ÆSCULAPIUS COMES TO
THE COLONIES

BENJAMIN FRANKLIN (1706-1790)

The statue of Benjamin Franklin by James Earle Fraser stands today in the Franklin Institute in Philadelphia, a memorial to "America's first great American." (*Courtesy of The Franklin Institute of Philadelphia.*)

ÆSCULAPIUS COMES TO THE COLONIES

The Story of
the Early Days of Medicine in
the Thirteen Original Colonies

MAURICE BEAR GORDON, M.D.

ARGOSY-ANTIQUARIAN LTD.

1969

FIRST PRINTING
1949

Reprinted & Published by

ARGOSY-ANTIQUARIAN LTD.
116 E. 59th Street
N. Y. C. 10022

Library of Congress Catalog Card Number 70-101590

PRINTED IN THE UNITED STATES OF AMERICA
by SENTRY PRESS, NEW YORK, N. Y. 10019

THIS BOOK IS DEDICATED

TO MY MOTHER

DOROTHY GORDON

WHOSE MATERNAL DEVOTION

WILL REMAIN A CONSTANT

SOURCE OF INSPIRATION TO

ME ALL THE DAYS OF MY LIFE

AND TO MY FATHER

BENJAMIN LEE GORDON, M.D.

PHYSICIAN, SCHOLAR, AUTHOR AND DEVOTED FATHER.

PREFACE

ONE HUNDRED AND seventy-two years have elapsed since the signing of the Declaration of Independence. It seems strange that this long interval of time has passed without the production of a comprehensive work devoted to the history of medicine in the thirteen original colonies that later amalgamated to form the felicitous union known as the United States of America.

In 1931, Francis R. Packard published his excellent corpus, "History of Medicine in the United States", but as the title implies, this work covers too much ground to devote excessive space to colonial medicine. None-the-less, Packard's work contains a great deal of valuable colonial medical data, particularly with regard to Virginia, New York, Pennsylvania, and Massachusetts, and, with the generous permission of author and publisher, I have freely partaken of this wealth of material in this present book.

"The Dictionary of American Medical Biography", published by Howard A. Kelly and Walter B. Burrage in 1928 has proved most helpful in filling in many of the numerous blank spaces that of necessity must crop up in the production of a work of this type. Dr. Edmund B. Kelly, on behalf of the Kelly family, was kind enough to permit me free access to this work.

Concise summaries of general colonial history which precede the medical historical data in the various chapters have been based largely on articles appearing in the Encyclopædia Britannica (11th edition). Walter Yust, present editor of the Encyclopædia Britannica, has graciously given permission for the use of this material.

It has been deemed advisable not to encumber the text with numerous footnotes. The reader is asked to constantly refer to Chapter Fourteen in which all major sources are listed, chapter by chapter. It is hoped that this system will render the reading of the book more enjoyable and at the same time enable the reader to delve more deeply into any particular aspect of colonial medicine that has aroused his interest and curiosity.

The author has attempted to minimize the data presented in those chapters which cover colonies and states, for which good works are readily available. The reader, in such cases, is referred to the names of such comprehensive works in Chapter Fourteen. Several of the original thirteen colonies, to the best of the present author's knowledge, have never been covered at all in any previously published book. It is hoped that this latter material particularly will prove useful to the interested reader.

The author, of course, is fully cognizant of the fact that, to employ a nautical metaphor, the hull of his work leaves more seams to be caulked than those which he has successfully filled in. Such is the nature of a pioneer historical work. He also is aware that he must have inadvertently committed sins of commission as well as omission. He hopes that the product of his handiwork will serve to stimulate others to produce more complete and more accurate works on the history of colonial medicine.

One last thought: "Æsculapius Comes to the Colonies" was written by the present author during the busiest period of his professional life. Its preparation provided a welcome relaxation for him from the cares of a busy practitioner. Until its completion, whether his day's professional duties were completed at 10:00 P.M., midnight or 2:00 A.M., he made it his habit to devote at least two hours in each twenty-four to the pursuit of this study. He avidly hopes that the reader will derive at least a portion of the pleasure and instruction out of reading this book that he obtained from writing it.

Maurice Bear Gordon

CONTENTS

ILLUSTRATIONS

Chapter One

I N T R O D U C T I O N

Iɴ ᴛʜᴇsᴇ ᴅᴀʏs of great medical advance in America, when the average family doctor is a thoroughly trained medical scientist with precision diagnostic instruments and effective therapeutic weapons at his disposal, and the average citizen can literally walk down to the corner and receive efficient medical care, it is fitting to trace back the history of medicine in America to its infancy—for medicine in America was not born with a silver spoon in its mouth.

The present work concerns itself with the story of the early days of medicine in America. In so far as the men and phenomena that pass in sequence before our scrutiny adequately mirror the conduct of the general population and reflect the trends of the times, it is, in a larger sense, also the story of the origin of the United States. Our early heroes are virile souls whose essential attribute, "guts" ("intestinal fortitude" is much too polite a term), pervades their every action. Yet their courage and audacity do not always prevent them from being extremely narrow-minded—at times even bigoted. The Pilgrim Fathers do not brook controversy. The only right they recognize is the right that their limited vision perceives. Tolerance is weakness.

Our heroes love their friends avidly and hate their enemies with a burning passion. No monument to the former can be too great, and no calumny against the latter can be too base.

Old World chicanery and intrigue were matched and at times even exceeded in the colonial general and medical history: The colonization of few, if any, of the colonies was on an entirely honest plane. The corruption and inefficiency in the medical department during the Revolutionary War, particularly under the machinations of Shippen, remains one of the blots on the pages of American medical history.

It is a difficult task, indeed, to properly evaluate the available source material. Unfortunately, most of the contemporary authors had a product to sell. Much of the material is pro this or anti that. Thacher, for example, eulogizes nearly everyone. The press agents of the proprietors tend to present a rosy picture of colonial health and life. Their enemies paint colonial conditions as a living hell.

Writers praise their medical friends and denounce their medical enemies. The colonial newspaper advertisements and articles promote this or condemn that. From a maze of information and misinformation, the present author has attempted to construct a representative evaluation of colonial medicine in the following chapters. An effort has been made to eliminate pure propaganda. Only when such propaganda unintentionally gives an insight into actual conditions is it presented.

In his desire to reproduce a fair cross section of the status of medical practice in colonial America in the thirteen original states, qualitative rather than quantitative considerations have been the keynote. Certain of the colonies, particularly Virginia, Massachusetts, Pennsylvania and New Jersey, have been covered more or less completely elsewhere. Others such as Georgia, the Carolinas, Delaware, New Hampshire and Rhode Island, have been scarcely touched in any previous volume. A more or less balanced picture of doctors and medicine in all the original colonial states has never been published.

To understand what the successful establishment of the settlement of Jamestown meant to the history of the United States and the world in general and to medical history in particular, it is urgent to review the forces that were at work in Western Europe during the time when medieval darkness was being illuminated by the light of experimental science. The hitherto enslaved mass of humanity, directly and indirectly, was eventually touched by all of the following: (1) the use of the mariner's compass and other nautical devices in Europe; (2) the employing of gunpowder in Europe; (3) the development of the printing press with movable type; and (4) the development of experimental physical science and its gradual divorce from metaphysical pseudoscience. With the advent of the reformation, human slaves severed the shackles that hitherto had bound them.

The antagonistic forces that fought for and against the status quo erupted violently into the lives of men, necessitating great readjustment. Two peoples and civilizations found themselves face to face at this crossroads of history: The Latin race intimately connected with the Roman Church and the Anglo-Saxon race founded on the Common Law and a highly modified religious system. In the New

World, it was Jamestown that definitely led to the defeat of the former and the victory of the latter.

When Jamestown was established, although the beginnings of modern medicine, like the first rays of the morning sun, were beginning to appear on the European horizon (under the tutelage of Paracelsus, Harvey, Malpighi, Paré, Vesalius, Fallopius, Fabricius and Sydenham), the men who brought medicine to the New World (and most of their colleagues in the Old World) were still under the spell of Galen and the theory of signatures.

Numerous medical books were published prior to 1500. These printed works cost much less and were distributed much more widely than the relatively rare and costly manuscript copies that had previously been the lone mode of distribution of medical education. Galen's works were translated into Latin, which was of course the language of all men of letters, by Dr. Thomas Linacre (1460-1524) and published between the years 1517 and 1524. These translations were widely employed by physicians not only in the British Isles but also on the European continent. Their contents penetrated the New World through the agency of the early colonial priest-physicians. The Galenic system persisted in America until the advent of the eighteenth century.

Galen's theory, an elaboration of the old Aristotelian Doctrine, held that the body was composed of four cardinal elements (water, fire, air, and earth) comprising four principal humors (phlegm, blood, bile and black bile). Excessive quantities or improper temperature of these humors resulted in disease. Dietary measures, herb remedies and phlebotomy were employed to secure a proper humoral balance in case of disease. According to Galenic physiology, the *natural spirit* taking its origin in the liver, passed on to the heart to unite with air and form the *vital spirit*, thence to pass via the arteries to the head to become the *animal spirit*.

Galen based his pathology on the premise that disease was merely a derangement of function. Cure was effected by overcoming the derangement and restoring normalcy. This could be accomplished by employing medicine which would allegedly drive out the forces which were upsetting the patient's normal equilibrium.

Paracelsus (1493-1541), the radical, violently opposed all Galenism. He denounced the humoral theory and introduced straight chemistry into the therapeutic armamentarium. His favorite drugs included arsenic, laudanum, lead, mercury and sulfur. In an age when it was a sacrilege to question ancient authority, Paracelsus exploded an atomic bomb on the status quo and rejected the time-accepted on principle. Paracelsus wrote, not in Latin, but in the language of the common man. His chemotherapeutic agents found their way to the New World.

Ambroise Paré's (1510-1590) modern surgical techniques (also written in the vernacular), including his rational treatment of gunshot wounds, were transferred to America via the English surgeons.

Andreas Vesalius (1514-1564), although he wrote in Latin, was truly an independent spirit. His anatomy was based on actual dissection and he violently opposed the mistakes of Galenism. He, too, indirectly influenced the physicians of the New World.

The theory of signatures, even more primitive than the humoral theory, postulated as a natural law the alleged fact that each illness has a corresponding cure in nature. According to this theory, walnut meats, because of their rough resemblance to the convolutions of the brain, would afford a natural cure for all cranial ailments.

Reverend John Saffrin, of Rhode Island, was one of the many who favored the humoral interpretation of disease and believed that the domination of a particular humor was dependent on the time factor: Blood was dominant from nine P.M. until three A.M., bile from three A.M. until nine A.M., black bile from nine A.M. until three P.M., and phlegm from three P.M. until nine P.M. Saffrin declares that if you become sick, "mark well the hour when it begins; and the humour then reigning, the better to find the remedy."

In Fuller's *Pharmacopoeia*, the lunar cycle is said to exert great influence on disease. A julep "used with benefit against epilepsy should be given for the prevention of paroxysms, near the lunary period; for these times the brain suffers wonderful alterations."

It will be recalled that the New England settlers who came over on the Mayflower were already toughened by adverse experience to the whips and scorns of fate. Excluded from the craft guilds and treated like undesired foreigners, they had dwelt in Holland for twelve years prior to their setting forth for the New World, and had supported themselves by long hours of manual toil. This was good preparation for the enormous task before them. Theirs was not a task of picking gold off the streets. Work, insecurity and drudgery were the watchwords of the day. Financial return was not forthcoming. Even the money actually invested in the enterprise was never more than partially returned.

Whereas the climate and soil of the Virginia colonies, ideally suited toward intensive cultivation of tobacco—a money-making crop —led directly to the plantation system, the same elements in New England, which did not offer a single money-making harvest, but rather a wide variety of produce, plus the fact that there was a great abundance of fish in the north, led away from the plantation system toward the establishment of the independent town. Each town had a church, a court, a school and a mill to process the grain from the outlying farms. The entire set-up was much as in the Old Country.

To a successful practicing English physician, the colonial life of drudgery could hardly have any appeal. Medicine, in this outpost of civilization, like all arts, must decline over the standard of the Old Country. The doctor was a luxury that the hard-working colonist could ill afford. Thus, more often than not, the duties of the physician were undertaken by the village priest, who was the only one who had any time for intellectual pursuits.

In early colonial days, physicians, when remunerated at all, received their salaries as ministers, government officials, or teachers, or earned their livelihood as farmers, or retailers. As time progressed, particularly in urban areas, the doctor was given a better opportunity to earn a living from the practice of medicine.

The original colonial physicians (e.g. John Winthrop, Jr., Giles Firmin) received their training in Europe. These fairly well trained medical men, through the medium of apprenticeship, passed on their medical knowledge to the generation born on American soil. Naturally these recipients of the serpent and the staff, although having adequate bed-side manners and instruction, were markedly lacking in organized fundamentals. This process of apprenticeship, excluding new medical immigrees and those native Americans who went to Europe for training and returned to practice, continued throughout the colonial period. Such a procedure was definitely not conducive to improving the standards of medical practice.

Of course there were doctors who braved all hazards to make the voyage to the Old World to improve their medical education. Most of this group were amply repaid for their journey after they returned home.

The intimate relationships existing between the practicing of medicine and theology all too often served to stifle medical progress, for there was a natural tendency to blame all bodily ills on divine punishment for sin.

The colonial pharmacopea, to be just and fair, contained few bonafide therapeutic agents. "Faith" was the main beneficial active ingredient which the many medications contained. A doctor was indeed a great therapeutic genius if his drugs were relatively innocuous and did not actually harm the patient.

Witness Doctor John Barton's list of "Medicines Expended upon A Voyage from Dartmouth to New England in ye Shipe Hannah & Elizabeth:"

1679	Names	Maladies	Medicines	£	s	d
May 27	Hen Dawson	An Itching Humour	letting a s blood .....o	1	0	
	Nath Stanbury	paine in his head & teeth	6 purging pills wth Resin of Jallup ....o	2	0	
			oile of Cloues & origanû for his teeth ....o	1	0	
June 28	Rich Goarding	Bite wth a Dogg on ye wrist	Oyntments & Emplaisters Balsam for seauen dayes ....o	5	0	
July 4	Robt Cann	A Bruise vpon his fingers wth a chest in ye Hold	Oyntments & Emplaisters for seuerall dayes .o	2	0	
July 10	Jos Manning	A Broken shinn	Seuerall Emplaisters ..o	1	0	
	Annis fford	An Extream Cold	A Diaphoritick Bolus .o	1	0	
12	Goodwif Martin	Naturall Obstructions & very faint	Syrup of Saffron ℥ iiij Gascons powder ℈ s ..o	3	6	
	Annis Jackson	Stomachacall paines	Syrup of Saffron ℥s ..o	1	0	
	Richard Goarding	A great Cold, swelling of ye Amigdalls & a feauer	An Oyntment for his throat ....o	0	6	
			A sweating Bolus ....o	1	0	
			A potion of physicke .o	1	6	
13	— — — —	— — — —	A Refrigerating powder ℥f ....o	1	0	
			A somniferous Bolus ..o	1	0	
			More oyntment ......o	0	6	
			A pectoral syrup ℥ iiij.o	1	4	
			A liquorish sticke ... o	0	2	
			A pectorall Refregerating Decoction ....o	2	0	
14	Margtt Manning	paine in her head	Emplaisters for her temples ....o	1	0	
15	Thō Knollman	Blistred his hand and fingers	Emplaisters & oyntment ....o	1	0	
	Annis Jackson	Costiue body	A suppository ....o	0	6	
16	Anne Killigroue	Costiue body	A suppository ....o	0	6	
			purging pills 6 ....o	1	6	
17	Annis Jackson		purging pills 6 ....o	2	0	
20	Mary peirce	Cutt finger	Emplaisters ....o	0	6	
	Nath. Stanbury	Bruised ffinger	Emplaisters Unguents .o	1	0	
21	Ben: Threenedles	A Roosty naile in his hand	Emplaisters ....o	1	0	
	mr Tom Towsey	paine in his head & Swelling of ye Amigdalls	A suppository ....o	1	0	
			A sweating Bolus ....o	0	6	
22	Goodwife Hutchins	Tooth ach	Blistering Emplaisters .o	1	6	
			Oile of Cloues ....o	0	6	
23	— — — —	— — — —	Oile of Cloues ....o	0	6	
			Emplaister for her temples ....o.	0	6	
	Goodman Hutchins	Much trouble wth ffemye	A pectoral Syrup ....o	1	0	
29	Stephen Bickford	Wormes	purging pills wth Mercurius dulcis .....o	1	0	
			flower of Brimston ...o	1	0	
31	mr. Goarding	Broken hands & fingers	Emplaisters ....o	1	0	

1679	Names	Maladies	Medicines.	£ s d
	margrett Bouy	Cutt & Bruise in her nose & eyebrow	Emplaisters & Balsams for 6 dayes ....o 6 o	
Aug. 4	Anne Killigroue	Histericall vapors	Suppository ....o o 6 A compound Clyster wth Histericall Carmanitiue seeds ....o 2 6 A stomachicall Emplaister ....o 1 o	
8	Joane Brownstist	Hysticall ffitts	Spiritt of Castar & oile of Amber seuerall times ....o 3 o	
Aug. 9	Thō Knollman	A Cold & feauer	A Diaphoretic bolus .o 1 6 A somniferous Julap .o 1 o	
10	— — — —	— — — —	both ye same againe ..o 2 6	
				3 5 0

That I John Barton, chyrurgeon doe wone this to be ye whole truth as witnesse my hand.

J. Barton.

Note in this itemization that purging is frequently mentioned to drive off the evil principles from the body. John Barton was clever enough to employ extensively, the relatively harmless external applications for a rusty nail wound, dog bite, bruised finger, cut finger, broken shin, headache, cuts and bruises of nose and eyebrows, toothache, blisters and broken hand.

One of the powerful influences brought to bear on the colonists engaged in the practice of medicine was wrought by the Indians. Friend or foe, the medical practices of the red man could not help but seep into the therapeutics of the pioneers in the New World. In the first place, as intimated previously, the medical practitioners, especially the native-born ones, were on the whole, but poorly equipped to treat the sick and were willing to receive useful information from any source. Then, too, since the early colonists were in a "New World," foreign to them, but well known to the Indian, it was only natural to ferret out the red man's therapeutic secrets which were apparently well adapted to the strange climate and had stood the test of time.

Let us, then, delve into the medical practices of the American Indians prior to their contact with the colonists. The forte of Indian art was richly beautiful decorative design and lovely folklore and poetry. This art, whether pictorial or verbal, always was dedicated to some deity. For that matter, every step of daily life necessitated obeisance to the proper god. Whether seeds were sown, or a tepee entered, an elaborate religious cermony had to be executed. No wonder, then, that Indian medicine was deeply engendered with mysticism and religion. Certain rituals were practiced in essentially the same way by ethnologically divergent tribes. From the upper half of the Mississippi to the Hudson Bay, and from the foothills of the Rocky Mountains to the Hudson River, *The Medicine Dance* was engaged in alike by the Ojibwa, the Plains Cree, the central Algonkian and the Siouan tribes.

The word "medicine" itself is a good example of the American Indian's dualism of theology and medicine. To the red man, this term connoted something far more than a mere chemical or physical combination of ingredients. He employed the term not only for a drug or herb but also for some supernatural agency which may be invoked to cure disease or even insure the success of an undertaking. The consecrated item might be a pipe, a spear, an adversary's toe or an animal. Once invoked, however, this "medicine" was carefully guarded against harm and never used for menial purposes. Articles or herbs producing evil were "bad medicine."

Medicine men ranked high in Indian society. Often they were chiefs. If not, they were considered next to the chiefs. The deities, especially the earth gods in animal form, deputed the following types of power to these chosen ones: They could cure the sick. They could perform magic feats. They could subject a patient to their will and thus make him amenable to the divine powers they invoked. They could obtain divine aid in favoring any undertaking. They interpreted the divine meaning behind dreams and omens.

Women were not prohibited from joining the ranks of the medicine men. Like the men, they might achieve this position by the reception of an unusual vision of or communication from the gods, through the possession of a psychic personality, or through a sequence of miraculous circumstances. An Apache female became a shaman after she survived being mangled by a lion and being struck by lightning. Among the Hopi and Navajo, medicine men were duly trained by the elders. Medicine men usually were organized in societies; rarely they performed their duties as individuals (e.g. among the Apache). It should be emphasized that all medicine men, despite their awe-inspiring antics and sleight-of-hand tricks, had complete faith in the efficacy of their practices.

The American Indians only knew the rudiments of agriculture. Essentially they represented a true hunting and fishing stone age culture. Their highly active life and their extensive warfare predisposed them to wounds, fractures and dislocations, in which fields of medical practice they excelled. Their knowledge of anatomy was unquestionably better than that of their colonial contemporaries.

It must be remembered that the Indian had no racial immunity against the white man's diseases. His therapy, therefore, against measles, scarlet fever, smallpox and yellow fever, was very ineffectual. Without committing ourselves on the unsolved and highly controversial issue as to whether the Indians were the source of European epidemic syphilis, we do know that the Indians never had gonorrhea until the white men visited them. Even today, in pure American strains, malignancy is a rarity. Conjunctivitis was a common ailment due to life in the smoke-filled tepees. Neuralgia and rheumatism were prevalent, for the Indians lived an exposed outdoor life. Digestive dysfunctions were common because periods of semi-starvation all too often alternated with spells of gourmandy.

The physical drugs of the Indian included herbs, roots, animal products, leaves and barks. Some substances operated purely through divine power (e.g. hoddentin, Chalchihuit, Killikinick and Kungue). Others operated according to the law of signatures (i.e. they seemed to resemble the disease or the alterations which appear on the surface) to relieve the condition (e.g. decoctions of milk weed were given to mothers with faulty lactation). And lastly, others were employed for a specific pharmacological action. Since disease-demons or spirits were believed to enter the body, charms to prevent or cure disease were naturally employed. The Apache suspended a small cactus stick (Opuntia emorcyi) around their childrens' necks to protect them against disease.

Drugs were usually administered in a massive single dose as a decoction, infusion, powder or inhalation. If this failed, complicated rituals were resorted to.

The Indians were aware of the fever syndrome—hot, dry skin, muscular ache and pain, thirst, chills and prostration. They recognized the favorable prognosis when the skin became cooler and moister and the chills and thirst disappeared, To treat fever, they employed rest, sweating, purgation, diuresis and liquid diet. The plains and Great Lakes tribes employed phlebotomy in fevers, using a sharp piece of flint to gain entrance to the vein.

Gastrointestinal disorders were diagnosed according to the symptoms prevailing: pain, colic, gastric distress, flatulence, nausea and vomiting and evacuatory disorders. Emesis was the popular therapy for all gastrointestinal dysfunctions.

Coryza was differentiated from other respiratory disorders. The various forms of bronchitis, pleurisy and lung infections were, as a rule, not differentiated and the same medicines were used for all. The Sac and Fox group alone differentiated pleurisy with effusion and treated it by incision and drainage as early as 1750. The Indians of

New England used Lobelia syphilitica to treat asthma. Cupping was widely used for chest pains (often scarification followed by mouth sucking was employed.) Counterirritants were widely used.

There are only four examples of drugs used by the Amerinds as cardiac stimuli. The North Carolina Indians made use of holly infusion (Hex vomitoria). The Dakota and Winnebago employed horsemint (Monarda punctata). The Delaware prescribed Virginia poke (Phytolacca decandra). The Paunee administered Irish morning glory (Ipomoea leptophylla, Torr.).

Most plains tribes used decoctions of sumac (Rhus copallina) as a diuretic. The Dakota and Winnebago administered decoctions of wintergreen (Chimaphila maculata) for the same purpose. The Ottawa and Chippawa employed decoctions of shrub yellow root (Xanthorrhiza apifolia) to induce diuresis. The Tewa, to effect the same result, prescribed decoctions of juniper berries (Juniperous monasperma). The plains tribes were partial to decoctions of magnolia (Magnolia macrophylla) and sarsaparilla (Aralia mediculilis) to stimulate the urinary output. These drugs were all employed regardless of whether the edema was renal or cardiac in origin. They were also used for oliguria without dropsy.

The American Indians, because of their constant exposure to the elements (and possibly also because of their dietary habits), were very often affected with rheumatism, arthritis and neuritis. Sweat baths were considered a good therapy for such conditions by all tribes. The Carolina Indians often buried the patients in hot mud or poured cold water on the affected limbs. Scarification, cupping and moxas were frequently used. The Dakota and Omaha-Poncha believed in counterirritation with crushed leaf of pasque flowers (Pulsatilla pratense). Many internal and external remedies were employed.

The action of the indigenous narcotics and intoxicants were, as a rule, well understood, especially by the Indians of the Southwest.

As previously mentioned, the aboriginal Indians had practically no experience with the contagious diseases which were introduced by the white man and which exacted a deadly toll.

The Amerinds very successfully treated hysteria with sound (although unwitting) psychotherapy as practiced by the medicine men.

The sweat house or sudatory was the most widely used system of therapy for almost every malady known to the Indians.

At the site of snakebite, the Indians universally employed suction and many tribes even excised the area. They also often employed substances (e.g. portions of a snake) locally according to the Law of Similars. On the other hand, Kuk-bi-ze root was often plucked and chewed with the quid being applied to the bite. This often quickly reduced the swelling and pain and seemed to neutralize the venom. Certain Indians practiced immunization against snakebite by periodically allowing themselves to be bitten by larger and larger snakes, using a small one as a starter.

Compared to other stone age peoples, the Amerinds' medical practices were of an exceptionally high standard. In a fair evaluation, the medical status among the Indians was in many ways, on a par with the Assyrians, Hebrews and Greeks. The American Indians handled their wounds, empyemas, fractures and dislocations as well, if not better, than the 18th century white physicians. Their method of removing a retained placenta preceded Credé by a hundred years. The Indians definitely added 59 drugs to our modern pharmacopeia, including cascara sagrada, lobelia, puccoon, cohosh, pipsissewa and dockmackie.

To improve the standard of colonial medical education, the establishment of a medical school in the colonies was a prime requisite. The earliest expression of this need goes back to a letter written by the Apostle Eliot (dated Sept. 24, 1647) to Mr. Shepherd, the minister at Cambridge. He is most anxious that "Our young Students in Physick may be trained up better than yett they bee, who have onely theoreticall knowledge, and are forced to fall to practice before ever they saw an Anatomy made, or duely trained up in making experiments, for we never had but one Anatomy in the Countrey, which Mr. Giles Firmin (now in England) did make and read upon very well, but no more of that now."

On October 27, 1647, the Massachusetts General Court issued the following declaration: "We conceive it very necessary that such as studies physicke and chirurgery may have liberty to reade anatomy" (i.e. perform dissection). It took 118 years however, before the first medical school (University of Pennsylvania Medical School) was actually established in the United States.

New Jersey and Pennsylvania were primarily populated by Quakers and Swedes, who do not appear to have had the difficult time that the Virginians and New Englanders had. The early settlers in these places profited by the experience of their predecessors. They were better equipped, were not so overcrowded enroute, and by and large, had much more even distribution of wealth.

From the beginning, colonial doctors showed a great interest in statesmanship. This interest culminated in the fact that five physicians were included as signers of the Declaration of Independence. This group included Oliver Wolcott of Connecticut, Josiah Bartlett and Matthew Thornton of New Hampshire, Benjamin Rush of Pennsylvania, and Lyman Hall of Georgia.

The colonial doctors displayed great skill and daring, both as military physicians and military leaders. That the ability of American physicians as military surgeons has by no means been lost has been amply demonstrated during World War II.

Every effort has been made to make the illustrations in this book the most complete collection pertaining to early American medical history yet published.

An interesting observation that anyone must make after going through this book is the average longevity of the early doctors' lives. Considering all aspects of this question, the present author is unable to adequately explain this phenomenon.

Benjamin Rush refers to so many early American doctors as "second to none in the United States," that this endorsement loses its vigor and can only be interpreted as a statement of moderate approbation. Incidentally, Rush, who is considered by many authorities to have been the greatest early American physician, did no one single thing that warrants listing in the compilation of major events in the early history of medicine in America which is appended at the end of this chapter.

Various means have been employed to bring the reader into contact with colonial medicine. These include the employing of quotations from original accounts, the reproduction of colonial documents, the use of illustrations pertaining to colonial medicine, and the quoting of contemporary newspaper articles and advertisements.

The general historical survey at the beginning of each chapter, it is hoped, will orient the reader sufficiently to place the time and the locale of the medical events that follow.

No arbitrary date limits have been set on the material contained in this study. In the event that a particular colonial personality extends his influence into the post-Revolutionary period, such material is not excluded. As a rule, in most chapters, the material employed does not date beyond the War of Independence. In a few chapters, particularly where the author found a scarcity of material, events are calendared up until the early 1800's.

In those chapters where there is a paucity of available material, lists of medical men who took part in the War of Independence are included. In the chapters where the available material far exceeds the space alloted, such lists are not included. The reader, in the latter circumstance, is referred to the list of medical men who served in the Revolutionary War contained in the Army Medical Bulletin, Number 25.

The reader is led from the corridors of colonial general history into the vestibule of colonial medical history via a group of original documents pertaining to the early days of Virginia. Since, in the author's opinion, the actual presentation of original sources is often of far greater interest than any summation made on such sources, there has been a persistent attempt to directly quote as many authentic colonial manuscripts as possible. The documentation of the organization of the first colonial medical society is particularly complete.

The arrangement of the chapters is based on the order in which the colonies were first permanently settled.

A listing of the major events in the early history of medicine in America would include the following:

1620: The first attempt to build a hospital in America at Henricopolis, Virginia.

1647: Declaration of General Court of Massachusetts permitting dissection. Massachusetts passes first quarantine in America to prevent spread of yellow fever.

1657: New York passes first ordinance employing doctors to combat crime.

1664: John Cranston of Rhode Island becomes the recipient of the first colonial M.D. degree.

$167\frac{7}{8}$: Thomas Thacher (1620-1678) publishes, "A Brief Rule to Guide the Common People of New England How to Order Themselves And Theirs in the Small Pocks or Measels"—the first medical article published and written in America.

1721: Zabdiel Boylston (1679-1766) successfully performs smallpox inoculation for the first time in America.

1723: General Court of Massachusetts passes first law to control any disease process other than of an infectious or contagious nature by forbidding the use of lead pipes in the distilling of rum.

1730: Bishop Berkeley plays a major role in establishing the Newport (Rhode Island) Philosophical Society which antedates the Philosophical Society of Philadelphia.

Thomas Cadwalader (1708-1779) presents earliest known American anatomical lectures in Philadelphia.

1741: Silvester Gardiner (1707-1786) performs rapid and successful operation for stone on six year old boy.

1743: Cadwallader Colden publishes first American public health articles in The New York Weekly Post Boy.

1750: John Bard (1716-1799) and Peter Middleton (?—1781) present systematic dissection for purpose of instruction in New York.

1751: The Pennsylvania Hospital, the first large scale hospital in colonial America, opens its doors in Philadelphia.

1752: Benjamin Franklin (1706-1790) designs first flexible catheter in America.

1755: William Hunter (1730-1777) presents first publicly advertised systematic lectures on anatomy with dissection in Newport, Rhode Island.

1757: Thomas Walker (1715-1794) of Virginia trephines bone for suppurative osteomyelitis.

1759: John Bard (1716-1799) reports a case of extrauterine pregnancy.

1762: William Shippen, Jr. (1736-1800) starts his famous anatomical lectures in Philadelphia with demonstration on cadaver.

1765: The forerunner of the University of Pennsylvania Medical School opens it doors.

William Shippen, Jr. (1736-1800) presents first lectures on obstetrics.

1766: Establishment of The New Jersey Medical Society, the first state society in America.

Thomas Bond (1712-1784) presents first systematic course of clinical or bedside lectures in America.

1767: Medical school attached to King's College, N.Y., organized.

John V. B. Tennent becomes first professor of obstetrics in America by being placed on staff of King's College.

1773: First insane asylum in America opened at Williamsburg, Virginia.

1775: John Jones (1729—?) publishes first American book on surgery and military surgery.

1782: Harvard Medical School is founded.

1784: Benjamin Franklin (1706-1790) invents bifocals.

1786: Benjamin Waterhouse (1754-1846) presents first lectures on natural history at Rhode Island College.

1787: The College of Physicians of Philadelphia is founded.

1788:   Hezekiah Beardsley (1748-1790), of Connecticut, describes congenital hypertrophic pyloric stenosis for the first time.

1790:   William Baynham (1749-1814), of Virginia, reports cases of extra-uterine gestation in 1790 and 1799. Both patients recovered. He also is discoverer of the vascularity of the rete muscosum.

1794:   Jessee Bennett performs first caesarean section in America and also bilateral oophorectomy.

1797:   Andrew Wiesenthal (1762-1798) is first to discover an organism producing an epidemic disease.

1799:   Noah Webster publishes "A Brief History of Epidemics and Pestilential Diseases" and thus becomes first epidemologist in the United States.

1800:   Benjamin Waterhouse (1754-1846) introduces vaccination in America.

Chapter Two

V I R G I N I A

THE GREAT HONOR of being the first permanent English settlement in North America goes to Jamestown, Virginia. On May 13, 1607, this city was founded on what is now Jamestown Island in the James River.

The location of this city of destiny consisted of marshy lowlands in which disease was prevalent. Jamestown was destroyed by accidental fire in January 1608. Nathaniel Bacon almost erased it from the map in September 1676. The destruction by fire of the state house and other buildings was one of the factors that led to the transferring of the seat of government of Virginia from Jamestown to the Middle Plantations (now Williamsburg) in 1699. Following this, Jamestown, having done its great deed, sunk into oblivion. By the time half of the 19th century had rolled past, Jamestown peninsula had been cut off into an island by the James River. By the advent of the 20th century this stream had eaten away the shoreline but had left "New Towne" (1619), just east of the first settlement, unscathed. Still visible were several gravestones and the tower of the brick Anglican church.

In 1893, this historic sight was deeded to the Association for the Preservation of Virginia Antiquities. In 1900, the federal government erected a bulkhead to hold the James River at bay and thus spare this American shrine. The foundations of the old buildings and numerous relics were then uncovered. In 1907 a reconstruction of the fourth colonial church built in 1639-1647 was erected. The site of the first settlement and the location of the first house of burgesses were suitably marked with shafts.

Prior to the establishment of Jamestown, it should be recalled that from 1583 to 1588 attempts had been made by Sir Walter Raleigh and others to found colonies on the coast of what is now North Carolina. These attempts ended in dismal failure, their only result being the fact that the area was named Virginia in honor of Queen Elizabeth. It was the fabulous accounts brought back by the early explorers that stimulated the London Company to organize an expedition in 1606. The London Company's intrepid band of adventurers landed at Jamestown on May 13, 1607, and established numerous plantations along the James River. The London Company's stockholders do not appear to have been motivated by pure philanthropy. They appear to have been more interested in setting up a profitable commercial and agricultural community. However, unfavorable climate and the hostile propensities of the native aborigines and the colonists themselves, teamed up to inhibit the healthy growth of the new community.

In September 1608, Captain John Smith came into authority and demanded that the colonists submit to law and order. He guided the colonists in the establishment of various extensive agricultural and fishing operations and supervised the erection of a church. One year later, the London Company was reorganized, auxiliary colonists were dispatched and the boundaries of Virginia were fixed to extend from a point 200 miles south of Old Point Comfort, at the mouth of the Chesapeake Bay, to another point 200 miles north, "west and northwest to the South Sea."

The London Company, in the beginning, was the direct ruling body over the colonists. Local and administrative affairs were controlled by a resident governor and council established by the Company. Prior to the arrival of the governing body and reinforcements of settlers, the original colony was in a bad way. At long last, the appointed ruling body including Captain Christopher Newport, Sir Thomas Gates and Sir George Somers reached Jamestown with 150 colonists. They found the colony reduced to such dire straits that all agreed on June 10, 1610, to give up colonization in this area as a lost cause and set sail for Newfoundland. However, at the mouth of the river, they met destiny in the person of Lord Delaware, who had brought numerous colonists and adequate supplies. The group turned back, set up a trading post at what is now Hampton, and began active measures to cope with the hostile natives.

In 1611, the enterprising English landed 650 additional colonists, conducted exploration of the James and Appomattox Rivers and established "plantations" at Henrico and New Bermuda. In 1617 the rule of Virginia was left to Captain Samuel Argall, a rigid puritan. Death was the penalty for colonists who failed to accept the doctrine of the trinity, who declined to respect the authority of the Bible and who proved their heresy by not attending church. This puritanical government lasted until 1619 when a milder system under Sir George Yeardley was instituted. In 1619, twelve hundred new colonists appeared on the scene, and negro slaves and many "indentured" servants were imported as laborers for the first time. Thus the curse of negro slavery came to the New World.

In Virginia's early colonial days, the colonists held their lands and improvements in common. In 1616 the land was parcelled out to the colonists and plantations were erected along the shores of the James and Appomattox Rivers for many miles inland. In 1619, the Virginia colonists were already self-supporting and they exported twenty thousand pounds of tobacco in this year alone. This fateful year, which had witnessed the start of slavery, also saw the organization of the first representative assembly in North America, the Virginia House of Burgesses. This body consisted of planters sent from the plantations to help the governor in reframing the laws of the colony.

In 1621 a constitution was granted Virginia whereby the London Company appointed the governor and Council, and the people chose delegates to the House of Burgesses. It was the colonists' group which granted supplies and originated laws. The governor and Council could only revise or veto the popular legislation. The Council had Supreme Court powers in reviewing all county courts. This division of power continued until the War of Independence with the exception that, in 1624, the king replaced the London Company.

By 1622, the population of the Virginia colonies consisted of about 4000 souls and the native Indians who saw their territories threatened, rose to action. On March 22, 1622, the red men fell upon the whites and slaughtered 350 persons. Following this catastrophe, illness and starvation again reared their ugly heads in the colony and the population was promptly reduced by almost fifty percent. But the die had already been cast and the beach-head of English colonization in North America established. The losses were promptly replenished, tobacco cultivation developed into a great industry and the settlers expanded deep into the interior. This mushroom growth was hardly influenced by another Indian attack in April 1641, which resulted again in the destruction of about 350 settlers. By 1648, Virginia's colonial population had reached the 15,000 mark.

In our quest for details as to the medical conditions under which the early colonists dwelt, let us examine some of the early documents. George Percy's "Observations" give minute detail of the journey to and the early days of Jamestown.

George Percy (1580-1632) was the eighth son of Henry, eighth earl of Northumberland. After serving as a soldier in the Netherlands, he set sail for Virginia in the first expedition (December 20, 1606). He was president during the nightmare period from September, 1609, to the arrival of Gates in May, 1610. When Lord Delaware departed from Jamestown in March, 1611, Percy was again made head of the colony until the arrival of Dale the following May. He left Virginia on April 22, 1612, and reached England in the following summer.

The original manuscript of Percy is not preserved and what has come down to us is merely an abridgment published for the first time in 1625 by Samuel Purchas, who assigns as a reason for the omissions he made in it that "the rest is more fully set downe in Capt. Smith's Relations." The narrative is to be found in *Purchas his Pilgrimes, IV*. 1685-1690. It gives the most complete account extant (to 1607) of the voyage and the early events in the settlement. Of the other accounts of the earliest months of the colony, Wingfield's *Discourse of Virginia*, printed in the fourth volume of the *Archaeologia Americana* and separately (Worcester, 1860), begins at that point; but it is too largely a partisan account of the author's quarrels with his fellow-members of the council to have the same sort of value as Percy's story. There is also the *Relatyon* called Newport's although perhaps written by Archer, likewise printed in the *Archaeologia*, Vol. IV.; but this is almost confined to the exploration of the James River (May 21-27). Captain John Smith's *True Relation*, the most important narrative of the early days, begins to be explicit about where Percy leaves off. Purchas' text was reprinted by Edward Arber, in his edition of *Smith's Works* (Birmingham, 1884), to which Wingfield and Archer are also prefixed. The following are excerpts from Percy's own pen; please note especially italicized parts:

OBSERVATIONS BY MASTER GEORGE PERCY, 1607

Observations gathered out of a Discourse of the Plantation of the Southerne Colonie in Virginia by the English, 1606. Written by that Honorable Gentleman, Master George Percy.

On Saturday the twentieth of December in the yeere 1606, the fleet fell from London, and the fift of January we anchored in the Downes: but the winds continued contrarie so long, that we were forced to stay there some time, where wee suffered great stormes, but by the skilfulnesse of the Captaine wee suffered no great losse or danger.

The twelfth day of February at night we saw a blazing Starre, and presently a storme.

The three and twentieth day (of March.) we fell with the Lland of Mattanenio (Martinique) in the West Indies. The foure and twentieth day we anchored at Dominico, within fourteene degrees of the Line, a very faire Lland, the Trees full of sweet and good smels; inhabited by many Savage Indians.

The sixt of August *there died John Asbie of the bloudie Flixe*, (bloody flux or dysentery). The ninth day *died George Flowre of the swelling*. The tenth day died William Bruster Gentleman, of a wound given by the savages, and was buried the eleventh day.

The fourteenth day, Jerome Alikock, Ancient, died of a wound, the same day, Francis Midwinter, Edward Moris Corporall died suddenly.

The fifteenth day, their died Edward Browne and Stephen Galthorpe. The sixteenth day, their died Thomas Gower Gentleman. The seventeenth day, their died Thomas Mounslic. The eighteenth day, there died Robert Pennington, and John Martine Gentleman. The nineteenth day, died Drue Piggase Gentleman. The two and twentieth day of August, there died Captaine Bartholomew Gosnold, one of our Councell: he was honourably buried, having all the Ordnance in the Fort shot off, with many vollies of small shot.

After Captaine Gosnold's death, the Councell could hardly agree by the dissention of Captaine Kendall, which afterwards was committed about hainous matters which was proved against him.

The foure and twentieth day, died Edward Harington and George Walker, and were buried the same day. The six and twentieth day, died Kenelme Throgmortine. The seven and twentieth day died William Roods. The eight and twentieth day died Thomas Stoodie, Cape Merchant.

The fourth day of September died Thomas Jacob Sergeant. The fift day, there died Benjamin Beast. *Our men were destroyed with cruell diseases, as Swellings, Flixes, Burning Fevers, and by warres, and some departed suddenly, but for the most part they died of meere famine. There were never Englishmen left in a forreigne Countrey in such miserie as wee were in this new discovered Virginia.* Wee watched every three nights, lying on the bare cold ground, what weather soever came, (and) warded all the next day, which brought our men to bee most feeble wretches. *Our food was but a small Can of Barlie sod in water, to five men a day, our drinke cold water taken out of the River, which was the destruction of many of our men.* Thus we lived for the space of five moneths in this miserable distresse, not having five able men to man our Bulwarkes upon any occasion. If it had not pleased God to have put a terrour in the Savages hearts, we had all perished by those wild and cruell Pagans, being in that weake estate as we were; our men night and day groaning in every corner of the Fort most pittifull to heare. If there were any conscience in men, it would make their harts to bleed to heare the pitifull murmurings and out-cries of our sick men without reliefe, every night and day, for the space of sixe weekes, some departing of the

World, many times three or foure in a night; in the morning, their bodies trailed out of their Cabines like Dogges to be buried. In this sort did I see the mortalitie of divers of our people.

It pleased God, after a while, to send those people which were our mortall enemies to releeve us with victuals, as Bread, Corne, Fish, and Flesh in great plentie, which was the setting up of our feeble men, otherwise we had all perished. Also we were frequented by divers Kings in the Countrie, bringing us store of provision to our great comfort.

The eleventh day (of September, 1607), there was certaine Articles laid against Master Wingfield which was then President; thereupon he was not only displaced out of his President ship, but also from being of the Councell. Afterwards Captaine John Ratcliffe was chosen President.

The eighteenth day, died one Ellis Kinistone, which was starved to death with cold. The same day at night, died one Richard Simmons. The nineteenth day, there died one Thomas Mouton.

In this accurate and unbiased account, Percy gives a factual picture of the wretched plight of the early colonists who were decimated by famine, cold, injuries and disease.

A short account of John Smith and his works would not be out of place at this juncture. In his *True Relation*, Captain John Smith briefly tells the story of the Virginia colonists from the time of their leaving London on December 20, 1606, to the departure of the *Phoenix* for England on June 2, 1608. Smith was the son of George and Alice Smith, tenants of Peregrine Bertie, Lord Willoughby, and he was baptized at Willoughby on January 9, 1580.

At the age of fifteen he was apprenticed to a merchant, but the wanderlust waxed strong within him. During the next nine years his life was spent on the continent of Europe in constant travel and adventure. Adventure followed him day by day. He was robbed and beaten by outlaws, was thrown into the sea as a heretic, and was a slave to a Turkish pasha. He had many hairbreadth escapes, but the most notable incident of his early career was his three combats before the city of Regall with the three Turkish champions, whose heads he cut off one after another. As a reward he received from Sigismund Bathori, a prince of Transylvania, a coat of arms with three Turks' heads on a shield.

In 1604, Smith went back to England and immediately became interested in the movement to establish a colony in Virginia. His reputation had preceded him, and he was picked out as one of the council to direct affairs in Virginia. He remained in this service until October, 1609, having been from September 20, 1608, to September 20, 1609, president of the colony. His wonderful talent for hairbreadth escapes did not desert him. He was charged on the way over with conspiracy and kept under arrest until three weeks after the settlers landed at Jamestown. In December, 1607, he was captured by the Indians and was saved from death by Pocahontas. He returned to Jamestown only to run into a new danger. He was arrested by the council and condemned to death but escaped hanging by the timely return of Captain Christopher Newport, who intervened and saved his life.

The doughty Captain left the colony at the end of his presidency, and for several years was in the employ of the Plymouth Company, giving the name to New England and making a valuable chart of the country. From 1615 to his death in 1631 he lived quietly in England, where he was known as a prolific writer. In 1612 he published his *Map of Virginia*. In 1624 *The Generall Historie of Virginia, New England and the Summer Isles*, and in 1630 *The True Travels*.

To further our insight into life in the early days of the colony, let us quote from Chapter II of his *True Relation*:

WHAT HAPPENED TILL THE FIRST SUPPLY

Being thus left to our fortunes, it fortuned that, within tenne daies, scarse ten amongst us coulde either goe, or well stand, such extreame weaknes and sicknes oppressed us. And thereat none need mervaile, if they consider the cause and reason, which was this; whilst the ships staied, our allowance was somewhat bettered by a daily proportion of bisket which the sailers would pilfer to sell, give, or exchange with us, for mony, saxefras, furres, or love. But when they departed, there remained neither taverne, beere-house, nor place of relife but the common kettell. Had we been as free from all sinnes as gluttony and drunkeness, we might have bin canonized for Saints. But our President would never have bin admitted, for ingrossing to his privat Otemeale, sacke, oile, aquavitæ, beefe, egs, or what not, but the kettel; that indeede he allowed equally to be distributed and that was halfe a pinte of wheat, and as much barly, boyled with water, for a man a day, and this having fryed s me 26. weeks in the ships hold, contained as many wormes as graines, so that we might truely call it rather so much bran than corne. Our drinke was water, our lodgings castles in the aire. With this lodging and diet, our extreame toile in bearing and planting pallisadoes, so strained and bruised us, and our continuall labour in the extremity of the heat had so weakened us, as were cause sufficient to have made us as miserable in our native tember, those that escaped lived upon Sturgion and sea-Crabs. 50. in this time we buried. The rest seeing the Presidents projects to escape these miseries in our Pinnas by flight (who all this time, had neither felt want nor sicknes), so moved our dead spirits, as we deposed him; (September 10, 1607.) and established Ratcliffe in his place: Gosnoll being dead, (August 22, 1607.) Kendall deposed, Smith newly recovered; Martin and Ratcliffe was, by his care, preserved and relieved. But now was all our provisions spent, the Sturgeon gone, all helps abandoned, each houre expecting the fury of the Salvages; when God, the patron of all good indeavours in that desperate extreamity, so changed the harts of the Salvages, that they brought such plenty of their fruits and provision, as no man wanted.

And now where some affirmed it was ill done of the Councel to send forth men so badly provided, this incontradictable reason will shew them plainely they are too ill advised to nourish such il conceipts. First, the fault of our going was our owne. What could be thought fitting or necessary wee had, but what wee should finde, what we should want, where we shoulde bee, we were all ignorant, and supposing to make our passage in two monthes, with victuall to live, and the advantage of the spring to worke: we weare at sea 5. monthes, where we both spent our victuall and lost the opportunity of the time and season to plant.

This indeed is a graphic presentation of the early days which requires no elucidation! The *Relation of the Lord De-La-Ware* (1611) is particularly replete with medical phenomena. The author, Thomas West, third Lord Delaware (1577-1618), was the son of Thomas West, second Lord Delaware, and Anne, daughter of Sir Francis Knollys by Katherine Cary, first cousin to Queen Elizabeth and sister of Henry Cary, first Lord Hunsdon. He received his master of arts degree at Oxford, and was knighted by Essex at Dublin, Ireland (July 12, 1599). He served with distinction in the Low Countries, was implicated in the Essex Rebellion on February 8, 1601, was imprisoned and pardoned. His father, the second lord, died on March 24, 1602, and he succeeded as third Lord Delaware and also as member of the privy council of Queen Elizabeth, and on her death became a privy councillor to James I.

In 1609 he became a member of the superior council of the Virginia Company, and on February 28, 1610, was appointed governor and captain-general of the Virginia colony for life. He arrived at Jamestown on June 10, 1610, and re-established the colonists whom he found deserting the settlement. After a stay of a year he was compelled to leave on account of his health, and went first to the West Indies and then to England. He remained in the latter country until 1618; in his absence the government in Virginia was administered by deputy-governors—Gates, Dale, Heardey, and Argall. In the latter year he was sent again to Virginia to rescue the government from the hands of Samuel Argall, who had incurred the strong censure of the London Company, but on his way over he died (June 7, 1618).

He married Cecily, daughter of Sir Thomas Sherley. His son and successor was Henry, fourth Lord Delaware, who married Isabella, daughter of Sir Thomas Edmonds, the ambassador. Governor Delaware had three brothers, Francis West, John West and Nathaniel West, who all lived in Virginia, and the first two of whom were deputy-governors at different times; William West, a nephew, was killed by Indians at the Falls of James River, Virginia, in 1611.

The chief value of the narrative proceeds from the strong defense it unconsciously affords of the character of the Virginia colonists. Here was Delaware given absolute power by a new charter established under the idea that the calamities in Virginia were due to the inveterate disposition of the Virginia colonists to quarrels and shiftlessness—a man toughened in war and given all the advantages of good living and the best medical attention. And yet what a doleful complaint he makes of the ague, the dysentery, and the scurvy, which in short order bombarded him out of the colony. The London Company and its servants—Smith, Delaware, Gates, Dale, and others—"boomed" the company's management and the natural advantages of Virginia, and very unjustly threw the responsibility on the poor colonists, who suffered untold horrors from starvation and disease.

THE RELATION OF THE LORD DE-LA-WARE, 1611

The Relation of the Right Honourable the Lord De-La-Warre, Lord Governour and Captaine Generall of the Colonie, planted in Virginea. London: Printed by William Hall, for William Welbie, dwelling in the Pauls Churchyeard at the Signe of the Swan. 1611.

A Short Relation made by the Lord De-La-Warre, to the Lords and others of the Counsell of Virginia, touching his unexpected returne home, and afterwards delivered to the generall Assembly of the said Company, at a Court holden the twenty five of June, 1611. Published by authority of the said Counsell.

My Lords, etc.

Being now by accident returned from my Charge at Virginea, contrary either to my owne desire, or other men's expectations, who spare not to censure me, in point of duty, and to discourse and question the reason, though they apprehend not the true cause of my returne, I am forced, (out of a willingnesse to satisfie every man) to deliver unto your Lordships, and the rest of this Assembly, briefely (but truely), in what state I have lived, ever since my arrival to the Colonie; what hath beene the just occasion of my sudden departure thence; and in what termes I have left the same: The rather because I perceive, that since my comming into England, such a coldnesse and irresolution is bred in many of the Adventurers that some of them seeke to withdraw those paiments, which they have subscribed towards the Charge of the Plantation, and by which that Action must bee supported and maintained; making this my returne the colour of their needlesse backwardnes and unjust protraction. Which, that you may the better understand, I must informe your Lordships, that *presently after my arrival in James Towne, I was welcommed by a hote and violent Ague, which held mee a time, till by the advice of my Physition, Doctor Laurence Bohun, (by blood letting) I was recovered,* as in my first Letters by Sir Thomas Gates I have informed you. *That disease had not long left me, til (within three weekes after I had gotten a little strength) I began to be distempered with other greevous sicknesses, which successively and severally assailed me: for besides a relapse into the former disease, which with much more violence held me more than a moneth, and brought me to great weakenesse, the Flux (Dysentery) surprised me, and kept me many daies: then the Crampe assaulted my weak body, with strong paines; and afterwards the Gout (with which I had heeretofore beene sometime troubled) afflicted mee in such sort, that making my body through weakenesse unable to stirre, or to use any maner of exercise, drew upon me the disease called the Scurvy; which though in others it be a sicknesse of slothfulnesse, yet was in me an effect of weaknesse, which never left me, till I was upon the point to leave the world.*

These severall maladies and calamities, I am the more desirous to particularise unto Your Lordships (although they were too notorious to the whole Colonie) lest any man should misdeeme that under the general name and common excuse of sicknes, I went about to cloke either sloth, or feare, or anie other base apprehension, unworthy the high and generall charge which you had entrusted to my Fidelitie.

In those extremities I resolved to consult my friends, who (finding Nature spent in me, and my body almost consumed, my panes likewise daily encreasing) gave me advise to preferre a hopefull recovery, before an assured ruine, which must necessarily have ensued, had I lived, but twenty dayes longer, in Virginia: wanting at that instant, both food and Physicke, fit to remedy such extraordinary diseases, and restore that strength so desperately decayed.

Whereupon, after a long consultation held, I resolved by generall consent and perswasion, to ship my self for Mevis, an Island in the West Indies, famous for wholesome Bathes, there to try what help the Heavenly Providence would afford me, by the benefit of the hot Bathe: But God, who guideth all things, according to his good will and pleasure, so provided, that after wee had sailed an hundred Leagues, we met with

Southerly windes which forced me to change my purpose (my long voyage) and so sterne my course for the Western Islands (Azores), which I no sooner recovered, then *I found help for my health, and my sicknesse asswaged by meanes of fresh diet, and especially of Orenges and Lemonds, an undoubted remedy and medicine for that disease,* which lastly, and so long, had afflicted me: which ease as soone as I found, I resolved (although my body remained still feeble and weake), to returne backe to my charge in Virginia againe, but I was advised not to hazard my selfe before I had perfectly recovered my strength, which by Counsell I was perswaded to seeke in the naturall Ayre of my Countrey, and so I came for England. In which Accident (State of affairs) I doubt not but men of reason, and of judgement will imagine, there would more danger and prejudice have hapned by my death there, then I hope can doe by my returne.

In the next place, I am to give accompt in what estate I left the Collony for government in my absence. It may please your Lordships therefore to understand that upon my departure thence, I made choise of Captaine George Pearcie, (a gentleman of honour and resolution, and of no small experience in that place) to remaine Deputie Governour, untill the comming of the Marshall, Sir Thomas Dale, whose Commission was likewise to be determined, upon the arrivall of Sir Thomas Gates, according to the intent and order of your Lordships, and the Councill here.

The number of men I left there were upward of two hundred, the most in health, and provided of at least tenne moneths victuals in their store-house, (which is daily issued unto them) besides other helps in the Countrey, lately found out by Captaine Argoll, by trading with pettie kings in those parts, who for a small returne of a piece of Iron, Copper, &c. have consented to trucke great quantities of Corne, and willingly imbrace the intercourse of Traffique, shewing unto our people certaine signs of amitie and affection.

And for the better strengthening and securing of the Collony, in the time of my weaknesse there, I tooke order for the building of three severall Forts, two of which are seated neere Poynt Comfort, to which adjoyneth a large Circuit of ground, open, and fit for Corne: the thirde Fort is at the Falles, upon an Island invironed also with Corne ground. These are not all manned, for I wanted the Commoditie of Boates, having but two, and one Bardge, in all the Countrey, which hath beene cause that our fishing hath beene (in some sort) hindered, for want of those provisions, which easily will be remedied when wee can gaine sufficient men to be imployed about those business, which in Virginia I found not: But since meeting with Sir Thomas Gates at the Cowes neere Portsmouth (to whom I gave a perticular accompt of all my proceedings, and of the present estate of the Collony as I left it) I understood those wants are supplyed in his Fleete.

The countrey is wonderfull fertile and very rich, and makes good whatsoever heretofore hath beene reported of it, the Cattell already there, are much encreased, and thrive exceedingly with the pasture of that Countrey: The Kine all this last Winter, though the ground was covered most with Snow, and the season sharpe, lived without other feeding than the grasse they found, with which they prospered well, and many of them readie to fall with Calve; Milke being a great nourishment and refreshing to our people, serving also (in occasion) as well for Physicke as for Food, so that it is no way to be doubted, but when it shall please God that Sir Thomas Dale, and Sir Thomas Gates, shall arrive in Virginia with their extraordinary supply of one hundred Kine, and two hundred Swine, besides store of all manner of other provisions for the sustenance and maintenance of the collony, there will appeare that successe in the Action as shall give no man cause to distrust that hath already adventured, but encourage every good minde to further so worthy a worke, as will redound both to the Glory of God, to the Credit of our Nation, and to the Comfort of all those that have beene Instruments in the furthering of it.

The last discovery, during my continuall sicknesse, was by Captaine Argoll, who hath found a trade with Patomack (a King as great as Powhatan, who still remaines our enemie, though not able to doe us hurt.). This is a goodly River called Patomack, upon the borders whereof there are growne the goodliest Trees for Masts, that may be found elsewhere in the World: Hempe better than English, growing wilde in aboundance: Mines of Antimonie and Leade.

There is also found without our Bay to the Northward an excellent fishing Bancke for Codde, and Ling as good as can be eaten, and of a kinde that will keepe a whole yeare, in Shippes hould, with little care; a tryall (sample) whereof I now have brought over with mee. Other Islands there are upon our Coasts that doe promise rich merchandise, and will further exceedingly the establishing of the Plantation, by supply of many helpes, and will speedily afford a returne of many worthie Commodities.

I have left much ground in part manured to receive Corne, having caused it the last Winter to be sowed for rootes with which our people were greatly releeved.

There are many Vines planted in divers places, and doe prosper well, there is no want of any thing, if the action can be upheld with constancy and resolution.

Lastly concerning my selfe, and my Course, though the World may imagine that this Countrey and Climate will (by that which I have suf-

fered beyond any other of that Plantation) ill agree with the state of my
body, yet I am so farre from shrinking or giving over this honourable
enterprise, as that I am willing and ready to lay all I am worth upon the
adventure of the Action, rather than so Honourable a worke should
faile, and to returne with all the convenient expedition I may, beseeching
your Lordships, and the rest, not onely to excuse my former wants, happened by the Almighty hand: but to second my resolutions with your
friendly indeavours: that both the State may receive Honour your selves
Profit, and I future Comfort, by being imployed (though but as a weake
Instrument) in so great an Action.

And thus having plainely, truely, and briefely, delivered the cause of my
returne, with the state of our affayres, as wee now stand, I hope every
worthy and indifferent hearer will by comparing my present resolution
of returne, with the necessitie of my comming home, rest satisfied with
this true and short Declaration.

The first English physician to land on American shores was Henry
Kenton who arrived on the eastern shore of Virginia in 1603. Dr.
Thomas Wotton was among the first colonists at Jamestown, and was
listed as fleet's physician and general of the colony His stay in the
New World must have been very short as the old archives hardly
mention him. Dr. Walter Russel arrived at Jamestown one year after
its founding. He accompanied John Smith on one of his voyages of
exploration up the various rivers and bays of the coast of Virginia
and attended him for injuries which he sustained en route. He also
is mentioned as administering to an Indian chief who had a gunshot
wound of the knee.

In 1608 Dr. Anthony Bagnall was surgeon to the fort at Jamestown and he accompanied Captain Smith on a voyage from Jamestown to Nausamond (Norfolk). It is related that Dr. Bagnall, while
making a professional call, was shot at by an Indian. The arrow conveniently perforated his hat leaving his cranium intact.

These physicians evidently did not linger in the colony, however,
for in 1609 when Captain Smith was injured by the explosion of some
gunpowder, he was obliged to set sail for England to secure treatment. ("there was neither chirurgeon nor chirurgery at the fort.").

Just when Dr. Lawrence Bohune (——1622), first physician-general
to the colony of Virginia, arrived is not known, but it was within the
first half of the year 1610. He was the first physician-general of the
London Company appointed for service in the colony.

Lord Delaware and the members of the Council sent a letter to the
London Company dated July 7, 1610:

"I only will entreate yee to stand favourable unto us for a new supply in such matters of the two-fold physicke, which both the soules and bodies of our poor people here stand much in need; the specialties belonging to the one, the phisitions themselves (whom I hope you will be careful to send to us) will bring along with them the peculiarities of the other we have sent herein, inclosed unto us by Mr. Dr. Bohune, whose care and industrie for the preservation of our men's lives (assaulted with strange fluxes and agues), we have just caused to commend unto your noble favours; not let it, I beseech yee, be passed over as a motion slight and of no moment to furnish us with these things, so much importuning the strength and health of our people, since we have true experience how many men's lives these physicke helps have preserved since our coming in, God so blessing the practice and diligence of our doctor, whose store is now growne thereby to so low an ebb, as we have not above three weekes physicall provisions."

As previously intimated, the colonists were as yet unacclimated, and much sickness prevailed; thus Dr. Bohune's pharmacopœia was enlarged by the use of sundry new vegetables and minerals, rhubarb being found "to be of service in cold and moist bodies for the purginge of fleame and superfluous matter."

Besides acting as physician, Dr. Bohune was a share-holder in the London Company and a member of the General Court which met on January 26, 1619, and February 2, 1620. He and James Swift, in the 1619 session, laid claim for such lands as were patentable to those "who have undertaken to transport to Virginia great multitudes of people with store of cattle." Bohune and Swift gave the number of immigrants so transported by them as three hundred. Bohune subsequently bought out Swift's interest.

The General Court, on December 13, 1621, ordered: "Mr. Doctor Bohune havinge desired yt hee might be a Phisition generall for the Company according to such conditions as were formerly set downe by way of Articles unto which place they had allotted five hundred acres of land and twenty Tenants to be placed thereupon att the companies charge."

By the end of 1621, Dr. Bohune returned to England to secure new supplies and colonists and early in 1622 he set sail with eighty-five immigrants on the *Margaret and John*. At Guadeloupe they took on six Frenchmen. On March 19, 1622, while nearing the West Indies to obtain water, they fell in with two large ships who feinted to be Hollanders until they had secured the advantage of position, when they broke the Spanish colors and fired upon the English ships. The unequal combat continued for six hours with the most desperate courage on the part of the English; and then they beat off the enemy with the loss of the latter's captain, making "their skuppers run with blood, coloring the sea in their quarter."

In this herioc defense Dr. Bohune fell, while encouraging the crew to resistance. Seven others were killed outright, two died and twenty were wounded. The victory fired the English mind and high tribute was paid the memory of the gallant Bohune.

Purchas used the incident in "Purchas his Pilgrimage," and Captain John Smith recited an account of it in his History of Virginia. George Deseler wrote of it in Amsterdam, and Thomas Hothersell, "late zitysome and groser of London being an I witness and interpreter in this exployte," left a description in a manuscript which is still in existence.

The first attempt to build a hospital in continental United States occurred at Henricopolis in 1620.

Dr. John Pott was appointed by the London Court to succeed Lawrence Bohune as physician to the colony of Virginia. He sailed with his wife Elizabeth on the *George* and landed at Jamestown in 1622.

The records of the London Company for the sixteenth of July, 1622, demonstrate that he was recommended for the position of physician-general by Dr. William Gulstone: "For so much as the physicians place to the company was now become voyde by reason of the untimely death of Dr. Bohune, slain in the fight with two Spanish shipps of Warr the nineteenth of March last, Dr. Gulstone did now take occasion to recommend unto the company for the said place one Mr. Potts, a Mr. of Artes, well practised in Chirurgerie and Physique, and expert also in distillinge of waters, and that he had many other ingenious devices so as he supposed his service would be of great use unto the colony in Virginia."

The Council ordained that "If Mr. Pott would accept of the place upon the same conditions as Dr. Bohune did, he should be specially recommended to the Governor to be well accommodated and should have a chest of Physique £20 charge unto the company, and all things thereunto apertaining together with £10 in books of Physique which should always belonge unto the company, which chest of Physique and Books Dr. Gulstone was desired to be, and seeing he intended to carry over with him his wife a man and a maid they should have their transporte freed, and if one or more Chirurgions could be got they likewise should have their passage freed which conditions Mr. Pott having accepted of was referred to the committees to be further treated and concluded with."

Dr. Pott became a member of the Council on May 24, 1625, and governor by election of the Council on March 5, 1628. He only lasted a little over a year as governor when Sir John Harvey succeeded him. Hardly had Harvey assumed office when Dr. Pott's enemies charged him with having pardoned and restored the privileges of a wilful murderer, and with holding some cattle not his own. Harvey confiscated Pott's property and ordered him to remain under arrest at his home until the General Court of July 9, 1630, when he was arraigned before a jury of thirteen on the charge of "felony." The doctor vehemently protested his innocence and declared the evidence against him was hypocritical and unreliable. The jury none-the-less convicted him. Governor Harvey held off sentencing him until he could correspond with the King, writing him that the prisoner "was the only physician in the Colony skilled in epidemical diseases." He pleaded for his pardon, and the restoration of his estate because of his lengthy residence and valuable service. Mrs. Pott personally set sail for England to importune the King in person.

Charles investigated and reported that the condemning of Dr. Pott "for felony" upon superficial evidence was drastic and very errone-ous. The King signed his pardon restoring all rights and privileges on July 25, 1631, most particularly for the reason that he was "the only physician in the Colony."

After his pardon Dr. Pott retired from all public life and devoted his time to the practice of medicine. He had acquired a grant of three acres on Jamestown Island in 1624, which was increased to twelve acres in 1628, but the unhealthiness of the Island drove him inland. In 1632 he purchased a plantation and erected the first home in Mid-dle Plantation, seven miles from James City, which he called "Harop." The fact that the "Surgeon of the Colony" had moved to Middle Plantation was a convincing argument in favor of its health-fulness. Surveys were quickly made and new homes erected so that there grew up around "Harop" a village which later was given the name of Williamsburg.

Notwithstanding the aforementioned factual accounts of the woe-ful days of the early colonists, there is at least one voice that plays down the disagreeable features and promotes a measure of optimism. William Strachey, recorder and secretary of Jamestown, declares:

The temperature of this country doth well agree with the English constitucions, being sometymes seasoned in the same, which hath ap-peared unto us by this that albeyt, by many occasions, ill-lodging at the first (the poorer on the bare ground and the best in such miserable cot-tages at the best, as through which the fervent piercing heat of the sun, which there (it is true) is the first cause creating such sommer fevers amongst them, found never resistance) hard fare, and their owne judge-ments and saffeties instructing them to worke hard in the faint tyem of sommer, (the better to be accommodated and fitted for the wynter,) they have fallen sick, yet have they recovered agayne, by very small meanes, without helpe of fresh diet, or comfort of wholesome physique, there being at the first but few physique helpes, or skillful surgeons, who knew how to apply the right medicine in a new country, or to search the quality and constitucion of the patient, and his distemper, or that knew how to councell, when to lett blood, or not, or in necessity to use a launce in that office at all.

According to Purchas, three thousand five hundred and seventy immigrants arrived in Virginia during the years 1619, 1620 and 1621. Before these arrived there were six hundred settlers there, so that the total number of settlers of that colony up to 1621 has been estimated at four thousand one hundred and seventy. In the Indian war of 1622 three hundred and forty-nine whites were killed, but by 1624 the total number of the settlers was but eighteen hundred. This shows a very heavy rate of mortality, especially when it is considered that the majority of the colonists were adult males.

Edward Ingle points out that some interesting medico-legal problems concerning medical practice in colonial Virginia appear in William Waller Hening's "Statutes at Large," a collection, in thirteen volumes, of the laws enacted by the General Assembly of the Colony.

This collection affords one of the primary sources of deducing the history of Virginia. In analyzing these documents, it is proper to remember that there was a tendency of colonial law-making bodies to reproduce English laws or customs.

The fundamental legislation calculated to control the practice of medicine was first passed in 1639. Essentially the same law was repeated in 1646. Let us permit the statutes to speak for themselves:

ACT XV—1643-6

Whereas by the 9th act of Assembly held the 21st of October, 1639, consideration being had and taken of the immoderate and excessive rates and prices exacted by practitioners in physick and chyryrgery and the complaints made to the then Assembly of the bad consequence thereof, It so happening through the said intollerable exactions that the hearts of divers masters were hardened rather to suffer their servants to perish for want of fitt meanes and applications than by seeking reliefe to fall into the hands of griping and avaricious men, It being apprehended by such masters who were more swayed by politick respects than Xian (Christian) duty or charity, That it was the more gainfull and saving way to stand the hazard of their servants than to entertain the certain charge of a physitian or chirurgeon whose demands for the most parte exceed the purchase of the patient, It was therefore enacted for the better re-drese of the like abuses thereafter vntil some fitter course should be ad-vised on, for the regulating phisitians and chirurgeons within the collony, That it should be lawfull and free for any person or persons in such cases where they should conceive the acco't of the phisitian or chirurgeon to be vnreasonable either for his pains or for his druggs or medicines, to arrest the said phisitian or chirurgeon either to the quarter court or county court where they inhabitt, where the said phisitian should de-clare vpon oath the true value worth and quantity of his druggs and medicines administred for the vse of the plt. whereupon the court where the matter was tryed was to adjudge and allow to the said phisitian or chirurgeon such satisfaction and reward as they in their discretion should think fitt, and it was further ordered that when it should be sufficiently proved in any of the said courts that a phisitian or chirurgeon had neglected his patient, or that he had refused, being thereunto required, his helpe and assistance to any person or persons in sickness or extremity, That the said phisitian or chirurgeon should be censured by the said court for such his neglect or refuseall, which said act and every clause therein mentioned and repeated, *this present Assembly to all intents and purposes doth revive, rattifie, allow, and confirme with this only ex-ception* that the plts. or patients shall have their remedie at the county courts respectively vnless in case of appeale.

The following enactment of March 1660-1661, is designed to pro-tect the physician where he is called in on a case that terminates fatally:

Whereas by a former act of assembly no accompts are pleadable against dead men's estates whereby some scruples have been made about the accompts of phisitians and Chirurgeons cannot possibly take bills, *Bee itt therefore enacted* that phisitians and chyrurgeons accompts shall be pleadable and recoverable for meanes administred and paines taken in the fitt of sickness whereof the patient dyes, and where the patient re-covers six months after such recovery and noe longer.—

The next statute is designed to protect the patient from "avaricious practitioners." It was passed in 1661-1662:

ACT XCII—1661-2
Chirurgions accounts regulated.

Whereas the excessive and immoderate prices exacted by diverse avari-tious and gripeing practitioners in physick and chirurgery hath caused several hardhearted masters swayed by profitable rather than charitable respects, rather to expose a sick servant to a hazard of recovery than put themselves to the certaine charge of a rigorous though unskilfull phisician, whose demands for the most part exceed the purchase of the patient, many other poore people also being forced to give themselves over to a lingering disease, rather than ruine themselves by endeavouring to procure an uncertaine remedy, for the redrese thereof for the future, *Be it enacted* that it shall be lawfull for any person or persons conveiving the accompt of the physician or chirurgeon unreasonable to arrest the said phisitian or chirurgeon to the generall or county court where the said phisitian or chiryrgion shall declare upon his oath the true value, cost and quantity of the drugs administered, for which the court shall grant order against the plaintiff with fifty percent advance, and such consideration for his care, visitts and attendance as they shall judge he hath deserved, and if it shall appear by evidence that the said phisitian or chirurgeon hath neglected his patient while he was under cure, the court shall censure him to pay so much as they in their discretion shall think reasonable.—

ACT III, April 1692 amended the Act of 1661-2 characterizing the "arrest" to court as "being in itselfe unreasonable," and permitting the court to increase the allowance for medicine, etc. In a later general law, relating to administration of estates, courts were permitted to "put such a reasonable valuation upon the medicines administered, and the visits, attendance and other services performed, as to them shall seem meet and just."

The following statute enacted in 1736, establishes a "ceiling" in physician's fee:

ACT, CHAPTER X, 1736

An Act for regulating the Fees and Accounts of the Practicers in Phisic.

I. Whereas the practice of the phisic in this colony, is most commonly taken up and followed, by surgeons, apothecaries, or such as have only served apprenticeships to those trades, who often prove very unskilful in the art of a phisician; and yet to demand excessive and exact unreasonable prices for the medicines which they administer, and do too often, for the sake of making up long and excessive bills, load their patients with greater quantities thereof, than are necessary or useful, concealing all their compositions, as well to prevent the discovery of their practice, as of the true value of what they administer: which is become a grievance, dangerous and intolerable, as well to the poorer sort of people, as others, and doth require the most effectual remedy that the nature of the thing will admit:

II. *Be it therefore enacted, by the Lieutenant-Governor, Council, and Burgesses, of the present General Assembly, and it is hereby enacted, by the authority of the same.* That from and after the passing of this act no practicer of phisic, in any action or suit whatsoever, hereafter to be commenced in any court of record in this colony, shall recover, for visiting any sick person, more than the rates hereafter mentioned: that is to say,

Surgeons and apothecaries, who have served an apprenticeship to those trades, shall be allowed,

	£	s.	d.
For every visit, and prescription, in town, or within five miles,	00	5	00
For every mile, above five, and under ten,	00	1	00
For a visit of ten miles,	00	10	00
And, for every mile, above ten,	00	00	00
With an allowance for all ferriages on their journeys,			
To Surgeons, For a Simple fracture, and the cure thereof,	02	00	00
For a compound fracture, and the cure thereof,	04	00	00
But those persons who have studied phisic in any university, and taken any degree therein, shall be allowed,			
If above five miles, for every mile more, under ten,	00	1	00
For a visit, if not above ten miles,	1	00	00
And, for every mile, above ten,	00	1	00
With an allowance of ferriages, as before.			

III. And to the end the true value of the medicines administered by any practicer in phisic, may be better known, and judged of, *Be it further enacted, by the authority aforesaid,* That whenever any pills, bolus, portion, draught, electuary, decoction, or any medicines in any form whatsoever, shall be administered to any sick person, the person administering the same shall, at the same time, deliver his bill, expressing every particular thing made up therein; or if the medicine administered, be a simple, or compound directed in the *dispensatories,* the true name thereof shall be expressed in the same bill, together with the quantities and prices, in both cases. And in failure thereof, such practicer, or any apothecary, making up the prescription of another, shall be nonsuited, in any action or suit hereafter commenced, which shall be grounded upon such bill or bills; nor shall any book, or account of any practicer in phisic, or any apothecary, be permitted to be given in evidence, before a court; unless the articles therein contained, be charged according to the directions of this act.

IV, *And be it further enacted, by the authority aforesaid,* That this act shall continue and be in force, for the during two years, next after the passing thereof, and from thence to the end of the next session of assembly.

Virginia enacted a law "to regulate the inoculation of small pox within the colony" in 1769 and amended it in 1777.

Virginia has the honor of being the first colony to provide an institution for the mentally ill. A committee was appointed on November 15, 1769 to formulate a bill "to make Provision for the Support and Maintenance of Ideots, Lunatics, and other persons of unsound Minds." It was not until June 27, 1770 that the House of Burgesses passed this enactment. In 1773 the structure was completed in Williamsburg with a full complement of cells, chairs and other instruments for dealing with the insane. On October 12, 1773, the asylum was opened for the admission of patients.

Unfortunately, but naturally enough, all the barbarities of European mental institutions were introduced into the Williamsburg establishment. The inmates were restrained, chained and whipped when such was deemed necessary. Narcotics, emetics and purges were used routinely. Bleeding was a therapeutic procedure which was performed frequently and profusely. Such practices continued until the time that the reforms of Philippe Pinel were introduced.

In the colonial and revolutionary history of Virginia, the following physicians deserve special mention: Doctors John Mitchell, John Clayton, William Cabell, Thomas Walker, George Gilmer, Theodoric Bland, Arthur Lee, Adam Stephen, James Craik, Jessee Bennett, John Minson Galt, Andrew Robertson, Robert Honyman, John Hale, James McClurg, Gustavus Richard Brown, William Brown, William Baynham, Robert Wellford and Elisha Cullen Dick. All did their part to advance the science or art of medicine in their beloved state.

At the dawn of the eighteenth century, Dr. John Mitchell, an English physician, came to the New World and settled in Urbanna, a village on the Rappahannock. He authored a monograph on the 1737, 1741 and 1742 Virginia yellow fever epidemics. "An Account of the Yellow Fever which prevailed in Virginia in the years 1737, 1741 and 1742, in a Letter to the late Cadwallader Colden, Esq., of New York, from the late John Mitchell, M.D., F.R.S. of Virginia" was published in the American Medical and Philosophical Register. Dr. Mitchell treated quite a few cases and did a few autopsies. Mitchell's manuscript fell into the hands of Benjamin Franklin who turned it over to Dr. Benjamin Rush. Dr. Rush credited Dr. Mitchell's description of this dread disease for enabling him to detect yellow fever in Philadelphia in 1793.

Dr. Mitchell became famous for his botanical works. He corresponded with Linnaeus, who named the partridge vine or squawberry after him, "Mitchella repens." Many fresh plants were sent by Mitchell to the famous botanist and he always courteously thanked his friend for remembering him. Mitchell's "Dissertatio Brevis de Principlis Botanicorum et Zoologogorum" was dated Virginia, 1783, and "Nova Plantarum Genera," 1741.

John Mitchell sailed back to England in about 1747 and was elected a fellow of the Royal Society. The results of his researches in America were presented to the learned Society in several addresses, among them "The Preparation and Use of Various Kinds of Potash," 1748, and "The Force of Electrical Cohesion." Another paper was entitled "Essay on the Causes of the Different Colours of People in Different Climates," read before the Royal Society, by Peter Collinson in 1744. "The Contest in America between Great Britain and France, by an Impartial Hand," anonymous, about 1757 and "The Present State of Great Britain and North America," 1767, are credited to Mitchell. Mitchell died in March, 1768.

John Clayton (1693-1773), whose chief fame rests on his botanical researches, was born in England in 1693. After receiving his education in his home county, Dr. Clayton came to Virginia in 1705, and settled in Gloucester County where he remained until his demise in 1773. Toner states that he had a medical education and was a physician. As one of the leading botanists of his day, Clayton, like Mitchell, was a regular correspondent of Linnaeus. Laurence Gronovius named "Claytonia virginica," after him.

Clayton maintained an excellent botanical garden and wrote a two volume opus on botany and a "hortus siccus" of folio size, with marginal notes and directions to the engraver in preparing the plates for the proposed work. These pioneer works were left in charge of the county clerk of New Kent only to be burned with the county records at the start of the War of Independence.

Many articles descriptive of the plants he discovered were published in the "Philosophical Transactions," in London. Several of these treated of medicinal plants, and others, of the different species of tobacco and their cultivation. His main work was his fine "Flora Virginica," editions of which were issued from the press at Leyden in 1739, 1743, and 1762, and is referred to by all writers who treat of North American plants. John Frederick Gronovius, the celebrated Swedish naturalist, and the Dutch naturalists of the same name, collaborated with Clayton on the book.

John Clayton was assistant, and later for half a century, clerk of

Gloucester County and this seems to indicate that he was not an active practitioner.

After reaching the ripe old age of seventy-seven, Clayton made an extensive botanical exploring tour of Orange County, then largely a wilderness, and he is said to have visited almost every part of the colony in botanical research.

His fame as a naturalist was world wide. Clayton was religious and a sincere follower of the Church of England. He felt that no botanist could be an atheist, for, without God, how could one explain the infinite wisdom and contrivance displayed in the structure of the smallest plant?

John Clayton passed away on the fifteenth of December, 1773.

William Cabell (1700-1774) was born in Warminster, England, on March 9, 1700. After pursuing a medical course in London, he graduated from the Royal College of Surgeons. It is said, without positive confirmation, that he practiced for several years in London with success, and then entered the British Navy as a surgeon. He arrived in Virginia in 1724 or 1725, and after residing for a time in Williamsburg and in Henrico County, he bought land in Goochland County and set up his permanent residence there.

Cabell is described as tall, spare, lithe and active, with a great capacity of endurance. Before he was disfigured by wounds inflicted by an exploding gun, he was quite handsome. His fortitude and physical courage are attested to by the fact that he carried "the settlements at least fifty miles to the westward, when no other man would attempt it." He maintained an up-to-date medical library.

In 1726, Cabell married Elizabeth Burks who passed away in September, 1756, of "billious fever and coma" (presumably malaria).

In 1726, he was deputy to the high sheriff of Henrico. In 1728-1729, he became one of the justices of the county of Goochland, and in 1729 was appointed county coroner. In 1735 he returned to England and left his wife to manage his affairs in Virginia.

He returned to Virginia in 1741 and secured a tract of land in Nelson County, fifty miles west of any settlement, and extending for twenty miles along the James river. This land grant contained 8,000 acres of river-bottom land. He erected an edifice, Liberty Hall, and lived there for the remainder of his life. He also founded a town on his holdings named Warminster after his birthplace.

Early in this new development there was no population sufficient to support a physician. Consequently he became assistant surveyor to his friend, Col. John Mayo. After Mayo died in 1744, he acted as assistant surveyor to Col. Joshua Fry until 1753, at which date he turned over this business to his son, John.

The population now markedly increased, William Cabell went back to his profession, and built up an extensive practice in the counties of Nelson, Albemarle, Augusta, Bedford, and Prince Edward.

Cabell ran a private hospital in his house and did plenty of surgery. His fee records show that he did not hesitate to guarantee cures, but at a price. Whereas his regular charge for amputation of the leg or arm was seven pounds ten shillings, twelve to fifteen pounds was charged for a guaranteed job. He furnished wooden legs to his patients at ten shillings each. Hospital patients paid for their board and "necessaries furnished," but professional services were contracted for, generally on the "no cure no pay" plan. His fee for a house call was from one to five pounds, Virginia currency, according to distance. His therapeutic armamentarium included purges, boluses, cordials, pills, blisters, drops, powders, plasters, diaphoretics, and emetics. Turlington's balsam, Bateman's drops, Stoughton's bitters and Anderson's pills were favorites of his.

Cabell continued his medical activities until at least as late as 1770 as is demonstrated by the following entry in his diary: "Attended (September 1770) Col. John Fry's wife with dead child three nights and two days."

He died on April 12, 1774, after ailing for two years.

Thomas Walker (1715-1794) was born in Gloucester County, Virginia, on January 25, 1715. After attending William and Mary College, he settled in Fredericksburg, Va. and became famous as a physician. He is credited with having trephined bone for suppurative osteomyelitis in 1757, making him one of the first known to have done that operation. He married the widow of Nicholas Merriweather and so acquired Castle Hill in Albemarle. He ably filled many important positions of trust, and was the guardian of Thomas Jefferson, as well as being an intimate friend of General Washington to whom he was related by marriage.

He was first to explore Kentucky, which he visited in 1745 and again in 1750. In the French and Indian wars he served as the commissary general of the Virginia troops. He was a member of the House of Burgesses, of the Virginia Convention of 1775, commissioner to treat with the Indians after their defeat by Andrew Lewis, and also a commissioner to run the boundary line between North Carolina and Virginia, which was known as "Walker's Line." He wrote, "Journal of an Exploration in the Spring of the Year 1750," with a preface by William Cabell Rives (Boston). He died at Castle Hill on November 9, 1794 at the ripe old age of eighty.

George Gilmer (1742-?) was born at Williamsburg, Virginia on January 10, 1742. He was a son of Dr. George Gilmer who migrated from Scotland to become an eminent and successful physician, surgeon and druggist of Williamsburg for half a century. His uncle was the aforementioned Dr. Walker, who aided him in his medical studies. Later he received his medical degree at Edinburgh University. Gilmer first settled in his native town, but later he moved to Albermarle County and opened his office there. In 1774 he served his county in the House of Burgesses, and was the mover of a resolution on the subject of the Crown Lands which was seconded by William Henry. An energetic orator, when Dunmore seized power in the colony, he aroused his countrymen so efficiently that a company was formed to march to Williamsburg and demand redress. Gilmer was lieutenant of this company. His county sent him to the convention of 1775 as the alternate of Thomas Jefferson.

His wife, Lucy, the daughter of Dr. Walker, gained a reputation commensurate with her patriotic husband for in the early days of the War, she handed Mr. Jefferson her jewels and exhorted him to sell them to help finance the War.

Theodorick Bland (1740-1790), after receiving a European medical education, returned to Virginia in 1765 and practiced medicine for seven years, at which time he gave up his practice and issued the following statement:

"With a constitution weak and infirm from my cradle, I buffeted the winds and faced the weather in all its extremes from the severest cold to the most intense and scorching heat; I exposed myself to every inclemency both by night and by day; and have for near seven years undergone all the distresses, cares and anxieties, which are the constant and unremitting attendants of a conscientious practitioner of physic, and all this in direct opposition to my leading and strongest inclinations to a calm, quiet, and philosophical life in a rural situation, and with a loss of every social and domestic enjoyment; for what enjoyment of time can a man have who is subject to perpetual alarms? My resolution to renounce the practice of physic is not the effect of whim or caprice, but of absolute and cogent necessity."

Arthur Lee (1740-1792) was born in Westmoreland County, Virginia, on December 20, 1740. He came from substantial stock being the sixth son of Thomas Lee of Stratford, who is remembered as the first native Virginian to be appointed governor. All six of the elder Lee's sons attained prominence. Concerning them, Washington wrote: "I know of no county that can produce a family all distinguished as clever men, as our Lees."

Arthur Lee received his medical degree from Edinburgh University, at which institution he excelled in botany and in materia medica. He wrote a prize winning monograph in Latin on the botanical character and medicinal uses of Peruvian bark. The university thought so much of this work that it published it.

But Virginia called and Lee settled in Williamsburg where he built up a large practice. The practice of medicine, however, did not satisfy the young physician so he gave it up and went to London to study law in the Temple. While in London, he greatly aided his country by reporting to America the earliest information concerning the plans of the British Ministry. Thus, when instructions were forwarded to Governor Bernard, Lee communicated their contents to the patriots of Boston. In 1775, while in London, he acted as agent for Virginia, and presented the King in August 1775 the second petition from Congress. Lee was later selected as minister to France, and he met Dr. Franklin and Mr. Deane, at Paris in December 1776. Dissention arose between Lee and his colleagues which resulted in him being recalled to America. However, his honor was so obvious that the public did not harbor ill will against him, and in 1781 he was elected to the State Assembly. From 1782 to 1783 he served in Congress, and in 1784 he was appointed commissioner for consummating a treaty with the Indians of the Six Nations, a trust which he executed ably and with great integrity. In 1790, by special permit, he was admitted as a counsellor of the Supreme Court. Arthur Lee passed away following a short illness on December 12, 1792, at Urbanna, Middlesex County, Virginia.

Adam Stephen was born in Scotland, date unknown. He attended Edinburgh University for six years, and excelled as a scholar. After leaving the gates of Edinburgh he passed the examination for naval surgeon, "but discovering that officers and men were a parcel of bears," he joined the army as a hospitalship surgeon in the expedition against Port L'Oriente. Eventually he settled in Virginia.

Stephen served with honor in the French and Indian War, and together with Dr. James Craik, accompanied Washington on that dangerous mission that terminated at Fort Necessity. When war with the mother country blazed forth, he was found to be solidly on the side of his adopted country. The third and fourth Virginia regiments were commanded respectively by Hugh Mercer and Adam Stephen. Stephen later was elevated to the rank of general in the Continental Army. He served also as peace commissioner to the Indians. Martinsburg, nestled in Berkeley County (now West Virginia), was founded and planned by Stephen.

The following quotations are from an old manuscript endorsed in the handwriting of Dr. Rush in 1775: "Stephen made himself known by making an incision into the liver of Mrs. Mercer of Stafford County, cleansing and healing the ulcers there, contrary to the opinion of all the faculty employed to cure the lady." Was this a case of abscess of the liver cured by operation? Stephen also performed an operation on Abraham Hill for aneurysm, "restoring him the use of his arm and hand."

Dr. Stephen lived to an old age, dying in Martinsburg in November, 1791.

James Craik (1731-1814) came into the world at his father's county seat, Arbigiand, near Dumfries, Scotland. Following his medical course at Edinburgh, he decided to migrate to the New World. For a time he engaged in practicing in the West Indies, but later he moved to Virginia. It was in the latter place that Craik met the young planter and surveyor, George Washington, and a friendship between the two was established.

In 1754 Craik was appointed surgeon of the Virginia Provincial Regiment which was led by Washington and he took part in the battles of Great Meadows and Monongahela, where he treated the wounds of Braddock. When the Virginia Provincial Army was organized, Craik was chosen chief medical officer. During the period when he practiced medicine in Charles County, Maryland, Washington and he made exploring trips into the west which became famous in the annals of colonial blood and thunder drama.

Such a man as Craik naturally became a fiery patriot and at the start of the War of Independence he became assistant medical director of the hospitals in the Middle Department at the request of Washington. He also organized the medical department of the forces of Count Rochambeau. He became next in rank to the director general and held this post until the end of the war. He personally engaged in many important campaigns, including the capitulation at Yorktown. Through his agency the Conway Cabal against George Washington was exposed.

In 1782 the University of Pennsylvania conferred the M.D. degree on one James Craik, thought to be the one now under discussion. After the war, Craik moved to Alexandria so that he could be near his beloved friend's Mount Vernon home, and remained there until 1798, when war with France seemed inevitable and Washington was again summoned to lead the army. Washington insisted that Craik be selected head of the medical department and so he was duly commissioned physician-general, retaining this office until the army was disbanded in 1800. Craik survived Washington by fifteen years, dying in Fairfax County, Virginia, on February 6, 1814.

Dr. Craik was called in first during the last illness of George Washington in 1799. Realizing the seriousness of the great one's condition, he summoned Dr. Elisha Cullen Dick to Mount Vernon at once.

Craik and Dick were shortly joined by Dr. Gustavus Richard Brown and the following statement was issued after the patient's demise:

Some time in the night of Friday, the 13th inst., having been exposed to rain on the preceding day, General Washington was attacked with an inflammatory affection of the upper part of the windpipe, called in technical language, cynanche trachealis. The disease commenced with a violent ague, accompanied with some pain in the upper and fore part of the throat, a sense of stricture in the same part, a cough, and a difficult rather than painful deglutition, which were soon succeeded by fever and a quick and laborious respiration. The necessity of blood-letting suggesting itself to the General; he procured a bleeder in the neighborhood, who took from the arm in the night, twelve or fourteen ounces of blood; he would not by any means be prevailed upon by the family to send for the attending physician till the following morning, who arrived at Mount Vernon at eleven o'clock on Saturday morning. Discovering the case to be highly alarming, and foreseeing the fatal tendency of the disease, two consulting physicians were immediately sent for, who arrived, one at half past three and the other at four in the afternoon. In the interim were employed two copious bleedings; a blister was applied to the part affected, two moderate doses of calomel were given, an injection was administered which operated on the lower intestines, but all without any perceptible advantage, the respiration becoming still more difficult and distressing. Upon the arrival of the first of the consulting physicians, it was agreed, as there were yet no signs of accumulation in the bronchial vessels of the lungs, to try the result of another bleeding, when about thirty-two ounces were drawn, without the smallest apparent alleviation of the disease. Vapours of vinegar and water were frequently inhaled, ten grains of calomel were given, succeeded by repeated doses of emetic tartar, amounting in all to five or six grains, with no other effect than a copious discharge from the bowels. The powers of life seemed now manifestly yielding to the force of the disorder. Blisters were applied to the extremities, together with a cataplasm of bran and vinegar to the throat. Speaking, which was painful from the beginning, now became almost impracticable, respiration grew more and more contracted and imperfect, till half after eleven o'clock on Saturday night, when, retaining the full possession of his intellect, he expired without a struggle.

Dr. Craik, years later, received a letter from Dr. Brown, which contained the following:

You must remember he (i.e. Dick) was averse to bleeding the General, and I have often thought that if we had acted according to his suggestion when he said, "he needs all his strength—bleeding will diminish it", and taken no more blood from him, our good friend might have been alive now. But we were governed by the best light we had; we thought we were right, and so we are justified.

In 1794 Jessee Bennett is said to have performed the first Caesarean section in the New World. The patient was his wife and he did a bilateral oophorectomy at the same time. Unfortunately, he failed to report the case in deference to his wife's feelings and because he felt that no doctors would believe that that operation could be performed in the Virginia backwoods.

John Minson Galt's (?-1808) native country, place of education and birthdate remain unknown. The first we hear of him is as chief surgeon of a military hospital at Williamsburg during the War of Independence. In 1795 he was appointed visiting physician to the hospital for the Insane at Williamsburg. This institution, as has been previously intimated, was the first insane asylum in the United States and had been founded in 1773. He held the post until his death in 1808. His son, Dr. A. D. Galt and his grandson, Dr. John M. Galt II, continued in this position for forty-one years. Starting with James, the first keeper, who was appointed in 1773, and ending with the death of Dr. J. M. Galt II, in 1862, the Galt family maintained a close connection with this pioneer mental institution for nearly 100 years.

Andrew Robertson (1716-1795) was born in Scotland in 1716. After receiving his medical degree from the University of Edinburgh, he joined the British Army as a surgeon. He was with the army for three years in Flanders, and in 1745 took part in the battle of Fontenoy. In 1755, his regiment was transferred to America and Robertson served on the ill-fated attack against Fort Du Quesne. He fled after Braddock's defeat with twenty men, who, living primarily on acorns, made their way to Dunbar's camp, where the sorry remains of the army under Colonel Washington had retreated.

Following this tragic episode, Robertson gave up his commission and moved with his wife and child to Virginia. He set foot on Virginia soil at Indian Banks in Richmond County, where he received a royal reception at the hands of a wealthy Scotch merchant, Mr. Glasscock. During this visit, his host's little daughter developed measles so Robertson prescribed for her. This, his first patient in Virginia, eventually became his fourth wife in 1771.

Robertson settled in Lancaster County and built up a fine reputation and a lucrative practice, but he never forgot the poor and downtrodden, whom he treated without remuneration and to the best of

his ability. He practiced until the very day of his death on March 1,
1795.

Robertson wrote quite a few contributions to medical literature.
Some of his articles appeared in the "Medical Inquiries and Observations," London.

Robert Honyman (1752-1824) was born in Scotland in 1752. He
received his M.D. from Edinburgh University, following which he
joined the British Navy. He did not care for the position, however,
and he resigned and set sail for America. Upon his arrival in 1774,
he settled in Louisa County, Virginia. Although new to the New
World, he promptly became an avid patriot. When the War of Independence started, he voluntarily joined up as a private. Before
long he was appointed regimental surgeon. When the calm of peace
again fell on his adopted shores, Honyman went back to private
practice in Louisa and Hanover counties for the prolonged period
terminated by his death in 1824.

Honyman was an avid reader and possessed an amazing memory.
It is said of him that he read more and remembered more of what
he read than any man in Virginia. The advent of old age did not dull
his incessant desire for knowledge. At the age of sixty he took up
Italian so that he would not miss literature in that language.

Honyman did not tolerate any criticism on the part of his patients.
If any one complained about the bill the good doctor was through
with the patient forever. His will includes the following stipulation:
"I also give and bequeath to my son my thermometer, my diploma
of doctor of physic, and also a human rib, which will be found in a
small trunk in my chest, with my earnest request that he will carefully
keep the said rib, which is of James V. King of Scotland, and transmit it carefully to his descendants."

John Hole (1754-1813) was born in Virginia in 1754. He was a
member of General Montgomery's medical staff when the General
was mortally wounded at the storming of Quebec on December 31,
1775.

A true patriot, Hole answered the first call for troops in the War
of Independence and went with the Virginia militia to the general
camp near Boston. He was appointed surgeons' mate in the Continental Army and he continued in active service until the end of the war.
Hole witnessed such memorable events as the Battle of Bunker Hill,
and Washington's assumption of command.

Hole was afflicted with the wanderlust and after the war, he
settled in New Jersey, where he married in 1778. In 1790 he travelled
to Cincinnati and started practice in the winter of 1792-3, inoculating for smallpox in this area for the first time. In 1797 he bought a

tract of land in Washington Township, Montgomery County, Ohio, paying for it with Revolutionary land warrants. He promptly built a cabin and took his family to the new home. Hole evidently accepted any kind of merchandise in payment of fees. A promissory note has been found as follows: "I owe Dr. John Hole one pair of leather shoes for a boy child.

Benj. Robbins."

At the start of the War of 1812 he was offered a position on the medical staff of the army, but his health did not permit acceptance.

Hole died on January 6, 1813.

James McClurg (1745-1823) the son of Dr. Walter McClurg, a wealthy physician of Elizabeth City County, Virginia, was a surgeon in the Virginia State Navy during the War of Independence. He graduated from William and Mary College in 1762 and received his M.D. from the University of Edinburgh, where he was held in high regard by Cullen, Black and other members of the faculty. He continued his medical studies in Paris and London and in 1773 returned to Virginia opening his office in Williamsburg, where Arthur Lee was practicing at that time. In 1779 he was elected professor of anatomy and medicine at William and Mary.

During the war with England he served first as a surgeon and later as a medical director. In 1787 he was a member of the convention which framed the Federal Constitution in Philadelphia, but he did not sign that document.

McClurg belonged to the Medical Society of Virginia and was elected its president in 1820 and 1821. When Richmond became the capital of Virginia, Dr. McClurg moved from Williamsburg to that city to become its most eminent physician for the next forty years. Toward the end of his life he confined his practice to consultations only.

That McClurg's reputation was widespread can be deduced from the fact that the Philadelphia Journal of Medical and Physical Sciences was dedicated to "The Elegant Scholar and Accomplished Physician, Dr. McClurg" in 1820.

His works included his "De Calore" which was regarded as an original and profound production; however it was never published. This essay is thought to have contained suggestions which profoundly affected some of the opinions afterwards presented by the founders of the French school of chemistry. While in London he wrote "Experiments upon the Human Bile and Reflections on the Biliary Secretions, with an Introductory Essay" (London, 1772), which attracted much attention both because of its content and style. This was translated into several languages. He made several contributions to the

"Philadelphia Journal of Medical and Physical Sciences," including an article about "Reasoning in Medicine."

McClurg died in Richmond on July 9, 1823, at the age of seventy-seven.

Gustavus Richard Brown (1747-1804) was a son of Dr. Gustavus Brown Sr. by his second marriage. He was born near Port Tobacco, Maryland, on October 17, 1747. He attended Edinburgh University and graduated in 1768. Dr. Benjamin Rush, who was a schoolmate of Brown's, stated that he was second to no student in the university. After spending several months in London hospitals, he returned to Maryland, stopping on the way for some time at the Madeira Islands, where he collected numerous rare plants and flowers.

He opened his office at Port Tobacco. During the War of Independence, he was an unquestioned patriot and was county judge in 1776 and 1777. In the spring of 1776, with his nephew, Dr. James Wallace, he set up a smallpox inoculation hospital near the Potomac river, on the Virginia side. He was a member of the State Convention which was called to ratify the constitution of the national government in 1788.

Dr. Brown is described as a handsome six-footer, of good breeding and manners. He was a well read physician and fine classical scholar. His love of botany led him to raise an extensive garden of rare flowers and plants, not for their beauty alone, but for their medicinal qualities.

Dr. Hosack was a frequent visitor to Brown during the former's residence in Alexandria, Virginia, about 1791, and it is from Brown that he got the idea for the public botanical garden which he afterwards founded in New York City.

Brown's office was a favorite rendezvous of medical students from Maryland and Virginia. He is said to have employed few remedies, but to have used these very effectively. He was called in on consultation during General Washington's last illness.

On May 15, 1769, Dr. Brown married Miss Margaret Graham, of Prince William County, Virginia, and had four children, two daughters and two sons; both of the latter became doctors.

He died at his house "Rose Hill," on September 30, 1804 at the age of fifty-six.

William Brown (17—-1792) was born in Haddingtonshire, Scotland, at his grandfather's estate. He was the grandson of Dr. Gustavus Brown, Sr. of Rich Hill, near Port Tobacco, Maryland, and the son of the Rev. Richard Brown. He studied medicine at the University of Edinburgh, and received his medical degree in 1770. His thesis was entitled "De Viribus Atmosphere." He returned to Virginia and became a citizen of Alexandria. He rapidly built up a large practice, and being a man of culture and polish, became close to Washington, Jefferson and Madison.

At the start of the War of Independence he became surgeon to Col. Woodford's regiment of Virginia troops. On September 20, 1776, he was appointed assistant to Dr. Shippen, chief physician of the Continental Army. Largely on the basis of the high recommendation of Dr. Hugh Mercer, he was appointed by Congress, on February 7, 1778, to be physician-general of the middle department to supplant Dr. Rush. On July 21, 1780 he resigned this position and went back to private practice. Although his resignation automatically forfeited his right to be paid in bounty lands, he was held in such high regard that the General Assembly of Virginia made an exception in his case and decreed that he should receive the pay due him, and also that he should be entitled to the bounty of land allowed surgeons of regiments raised under the authority of the state.

William Brown had a son, Gustavus Alexander Brown, who became a physician and practiced in Alexandria for many years.

William Brown compiled the "Pharmacopœia for the Use of Army Hospitals," a copy of which is now in the Toner collection in the Library of Congress.

He died in January, 1792.

William Baynham (1749-1814) was born to Dr. John Baynham of Caroline County, Virginia, on December 7, 1749. After a five year apprenticeship under Dr. Walker, a physician of Caroline County, he went to London to complete his medical education. In 1769 he began his studies at St. Thomas' Hospital and his anatomical knowledge soon attracted the attention of the professor of anatomy, Mr. Eise, who encouraged him greatly in the study of anatomy and surgery.

He soon became so proficient in anatomy that in 1772 he was engaged by the professor of anatomy at Cambridge as his prosector, a position he held for several years. During those months in which he was not occupied at Cambridge, he practiced most successfully at Margate as a partner of Mr. Slater, a surgeon of that place.

Mr. Eise asked him to return to London and become his assistant demonstrator, and it was in this work that he acquired that minute and comprehensive knowledge of anatomy for which he became so famous. During the five years in which he held this position he prepared for the museum many valuable and beautiful specimens.

Eise died prematurely and suddenly without having completed a promised arrangement that Baynham should succeed to his professorship. On the election before the governors Baynham lost out to Mr. Cline, by only one vote. On June 7, 1781, he was elected to the

A letter sent by Elisha Cullen Dick to James A. Hooe in 1815. This letter deals with a case of enterocolitis and the use of Eupatorium (thorough-wort boneset) in some disease not mentioned. (*Courtesy Army Medical Library, Surgeon General's Office.*)

7 1 1/2 drachms of chalk. 20 drops of laudanum a little cinnamon water with lime water. A mixture that will always be found useful in cholera after the exhibition of Calomel in the manner directed. And where it does not entirely subdue the complaint Calomel as at first must be occasionally resorted to, giving one two or three broken doses as the obstinacy or inveteracy of the complaint may seem to require.

Send a supply of the certain ointment for thy mother. The plant recommended I expect was the Eupatorium or what is called Thoroughwort. It is found mostly in meadows bears a white flower and is now in bloom. A teacupful of the tea of moderate strength should be taken three or four times a day and the affected skin should be washed with a

trans description of it being no
thinks in due. Thy friend
B. C. Dick

Company of Surgeons of London and he began to practice in that city on a par with such men as Abernethy, Cooper, John Hunter and Pott.

After the lapse of sixteen long years in the British Isles, he returned to Virginia in 1785 and settled in Essex County, where he remained until his death. He built up a huge surgical practice and it was said that there was scarcely any known operation that he did not perform with success. He became renowned for his operations for stone, cataract and extrauterine gestation. As a surgeon, none surpassed him and as an anatomist none in the New World could compare with him. Baynham was also a superb diagnostician. He was consulted from wide areas, even in other states, and he travelled long distances to perform operations.

His greatest contribution to anatomy was the discovery of the vascularity of the rete mucosum. He operated for ectopic pregnancy in 1790 and in 1799 and both patients recovered. He recorded these cases in the "Philadelphia Journal of Medical and Physical Sciences."

Dr. Baynham died on December 8, 1814, at the age of sixty-five.

Robert Wellford (1753-1824), although a surgeon in the British Army during the War of Independence, lived to win the admiration of America and to become the personal friend of George Washington. The son of William Welford (note the single "l" in the English spelling), a surgeon of Ware in Hertfordshire, England, Robert was born on April 12, 1753. He is said to have studied medicine in London and he was a licentiate of the Royal College of Surgeons, London. Shortly after starting practice in his home town, a traveler sustained a fracture of the thigh, and in the absence of Wellford's father, young Wellford managed the case so successfully that the patient, who had influence at court, obtained for the young surgeon an appointment, in the medical service of the British Army. Thus, Robert Wellford came to this country as surgeon of the First Royal Grenadiers for service in the War of Independence.

Mention should here be made that after the battles of Brandywine and Germantown, many patriots became prisoners of war of the British. The prisoners incarcerated in Philadelphia were treated as a rule unkindly and often brutally by the British surgeon and many died unnecessarily. General Washington, informed of this situation, complained vehemently to General Howe, who, after an investigation, replaced the guilty surgeon by Wellford.

Wellford was conscientious, kind and human and his efforts alone achieved a great improvement in the care of the prisoners. The prisoners, their friends and their families never forgot the good doctor and General Washington, very grateful, became his life-long friend.

Needless to say, the Tory and Hessian officers of the British Army did not like Wellford's humane policy and they treated him so badly that his position rapidly became intolerable. A man of pride, he resigned from the army and determined to make the New World his future home.

For a time, he practiced in Philadelphia, but one of the afore-mentioned prisoners, Col. John Spotswood (a grandson of the old colonial governor of Virginia), persuaded him to come to the Spots-wood home in the vicinity of Fredericksburg, Virginia.

Wellford brought with him letters of commendation and of intro-duction from Washington. The Spotswood family accepted him as their own. He rapidly built up a large practice. He married a grand-daughter of Edward Randolph, the youngest of the seven sons of William Randolph, of Turkey Island, named Catherine Yates.

In 1794, the "Whiskey Rebellion" in Pennsylvania broke out and assumed such serious proportions that the federal government raised troops to quell it. The president appointed Wellford surgeon-general of these troops. Fortunately his services never were actually needed for the presence of the troops alone was sufficient to stamp out the uprising.

Robert Wellford died in Fredericksburg in 1823. His son, Beverly R. Wellford, became a physician, and from 1854 to 1868 was profes-sor of materia medica and therapeutics in the Medical College of Virginia.

Elisha Cullen Dick (1762?-1825) was born on his father's farm in Delaware County, Pennsylvania, in about 1762. Archibald Dick, his father, was a well-to-do man of considerable culture who contributed largely to the fund for the support of the Pennsylvania Hospital in 1771. Voluntarily, he emancipated and provided for his slaves in his will. He was assistant deputy quarter-master general of the army dur-ing the War of the Revolution.

The young Dick naturally was given every educational oppor-tunity. He became a good classical scholar and studied medicine with Benjamin Rush and William Shippen, Jr., at the University of Penn-sylvania and received an M.B. on March 21, 1782. He later obtained his M.D. After his father's death, he fell heir to one-half of the paternal estate.

Dr. Dick, set upon opening an office in Charleston, South Carolina, stopped over in Alexandria, Virginia, on his way. He never left this city. In 1804 he was elected Mayor of Alexandria and continued in this office for several terms. As colonel of a cavalry regiment, he took part in quelling the Whiskey Rebellion in Pennsylvania.

That he was known as a great physician is proven by the fact that he was frequently called into consultation by his colleagues. Together with Drs. Craik and Brown, he was called to the deathbed of Washington to render his sage advice. Known for his confident manner, his sympathy toward humanity, his fine manners and his diagnostic perspicacity, Dick, indeed must be reckoned as a scholar and a gentleman. His loathing of great ostentation and braggadocio he carried to the grave, for, according to the Quaker custom, he was buried in an unmarked grave.

Elisha Dick authored "Yellow Fever at Alexandria," which appeared in the *New York Medical Repository*, and in an account of the epidemic of yellow fever which occurred in Alexandria in 1803, and "Facts and Observations Relative to the Disease Cynanche Trachealis, or Croup," written in 1808, and published in the *Philadelphia Medical and Physical Journal*. The surgeon-general's library contains an autographed letter "On Treatment of a Case of Enterocolitis, called Cholera of Infants," by Dr. Dick, which is dated July 27, 1815, and is addressed to James H. Hooe, of Prince William County, Virginia.

In 1783 Dr. Dick married Hannah Harman, daughter of Jacob Harman of Darby, Pennsylvania and by her had three children, two of whom lived to maturity: Archibald and Julia. Archibald graduated in medicine from the University of Pennsylvania in 1808.

Chapter Three

M A S S A C H U S E T T S

IN 1602 BARTHOLOMEW GOSNOLD sailed to and provided the name for Cape Cod and sailed as far south as No-Man's Land, which he named Martin's or Martha's Vineyard, a name later transferred to a neighboring larger island. Pring and Champlain, a few years later, sailed along the coast of Massachusetts, but Champlain's map of this area is very unsatisfactory. It was left for John Smith in 1614 to make sufficient exploration to construct a satisfactory map.

The first permanent colony in Massachusetts, of course, dates from the voyage of the "Mayflower," which landed one hundred and two Puritan separatists at Plymouth in 1620. Plymouth had already been named by John Smith on his maps of 1614 and 1616. The settlers had intended to colonize farther south, within the territory controlled by the Virginia Company, but storms drove them farther north. The leaders of the group realizing that their settlement was without warrant in a region beyond their patent, and noting the threatened desertion of many members of the company unless concessions were made to these, drew up and signed before landing a democratic compact of government.

This document, the democracy of which markedly differentiates between the government of Plymouth Colony and that of Massachusetts Bay, is signed by a group of colonists who "...mutually ...covenant and combine ourselves together into a civil body politic, for our better ordering and preservation and furtherance of the ends aforesaid; and by virtue hereof to enact, constitute and frame.... (laws) ...unto which we promise all due submission and obedience."

The first winter was a cruel one. Nearly one-half of the colonists died from disease and exposure, and the relations of the survivors with their partners of the London Company, who had insisted that for seven years the plantation should be managed as a joint stock company, were at low ebb. Notwithstanding, about thirty-five new colonists arrived in 1622 and ninety-six additional ones came in 1623.

By 1623, abandonment of the communal system was instituted, and with the liquidation of the partnership with the London Company in 1627, Plymouth became a corporate colony ruled by all the freemen. In 1621, the first governor, John Carver, died and the General Court (the freemen's assembly) appointed William Bradford. One assistant was also chosen at the same time as Bradford. Yearly elections were held and in a few years the number of assistants was increased to seven.

A balance of power was effected between the General Court, which acted as the legislature and electoral body, and the governor and assistants who officiated over executive and judicial matters. The General Court consisted of all freemen until Scituate was organized in 1636 and Duxbury in 1637. Then a representative form of government was adopted and Plymouth the town gradually became differentiated from Plymouth the colony.

The Plymouth colony was held to be part of the territory of the New England Council, and, in 1621, John Pierce received from that body a grant which in effect made the colonists his tenants. Pierce surrendered this document in 1622 and secured another, which made him proprietor of the colony. He was twice shipwrecked, however, and was forced to assign to the adventurers his second patent. In 1629 Governor Bradford obtained from the New England Council a grant of the tract which corresponds to the south-eastern portion of present Massachusetts. All efforts to secure a royal charter for Plymouth Colony were doomed to failure and in 1621 it was annexed to the Colony of Massachusetts Bay under the Provincial Charter.

It must be recalled that in 1620 King James created the Council for New England and transferred to this body a large piece of territory. The council in 1628 issued a sub-grant, to the "Governor and Company of the Massachusetts Bay in Newe England." A few small coastal expeditions had been conducted following John Smith's before this company in 1628 sent over John Endicott with a party of Puritans to what is now Salem. In 1630 the government of the company, with dubious legality (for the charter seems to have contemplated the residence of the company in England), transferred itself to this territory. Under the leadership of John Winthrop, this group built the foundation of the Massachusetts colony by settling Boston.

Winthrop was reelected governor repeatedly until his death in 1649. He lost one election in 1636 because of a theological revolutionary party which chose Henry Vane to the office. This was merely an incident in an important episode: the Antimonian controversy, "New England's earliest protest against formulas," in which the aforementioned Vane and Ann Hutchinson, who we shall hear more about later, openly criticized the official orthodoxy of the colony.

The magistrates successfully wreaked their vengeance on their critics and Ann Hutchinson was banished. The charter gave the company control over the admission of "freemen" (co-partners in the enterprise, and voters), "full and absolute power and authority to correct, punish and rule" subjects settling in the territory comprised in their grant, and power to "resist... by all fitting ways and means whatever" all persons attempting the "destruction, invasion, detriment or annoyance" of the plantation.

What the company did was to make the suffrage dependent on stringent religious tests, and to repress with determined zeal all theological "vagaries" and "whimsies." Criticism of church or magistrates was forbidden under dire penalties. Laws were based on strict biblical teaching. The clergy was the ruling class and the government was frankly theocratic. In 1637 Winthrop said: "We see not that any should have authority to set up any other exercises besides what authority hath already set up." In 1637 a synod at Cambridge collected eighty-two "opinions, some blasphemous, others erroneous and all unsafe," besides nine "unwholesome expressions," all of which were consigned "to the devil of hell from whence they came."

In 1647, yet another synod at Cambridge formally established the principle of state religious control. Legislation against Baptists was promulgated between 1644 and 1678. The persecution of the Quakers (especially between 1656-1662) included such choice systems of torture as scourging tongues, slitting ears, amputation and even capital punishment. In all fairness it must be admitted that dissenters like Roger Williams and some of the persecuted Quakers, exhibited a spirit which seems higher in tolerance and humanity than the essence of Puritanism. While it is true that the Puritans left England to seek liberty they definitely did not desire religious liberty in the modern sense of the term. They abhorred such a principle and they subjected their own persons to all the rigid restrictions to which they subjected others. Their frailties were small when compared with those of their contemporaries in England and elsewhere in Europe, and public opinion did not long sustain violent persecution of opinion. More than once mobs freed Quaker prisoners. Religious toleration excepted, the record of the Puritans with regard to human rights was from the first excellent.

Aside from the few persons banished to Rhode Island, theological and political differences led many to emigrate there. Others, discontented with Massachusetts autocracy and wishing, too, "to secure more room," went to Connecticut.

The evil specter of witchcraft (especially from 1691 to 1697) led to another tragedy of ignorance. In all, thirty-two persons were executed (according to W. F. Poole, about a thousandth part of those executed for witchcraft in the British Isles in the 16th and 17th centuries). Salem was the scene of the greatest excitement in 1691-1692.

The devotion of the early colonists to education is especially noteworthy. Massachusetts Bay boasted many learned men. According to one estimate, in 1640 there was an Oxford or Cambridge graduate to every 250 persons in the colony. The earliest printing in the British-American colonies was done at Cambridge in 1639. It was not until 1674 that the authorities of the colony permitted printing, except at Cambridge. The *Boston Newsletter*, was the pioneer publication of the American newspaper press.

Sporadic war with the Indians was commonplace in early colonial times. The main disturbances were the Pequot War in 1637, and the King Philip's War in 1675-76. To more effectively combat the mutual enemies, Massachusetts, with Connecticut, New Haven and New Plymouth, formed a confederacy in 1643.

The conflict between the colonies and the mother country began at the foundation of the colony, with assumptions of power under the charter which the colonial government was always trying to maintain, and the crown was as assiduously endeavouring to counteract. After fifty years of constant bickering, England finally annulled the charter of the colony in 1684, although not until 1686 was the old government actually supplanted on the arrival of Joseph Dudley, a native of the colony, as president of a provisional council. Sir Edmund Andros was later sent over with a commission to unite New York and New England under his rule.

The colonists had for a prolonged period enjoyed relatively great independence: They had enacted their own laws; the king customarily selected natives as officials; and the colonial interpretation of the old charter had by and large, been allowed to stand. Massachusetts without interference from the Mother Country, had actually forbidden the use of the English Book of Common Prayer, had placed restrictions on the franchise, had placed a death penalty on religious violations, and had freely enacted other laws obnoxious to Charles II, and James II. Laws and writs were customarily used in the name of the colony. No oath of allegiance to the sovereign was ever required although an oath of loyalty to Massachusetts was methodically demanded. Massachusetts protected the regicides, coined her own money, blocked legal appeals to the English courts, and did not bother enforcing the navigation acts.

The colonists, long accustomed to transact their own business, were furious when the charter was revoked.. Andros met determined opposition in his efforts to exact taxation, secure a church for Episcopal services, and curb the town meetings. His government was supported primarily by a small Anglican Church party, and was repugnant to the bulk of the people. In April 1689, the citizens of Boston rose in revolution, deposed Andros, imprisoned him and reestablished their old colonial form of government.

In England, Increase Mather, acting as agent (1688-1692) of Massachusetts, attempted to secure a more liberal form of government under a new charter. Plymouth Colony endeavored to secure a separate existence by royal charter, but accepted union with Massachusetts when association with New York became the probable alternative. The province of Maine was also united in the new provincial charter of 1691, and Sir William Phips came over as the first royal governor. The new charter softened religious tests for office and suffrage, and accorded "liberty of conscience" except to Roman Catholics. The old religious narrowness had begun to subside and the clergy had lost most of its power.

Under the provincial charter, there was always bickering between the prerogative party, headed by the royal governor, and the popular party, which was mindful of the practical independence under the colonial charter. This conflict finally resulted in the War of Independence. The inter-charter period, 1686-1691, is of great importance in this connection. The popular majority kept up the feeling of hostility to the royal authority in the ever increasing battles in the legislative assembly over the salary to be voted to the governor, although these antagonisms were from time to time forgotten in the wars with the French and Indians. During the Earl of Bellomont's administration, New York was again united with Massachusetts under the same executive (1697-1701).

Massachusetts was a pioneer in protesting against the exercise of sovereign power by the crown and the first general moral and political revolt that marked the approach of the Revolutionary War occurred in this state. The first active opposition to the crown was the resistance, led by James Otis, to the issuing of writs to compel citizens to assist the revenue officers; followed later by the outburst of feeling at the imposition of the Stamp Act (1765), when Massachusetts took the lead in confronting the royal power.

The governors appointed by the crown were far from conciliatory and the measures instituted in parliament aroused the colonists further. Royal troops sent to Boston in 1768 intensified the ire of the populace. In an outbreak on March 5, 1770, garrison troops shot down a few citizens in a crowd which assailed them. This is known as the "Boston Massacre."

The merchants combined to prevent the importation of goods which by law would yield the crown a revenue; and the patriots under the leadership of Samuel Adams, instituted regular communication between the different towns, and afterwards, following the initiative of Virginia, with the other colonies through "committees of correspondence"; a method of the utmost advantage thereafter in forcing on the Revolution by intensifying and unifying the resistance of the colony, and by inducing the cooperation of other colonies.

On December 16, 1773, a party of citizens, disguised as Indians and instigated by popular meetings, boarded some tea-ships in the harbor of Boston, and, to prevent the landing of their taxable cargoes, threw them into the sea. In retaliation to the Boston Tea Party, Parliament closed the port of Boston (1774), which of course further enraged the colonists. The governorship was now given to General Thomas Gage, who commanded the troops which had been sent to Boston.

Events pointed to an early outbreak of hostilities. Agitation was conducted by Samuel Adams and John Hancock, a rich merchant who had deserted the crown, which forced on the war in April 1775, when Gage sent an expedition to Concord and Lexington to destroy military stores accumulated by the patriots and to capture Adams and Hancock, temporarily staying at Lexington. This detachment, commanded by Lord Percy, was assaulted, and returned with heavy loss.

The country towns now poured their militia into Cambridge, opposite Boston; troops came from neighboring colonies, and Artemas Ward, a Massachusetts general, was placed in command of the irregular force, which with superior numbers, at once shut the royal army up in Boston. An attempt of the provincials to seize and hold the commanding hill in Charlestown brought on the battle of Bunker Hill (June 17, 1775), in which the provincials were driven from the ground, although they lost much less heavily than the royal troops.

General Washington came to Cambridge in July 1775, surrounded Boston and forced its evacuation in March 1775. Generals Henry Knox and Benjamin Lincoln were the most distinguished Massachusetts officers in the revolutionary army. Massachusetts gave more soldiers and sailors and contributed more money to the war effort than any other state.

After the outbreak of the War of Independence, a temporary government with vague power persisted until a constitution was adopted in 1780, at which time John Hancock became the first governor.

The outcome of the famous Shays Rebellion was an encouraging test of loyalty to the commonwealth of Massachusetts and this insurrection was a potent factor influencing public opinion throughout the country for the adoption of the stronger national government. The Federal Constitution was ratified by Massachusetts by only a small majority on February 6, 1788, but Massachusetts became a strong Federalist state.

Among the early events of interest connected with the history of their new country which the 102 Puritan separatists learned on landing at Plymouth in 1620, was that the natives of the area which they settled had recently been almost wiped out by a horrible plague. Soon after they had founded their colony, an Indian, Samoset, entered it, who amazed everyone by welcoming them in English (which he had learned from some fishermen on the Maine coast). He told them of this dreadful disease which had decimated the population and turned the skin of its victims yellow. From the colonial descriptions given, it seems probable that the epidemic referred to was bubonic plague.

It should be recalled that the Pilgrim Fathers landed at Plymouth toward the end of December. Three months later, out of one hundred and two who had landed, but fifty survived. Bradford attributed this high death rate to "being Infected with ye Scurvie and other diseases, which this long voiage & their Inacommodate condition had brought upon them; so as there dyed some times 2 or 3 of a day, in ye foresaid time." Ten years later John Winthrop arrived with a much larger group, and each year was followed by a large increase in New England settlers.

C. F. Adams describes the unsanitary conditions at Charlestown, where the first Boston immigrants settled prior to departing for that city:

A state of things better calculated to breed sickness could not well have existed. Several hundred men, women and children were crowded together in a narrow space, almost without shelter and with unaccustomed and improper food. . . . When they arrived they had been living for months on shipboard, fed on the salt meat which was then the only sea fare. Their systems had become reduced and the scurvy had broken out. They were in no condition to bear exposure. Then, landed suddenly in midsummer, they had their first experience of a climate quite different from that which they had known before,—a climate of excessive heat and sudden change. Their clothing was not adapted to it. As a matter of course dysentery and all sorts of bowel complaints began to appear. These they did not know how to treat, and they made things worse by the salt food to which they doubtless recurred when they found that an improper use of the berries and natural fruits of the country caused the disorders under which they suffered. Their camp, too, could not have been properly policed. By degrees the hill at Charlestown, covered with decaying vegetables and animal matter, became unfit for human habitation; the air reeked with foul odors.

Dr. Fuller arrived from Plymouth on an errand of mercy, but he wrote back in despair, "Many are sick, and many are dead, the Lord in mercy look upon them...I here but lose time and long to be home." Finally, after every family in the settlement had lost at least one of its members, the immigrants moved over to the healthy location on which Boston now stands.

Samuel Fuller (1580-1633), the earliest practitioner of medicine in Massachusetts, was born in Norfolk County, England, on January 20, 1580. Little is known of his education. While in Leyden he became deacon of the church and formed an intimate friendship with William Bradford, with whom he emigrated to America. The records indicate that Fuller was married three times prior to coming to America. His last wife was Bridget Lee of Leyden and she survived him.

In the passenger list of the *"Mayflower,"* Samuel Fuller is referred to as a physician. Fuller unquestionably served the colonists during the epidemics of typhus and smallpox in 1621. Fuller cared for the sick in Plymouth where he was deacon of Reverend John Robinson's Church.

After Endicott came to Salem in 1628 many of his colonists became afflicted with scurvy, and quite a few died from lack of proper food and shelter. Endicott asked Fuller to visit Charlestown and Salem and help the ailing in these towns. Fuller promptly complied with this request. He visited Salem in 1628, and again in 1629, the reason for his second visit being the fact that there was an outbreak of disease among some newly arrived colonists. Upon Fuller's return to Plymouth, Governor Endicott sent the following letter to Governor Bradford on May 11, 1629:

I acknowledge myself much bound to you for your kind love and care in sending Mr. Fuller among us, and rejoice much that I am by him satisfied touching your judgements of the outward form of God's worship. It is as far as I can gather, no other than is warranted by the evidence of truth, and the same which I have professed and maintained ever since the Lord in mercy revealed himself unto me, being far from the common report that has been spread of you touching that particular.

Fuller had evidently brought religious calm as well as medical healing on his visits to Endicott's colonists.

Dr. Fuller wrote to Governor Bradford on June 28, 1630: "I have been to Matapan (a part of Dorchester) and let some twenty of those people's blood." Writing again to the same correspondent in the same year, he says: "I have had conferences with them all till I was weary. Governor Endicott is a goodly wise and humble gentleman and very discreet, and of a firm and good temper."

That Fuller performed a useful function among the early settlers of Massachusetts cannot be doubted. Also it is plain that he was a physician and not a preacher. The friendly and efficient professional services rendered by Dr. Fuller to the Puritan settlements did much to dissipate the distrust and hostility of the Puritans, both at Salem and in England, to the Pilgrim settlement at Plymouth, thus encouraging further immigration to this country.

According to Thacher, in his medical character, and for his Christian virtues and unfeigned piety, Dr. Fuller was held in the highest estimation and was resorted to as a father and wise counsellor during the perils of the day.

Mowrt's "Relation" refers to several occasions when Fuller proffered his medical services to Indians who were in need of professional attention. When a punitive expedition was despatched against Indian Chief Corbitant to avenge the alleged death of Tisquantum, their interpreter, two wounded Indians were conveyed back to the settlement and Fuller took care of their injuries. Fuller even made professional visits to the sick in Thomas Weston's colony at Wessagusset (Weymouth), although the colonists of this town had behaved with ill will towards the residents of Plymouth.

Fuller died with some twenty others in the smallpox epidemic during the summer of 1633. His widow became an eminent midwife, and in 1663, was asked to settle in Rehoboth, Massachusetts, to practice midwifery. She declined this invitation and passed away in 1664. Dr. Fuller's son, Samuel, became first minister of the church in Middleboro, Massachusetts.

Occasionally, regularly appointed physicians accompanied expeditions to colonize the New World.

The London Court of Assistants issued the following declaration on March 5, 1628:

A Proposicon beeinge made to Intertayne a surgeon for (the) plantacon Mr. Pratt was apoinded as an abell man vp (on) theis Condicons
Namely That 40 lb should be allowed him viz for his Chest 25s Rest
(for) his owne sallery for the first yeere prouided yt he (continue) 3
yeeres the Comp. to bee at Charge of transporting his wiffe & a ch (ild)
have 20' a yeere for the other 2 yeeres & to acrs of ground but if he stay
but one yeere then the comp to bee at chardge of his bringing back for
England & he to Leaue his seru (ant) and the Chist for the Comp service.

Agreed with Robert Morly seruant to Mr. Andrew Matthewes late
barber surgeon to srve the Comp. in Newe England for three y (ears) the
first yeere to have 20 nobles the second yeere (30) and the third 20
markes, to serve as a barber & a surgeon (on all) occasyons belonging to
his Calling to aney of this (Company) whereof he hath geeuen an Inventory... sight of It be approoued ffive pounds Is—and payd to him
ffor it the same to bee fo (rthwith payd).

Pratt practiced medicine in Cambridge and, according to Governor
Winthrop, in 1645 he sailed for Spain with Thomas Hawkins, of
Boston. Catastrophe overtook the vessel within actual sight of the
Spanish coast, for it struck a projecting rock and sank. Pratt died
in this shipwreck. Winthrop declares:

"He was above sixty years of age, an experienced surgeon, who had
lived in New England many years, and was of the first church at
Cambridge in Mr. Hooker's time, and had good practice and wanted
nothing. But he had long been discontented because his employment was not so profitable to himself as he desired, and it is like he
feared lest he should fall into want in his old age."

The earliest actual record of the apprentice method of medical
training is found in the first letter of instruction sent to Governor
Endicott of the Massachusetts Bay Colony, dated April 17, 1629. It
informs Endicott that Lambert Wilson, a chirurgeon, has been employed to treat the colonists and neighboring Indians for a three
year period. "Moreover, he is to educate and to instruct in his art
one or more youths, such as you and the said Councell shall appoint,
that may bee helpful to him, and if occasion serve, succeed him in
the Plantacon, which youth or youths fitt to learne that profession,
lett bee placed with him." The Governor mentioned Mr. Higginson's
son as a suitable candidate for training as "he hath been trayned vp in
litterature." This thirteen year old later became Reverend John Higginson and lived to the grand old age of ninety-four. He became one
of the most noteworthy men in the early history of Salem. He
probably did not become a physician, because Lambert Wilson left
the Colony a little over a year after his arrival.

The earliest autopsy in New England goes back to September 1639. Mention is made in Winthrop's History of New England of a boy who was treated badly by his master. "After the boy gate a bruise on his head, so as there appeared a fracture in his skull, being dissected after his death."

On February 23, 1643, a jury of twelve men rendered a report on the body of an Indian lad, that implied that an autopsy had been performed. "We find that this Indian came by his death by a bullett shot by John Dandy, which bullett entered the epigastrium near the navell on the right side, obliquely descending and piercing the gutts, glancing on the last vertebra of the back, and was lodged in the side of the ano."

The aforementioned Dandy, since he was an irreplaceable man—a blacksmith, was punished for this crime by being appointed public executioner. However, when he murdered Henry Gouge in 1657, the court called in two physicians, Richard Maddokes and Emperor Smith, to perform an autopsy. The jury report declared that the head being laid open to us by the Chirurgeons which was Ordered by the Court to View and Lay it open unto us. We here attest under our hands that we can See nor find nothing about the Said head but only two places of the Skin and flesh broke on the right Side of the head and the Scull perfect and sound, and not anything doth or can appear to us to be any cause of the Death of the said Gouge. And alsoe we doe attest that we did Endeavor what possible in us lay to Search the body of the Said Corps and could not possibly do it; It being so noysome to us all, and being put at first into the ground without anything about it, as the Chirurgeons and the Sheriffe can satisfie you.

Dandy was brought to trial, convicted and sentenced to death. Although he escaped to Virginia, he was apprehended and executed. Incidentally, the surgeons were each given half a hogshead of tobacco as payment for their fees.

We have intimated previously how unhygienic the conditions of the early colonists were. However bad the health factors were in the New World, let us consider for a moment the sanitation on board ship during the journey to the New World. Ships were small, over-crowded and poorly equipped. Food was of poor quality and insufficient very frequently because the time of the journey could not even be roughly estimated. It is the greater wonder then, how many survived the vicissitudes of the journey—not how many passed away before the sojourn was completed.

On July 23, 1630, when Governor Winthrop sent for his wife, he declared:

".... for the physick you shall need no other, but a pound of Doctor Wright's Electuaria lenitivii, & his direction to use it, a gallon of scurvy grease to drinke a little 5; or 6; morninges togither, with some saltpeter dissolved in it, & a little grated or sliced nutmete." On November 29, 1630, Winthrop mentions the high mortality in the settlement: "We conceive that this disease grew from ill diet at sea, & proved infectious. I write this not to discourage thee, but to warne theee & others to provide well for the sea & by God's helpe the passage will be safe & easy how longe so ever." On March 28, 1631 he declares: ".... remember to bringe juice of lemons to sea with thee, for thee and thy company to eate with your meate as sauce."

John Josselyn suggests that new colonists take with them on board boat

... juice of Lemons well put up to cure, or prevent the scurvy, (and) to prevent or take away Sea sickness, Conserve of Wormwood is very proper, but these following Troches I prefer before it. First make paste of Sugar and Gum-Dragagant (Tragacanth) mixed together, then mix therewith a reasonable quantitie of the powder of Cinnamon and Ginger, and if you please a little Musk also, and make it up into Roules of several fashion, which you may gild, of this when you are troubled in your Stomach, take and eat a quantity according to discretion.

It is fitting now to discuss what was probably the first recorded system of therapeutics to be used in the New World. It was contained in a letter by one Dr. Ed. Stafford of London to "my worthy friend Mr. Winthrop" in 1643. Entitled "Receipts to Cure Various Disorders," this document was thought by Dr. Oliver Wendell Holmes to have been addressed to Governor Winthrop of Massachusetts. C. E. Browne, however, expressed the opinion that his son, the Governor of Connecticut, was the recipient. Holmes declares:

Dr. Stafford's practical directions to so considerable a person as Governor Winthrop, in a strange land where he would be exposed to unknown causes of disease, might be taken as a fair sample of the better sort of practice of the time. There is no parade of polypharmacy; no display of learned names for aches and ailments. It was written for the special use of a friend, and evidently with care and forethought.

What were the diseases and injuries the physician expected the Governor would have to deal with? Plague, small pox, scurvy; all sorts of fevers, poisons; madness, epilepsy, hysteria, lethargy, vertigo; dysentery, jaundice; pains, rheumatic or other; affections of the urinary organs; pleurisies; watery humors, or dropsies; phlegm, or catarrhal affections,—

such are the inward complaints for which he prescribes. Fractures, dislocations, wounds, bites of venomous creatures, boils, ulcers, gangrene, scro-
fula, burning with gunpowder, etc. are the external maladies.

Herewith is the manuscript:

(1) For Madnesse: Take ye herbe Hypericon (: in English St. John's
Wort) and boile it in Water or drinke, untill it be strong of it, and redd
in colour: or else, putt a bundle of it in new drinke to Worke, and give
it ye patient to drinke, permitting him to drinke nothing else. First
purge him well with 2 or 3 seeds (: or more, according to ye strength
of the partie:) of Spurge. Let them not eat much, but keepe dyet, and
you shall see Wondrous effects in fewe dayes. I haue knowne it to cure
perfectly to admiration in five dayes.

(2) For ye Falling Sicknesse. Purge first with ye Extract of Hellebore
(:black hellebore I meane:) and in stead of St. Johns Wort, use penta-
phyllon, (or meadow Cinquefoile:) use it as aboue is said of St. Johns
Wort, & God Willing he shall be perfectly cured in short or longer tyme,
according as disease hath taken roote.

(3) For ye Mother. Give ye patient as much as will goe upon 6 pens,
or a shilling, each morning, of ye powder of ye great Bryonie roote.

(4) For Implicat or Mixt diseases, as Lethargie or Vertigo, & Mixe
either two or more of these above said in ye patient's drink.

(5) For disease of ye Bladder,—Give ye partie to drinke (: if it be an
inflammation heat of Urine:) emulcions made with barlie, huskt almonds,
and ye 4 great cold seeds, if his drinke hath been strong before; but if
small drinke and Water, give him old Maligo and Canarie, such to drinke
Warme either by it selfe or mixt with Water: and applie to the region of
his bladder, a poltis made with barlie meale, and ye rootes or leaves of
Aaron; make Injections of ye decoction of Hypericon, ye barke of a
young Oake (: the Outward black skinn being taken off:) and linnseede:
and by God's grace he shall finde present ease and cure with continuance.

(6) For ye stopping of ye Urine, or ye Stone. Give ye partie to drinke
of ye decoction of maiden hayre, fennell roots, and parsley rootes. Let
him drinke great quantitie. But before lett him drinke 2 or 3 Ounces of
ye Oyle of Allmonds newly extracted, or more: Or let him swallow a
quarter of a pound of new butter made into round bullets, and cast into
faire Water to harden them.

(7) For ye Bloodie Flix: Purge first with Rhubarbe torrified; and give
the partie to drinke twice a day a pint of this caudle following: Take a
dragme of ye best Bole-Armoniak, a dragme of Santalum Rubrum, and
dragme of Sangris draconis; and a dragme of ye best Sigillata of a yellow
colour seal'd with a Castle. Make these into fine powder, and with a quart
of red stiptick Wine, the yolks of halfe a dozen eggs, & a quantitie of

Sugar, make a Caudle, boyling the powder in a pipkin with the Wine; then adding ye yolks of ye eggs beaten, and lastly ye Sugar.

If his gutts haue bene fretted, give him ye Injection for ye bladder before mentioned, in a glister; and if you please you may adde to it the powders.

(8) For the yellow Jaundise or Jaunders. Boyle a quart of sweet milke, dissolve therein as much bay-salt, or fine Sal-peter, as shall make it brackish in taste; and putting Saffron in a fine linnen clout, rubb it into ye Milke, untill ye Milke be very yellow; and giue it ye patient to drinke.

(9) For paines in ye Brest or Limmes: Weare a Wilde Catts skin on ye place grieved.

(10) For a broken bone, or a Joynt dislocated, to knit them: Take ye barke of Elme, or Witch-hazzle; cutt away the Outward part, and cutt the Inward redd barke small, and boyle it in Water, till it be think that it Will rope; pound well, and lay of it hott, barke and all upon ye Bone or Joynt, and tye it on; or with ye Mussilage of it, and bole Armeniak make a playster and lay it on.

(11) My Black powder against ye plague, small pox; purples, all sorts of feavers; Poyson either by Way of prevention, or after, Infection. In the Moneth of March take Toades, as many as you will, alive; putt them into a Earthen pott, so yt it will be halfe full; Cover it with a broad tyle or Iron plate; then overwhelme the pott, so yt ye bottome may be uppermost; putt charcoales round about it, and in the open ayre, not in an house, sett it in fire and lett it burne out and extinguish of it selfe: When it is cold, take out the toades; and in an Iron-Morter pound them very well and searce them: then in a Crucible calcine them so againe: pound and searce them againe. The first time they will be browne powder, the next time black. Of this you may give a dragme in a Vehiculum (or drinke) Inwardly in any infection taken; and let them sweat upon it in their bedds; but lett them not cover their heads; especially in the Small pox. For prevention, halfe a dragme will suffice: moderate the dose according to ye strength of the partie; for I have sett downe ye greatest that is needfull. There is no danger in it. Let them neither eate nor drinke during their sweat, except now and then a spoonefull of Warme posset-drinke to wash their mouthes. Keep Warm and close, (for a child of 5 years, 10 graynes enough in infection, for prevention 4 or 5 graynes) till they be perfectly well: and eate but little and that according to rules of physicke.

The same powder is used playster wise with Vinegar for gangrene, or bite of anie Venomous beast, taking it likewise, Inwardly: it is used likewise for all Cankers, Fistulas & old Ulcers & Kings Evill, strewing it upon the core, and keeping them cleane.

(12) An other for old Soares. Take St. John's Wort, pound it small,

and mingle it with as much quicklime: powre on it raine Water, that may cover it, six fingers deepe in a broad earthen Vessell: putt in to ye sunne, and stirre it well once every day for a Moneth; then filter and reserve the Water for your use. Wash ye soares' with it; it cureth Wonderfully.

(13) For Burning with Gunn powder or otherwise. Take ye Inner green Rine of Elder, in latine Sambucus-Sempervive, and Mosse that groweth on an old thackt howse top, of each alike; boyle them in stale pisse, and sallet oyle, so much as may cover them 4 fingers: Let all the pisse boyle cleane away, and straine very well; putt new herbes and pisse as before, boyle that likewise away, and straine it as before. Then to to that oyle adde barrowes grease until it come to be an Oyntment, with which anoynt a paper, and lay it to ye burning anoynting the place also with a feather.

(14) For Soare Brests. Take yolkes of eggs and honie alike, beat them till they be very thinn; then with wheat flower beat them, till it be as thick as hony: spread it upon flax, and lay it upon the breast, defending the nibble with a plate of lead as bigg as an halfe crowne, and a hole in it so begg that ye nibble may come out—renewe it every twelve hours: and this will breake and coole the Brest. When it breakes, tent it with a salve of rosin, wax & terpentine alike quantitie.

(15) For Breaking of any Biles or great Swellings. If that poltis next above for the sore Brest doe not breake it, pound fox-glove, and lay it to it, and that will; then tent it as for the sore Brest.

(16) For a greene Wound. Take salve of Clownes Wort, or Clownes all-heall prescribed in Gerrits Herball; or the Oyle of Hypericon and Ballsam.

(17) For the King's evill. Take 2 Toades & let them fast 2 or 3 dayes that they may spewe out their Earth, then boyle them in a pint of Oyle in a newe pipkin covered so long, till they be brought to a black Coale broken in peeces, presse out the Oyle from the said Toades, reserve a 4th part, to the other three parts adde halfe a pound of yellow wax, shaved small. let the wax melt in the Oyle in wch. dippe the linned cloathes, that they may be well covered cerecloathes. with the 4th part of the Oyle left annoynt all the places infected, & then strewe of my black powder of Toades (mentioned before for an Antidote agaynst the Plague) upon the sores or swellings, & then put on of ye cerecloath.

dresse the running sores once everie 24 howres, but it will serve to dresse the swellings once in 4 dayes. Everie 4th day at furthest give of ye said black powder to the partie & let them swet upon it. You may proportion the dos from 5 graynes to a dragme according to the strength & constitution of ye partie. if the partie be strong, it is the better that they swet everie day or everie second day.

By this course ther is no doubt of the cure by God's assistance.

CAUTIONS IN PHYSICK.

1 That you doe not let Blood, but in a pleurisie or Contusion, and that necessitated.

2 yt in the beginning of all Feavers, you fast 2 or 3 dayes from meate and drinke, except ye last day, and that so litle, as only to sustain Nature; and afterward you come to your dyet by degrees.

3 yt you purge to follow Nature and not to contrarie her: as if the partie Vomit, you purge my vomit; if the partie be loose you purge downwards: if the partie bleed at ye nose, you draw blood.

4 yt in all purges you administer in long diseases, or to weake persons, you mixe Cordials, as Confectio Alchermes, etc. And yt you purge with simples and not compounds, except the disease be mixt.

The best purgers: Rhubarbe, or rather ye tincture of it for Choller.
Jallop for Watrie humors.
Agarick for flegme.
Extract of Scammonie, or black Hellebor, for Melancholie.
Pine de Inde halfe a Kernell for mixt humors.
Crocus Metallorum well prepared for mixt humors.
Spurge seede for ye head.
The Best Sudorificks being simples:
Snake roote:
Contra yerva.
The best gumms for drawing
Tackamahacka;
Caranna, Kereman; Burgundie pitch:
These may be used simple or mixt for old aches & paines.

Nota bene. No man can with a good Conscience take a fee or a reward before ye partie receive benefit apparent: and then he is not to demand any thing, but what God shall putt into the heart of the partie to give him. And he is not to refuse any thing, that shall be so given him, for it commes from God.

A man is not to neglect that partie, to whom he hath once administered, but to visit him at least once a day, and to medle with no more, then he can well attend. In so doeing he shall discharge a good Conscience before God & Man.

These receipts are all experimented.
London May 6th 1643.

In any history of medicine in early colonial Massachusetts it is essential to include John Josselyn, that erudite Englishman who sojourned for a prolonged period in the early Massachusetts settlements. He heartily endorses the great healing virtues of tobacco: "It helps digestion, the Gout, the Tooth Ache, prevents infection by scents, it heats the cold and cools them that sweat, feedeth the hungry, spent spirits restoreth, purgeth the stomach, killeth nits and lice; the juice of the green leaf healeth green wounds, although poysoned; the Syrup for many diseases, the smoak for the Phythisick, cough of the lungs, distillation of Rheoume, and all diseases of a cold and moise cause, good for all bodies cold and moist taken upon an emptie stomach, taken upon a full stomach it precipitates digestion." He warns, however, that immoderately taken "it dryeth the body; enflameth the blood, hurteth the brain, weakens the eyes and sinews."

Josselyn gives a listing of the diseases to which the Indians are subject. These include (1) great pox; (2) pestilent fevers; (3) plague; (4) black-pox; (5) consumption; (6) falling sickness; (7) Kings evil; (8) empyema. He mentions that the Indians are great believers in artificially induced pyrexia and diaphoresis. Perhaps their bark sealed wigwams with fire within is one of the earliest forms of fever therapy. Josselyn relates that after working up a great perspiration, the Indians rush from their wigwams to immerse themselves in a river or in the ocean. Then they "either recover or give up the Ghost."

Josselyn further declares that the colonists suffered from their native English diseases and also from local ailments:

Griping of the belly (accompanied with Feaver and Ague) which turns to the bloody-flux, carried away abundance of their children, for this the common medicines amongst the poorer sort are Pills of Cotton swallowed, or Sugar and Sallet-oyl boiled thick and made into Pills, Alloes pulverized and taken in the pap of an Apple. . . . they are troubled with a disease in the mouth or throat which hath proved mortal to some in very short time. Quinsies, and Imposthumations of the Almonds, with great distempers of cold. Some of our New England writers affirm that the English are never or very rarely heard to sneeze or cough, as ordinarily they do in England, which is not true. For a cough or stitch upon cold, Wormwood, Sage, Marygolds, and Crabsclaws boiled in posset-drink and drunk off very warm, is a sovereign medicine. Pleurisies and Empyemas are frequently there, both cured after one and the same way; but the last is a desperate disease and kills many. For the Pleurisie I have given Corianderseed prepared, Carduus seed, and Hartshorn pulverized with good success, the dose one dram in a cup of wine. . . The Stone terribly afflicts many, and the Gout, and Sciatica, for which take Onions roasted, pealed and stampt, then boil them with Neatsfeet oyle and Rhum to a plaister and apply it to the hip. Headaches are frequent, Palsies, Dropsies, Worms, Noli-me tangere, Cancers, pestilent Feavers, Scurvies, the body corrupted with Sea-diet, Beef and Pork tainted, Butter and Cheese corrupted, fish rotten, a long voyage, coming into the searching sharpness of a purer climate, causeth death and sickness amongst them . . . Men and Women keep their complexions, but lose their Teeth; The Women are pitifully Tooth-shaken; Whether through the coldness of the climate, or by sweetmeats of which they have store, I am not able to affirm.

Josselyn states that the colonists used white hellebore in place of opium and "Clownes would wort" for new wounds.

The interesting tale of the friendly Indian Massasoit should be briefly reviewed at this juncture. When news came to Plymouth that he was mortally ill, a delegation of colonists, including Edward Winslow, (later to be governor at Plymouth), came to tender their good wishes. They found him in an overcrowded house being massaged by 6 or 8 women to the raucous accompaniment of loudly proclaimed charms that "distempered us that were well, and therefore unlike to ease him that was sick."

Winslow administered "a confection of many comfortable conserves" on the point of knife which he could scarcely get between Massasoit's teeth. To quote Winslow:

When it was dissolved in his mouth, he swallowed the juice of it whereat those that were about him much rejoiced; saying, He had not swallowed anything in two days before. Then I desired to see his mouth, which was exceedingly furred; and his tongue swelled in such a manner, as it was not possible for him to eat such meat as they had, his passage being stopped up. Then I washed his mouth, and scraped his tongue; and got abundance of corruption out of the same. After which I gave him some more of the confection; which he swallowed with more readiness. Then he desiring to drink; I dissolved some of it in water and gave him thereof. Within half an hour, this wrought a great alteration in him, in the eyes of all that beheld him. Presently after, his sight began to come to him; which gave him and us good encouragement. In the mean time I inquired, how he slept; and when he went to stool? They said, he slept not in two days before; and had not had a stool in five.

Following this Winslow made Massasoit a broth which greatly improved his vitality. After a relapse due to dietary indiscretion from which Winslow also pulled him through, the grateful old patriarch tipped off Winslow that the Indians were plotting to massacre the English. Thus, this unsolicited act of medical benevolence may have been a great factor in preserving the colonists at Plymouth.

The colonists early appreciated the great need for an institution of higher education:

After God had carried us safe to New England, and wee had builded our houses, provided necessaries for our liveli-hood, rear'd convenient places for Gods worship, and setled the Civill Government: One of the next things we longed for, and looked after was to advance *Learning* and perpetuate it to Posterity; dreading to leave an illiterate Ministery to the Churches, when our present Ministers shall lie in the Dust. And as wee were thinking and consulting how to effect this great Work; it pleased God to stir up the heart of one Mr. Harvard (a godly Gentleman, and a lover of Learning, there living amongst us) to give the one halfe of his Estate (it being in all about 1700 pounds) towards the erecting of a Colledge, and all his Library: after him another gave 300 pounds, others after them cast in more, and the publique hand of the State added the rest: the Colledge was, by common consent, appointed to be at *Cambridge*, (a place very pleasant and accomodate) and is called (according to the name of the first founder) Harvard Colledge.

Physicians too needed adequate training and it was decided "that such as studies physick or chirurgery may have liberty to reade anatomy, and to anatomize once in fore years some malefactor, in case there be such as the Courte shall allow of." This enactment by the General Court on October 27, 1647 was an early promise of medical education in the New World.

According to Fitz:

There has always been a strange fascination in certain people's minds toward trying to manage other people's business. Before long amateur regulators of human affairs began to appear on the scene, ignorant amateurs who had never even "anatomized a malefactor", and yet who competed in the spiritual and physical management of souls in a manner thoroughly distasteful to competent professionals. . . . It became necessary to put a stop to such goings on. The manner in which medical licensure originated, also, was delightfully simple. Mistress Hawkins was said to have a knack at practical obstetrics and to be a good hand at the prescription of medicinal herbs. Unhappily for her, however, she was caught at these practices by someone who did not approve. There was no Board of Registration in Medicine and no Committee on Ethics and Discipline to contend with; all that was required to put a stop to her activities was a General Court ruling, easily obtainable, no doubt, if one knew the ropes; "Jane Hawkins, the wife of Richard Hawkins, had liberty till the beginning of the 3rd month, called May, and the Magistrates (if shee did not, depart before). to dispose of her, and in the meane time shee is not to meddle in surgery or physick, drinks, plaisters or oyles, nor to question matters of religion, except with the elders for satisfaction." These restrictions not proving sufficient, some months later, "Jane

Hawkins is injoyned to depart away to morrow morning, and not to return againe hither, upon paine of severe whiping and such other punishment as the courte shall think meete; and her sonnes stand bound in 20 pounds to carry her away, according to order."

More about Jane Hawkins, later.

The colonists early learned to fear epidemics with high mortality. Many favored the concept of the aforementioned Reverend Michael Wigglesworth of Malden, who declared that the country was going to pot and diseases were being engendered by deceitful young people.

> Our healthful days are at an end,
> And sicknesses come on
> From yeer to yeer, becaus our hearts
> Away from God are gone.
> New England, where for many yeers
> You scarcely heard a cough,
> And where Physicians had no work,
> Now finds them work enough.
> Now colds and coughs, Rhewms, and sore-throats,
> Do more & more abound:
> Now Agues sore & Feavers strong
> In every place are found.
> How many houses have we seen
> Last Autumn, and this spring
> Wherein the healthful were too few
> To help the languishing.
> One wave another followeth,
> And one disease begins
> Before another cease, becaus
> We turn not from our sins.
> We stopp our ear against reproof,
> And hearken not to God:
> God stops his ear against our prayer.
> And takes not off his rod.
> Beware, O sinful Land, beware;
> And do not think it strange
> That sorer Judgements are at hand,
> Unless thou quickly change.
> Or God, or thou, most quickly change;
> Or else thou art undon:
> Wrath cannot cease, if sin remain,
> Where judgement is begun.

Other individuals were sensible enough to be of the opinion that whereas prayer was efficacious in controlling disease, other methods were also beneficial.

The first recorded quarantine in the colonies took place in 1647 and was issued to prevent the spread of Yellow Fever to New England.

According to Winthrop, Massachusetts received a report in 1647 that there had been a draught in the Barbadoes . . . .

followed presently by a great mortality, (whether it were the plague or pestilent fever it killed in three days) that in Barbadoes there died 6,000 and in Christophers, of English and French men, near as many, and in other islands proportionable. The report of this coming to us by a vessel which came from Fayal, the Court published an order, that all vessels which should come from the West Indies, should stay at the Castle and not come on shore, nor put any goods on shore, without license of three of the council, on pain of 100 pounds, nor any to go aboard, etc., on like penalty. The like order was sent to Salem and other Haven towns. But one goodman Dell, of Boston, coming from Christophers in a small pinnance, and being put into Gloucester, and there forbidden to land, and informed of the order of Court yet coming into the Bay and being bailed by the Castle boat, and after by the Captain of the Castle, denied that he came from the West Indies, and having taken in 3 fishermen (whom the Captain knew) who joined with him in the same lie, they were let pass, and so came on shore at Boston, before it was known. But such of the Council as were near assembled the next day, and sent for some of the company, and upon examination finding that the sickness had been ceased at Christophers 3 months before they came forth, so as there could be no danger of infection in their persons, they gave them liberty to continue on shore, but for cotton and such goods as might retain the infection, they ordered them to be laid in a house remote, and for Dell, he was bound over to the next Court to answer his contempt. About 14 days after came a ship from Malago, which had stayed 9 days at Barbadoes. She was stopped at the Castle. The Captain brought the Master and 2 others to Boston (which he ought not to have done). Four magistrates examined them upon oath and finding they were all well, save two (who had the flux), and no goods from Barbadoes but 3 bags of cotton, which were ordered to be landed etc. at an island, the ship was suffered to come up, but none to come on the shore for a week after, etc.

The actual wording of the preceding enactment follows:

For as much as this Corte is credibly informed that ye plagu, or like grieves infectious disease, hath lately exceedingly raged in ye Barbadoes,

Christophers, and other islands, in ye West Indies, to ye great depopulating of those, it is therefore ordered, that all (our own) or other vessels coming from any pts of ye West Indies to Boston Harbor shall stop (and come to an) anchor before they come at ye Castle, under ye poenalty of 100 pounds, and that no person coming in any vessel from the West Indies shall go ashore in any towne, village or farme, or come within foure rods of any other person, but such as belongs to the vessels company that hee or shee came in, or any wayes land or convey any goods brought in any such vessels to any towne, village, or farme, aforesaid, or any other place within this jurisdiction, except it be upon some island where no inhabitant resides, without licence from ye councell, or some three of them, under ye aforesaid poenalty of a hundred pounds for every offence.

In the spring of 1649, after the decline of the epidemic, the quarantine was lifted.

Giles Firmin (1615-1697) engaged extensively in the practice of medicine although he is primarily famous as a religious dissenter in England, after he was thirty years old. In his early adult years, Firmin practiced medicine in Ipswich, Massachusetts for six years and it is possible that he administered to the professional needs of the inhabitants of Boston previously.

While in Ipswich, Firmin wrote the following: ".... only for matter of employment I have as much here as I desire and love my planting more than it, only the highest ambition of my thoughts and desires are to be useful and serviceable here in a common way. We have divers very ill; and fluxes and fevers, I observe are very dangerous."

Firmin studied under Dr. John Clerk of London (1582-1653), who became president of the College of Physicians (1645-1649). Robert Harmer wrote a letter in 1645 which included the following: "Quaeries put to some independents of C. (Colchester) upon an occasion of a sermon preached by Mr. F. (Firmin), an independent apothecary physician, sometime servant to Dr. Cl. (Clerk) of London."

In 1670, Firmin published the popular work, "The Real Christian," which was reprinted several times. He states that when his father passed away in 1634 he was "far distant." It is likely that he was studying in England at the time and that his father's demise ended his studies. He states in a pamphlet entitled, "A Serious Question Stated": "Being broken from my study in the prime of my years, from eighteen years of age to twenty-eight, and what time I could get in them years I spent in the study and practise of physic in that wilderness till these times changed, and then I changed my studies to divinity."

That Firmin visited Boston in March, 1637-8, may be inferred from the fact that he was present at the excommunication of Mrs. Ann Hutchinson on March 22d of that year. Firmin's name is first mentioned in the archives of Ipswich on January 4, 1638-9. At this time he was granted one hundred acres of land on condition that he would live there for three years. At this date, the town had been colonized for five years and the population was small. The town records mention that in the first nineteen years (1633 to 1652), the total number of male inhabitants over twenty years of age was only 332. Perhaps this is the reason that Firmin wrote to Governor Winthrop on October 10, 1639, and sought his permission to settle in another township and sell his land. He says: "I am strongly sette upon to study divinitie, my studyes else must be lost; for physick is but a meene help."

In the fall of 1644, Firmin set sail for England. While off the coast of Spain, his ship was wrecked and he did not reach England until 1645. He preached in Colchester on July 30, 1645 and he was violently attacked for expressing his non-conforming views. Firmin preached at every opportunity, plunged his dynamic spirit into theological controversies and wrote numerous pamphlets. In 1646, he moved to Shalford and was met there by his wife, children and father-in-law, who had just come over from Massachusetts. At the age of thirty-six, he was ordained minister of the Presbyterian church. In 1662 the Act of Uniformity led to the loss of his job. From then on, he was labelled a "Dissenter."

After the Declaration of Indulgence was promulgated in 1672, Firmin opened a meeting at Ridgwell and remained there until his death in April, 1697. During the ten years from 1662 to 1672, he supported his family by the practice of medicine. The Five Mile Act of 1665 forced dissenters to keep at least five miles away from any incorporated town, or any place they had previously served as clergymen.

Calamy says of Firmin:

He practised physic for many years, and yet was still a constant and laborious preacheer, both on the Lord's days and week days too—. He had one considerable advantage above his brethren which was the favour and respect which the neighboring gentry and the Justices of the Peace had for him, on account of their using him as a physician—. The poor applying themselves to him, had often both advice and physic too for nothing; and of those who were more able, he took but very moderate fees; whereby he lost the opportunity of getting an estate, which had been a very easy thing.

Oliver Wendell Holmes presents an interesting account of this distinguished preacher-physician during his rounds. Accompanying him is his disciple and student, Luke. On the first call, the patient is a strapping man with pain. The timid youth whispers: "He will die, Master, of a surety, methinks," but Firmin is sure he will recover for " 't is but a dry belly-ache," as the man does not have "the pulse of them with fevers. . . . We will steep certain comforting herbs which I will shew thee, and put them in a bag and lay them on his belly. Likewise he shall have my cordial julep with a portion of this confection which . . . hath juice of poppy in it, and is a great stayer of anguish. This fellow is at his prayers to-day, but I warrant thee he shall be swearing with the best of them tomorrow."

The master and disciple then visit the home of a young girl afflicted with tuberculosis. Luke is confident that she will recover soon because she has rosy cheeks and bright eyes. But the wise master points out that the "redness of the cheek is but the sign of the fever, . . . and that shining of the eyes is but a sickly glazing, and they which do every day get better and likewise thinner and weaker shall find that way leadeth to the churchyard gate." This patient "is not long for earth— but she knoweth it not, and still hopeth."

The embryo physician then inquires why Firmin prescribes treatment if he is so certain that the patient is going to die. The doctor replies: "Thou shalt learn, boy, that they which are sick must have somewhat wherewith to busy their thoughts."

Giles Firmin first came to Massachusetts in 1632, and he was one of the early teachers of anatomy and medicine in the New World, but not the first, for Lambert Wilson had been engaged in this task at an earlier date. He was educated at Cambridge at a time when this institution was the hotbed of Puritanism in England. Eliot, the apostle wrote to Mr. Shepard, a minister at Cambridge, on September 24, 1647, as follows:

"Our young students in Physick may be trained up better than yet they bee, who have only theoreticall knowledge, and are forced to fall to practise before ever they saw an Anatomy made, or duely trained up in making experiments, for we never had but one Anatomy in the Countrey, which Mr. Giles Firmin, (now in England) did make and read upon very well, but no more of that now."

One William Gager (?— -1630) of Boston, is referred to by Governor Winthrop as "a right godly man, skillful chirurgeon, and one of the deacons of the congregation." He passed away in September, 1630.

In 1637, a clerical physician named John Fisk settled in Salem. Samuel Bellingham and Henry Saltonstall both graduated at the first Harvard commencement in 1642, and later received their medical education in Europe.

John Glover sailed to Scotland in 1650 and was awarded a medical degree by the University of Aberdeen. He served as one of the chief men of Dorchester, as deputy to the General Court, and finally as assistant to the governor of Massachusetts. He has been referred to as "a man strong for the truth, a plain, sincere godly man, and of good abilities."

Charles Chauncy (1592-1672), although a clergyman by profession, was eminent as a physician. He distributed a high grade brand of medicine, obtained by him in England, to his students at a time when there was great need for such instruction.

Charles Chauncy was born in Yardley-Bury, Hertfordshire, England, in November, 1592, of old English stock. His preliminary education was at the Westminster school at the time of the Gunpowder Plot and he just missed being blown to bits. In 1613 Cambridge University awarded him his Bachelor of Arts degree and in 1613 he was appointed a fellow at Trinity College. He taught Hebrew and Greek at Trinity and left this institution to become vicar at Ware, Hertfordshire (1627-1633). Resigning this position, he became vicar of Marston St. Lawrence in Northamptonshire (1633-1637). Chauncy received an M.A. from Cambridge in 1617 and an S.T.B. in 1624. All this occurred prior to the time that his puritanical beliefs rendered him obnoxious to his ecclesiastical superiors.

In 1629, Chauncy appeared before the high commission on the charge that he had asserted in a sermon that "idolatry was admitted into the church" and that "an increase of atheism, popery, and Arminianism" existed in that body. In 1634 he was brought before the commission and accused of opposing the erection of an altar-rail as "a snare to men's consciences." For this so-called crime he was suspended and imprisoned until such time as he would openly admit the error of his ways. Chauncy was also forced to pay the heavy costs of his trial. Chauncy, to his everlasting dismay, lost his courage and issued a retraction in open court. His lengthy "Retraction" written in 1637 was not published until 1641, when he was in America. When, in the fall of 1637 Chauncy refused to read Archbishop Laud's book of "Lawful Sunday Sports," he found it necessary to leave his homeland and he set sail for Plymouth, where he arived in January, 1638.

After residing for three years in Plymouth as an assistant to Mr. Raynor, and spending thirteen years in Scituate as pastor of a church which developed a schism and was poorly supported, he determined to go back to England. While tarrying in Boston, the port of embarkation, he was offered the presidency of Harvard College made vacant by the death of the first president, Henry Dunster. He accepted this appointment in November 1654 and served the college until his death on February 19, 1672. That the New World appreciated Chauncy more than the Old is indicated by the statement of Cotton Mather, who declared that when Chauncy had been a year or two in town "the church kept a whole day of thanksgiving to God for the mercy which they had enjoyed in his being there."

It was Charles Chauncy's custom to get up at four in the morning and spend the early morning hours in study and devotion. A considerable number of his sermons were published as were some Latin and Greek verses. Perhaps the aforementioned retraction of his views made under coercion back in England led him to be sternly unchanging in all of his views. Until his death he continued to be firmly opposed to the baptism of the children of non-communicants, and the wearing of long hair. The latter custom he referred to as "a heathenish practice." In 1662, he published "Antisynodalia Scripta Americana," in opposition to the synod of 1662, which permitted the admission of all baptized persons, even if they had not professed a "change of heart" into the church.

Sad to relate, it is said that his writings came into the possession of his stepdaughter who gave them to her baker husband to line his pies.

All six of Charles Chauncy's sons graduated from Harvard and became preachers. Mather is the source of the statement that they were all physicians, also, just like their father. Chauncy advanced the interest of Harvard College and Massachusetts and was one of the early instructors of medicine.

Dr. Charles Chauncy's successor as president of Harvard College was Dr. Leonard Hoar (1629?-1675) who graduated from Harvard College, receiving the degree of B.A. in 1650. He then went to England and studied medicine at Cambridge University. Incidentally he was one of the few colonists to study medicine abroad and return to the colonies. He was made president of Harvard in 1672.

Hoar inaugurated the first system of technical education by adding a workshop and a chemical laboratory to Harvard. However, the College did not prosper under his leadership. A large faction opposed him, members of the board of trustees resigned, and the situation was grave. "As a scholar and a Christian" Hoar was said to be "very respectable," but he appears to have lacked in the power to govern. He resigned in March, 1675, developed tuberculosis and died on November 28, 1675.

Matthew Fuller (?—-1678) settled first at Plymouth in 1640. He moved to Barnstable in 1652, where he died in 1678. He was appointed surgeon-general of the provincial forces raised by Plymouth in 1673. His estate included "Surgeon's chest and drugs, 16 pounds. Library, 10 pounds."

Thomas Starr dwelt in Yarmouth from 1640 to 1670, and he is frequently referred to as "chirurgeon" in the town records. Comfort Starr practiced surgery in Newton, Duxbury, and Boston, where he expired in 1663.

Thacher mentions Samuel Seabury (?—-1680) and Thomas Little (1674-1712). The former died in Duxbury in 1680 in which city he had engaged in the practice of chirurgery, leaving an estate which included an antimonial cup, Culpepper's Practice of Physic, The Art of Distillation and surgeons' instruments. Little graduated from Harvard in 1695, engaged in medical practice in Plymouth in around 1700 and died at the age of 38 (1712).

Thomas Oliver is named by Winthrop as a physician of skill and experience. He was an elder of the Boston church, and is mentioned as a surgeon in 1644.

The first physician of Braintree (now Quincy), Massachusetts, was Dr. John Wilson, who died there in 1627. There was another John Wilson, the son of Rev. John Wilson, pastor of the first church built in Boston, who was born in 1621, and graduated from Harvard at its first commencement in 1642. He became a minister at Medfield, and lived there as "pastor, schoolmaster, and physician" until his death on August 29, 1691.

In Boston in 1646, there occurred the first recorded epidemic of syphilis in the colonies:

There fell out a loathsome disease at Boston, which raised a scandal upon the town and country, though without just cause. One of the town ... having gone cooper in a ship into..., at his return his wife was infected with Lues Venerea, which appeared thus; being delivered of a child and nothing then appearing, but the midwife a skillful woman, finding the body sound as any other, after her delivery she had a sore breast, whereupon divers neighbors resorting to her, some of them drew her breast, and others suffered their children to draw her, and others let ye child suck them, (no such disease being suspected by any,) by occasion whereof about sixteen persons, men, women, and children were infected, whereby it came at length to be discovered by such in the town as had skill in physic and surgery, but there was not any in the country who had been practised in that cure. But (see the good providence of God) at that very season there came by accident a young surgeon out of the West Indies, who had had experience of the right way of the cure of that disease. He took them in hand and through the Lord's blessing recovered them all in a short time. And it was observed that though many did eat and drink and lodge in bed with those who were infected and had sores, etc., yet none took it of them but by copulation or sucking. It was examined the husband and wife, but could find no dishonesty in either, nor any probable occasion how they should take it by any other, (and the husband was found free of it). So it was concluded by some that the woman was infected by the mixture of many spirits of men and women as drew her breast, (for thence it began). But this is a question to be decided by physicians.

The profound faith of the Puritans in the efficacy of prayer to cure disease is evident from the following:
In the year 1644:

... one of the deacons of Boston Church, *Jacob Eliot*, (a man of very sincere heart, and an humble frame of spirit) had a daughter of eight years of age, who being playing with other children about a cart, the hinder end thereof fell upon the child's head and drove a piece of the skull before it into the brain, so as the brains came out, and seven surgeons, (some of the country, very experienced men, and others of the ships which rode in the harbour) being called together for advice, etc., did all conclude that it was the brains (being about half a spoonful at one time and more at other times), and there was no hope of the child's life, except the piece of skull could be drawn out. But one of the ruling elders of the Church, an experienced and skillful surgeon, liked not to take that course but applied only plasters to it, and withal earnest prayers were made by the Church to the Lord for it, and in six weeks time it pleased God that the piece of skull consumed, and so came forth, and the child recovered perfectly, nor did it lose the senses at any time.

Another illustrative story presented by Winthrop, follows:

One Bumstead, a member of the church, had a child of about the same age (as the one mentioned before), that fell from a gallery in the meeting-house about 18 feet high, and broke the arm and shoulder, (and was also committed to the Lord in the prayers of the church, with earnest desires that the place where his people assembled to his worship might not be defiled with blood), and it pleased the Lord also, that this child was soon perfectly recovered.

July 3, 1644, was the first Massachusetts fast-day held for deliverance from sickness. The archives relate that "there was much sickness in the land" but do not attempt to further clarify the nature of the disease then prevalent.

Winthrop states that the spring of 1646 was very unhealthful because of a malignant fever "whereof some died in five or six days, but if they escaped the eighth they recovered, and divers of the churches sought the Lord by public humiliation, and the Lord was entreated, so as about the middle of the third month it ceased." On July 11, 1646, the conclusion of this epidemic was celebrated by a thanksgiving for this "Mercy of God in withdrawing his afflicting hand."

On July 22, 1647 the Barnstable church declared a fast because of the "sickness upon every family and everyone in the family."

On November 15, 1649, a fast was held in Plymouth because of an epidemic among the children of "chin-cough & the pockes." A thanksgiving day was celebrated upon the ending of this epidemic on March 13, 1650.

The story of the early days of colonial medicine must also include some pertinent facts about midwifery. In 1634, at the age of 34, Ann Hutchinson arrived in Boston from England. Primarily because her religious views did not coincide with those of the Puritan fathers, she became very much hated. One minister declared that she was of "....haughty and fierce carriage, of a nimble wit and active spirit, and a very voluble tongue, more bold than a man, though in understanding and judgement inferior to many women." She lasted four years in Boston from which city she was banished in 1638. She fled to Rhode Island, where she was later killed by the Indians.

On October 17, 1637, according to Winthrop, Ann Hutchinson was present at the delivery of a monstrosity to one Mary Dyer, although another midwife, Jane Hawkins, had officiated at the delivery. They buried the monster and kept mum, but the only other individual who had seen it, spread the good word. To quote Winthrop:

One of the elders hearing of it, asked Mrs. Hutchinson, when she was ready to depart, whereupon she told him how it was, and said she meant to have it chronicled, but excused her concealing of it till then, (by advice, as she said of Mr. Cotton) which coming to the Governor's knowledge, he called another of the magistrates and that elder, and sent for the midwife and examined her about it. At first she confessed only, that the head was defective and misplaced, but being told that Mrs. Hutchinson had revealed all, and that he intended to have it taken up and viewed, she made this report of it, viz. It was a woman child, stillborn, about two months before the just time, having life a few hours before; it came hiplings till she turned it, it was of ordinary bigness; it has a face, but no head, and the ears stood upon the shoulders, and were like an apes; it had no forehead but over the eyes four horns, hard and sharp; two of them were above one inch long, the other two shorter; the eyes standing out and the mouth also, the nose hooked upward; all over the breast and back full of sharp pricks and scales, like a thornback; the navel and all the belly should have been, behind, between the shoulders, it had two mouths, and in each of them a piece of red flesh sticking out, it had arms and legs as other children; but instead of toes it had on each foot three claws, like a young fowl, with sharp talons. The Governor speaking with Mr. Cotton about it, he told him the reason why he had advised them to conceal it. *First*, Because he saw a providence of God in it, that the rest of the women, who were coming and going in the time of her travail, should then be absent. 2. He considered, that, if it had been his own case, he should have desired to have had it concealed, and that he thought God might intend only the instruction of the parents, and such others to whom it was known, etc. The like apology he made for himself in publick, which was well accepted.

Jan. 2, 1638.

The Governor, with advice of some other of the magistrates and elders of Boston caused the said monster to be taken up, and though it were much corrupted, yet most of those things were to be seen, as the horns and claws, the scales, etc. When it died in the Mother's body, (which was about 2 hours before birth) the bed whereon the Mother lay did shake, and withal there was such a noisome savour, as most of the women were taken with extreme vomiting and purging, so as they were forced to depart; and others of them their children were taken with convulsions, (which they never had before nor after,) and so were sent for home, so as by these occasions, it came to be concealed.

Another thing observable was, the discovery of it, which was just when Mrs. Hutchinson was cast out of the church. For Mrs. Dyer going forth with her, a stranger asked what young woman it was. The others answered, it was the woman which had the monster; which gave the first occasion to some that heard to speak of it. The midwife, presently after this discovery, went out of the jurisdiction, and indeed it was time for her to be gone, for it was known, that she used to give young women oil of Mandrakes and other stuff to cause conception, and she grew into great suspicion to be a witch, for it was credibly reported, that, when she gave any medicines, (for she practiced physick), she would ask the party if she believed she could help her, etc. Another observable passage was that the father of this monster, coming home at this very time, was, the next Lord's day, by an unexpected providence, questioned in the church for divers monstrous errours, as for denying all inherent righteousness, etc., which he maintained and was for the same admonished.

Incidentally, Mary Dyer went to Rhode Island with Mrs. Hutchinson, and was spared by the Indians only to go back to Boston twenty one years later to be executed as a Quaker. It appears that the ill-fated Mrs. Hutchinson herself developed hydatid cyst of the uterus.

Returning to Winthrop:

Mrs. Hutchinson, being removed to the Isle of Aquiday, in the Narragansett Bay, after her time was fulfilled, that she expected deliverance of a child, was delivered of a monstrous birth, which being diversely related in the country, (and in the open assembly at Boston upon a lecture day declared by Mr. Cotton to be 27 several lumps of man's seed, without any alteration or mixture of anything from the woman, and thereupon gathered that it might signify her errour in denying inherent righteousness, but that all was Christ in us, and nothing of ours in faith, love, etc.) hereupon the Governor wrote to Mr. Clarke, a physician and preacher to those of the island, to know the certainty thereof, who returned him this answer. Mrs. Hutchinson, six weeks before her delivery, perceived her body to be greatly distempered, and her spirits falling, and in that regard doubtful of life, she sent to me, etc. and not long after (in immoderate fluore uterino) it was brought to light, and I was called to see it, where I beheld, first unwashed, (and afterwards in warm water), several lumps, every one of them greatly confused, and if you consider each of them according to form; but if they were considered in the parts of each lump of flesh, then there was a representation of immeasurable distinct bodies in the form of a globe, not much unlike the fins of some fish, so confusedly knit together by so many several strings, (which I conceive were the beginnings of veins and nerves,) so that it was impossible either to number the small round pieces in every lump, much less to discover from whence every string did fetch its original, they were so snarled one with another. The small globes I likewise opened, and matter of them (setting aside the membrane in which it was involved) to be partly wind and partly water. Of these several lumps there were about 26, according to the relation of those, who were narrowly searched into the number of them. I took notice of 6 or 7 of some bigness; the rest were small; but all as I have declared, except one or two which differed much from the rest both in matter and form and the whole was like the (blank) of the liver, being similar and everywhere like itself. When I had opened it the matter seemed to be blood congested. The Governor, not satisfied with this relation, spake after with the said Mr. Clarke, who thus cleared all the doubts: The lumps were 26 or 27, distinct and not joined together; there came no secundine after them; six of them were as great as his fist; the rest less . . . , and the smallest about the bigness of the top of his thumb. The globes were round things included in the lumps, about the bigness of a small Indian bean, and like the pearl in a man's eye. The two lumps, which differed from the rest, were like liver or congealed blood, and had no small globes in them as the rest had. Mr. Cotton, next lecture day, acknowledged his errour.

It is now fitting to discuss the advent of the first medical publication in the New World:

Thomas Thacher (1620-1678), physician and minister, wrote the first medical article written and published in America. He was born in England on May 1, 1620, and arrived in Boston on June 3, 1635, when fifteen years old, with his uncle, Anthony Thacher, on the *James*. Thomas and Anthony settled in Ipswich.

Thomas had a narrow escape from shipwreck, for Anthony, with the Rev. John Avery and a party of friends, sailed on August 11, 1635, from Ipswich to Marblehead, where Mr. Avery settled. Thomas, as fate would have it, traveled by land. A violent storm arose, and the ship was wrecked off a desolate island off the tip of Cape Ann, and Anthony and his wife alone were saved. The island, carrying two lofty granite lighthouses and lights of the first class, bears the name of Thacher's Island to this day.

Before coming to America, Thomas received a good preliminary education. Charles Chauncy instructed him for the ministry and probably also gave him something of a medical education. At all events, Thacher was learned in many things. He was a scholar in Arabic and composed a Hebrew lexicon. Dr. Mather tells us that, according to Eliot, he was a great logician, and understanding mechanics in theory and practice, could do all kinds of clock work to admiration. He was ordained as pastor in Weymouth, January 2, 1644, and on February 16, 1670, was installed as the first minister of Old South Church in Boston. He died of a fever on October 15, 1678, following "a visit to a sick person."

The title of the publication, issued by Dr. Thacher in the year 1677, was "A Brief Rule To guide the Common People of New England how to order themselves & theirs in the Small-Pocks, or MeaSels."

It will be recalled that smallpox existed in remote antiquity. It was left for Rhazes, however, that ninth century sage of the Orient, to adequately describe it. It is possible that Thacher had some translation of Rhazes on hand. It is more likely that recourse was had to Sydenham's works, however. The text of Thacher's broadside closely follows the account in Sydenham's *Observationes Medical* published in 1676. In *A Brief Rule,* a definition of the dread scourge is presented, a theory as to the cause of the symptoms is promulgated, an enumeration of the symptoms during the course of the ailment is listed and a summary of the early signs, doubtful signs, hopeful signs, and fatal signs are recounted.

According to Thomas Hutchinson, "In the year 1633, the small pox made terrible havock among the Indians of Massachusetts. Whether or no their food and irregular diet furnishes greater quantities of the morbific matter, than in more temperate persons, I leave to physicians. They were destitute of everything, proper for comfort and relief, and died in greater proportion than is known among the English. John Sagamore of Winesimet, and James of Lynn, with almost all their people, died of the distemper."

This makes reference to the first definitely recorded smallpox epidemic in New England. A previous epidemic in Plymouth in 1620, which had decimated the Indians, remains unproven.

Samuel Fuller, incidentally, was one of the victims of the 1633 epidemic.

Zabdiel Boylston (1679-1766), the first to inoculate for smallpox in America, was born in Brookline, Massachusetts, on March 9, 1679. Dr. John Cutter, of Boston, imparted to him a medical education and he opened his office in his preceptor's city. He built up a fine practice in short order. Throughout his life he maintained a great interest in botany and zoology and his collection of American plants and animals was very large.

He contracted smallpox in 1702 and narrowly escaped death. When an epidemic of the dread scourge broke out in Boston in 1721, Dr. Cotton Mather received accounts of inoculation from England and passed them on to Boylston. On June 26, 1721, Boylston successfully inoculated his six-year-old son and two Negro servants. So violently did the press, the public and especially his colleagues censure his experiments with inoculation, that it is said his life was actually in danger at times. However, seeing the excellent results of the practice, he steadfastly refused to step down. Cotton Mather at all times remained his staunch supporter.

Just to mention one of the incidents to which Boylston and Mather were subjected by the irate populace: On October 31, 1721, Mather's nephew, the Rev. Mr. Walter, a minister in Roxbury, was inoculated by Boylston. While he was convalescing at Mather's house, a desperate mob broke into the house, insulted its occupants, and actually hurled a bomb into the patient's room! Fortunately the fuse broke off before the missile exploded. According to "The Boston News

Letter" of November 20, 1721: "When the Granado was taken up there was found a paper so tied with a thread about the fuse that it might outlive the breaking of the shell, wherein were these words: "Cotton Mather, I was once of your meeting, but the cursed lye you told of——You know who, made me leave you, you Dog, and Damn You, I will inoculate you with this with a pox to you."

In 1721 Boylston published: "Some Account of what is said of Inoculation or Transplanting the Small-pox by the Learned Dr. Emanuel Timonius and Jacobus Pylarinus. With some Remarks thereon. To which are added a Few Queries in Answer to the Scruples of many about the lawfulness of this Method. Published by Dr. Zabdiel Boylston, Boston, 1721." With great zeal, Boylston inoculated 247 persons and his method gradually came into general use. In 1721 and 1722, 7590 cases of smallpox were reported in Boston alone. Out of this group 844 died. During the same period 286 persons were inoculated and only six of these died.

Isaac Greenwood dedicated his "A Friendly Debate; or Dialogue Between Academicus and Sawny (Douglass) and Mundungus (Archbold), Two Eminent Physicians, About Some of their Late Performance, Boston, February 15, 1721-2," "To my very worthy physician Mr. Zabdiel Boylston. Sir, I know of no person so proper to present the following dialogue to as yourself. . . . To you under the auspicious providence of God, we are indebted for the blessing of inoculation and you can claim the undivided honor of introducing it among us."

Boylston in his own writings declares:

I began the practice indeed from a short consideration thereof, for my children, whose lives were very dear to me, were daily in danger of taking the infection by my visiting the sick in the natural way; and although there arose such a cloud of opposers at the beginning yet finding my account in the success and easy circumstances of my patients (with the encouragement of the good ministers), I resolved to carry it on for the saving of lives, not regarding any, or all the menaces and opposition that were made against it.

In 1723 Boylston was honored in England by King George the First, and by the Royal Society which requested that he publish an account of his practice of inoculation in America. He wrote "An Historical Account of the Small-pox Inoculation in New England," which was published in London in 1726 and which was dedicated to Princess Caroline. He returned to New England and continued in active practice for many years. When aged, he retired to his farm in Brookline where he passed away a few days short of his eighty-seventh birthday on March 1, 1766.

It can be said of Boylston that his publication of 1721 introduced public education of the layman on medical affairs. Although numerous individuals fumed and cursed over its contents, it none-the-less directly resulted in a diminishing of the mortality from smallpox from around fourteen percent to a little over one percent. Boylston thus demonstrated for all time that physicians could wage successful medical propaganda and influence the populace through the medium of education.

In 1723, it was observed that the "Dry Gripes" afflicting the rum drinkers of New England were produced by the fact that their rum was distilled through lead pipes. Accordingly the General Court ordered:

Whereas, the strong liquors and spirits that are distilled through leaden pipes are judged on good grounds to be unwholesome and hurtful; notwithstanding which some persons to save charge may be led into the making or using of such heads, worms or pipes; for remedy and prevention whereof.—

Be it enacted by the Lieutenant-Governor Council and Representatives in General Court assembled, and by the authority of the same.

(Sect. 1.) That no person whatsoever shall make use of any such leaden heads or worms, for the future; and that whosoever shall presume to distil, or draw off any spirits or strong liquors thro' such leaden heads or worms, upon legal conviction thereof before any of his majestie's courts of record, shall forfeit and pay a fine of one hundred pounds.

And be it further enacted by the authority aforesaid.

(Sect. 2) That no brazier pewterer or other artificer whatsoever, shall presume to make any worm or head, for distilling, of coarse and base pewter, or such as hath any mixture of lead in it under the penalty of one hundred pounds.

This enactment marks the first time that steps were taken to control any disease process other than of an infectious or contagious nature.

Three important Massachusetts pre-revolutionary medical men were Nathaniel Williams, Benjamin Doolittle and Simon Tufts:

Nathaniel Williams (1675-1738) was born in Boston on August 23, 1675. He finished his course in Harvard College in 1693. In 1698 he was ordained as a minister for one of the West Indies Islands. However, the climate did not agree with him so he returned to Boston. Williams for a time tutored boys for he was a first-rate classical scholar. In 1703 he was appointed usher at the Boston Latin School. Later he attained the headmastership which he held until 1734. He studied medicine and chemistry under the tutelage of his uncle, Dr.

James Oliver, of Cambridge. Even while teaching he maintained a medical practice. He died on January 10, 1738.

He wrote a medical pamphlet published posthumously under the title: "The Method of Practice in the Small-Pox, with Observations on the Way of Inoculation. Published for the Common Advantage, more especially of the Country Towns, who may be visited with that Distemper," Boston, 1752.

The lone physician in Northfield, Massachusetts, prior to the pastorate of Benjamin Doolittle in 1717, was Patience Miller (?-1716), wife of a local tanner. Her period of practice included the first two settlements, in 1673 and 1685 respectively. It is said that this mother of eight children was a capable physician and surgeon. She lived to a ripe old age, dying on March 16, 1716. Northfield had to get along without expert medical attention until Benjamin Doolittle (1685-1749) arrived to start his pastorate. Doolittle hailed from Wallingford, Connecticut and arrived to preach his first sermon in Northfield, in November, 1717.

Benjamin Doolittle (1695-1749) was born in Wallingford, Connecticut, on July 10, 1695. He graduated from Yale in 1716. It seems likely that between this time and the time of his arrival at Northfield, he must have ardently pursued his studies, both in theology and medicine. He is referred to as a "regular educated physician and surgeon, furnished with books, instruments and drugs." After twenty years in Northfield, his medical and surgical practice had become so vast and remunerative that many of his townsmen claimed that he was neglecting his religious duties. An alleged statement of his that "he would not lay by doctoring and chirurgery under 400 pounds a year," aroused the wrath, and perhaps the jealousy, of his adversaries.

In 1737, during the period when Jonathan Edwards had been effectively preaching the "Great Awakening," Doolittle's religious doctrines fell out of favor. Accusations against him reached a climax when members of his congregation affixed their signatures to a document openly accusing him of leanings toward Arminianism and proposing that this matter be referred to a council to determine whether his views were sound and he should continue as pastor.

Doolittle did not even bother replying to this accusation until February, 1721, when he publicly read the following statement from the pulpit: "Brethren: There has been a great noise about my Principals which has been very wounding to Religion and hurtful to peace and unity among us: and I now make a demand of all those that have anything to object against my Principals to come to me and tell me ye very particular article they object against, to see if I cant satisfy them, and if I dont satisfie them, then to bring it to the church, or else to hold your peace forever hereafter. . . . Brethren, if it be your minds that those that have anything to object against my Principals should do so I have now demanded of them, manifest it by lifting up the hand. Voted in ye affirmative."

Doolittle was medically active ministering to the settlements about Northfield, the garrisons at Fort Dummer and the Ashuelots and the battles and skirmishes of the Old French War.

On June 3, 1746, "Cap. Stevens sent down a troop of men to guard Mr. Doolittle and Dr. T. Williams (of Deerfield) to cut off the arm of one of the soldiers that was sore wounded, broke off one of his arms." In September, 1747, a wounded cadet "was put under the care of Mr. Doolittle, by whose skill his wound was soon cured." On June 16, 1748, "a ranger, severely wounded in the thigh in an ambush, was brought on a horse the next day to Northfield to be treated by Mr. Doolittle."

Benjamin Doolittle died on January 9, 1749 at the age of fifty-four. He evidently sustained a massive coronary occlusion for it is recorded that he was "suddenly seized with a pain in his breast" while mending a fence.

Simon Tufts (1700-1747) was born on January 31, 1700, in Medford, Massachusetts. He received an A.B. from Harvard in 1724, and it is said that he studied medicine concurrently with his colleagues. He opened his office in Medford in 1724, the first physician to practice in this town. His oldest son, Simon (1727-1786), succeeding to his practice in Medford. His fourth child became the famous Cotton Tufts, M.D., of Weymouth. Simon Tufts built up a large practice and was frequently called to visit the sick at Harvard College. He steadfastly refused to accept fees from the students. He died on his birthday, January 31, 1747, at the age of forty-seven.

Silvester Gardiner (1707-1786), one of the most spectacular figures in colonial Massachusetts, was born on June 29, 1707, in "Boston Neck," South Kingston, Rhode Island. His childhood was marred by delicate health and his energies were directed away from physical effort to that unlimited realm of books. When he reached the age of thirteen, that fiery orator, Rev. James McSparran, married his sister and the boy was raised in their home, under an intellectual atmosphere.

When Silvester became interested in medicine, he was sent abroad, and studied eight years in London and Paris. While in London, Cheselden of St. Thomas' Hospital, who in 1723 had suggested the high operation for stone and in 1727, about the time when Gardiner reached London, the lateral operation for the same disease, became interested in this clever young American. The "Gentleman's Magazine" for 1731 mentions a case in which Cheselden removed from the bladder a stone in a single minute, and it prints in a later issue, in 1732, a poem from the patient, grateful to Cheselden for his cure.

Dr. Gardiner evidently settled in Boston as early as 1734, for in 1735 he was chosen to be one of the vestry of King's Chapel. An article on the examination of physicians by a board of physicians and surgeons to be appointed by the General Court, appearing in the newspaper in 1736, was written by him as also was a paper on "The Measels."

At this same period, Gardiner organized the "Medical Society of Boston, New England," and presented before it lectures on anatomy, illustrated with plates brought from Europe. On October 8, 1741, with the members of the body attending, he performed a rapid and successful operation for stone on a boy six years of age, named Joseph Baker. According to the history, young Joseph had had trouble from calculi from birth and at the time of the operation was emaciated and wasting away. Dr. Gardiner employed the lateral operation of Cheselden, and removed the stone which resembled a sand stone, only being harder and more compact. This calculus was oval and seven inches in circumference. For three days urine drained through the incision; following this it returned to the natural channels. By three weeks the urinary flow was natural.

Dr. Gardiner saw the waste of energy and time in the custom prevalent among physicians to compound their own prescriptions. He therefore opened an apothecary shop for himself and for other physicians. From a moderate start he built up a large trade in this shop, importing drugs and chemicals. His pharmacy, under the famous "Sign of the Unicorn and Mortar" on the corner of Washington and Winter Streets, made a wealthy man out of him. Always desirous of increasing his income, he also opened establishments in Meridon and Hartford, Connecticut, that also prospered. Gardiner's drug stores were famed for their "Galenical and Chymical Medicines," and "Ship's medicine Boxes, put up in the neatest manner for Merchant Ships as they are put up for the Royal Navy at Apothecary's Hall in London."

The equanimity of Gardiner's enterprises was not long lived for he soon discovered that he was being cheated by his partners. The newspapers were copious with bitter accusations between Dr. Gardiner on the one hand and Mr. James Flagg and Dr. Jepson on the other. Both partners at long last, were pushed against the ropes, and were more than willing to liquidate their debts, according to the decisions of the judicial referees.

In his palatial house on Winter Street, Dr. Gardiner was visited by such celebrities as General Gage, Admiral Graves, Earle Percy,

Governor Hutchinson, and Sir William Pepperell. His every action was conducted with complete devotion to the Crown of England. He constructed a hospital, surrounded with a stockade fence, for the men of His British Majesty's New England Fleet. In 1761, when smallpox inoculation became popular, he offered to construct another hospital at a cost to patients of £4 for inoculation and medicines and £3 per day maintenance. This last offer was not accepted.

In 1752 the Kennebec Company was established and this organization, largely financed with Gardiner's money, appointed him "Perpetual Moderator." By the terms of the charter title was granted seven and a half miles on each side of the Kennebec up as far as fifty miles from its mouth. It was in this area that the versatile physician built towns, sawmills, and churches, and induced people to settle by generous land offers at low interest.

Dr. Gardiner also controlled shares in the Pejepscot Company and conducted a prosperous lumber business in Saco with Dr. Donald Cummings.

When the War of Independence began, this magnate, naturally enough, sided with the mother country. He severed his long friendship with John Hancock. When Dr. John Morgan, surgeon-general of the army, acting on orders from Washington, confiscated his drugs, Gardiner became a violent enemy of the republic and called the Father of Our Country: "That Thief Washington." Feeling against Gardiner waxed heavy so he gathered some £2,000 in gold, and fled to Halifax. Thus, for the sake of an ideal, refusing to merely close his mouth about his feelings, this loyalist lost his practice, his stock in trade, his real estate in Boston, and his vast dominions in Maine. His books and furniture were sold at public auction for £8,000. His real estate in Boston was confiscated. Squatters overran the land grants of the Kennebec Company and cut down the timber at will.

Dr. Gardiner sailed from Canada to England and received a pension from the grateful Crown. He opened an office at Poole, in County Dorset, and travelled occasionally to London. He obtained financial assistance also from his son-in-law, Oliver Whippel, of Portsmouth, New Hampshire.

In 1785, already an old man, he returned to the United States with the idea of regaining control of his estates. His properties were eventually returned to his heirs. Despite his advanced age, he opened an office in Newport, Rhode Island.

Dr. Gardiner, unquestionably able and even public-spirited, was most obstinate with regard to his ideas. He became peeved at his oldest son because he was inefficient and at his second son because he became a Unitarian. Both were cut off in his will. He was a man of false humility and ill-concealed braggadocio. He left most of his estate to the children of a sister on condition that they change their name to Gardiner.

Loyal to the Church of England, he was appointed a warden in King's Chapel, Boston, and presented the finances for its communion wine. He also endowed the church in Gardiner, Maine. It is said that he was sincerely religious and God-fearing and given to prayer. He wrote a book of "Devotions," published in London in 1785. Silvester Gardiner passed away in Newport, Rhode Island, on August 8, 1786 of a "malignant fever." He was seventy-nine years old.

Reference to the Hersey brothers, Edward Holyoke, Oliver Prescott and Cotton Tufts must be made in any history of medicine in colonial and revolutionary Massacushetts:

Ezekiel Hersey (1709-1770) was born at Hingham, Massachusetts on September 21, 1709. After graduating from Harvard in 1728, he engaged in the study of medicine with Lawrence Dal'-Honde, a French physician of Boston, who was an active participant in the incessant argumentation concerning the value of inoculation for the smallpox. The unscientifically conceived arguments of Dal'-Honde and William Douglass were presented frantically to combat the progressive scientific elucidation of Boylston. Hersey, however, saw the error of his teacher's ways, and proved his impartiality by offering himself as one of the first Americans to submit to inoculation.

Hersey practiced in his native town and his fine reputation spread his practice into the counties of Plymouth, Norfolk and Barnstable. Concerning this erudite colonial physician, president Quincy of Harvard College declared: "His intellectual powers were strong, his manners pleasing and his professional attentions assiduous and faithful. To the rich his charges were proverbially moderate, and to the poor his services were ever ready, and even gratuitous. Yet he attained great wealth, according to the estimate of his contemporaries, and was among the most beloved and honored of the distinguished men of that period."

It seems a shame that Hersey did not live to see his country freed from the bondage imposed by the mother country, for he was very active in all patriotic endeavors, acting frequently as chairman of the committees from Hingham which dealt with similar committees from other towns of Massachusetts in formulating measures for defense. His fine oratorical ability was frequently put to test on behalf of the land that he loved.

Dr. Hersey's will left to Harvard one thousand pounds to be applied toward maintaining a professorship of anatomy and physic.

Since his death anteceded the founding of the Harvard Medical School by a dozen years, this money was placed at interest and later increased in 1791 by a similar sum from his widow. A further bequest of five hundred pounds was added later by his brother, Dr. Abner Hersey (1722-1787). Essentially from the total grant of 2500 pounds, the "Hersey Professorship of Anatomy and Surgery" and the "Hersey Professorship of the Theory and Practice of Physic" were founded and maintained at Harvard.

Abner Hersey, who guided the medical training of several apprentices, practiced all of his days in Barnstable, Massachusetts. His will is said by lawyers to represent one of the strangest documents on record. The legislature was compelled to put an end to his scheme for perpetuating his estate. It is said that Abner wore a coat made of seven tanned calfskins and that he vehemently denounced the fashions of the time.

Dr. Ezekiel Hersey expired on December 9, 1770 at the age of sixty-one.

Edward Augustus Holyoke (1728-1829) was born in Marblehead, Massachusetts on August 1, 1728. Edward Holyoke, his father, was elected president of Harvard College in 1737 and held this office for over thirty-two years. Edward Augustus graduated from Harvard in 1746. The following year he entered upon the study of medicine with Dr. Berry of Ipswich and remained with this learned physician for almost two years. In 1749, he opened his office in Salem and continued to practice there for the rest of his life. Slowly, but surely, he built up a large practice. In his later years, it was said that there was not a single house in town to which he had not been called to minister to the sick. In everything he did, he was meticulous, conscientious and industrious.

During the nearly eighty years of his medical practice it is said that he never travelled more than fifty miles from Salem.

As one of the original incorporators of the Massachusetts Medical Society in 1781, he called the first meeting and was elected the first president of this body, serving from 1782 to 1784, and again in 1786-7, after which term he refused re-election. He constantly reported medical cases and meteorological observations to the Society and by so doing stimulated interest in the organization.

He employed essentially only four drugs: mercury, antimony, opium and quinine, and his prescriptions were either compounded personally by him or by his pupils. He shied away from surgery. During his long career he guided thirty-five medical students in their medical pursuits.

Dr. Holyoke received the first honorary M.D. from Harvard in 1783. In 1813 Harvard conferred upon him an honorary LL.D. He was president of the American Academy of Arts and Sciences, the Salem Athenaeum, and the Essex Historical Society.

In a letter to John F. Watson, written on his hundredth birthday, he states: "My health is good. That is, I have a good appetite and sleep as well as at any period of my life and thanks to a kind Providence, suffer but little pain, except now and then pretty severe cramps,—but my mental faculties are impaired,—especially my memory for recent events."

His health was excellent until his last years when he suffered fainting spells. Edward Augustus Holyoke passed away in the town that he loved so well on March 31, 1829, one day short of one hundred years and eight months old, having lived a long and useful life as a family practitioner, unambitious for public acclaim.

Oliver Prescott (1731-1804) was born in Groton, Massachusetts on April 27, 1731. He attended Harvard College and received his degree in 1750. Following his graduation, he studied medicine with Dr. Ebenezer Roble, of Sudbury, Massachusetts. In 1791 Harvard awarded him its honorary M.D. He settled in Groton and rapidly developed a large practice. Legend has it that he acquired a habit of sleeping while making his rounds on horseback and his son, Dr. Oliver Prescott, Jr., states that he personally observed his father peacefully slumbering, "the horse continuing the whole time at the usual travelling pace." The younger Prescott further affirmed that his father would, when drowsiness came upon him, brace himself in the stirrup, rest one hand on the pommel of the saddle and resign himself without fear, for miles together, to quiet repose."

Oliver Prescott was one of the original incorporators of the Massachusetts Medical Society. He was president of the Middlesex Medical Society during this organization's entire life. He served as major, lieutenant-colonel and colonel of militia, under the Crown, and in 1775, an avowed patriot, he was appointed brigadier-general of Massachusetts militia, his command being assigned to guard duty, for the most part, and the work of organizing the town committees of correspondence. In 1779, when John Winthrop died, he was appointed his successor to the office of judge of probate for the county of Middlesex. Prescott was also the first president of the trustees of the Groton Academy, and a fellow of the American Academy of Arts and Sciences.

He died at Groton "of a pectoral dropsy" on November 17, 1804, at the age of seventy-three.

Cotton Tufts (1731-1815), the youngest son of Dr. Simon Tufts, Senior, of Medford and a brother of Dr. Simon Tufts, Junior, of Medford, was born in Medford on May 31, 1731. He was admitted to Harvard College at the age of fourteen and received an A.M. from this institution in 1749. In 1785 Harvard awarded him an honorary medical degree.

He taught school for a time and then studied medicine with his older brother, Simon, in Medford. He established his residence in Weymouth on April 8, 1752, but as early as 1749, he visited Weymouth as is demonstrated by the following entries in the diary of the Reverend William Smith, for that year: "Books lent, 1749, To Cotton Tufts, several books." "October 15, I preached. Mr. Thaxter and Cotton Tufts here."

During the year 1751, the Throat Distemper or Putrid Sore Throat, (diphtheria) was very prevalent and fatal among the inhabitants of Weymouth. The Reverend Mr. Smith records the death of nineteen children and four adults from the disease, between July 12, and November 15. On October 5, he declares: "11 died this week, 6 in our parish, 5 in Mr. Bayley's," and on November 21, he adds: "Fast Day at Mr. (James) Bayley's Parish on account of the throat distempers prevailing there. Mr. Cotton preached from 2 Jer. 30. 'In vain have I smitten yr children; ye rec'd no Correction,' and Mr. (Samuel) Porter P.M. fm. 2 Cor. 12, 8 and part of the 9, 'For ys thing I besought the Ld thrice that it might depart from me. And he said unto me, My grace is sufficient for thee.'"

James Thacher declares that Cotton Tufts' success was assured when he introduced a new and original treatment for the throat distemper. He made frequent trips to Boston and always kept in close touch with his brother in Medford.

Cotton Tufts planned for the formation of a Massachusetts state medical society and the following letter in his handwriting, but without signature or date, has been found among his papers:

Sirs:

Divers gentlemen of the profession have met together for the friendly purpose of forming an association for the advancement of medical knowledge, promoting good will and harmony and discountenancing empirics. This meeting was in consequence of a paper wrote by an anonymous writer proposing such a scheme in which were invited as underneath. The meeting is adjourned to the first Wednesday in June at Gardiner's Tavern on Boston Neck at two o'clock p.m. The gentlemen have desired me to invite you to attend the same and join them in accomplishing so benevolent a scheme and any plan that you can suggest for the (word illegible) of such meeting will be kindly received. In behalf of the gentlemen I now act as scribe, and am,

Your Very Obedient Servant,

To Dr. John Wilson,
of Hopkington.

A vehement patriot, Tufts as early as 1765, wrote instructions to the representatives of the town of Weymouth to act against the Stamp Act. In 1784 he was a member of the Massachusetts Senate. In 1781 Dr. Tufts acted as an interpreter for the Massachusetts Medical Society. He was elected second vice-president of the society from 1785 to 1787, and fourth president from 1787 to 1795. From the first meeting of the Council of this society on July 18, 1782, through his term as president, a period of thirteen years, Dr. Tufts, in spite of the fact that he lived twelve miles away, only missed two of the forty meetings. In 1780 Tufts was also one of the incorporators of the American Academy of Arts and Sciences. He also was a member of the convention to adopt the Constitution of the United States. He died in Weymouth on December 8, 1815.

Short mention must be made of a Boston physician who turned traitor in his Country's hour of need:

Benjamin Church (1734-1776) was born in Newport, Rhode Island on August 24, 1734. He graduated from Harvard College in 1754, following which he engaged in the study of medicine in London. When his training was completed he started practice in Boston and built up a large medical and surgical practice. On March 5, 1773, he was the orator at the "Commemoration of the Boston Massacre."

When the War of Independence broke out, Church was appointed physician-general of the army with the title "Director-General and Chief Physician." His salary at this post was four dollars a day, and his task was to "furnish medicines, bedding and all other necessaries, to pay for the same, and receive orders from the commander-in-chief." In 1774, he attended the Provincial Congress.

It seems certain that Church was anxious to improve the standards of the medical corps. Quarreling and quibbling between the hospital and the regimental surgeons obstructed him in this task at every turn. Perhaps disheartening experience turned this erudite physician whose past had always been one of patriotism into a traitor. Be that as it may, it was discovered that Church was in communication with the enemy, as revealed by a cryptic letter intercepted through the agency of a paramour of his. He was immediately arrested and incarcerated for some four months, following which he was unanimously convicted by a council of war, presided over by General Washington.

Following the conviction, he was, of course, expelled from Congress and confined to prison at Norwich, Connecticut. In May, 1776, he was released on account of failing health and allowed to sail to the West Indies. As far as is known, the voyage was never completed. At any rate, Church was never heard of again and it was supposed that his ship was lost at sea. His family was pensioned by the crown.

According to Drake, "He was an elegant orator and poet, and the best of the contributors to the "Pietas et Gratulatio." Church was the author of "The Choice," a poem; "The Times," 1760, a satire on the Stamp Act and its abettors; an elegy on Dr. Mayhew, 1766; an elegy on Dr. Whitefield, 1770; and "Address of a Provincial Bashaw, by a Son of Liberty," 1769.

In the later colonial and revolutionary periods, John Green, Samuel Holten and Samuel Danforth played important roles:

John Green (1736-1799), the son of Thomas Green, Baptist elder and physician, was born in Seicester (Greenville) on August 14, 1736. After his father tutored him in the wiles of Æsculapius, he came to Worcester and built his house on the hill now known as Green Hill, which, although, out of the way, was frequented by numerous patients. Medical students from Worcester and adjacent towns also came to Green's abode. Green Lane developed into a county road and, although during his later years, Dr. Green's office was in a little wooden shack on the present site of the Five Cents Savings Bank, the doctor maintained his home in the Green Hill house until his death.

First and last, Green was a staunch patriot. As early as 1763, he was the only medical member of the American Political Society, which organization was an outgrowth of the dissatisfaction of the times. Throughout the War of Independence, he was exceedingly active. In 1777 he served as representative to the General Court. In 1778 and 1779 he was town treasurer, and in 1780 one of the selectmen, the only physician who ever held that office.

Dr. Elijah Dix Green, his son, was born on July 4, 1769, received his A.B. from Brown in 1793 and practiced in Charleston, South Carolina. He was named after Elijah Dix, an early surgeon of Worcester, Massachusetts.

John Green passed away on October 29, 1799 at the age of sixty-three.

Samuel Holten (1738-1816) was born in Danvers, Massachusetts on June 9, 1738. As a lad, he was sickly and received no formal education. Holten, when a young man, apprenticed himself to Dr. Jonathan Prince of his home town. His preceptor was so impressed by his medical acumen that he considered him qualified to practice at the age of nineteen, at which age he opened an office in Gloucester.

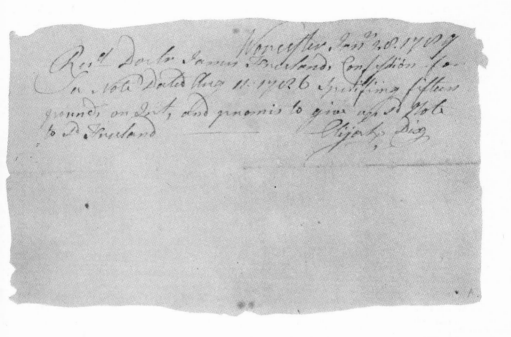

Legal Note Dated 1709 and Signed by Elijah Dix pertaining to a Loan Transaction with Dr. James Freeland. (*In author's possession.*)

After practicing for two years in this place he returned to his old home town where he practiced for the following sixteen years. By 1775, however, his time had become so occupied by his public duties that he was unable to devote enough time to medicine.

The first public office he held was in 1768 when the people of Danvers elected him representative to the General Court. In 1775 he was a member of the Provincial Congress at Watertown, the committee of safety of this body and also the examining board for the medical department of the Continental Army. In 1776, he was appointed judge of the court of general sessions of the peace, and also justice of the Quorum, a public office which he faithfully served for forty years. In 1777, he was elected a delegate from Massachusetts to the Federal Convention of the United States. He served as a member of the Congress, and was one of the signatories of the constitution. He was honored by being elected president of the Congress and for over a year he was the only congressional physician. All told, he served eight years as a representative in the General Court, five in the Senate, twelve in the council, five in the Congress under the confederation, and two under the federal constitution.

In 1781, Samuel Holten actively asisted in the organization of the Massachusetts Medical Society. One of the incorporators of this body, he aided the infant organization greatly as vice-president, and "counsellor." He was present at the early meetings of the society and of its council composed of only a few members, and in 1782 was the presiding officer at its second meeting.

James Thacher, who personally knew the good doctor, says concerning him: "His form was majestic, his person graceful, his countenance pleasing, his manners easy and engaging, his address courtly, his talents popular, his disposition amiable and benevolent, and he possessed good intellectual powers."

He died on January 2, 1816, at the age of seventy-seven.

Samuel Danforth (1740-1827) was born at Cambridge, Massachusetts, in August, 1740. He graduated from Harvard in 1758, the seventh Danforth to do so since 1634. He undertook the study of medicine with Dr. Rand, the elder, either in Charlestown or Boston. Harvard awarded him an honorary M.D. in 1790. His medical opinions appear to have been influenced by Dr. Philip Godfrid Kast. He started his practice in Weston, Massachusetts, but in a short time he moved to Newport, Rhode Island. In a year or two, he came back to Boston, married and settled there. Like Hunter, who also lived in Rhode Island, he sided with the British during the War of Independence and it is related that his wife and three children were forced to seek refuge with her father. When the British moved out of Boston,

Dr. Danforth was naturally treated roughly by many of the citizens. However, he lived to earn their forgiveness and build up a fine practice.

Samuel Danforth was one of the founders of the Massachusetts Medical Society and served this organization as its president from 1795 to 1798. He is described as an adequate surgeon and a good medical diagnostician, with polished manners and good carriage, but never overly formal. He employed few remedies, but these were of a potent and drastic nature, such as calomel, ipecacuanha, opium and peruvian bark. His common sense is illustrated by the following story: One day when called to visit several persons who had been injured by the fall of a house frame, he found another practitioner engaged in bleeding the injured persons. "Doctor," said the colleague, "I am doing your work for you." "Then," said Dr. Danforth, "pour the blood back into the veins of these men."

He died on November 16, 1827, at the age of eighty-seven.

And now we come to the medical martyr of the War of Independence:

Joseph Warren (1741-1775) was born at Roxbury on June 11, 1741. He graduated from Harvard in 1759, after which he was engaged as master of the Roxbury grammar school. Dr. James Lloyd guided his medical studies and at the age of twenty-three, he opened his office in Boston. His reputation became widespread because of his effective treatment of smallpox during a severe New England epidemic. John Adams, later to become president of the United States, thought so much of Joseph Warren that he employed him as family physician.

It is agreed that the patriotic ardor of Joseph Warren could not have been enhanced, and violently neglecting his brilliant medical prospects, he vociferously attended every town meeting held in Boston, from the arrival of the British troops in October, 1768, to their removal in March 1770, in the name of American freedom. In March, 1772, he presented the anniversary address upon the "Boston Massacre." On March 5, 1775, he gave a speech in Old South Church, scornful of threats of violence from the British. When the Provincial Congress held sessions at Watertown on May 31, 1775, Dr. Warren was unanimously elected president of the body.

On June 14, 1775, he was chosen second major-general of the Massachusetts forces. It was on June 17, 1775, that Joseph Warren met the committee of Safety at General Ward's headquarters on Cambridge Common. When he received the news that the British had landed at Charlestown, he immediately departed on horseback to Bunker Hill. When he reached the battlefield, he sought duty in the area where the need and danger were greatest. As the battle drew to a close and the Americans were retreating, it was Joseph Warren who vainly sought to rally the decimated forces of his countrymen. He was struck dead by a ball lodged in his skull.

The lives and works of Benjamin Shattuck, William Aspinwall, and William Baylies now come up for discussion:

Benjamin Shattuck (1742-1794) was born in Littleton, Massachusetts, on November 11, 1742. It is related that his father, Stephen, on April 19, 1775, already past sixty-five years of age, shouldered his musket and marched off to Concord to follow the retreating enemy to Cambridge. Benjamin received his preliminary education from Jeremiah Dummer Rogers. He graduated from Harvard in 1765, receiving an A.M. degree. Then he took up medicine with Dr. Oliver Prescott of Groton, Massachusetts, after which he moved to Templeton, where he practiced for the rest of his life.

The region where Shattuck settled had but few inhabitants and no medical conveniences. Yet, through patient and arduous labor he acquired a large practice and a wide reputation. He died on January 14, 1794 at the age of fifty-two.

William Aspinwall, (1743-1823) was born in Brookline, Massachusetts, on May 23, 1743, in the old house situated in what was later called "The Structure," on Aspinwall Avenue near St. Paul's church. In 1668 this property was constructed by Peter Aspinwall, the ancester of William, who came from England in 1630.

William Aspinwall received his preliminary education from Amos Adams, a minister of Roxbury. After graduating from Harvard in 1764, he proceeded to engage in the study of medicine with Dr. Benjamin Gale, of Killingsworth, Connecticut. His medical education was enhanced in the Pennsylvania Hospital, Philadelphia, where he spent seven months with Dr. William Shippen, Jr. Shippen granted Aspinwall a certificate of proficiency on May 27, 1769.

William then opened his office in Brookline, the town of his birth. When war with the mother country flared forth, he was induced by his friend and kinsman, Dr. Joseph Warren, to join the medical department of the provincial army, although at first he volunteered as a private during the battle of Lexington, conducted himself with distinction, and carried off the field the body of the commander of the Brookline Company, Isaac Gardner, father of his future wife. He was soon appointed surgeon to General Heath's brigade and later deputy director of the army hospital in Jamaica Plain, Massachusetts.

In 1776 he married Susanna Gardner who bore him seven children. His portrait was done by the famous Gilbert Stuart. The story is told that the painting was in the possession of his son-in-law, Lewis

Tappan, at the time when anti-slavery rioters broke into his home. Because the portrait resembled George Washington, the mob, thinking it a picture of the first president, spared it.

When Zabdiel Boylston passed away, Dr. Aspinwall vigorously took up the task of inoculation in a private hospital in Brookline. Quick to sense the value of vaccination he observed Dr. Benjamin Waterhouse's methods first-hand and, at great financial loss to himself, gave up inoculation in favor of vaccination. "This new inoculation will take from me a handsome annual income, yet as a man of humanity, I rejoice in it," is the way he expressed himself to Waterhouse.

For five years short of half a century, Aspinwall maintained a large practice, making the calls on horseback, and more often than not, covering forty miles in a day. In his youth he had the misfortune to lose one eye in an accident. Later in life, when the lens of the remaining eye became opaque with cataract, he had the greater misfortune to lose sight in this eye too after an unsuccessful operation.

He passed away in the house which he built on Aspinwall Hill on April 16, 1823, at the age of 79.

Aspinwall became a fellow of the Massachusetts Medical Society in 1812, and Harvard College awarded him an honorary M.D. in 1808.

Aside from his medical and military pursuits, William Aspinwall found time to be town treasurer, warden, surveyor, state representative, and senator. While studying medicine in 1769 he wrote a sketch of his ancestors, which has been preserved by his descendants.

William Baylies (1743-1826) was born at Uxbridge, Massachusetts on December 5, 1743. He was graduated from Harvard College in 1760. Following this, he undertook the study of medicine with Dr. Elisha Tobey, of New Bedford. When his studies were completed he married a daughter of Samuel White, of Taunton, speaker of the House of Representatives. Then he set up his office in the town of Dighton.

Dr. Baylies represented Dighton in the Legislature, and in three Provincial Congresses. He was also a member of the State Convention that adopted the Federal Constitution, a Common Pleas judge and a register of probate. Notwithstanding these extensive non-medical activities, he was much in demand as a consultant. It is said that his prognoses were usually very accurate.

William Baylies was one of the original members of the Massachusetts Medical Society and of the Massachusetts Historical Society. He was also a member of the American Academy of Arts and Sciences. In 1807 Harvard awarded him an honorary M.D. He wrote an article: "Ulcerated Sore Throat in Dighton, 1785-6," which was published in the Communications of the Massachusetts Medical Society, vol. I, series 1. He passed away on June 17, 1826, at the ripe old age of 83.

The "Blood and Guts" of the Revolutionary War was Eliphalet Downer (1744-1806). Known as the "fighting surgeon," he was born in Roxbury, Massachusetts, in 1744. When the War of Independence began, Downer occupied a house on Washington Street, Brookline, near the famous Punch Bowl Tavern. Downer has been called a "skillful surgeon, but a hard, rough man." As the battle of Lexington materialized, Eliphalet Downer, without any to-do, promptly shouldered a musket and set out for the front.

Major-General Heath tells the story that, while the young doctor was avidly pursuing the retreating British, he "came to single combat" with a British soldier. The enemy chided him with: "you damned rebel, do you dare face?" Downer promptly accepted the dare, and as they met head on, both fired their muskets and missed. Since there was no time to reload, a hand to hand struggle ensued. The enemy, possessing a large gun and having had better bayonet training, was getting the best of the rugged doctor. Suddenly the physician, in a fit of rage, reversed his musket, stepped back a few paces and bashed his antagonist with the butt of the gun. The weapon broke in the process of this maneuver. Downer promptly polished off his opponent by running him through with his own bayonet. Later that night, while recounting his experience, Downer remarked: "It was not ten minutes before I got another shot."

In December, 1775, Downer is mentioned as surgeon to one of General Putnam's regiments at Charlestown. This however, proved too dull for the lusty soul, for after the British evacuated Boston, he enlisted as surgeon on one of the first privateers fitted out in New England. Again, not content with confining his efforts to the healing art, he operated one of the guns on board the sloop "Yankee" when two sloops, loaded with rum and sugar, were captured. His luck held out until he was on board the "Alliance" when she was captured at sea after fighting seven and a half hours and losing both her masts. Badly wounded in the left arm, he was thrown into Portsea Prison near Portsmouth, England. Needless to say, stone walls could not confine this man of action. He promptly made his escape by tunneling out of the prison and succeeded in reaching France. Twice more he was captured by the British and imprisoned (in Dartmoor and Forten prisons) but on both occasions he managed to escape. His poor wife and four children were hard put financially during the three year period he was away from home. It is said that for the entire period his wife received only one letter from him.

On July 9, 1779, Downer was appointed chief surgeon to the Penobscot expedition, which he served for three months. During this time he lost all his surgical instruments and the Massachusetts Legislature appropriated fifteen dollars to reimburse him.

When the war was over, it must have been most trying for this fiery man of steel to settle down to private practice in Brookline. However, he did just that and built up a large practice. On April 4, 1806, at the age of sixty-two he died in Brookline.

We shall conclude our evaluation of the medical men of colonial and revolutionary Massachusetts with glimpses into the lives of John Jeffries, John Swett, William Eustis, Aaron Dexter, John Warren, David Townsend, Nathaniel Appleton, John Brooks, Josiah Bartlett and Abijah Cheever.

John Jeffries (1745-1819) was born in Boston on February 5, 1745. He graduated from Harvard in 1763 and then went abroad to continue his studies. He was awarded his M.D. at Aberdeen in 1769. In 1771 Admiral Montague, commander-in-chief of the British North American Squadron, appointed Jeffries assistant surgeon of a ship of the line, with a hospital on shore, a position he held until 1774. During the Revolution he was strictly a royalist. It is said that he identified the body of his friend, Dr. Joseph Warren, for General Howe after the battle of Bunker Hill. After the British departed from Boston he accompanied the troops to Halifax, where he was later appointed surgeon-major to the forces in America settling in England at the close of the war.

In 1784, it was John Jeffries who daringly made the first balloon ascension over London. It is said that he dropped cards of greeting to the awe-stricken populace below. During the trip he made studies of the air at high levels and carried with him a barometer, a thermometer, a hydrometer, an electrometer, a mariner's compass, and seven small bottles for obtaining samples of air at different levels. It is certain that he reached an elevation exceeding 6560 feet. His data were turned over to the Royal Society to be discussed and were studied by the famous chemist, Cavendish.

On January 7, 1785, just five weeks after the London balloon voyage, Jeffries daringly crossed the English Channel and landed with his balloon in the forest of Guines, in Artois. His "Narrative of Two Aerial Voyages" was published in London in 1786. He kept detailed records of the weather in Boston from 1774 until March 4, 1776, and later from 1790 until 1816. These records are now in the library of the Blue Hill Meteorological Observatory.

In 1790 Jeffries returned to Boston, and practiced surgery, medicine and midwifery until near the time of his death. Thacher declares that Jeffries presented the first public lecture on anatomy in Boston and that on the second evening a mob collected and carried off his subject, the body of a convict.

When he died of strangulated hernia on September 16, 1819, he had one of the most valuable private libraries in the country. His methodical habits are attested by the diary he kept for more than forty years, recording all his important cases in medicine and surgery and nearly two thousand pregnancy cases he had presumably attended. His son, John Jeffries (1796-1876), specialized in ophthalmic surgery and helped found the Massachusetts Charitable Eye and Ear Infirmary in Boston in 1824.

John Barnard Swett (1752-1796) was born in Marblehead, Massachusetts, on June 1, 1752. He attended Harvard from which college he received his A.B. in 1771. He was desirous of studying for the ministry, but perchance he witnessed autopsies "on the bodies of some persons who had come to a violent death." This led him to study medicine against the advice of his preceptor, the Rev. John Barnard.

He undertook his medical course at Edinburgh, under the direction of Dr. William Cullen. After finishing his study, he was appointed fleet surgeon in a merchant expedition to the Falkland Islands. With the pay he received on the trip he completed his medical education in the hospitals of France and England. He returned to America in 1778 and promptly enlisted as surgeon in the Continental Army. He accompanied the expedition to Rhode Island under Gen. Sullivan. In 1779, he served for several months in the expedition to the Penobscot River commanded by General Lovell.

Unfortunately, during the conflict with the mother country, Swett lost his valuable library and surgical instruments which he had collected abroad at great expense. In 1780 he opened his office in Newburyport, Massachusetts, and for the succeeding sixteen years, he performed a large part of the surgery of this town and adjacent areas.

He was a charter member of the American Academy of Arts and Sciences, and of the Massachusetts Medical Society. He was the first corresponding secretary of the latter organization from 1782 to 1789.

He built up another sizable library and his book-plate is described as follows in Currier's History of Newburyport. "At the top of the plate, resting upon a couch and attended by four cupids or cherubs, is the body of a patient about to undergo a surgical operation, while under the name 'J. B. Swett' the serpent of the Æsculapius is twisted about a rod standing upright between retorts, and herbs growing in flower pots."

Swett died on August 16, 1796, of yellow fever contracted during the epidemic of the summer of 1796 after he had fearlessly mingled among the victims of this dread plague.

William Eustis (1753-1825) was born in Boston on June 18, 1753. At the age of fourteen, he matriculated in Harvard and graduated from this institution in 1772. Dr. Joseph Warren, his preceptor, turned over his practice to him when he departed for Lexington.

Eustis served in New Jersey and New York as surgeon to Gridley's and Knox's Artillery until December 1776, when he declined a lieutenant colonelcy of artillery in favor of an appointment as hospital surgeon. He was placed in charge of a Connecticut hospital and later Robinson's House, near West Point, where he served at the time of Benedict Arnold's treason.

Eustis resigned from the army in 1783 and started to practice medicine in Boston. In 1786 he served as surgeon to the Massachusetts troops during an Indian campaign, and in Shay's Rebellion. He became a member of the General Court in 1788 and a Congressman in 1800. From 1809 to 1813, he served as Secretary of War.

In 1815, he became minister to Holland and in 1821 was again elected to Congress where he served two additional terms. Later he became governor of Massachusetts.

This versatile physician passed away on September 6, 1825.

Aaron Dexter (1750-1829) was born in Chelsea, Massachusetts, on November 11, 1750. Dexter entered Harvard College in 1772, receiving an A.B. from this institution in 1776. Following graduation he arranged to study medicine with the previously mentioned Samuel Danforth.

During the War of Independence, Dexter is claimed by some to have made several voyages to Europe as ship-surgeon and to have been captured and exchanged; however, it appears likely that this is not so and that he has been confused with William Dexter, a surgeon's mate from Massachusetts.

As the War drew to a climax, Aaron Dexter settled in Boston and proceeded to build up a fine practice and an eminent reputation. On May 22, 1783 he was selected as professor of chemistry and materia medica in the newly formed Harvard Medical School. In 1781, he had been one of the incorporators of the Massachusetts Medical Society and he served this organization as librarian for ten years. Dexter was one of the five originators of the Massachusetts Humane Society for the resuscitation of those apparently drowned, a society which still persists. He was also a fellow of the American Academy of Arts and Sciences and of the Massachusetts Historical Society. Harvard awarded him an honorary M.D. in 1786 and in 1805 Dartmouth followed suit. In 1791 his professorship was endowed by the will of his patient and friend, Major William Erving. Dr. Dexter retired from active teaching in 1816 and John Gorham succeeded him.

Dr. Oliver Wendell Holmes related the following incident concerning Dexter:

At one of Dexter's chemistry lectures he said to the class: "This experiment, gentlemen, is one of remarkable brilliancy. As I touch the powder you see before me with a drop of this fluid, it bursts into a sudden and brilliant flame.—" which it most emphatically does not do as he makes the contact. "Gentlemen," he says, with a serious smile, "the experiment has failed, but the principle, gentlemen, the principle remains as firm as the everlasting hills."

Dexter died in Cambridge at the age of 78 on February 28, 1829.

John Warren (1753-1815) was born in Roxbury, Massachusetts, on July 27, 1753, the descendant of John Warren, who came to the New World with Governor Winthrop as passengers on the "Arabella" which arrived in Salem on June 12, 1630. John's brother was the aforementioned Dr. Joseph Warren who lost his life at Bunker Hill. It is said that young John was a poor student and did not learn to read until the age of ten. However, he attended the Grammar School in Roxbury and eventually satisfactorily completed the requirements to enter Harvard College in July 1767, at the age of fourteen. John Warren not only proved to be a good student at Harvard, but also acquired a fluency in Latin which aided him greatly in communicating with numerous foreigners who had no other common tongue and with whom the political conditions of the times brought him much in contact. Graduating from Harvard in 1771 he at once undertook the study of medicine with his brother Joseph.

His medical education completed, John did not open his practice in Boston in competition with such physicians as Lloyd, Jeffries, Rand and Bulfinch. Instead he migrated to Salem and placed himself under the patronage of Dr. Holyoke who had furthered the careers of many budding doctors. Since a two-year course of study was required, John Warren opened up for himself in Salem in 1773. He received an honorary M.D. from Harvard in 1786.

It is said that on December 18, 1773, among those present at the Boston Tea Party, was our good doctor, John Warren. Soon afterwards, he became surgeon to a Salem regiment commanded by Colonel Pickering. In 1774, a true patriot, Warren openly urged the mechanics of New York to take no part in the construction of the fortifications of Boston. On June 19, 1775, as the battle of Lexington drew to a close, Warren's regiment arrived at Winter Hill, Somerville, encamped for the night, but returned to Salem the next day without having participated in that battle.

The morning after the battle of Bunker Hill, John Warren departed from Salem at two o'clock, and at Medford he was greatly grieved to learn of his brother Joseph's death. Frantically he rushed back to the battlefield to seek his brother's body, and a sentinel thrust a bayonet into his flesh, the scar of which he bore through life.

Anxious for vengeance, he volunteered as a private in the ranks of the American Army, but he was assigned to the care of the wounded. Warren took an examination on the basis of which he received the appointment of senior surgeon to the hospital established at Cambridge. Throughout the entire seige of Boston, Warren remained at his post, and after the evacuation of that city, he was one of the first surgeons to enter the city and make a report on the discovery that the departing British had mixed arsenic in the medicines left behind.

Upon departure of the army from Cambridge, the general hospital was transferred to New York. Warren set out for New York on May 11, 1776, and he was appointed senior surgeon of the hospital established at Long Island. He maintained his post in the army until July, 1777, and during this year concerned himself with the treatment of dysentery and what was probably typhoid fever. He was with the army at Trenton and narrowly escaped capture after the battle of Princeton.

Warren, having lost his health during the hardship of the campaign, applied for and received permission to return to Boston in April, 1777. Since considerable military preparations were then going on in Massachusetts, a hospital was established at the corner of Milton and Spring Streets near the site of the present Massachusetts General Hospital. On July 1, 1777, Warren became senior surgeon of the General Hospital in Boston, a position he held until the close of the war. This was the turning point in Warren's career. By now, most of the older physicians had left the city and Warren took advantage of this opportunity.

Warren, while in college, showed a keen interest in anatomy. Recognizing the importance of this subject in relation to the practice of medicine and surgery, he, in the winter of 1770, presented a course of anatomical lectures at the hospital which was attended by the army medical personnel, a few medical students, several Boston physicians and other scientifically inclined individuals. These demonstrations, which included work on the actual cadaver, were kept secret from the public on account of the popular wrath against dissection. The members of the Boston Medical Society, an organization formed the same year (May 14, 1770), elated by the lectures, passed a resolution to the effect ".... that Dr. John Warren be desired to demonstrate a course of anatomical lectures the ensuing winter." This course, presented at the hospital, was attended by literary and scientific men, including President Willard and members of the Harvard Corporation. In 1782, another anatomical series was given at the "Molineux House" on Beacon Street near Bowdoin Street, which was attended by the senior class at Harvard.

The success of Warren's anatomical presentations proved to the directors of Harvard that there was great need for a medical school. Thus, at a meeting of that Corporation held on May 16, 1782, a committee was appointed to consider the establishment of a medical professorship. After this committee reported on September 19, Warren was asked to organize a course of medical instruction. Shippen and Rush of Philadelphia aided Warren greatly in this work, and on November 22 of the same year, the corporation established three professorships: One of anatomy and surgery, one of theory and practice of physic and one of chemistry and materia medica. Warren was appointed professor of anatomy and surgery. On December 14, Benjamin Waterhouse was appointed professor of theory and practice of physic. Dr. Aaron Dexter was selected professor of chemistry and materia medica on May 22, 1783. It was on October 7, 1783 that Warren and Waterhouse were inducted into office at the Cambridge meeting house; Dexter's induction ensued a few weeks later. The first course of lectures was presented during the winter of 1783-4.

Early in his professional life, Warren performed one of the first abdominal sections recorded in this country. He opened and evacuated a dermoid cyst in the left hypochondrium with good recovery of the patient. He also successfully amputated a patient at the shoulder joint. Warren was always a patient, calm and thorough operator. He was among the first to recognize and practice the principle of the healing of wounds by first intention.

. Warren's extensive practice naturally brought him face to face with various epidemics. He helped greatly in the management of an epidemic of yellow fever which visited Boston in 1798, of which he wrote a report. In 1802 he was one of a commission to render a favorable report on the use of vaccine which had recently been brought from Europe, "as a complete security against smallpox."

Dr. Warren's most famous monograph is entitled "A View of the Mercurial Practice in Febrile Disease," published in 1813. In this work he refers to the treatment of many of the prevailing diseases of that period, such as measles, throat-distemper, consumption, dysentery, spotted fever and spinal meningitis.

John Warren wrote numerous articles published by the American

Academy of Arts and Sciences, the Communications of the Massachusetts Medical Society and the New England Journal of Medicine and Surgery. The first Boston Fourth of July oration was delivered by this erudite physician in 1783. In 1808, his oldest son, John Collins Warren was appointed to an adjunct professorship to aid him in lectures which were at that time delivered in inconvenient Cambridge.

Dr. Warren was one of the founders of the Massachusetts Medical Society in 1781 and served as its president from 1804 until his death. He also helped establish the Boston Medical Society in 1780, which set up a system of fees. In 1781, a year after its formation, Warren became a member of the American Academy of Arts and Sciences. Warren was also a corresponding member of the London Medical Society. In 1785, the Humane Society of the Commonwealth of Massachusetts was established and Warren became its second president. John Warren was the father of seventeen children, the youngest of whom was Dr. Edward Warren, his biographer.

Dr. John Warren died on April 4, 1815, after a short pulmonary ailment, at the age of sixty-two.

David Townsend (1753-1829) was born in Boston on June 7, 1753, a direct descendant of and four generations away from Thomas Townsend of Norfolk, England, who came to Massachusetts in 1637. David, a Harvard graduate of the class of 1770, received his honorary M.D. from that institution in 1813. A medical disciple of Joseph Warren, Townsend accompanied him as surgeon to his regiment at the battle of Bunker Hill. On January 1, 1776, he was commissioned surgeon to the sixth infantry regiment commanded by Colonel Asa Whitcomb. In March 1777, he was appointed senior surgeon to the General Hospital, Northern Department. He served the patriot army under Washington during the winter at Valley Forge. On October 9, 1781, he was appointed surgeon-general of the hospital department. For many years, and until his death, Townsend was physician in charge of the United States Marine Hospital in Chelsea, Massachusetts.

Dr. Townsend was a prominent member of the Massachusetts Medical Society from 1785 to 1824. He was also one of the charter members of the Society of the Cincinnati, which organization he served as secretary of the Massachusetts chapter from 1817 to 1821, vice-president from 1821 to 1825 and president from 1825 until his death on April 13, 1829 in his native town.

David Townsend's son, Solomon Davis Townsend, became a famous surgeon of the Massachusetts General Hospital.

Nathaniel Walker Appleton (1755-1795), the son of Nathaniel Appleton of the Harvard Class of 1749, and the grandson of Rev.

Dr. Nathaniel Appleton of the class of 1712, was born in Boston on June 14, 1755. Nathaniel received an A.B. from Harvard in 1773 and an A.M. in 1774. Following this he moved to Salem where he studied medicine with his father's cousin, Edward Augustus Holyoke.

Appleton opened his office in Boston and was elected first secretary of the Massachusetts Medical Society. During Appleton's secretary-ship, Holyoke and Cotton Tufts served as presidents.

Dr. Appleton developed a large practice. "The Boston Directory" of 1789 mentions the doctor's address as, "South Latin-School Street, near the Stone-Chappel" (at present School Street, near King's Chapel). In 1789 Appleton became a Fellow of the American Academy of Arts and Sciences and acted as chairman of the committee of the Massachusetts Medical Society that brought out the first volume of the "Medical Communications" in 1790. This publication was issued yearly until 1914, a total of one hundred and twenty-four annual issues.

Appleton was the author of two articles for the Massachusetts Medical Society which were published in "Medical Communications": "An account of the successful treatment of paralysis of the lower limbs, occasioned by a curvature of the spine," and "History of a hemorrhage from a rupture of the inside of the left labium pudendi."

Appleton also was a spark plug on the committee of the society on education that drafted the qualifications of candidates for licensure in conformity with the act of the Legislature of 1789. The Boston Town Records show that Appleton was elected as one of the twelve members of the 1789 school board which started the machinery rolling in the "New System of Education." He was reelected to the board each year through 1794.

Dr. Appleton is thought to have been in relatively poor health. In a letter dated March 23, 1782, he says that he was sending a messenger with his letter "being somewhat unwell myself and not daring to be out in the evening air.... At present I am confined with a bad cold." In 1788 he attempted to resign as secretary but the society prevailed upon him to serve for four more years.

Dr. Appleton's records as secretary of the Medical Society of Massachusetts are classic examples of precision and thoroughness. His penmanship was excellent. He kept accurate records of all the important doings of the society and its council through his entire term of office.

On January 2, 1793, his signature appeared on the records for the last time. However, he attended meetings of the society and council until April 3, 1794. On April 16, of this year, he presented the society with "a folio edition of Smellie's anatomical tables; a quarto edition of the medical works of Richard Smead, M.D., and a small box containing a few anatomical preparations." Appleton was elected an honorary Fellow of the society he had struggled so diligently to foster. He then moved to Marietta, Ohio, later returning to Boston, where he died on April 15, 1795, just two months prior to his fortieth birthday.

John Brooks (1752-1825) was born in Medford, Massachusetts, on May 31, 1752. When fourteen years old, after a common school education, he was apprenticed to Dr. Simon Tufts, Jr., of his home town, whom he served for seven years, after which he opened his office in nearby Reading.

During the War of Independence, Brooks raised a company in his town, and was chosen commander. At the Battle of Lexington his company harassed the British on their retreat. A fiery participant in the Revolution, with the rank of colonel, Gen. Washington appointed him the commander of a brigade at its close.

After peace was established, Brooks moved back to his birthplace and opened an office. He was one of the early members of the Massachusetts Medical Society and served as its president from 1823 to the time of his death in 1825. He was elected Governor of the Commonwealth in 1816 and served until 1823 in that office. Yale and Harvard both awarded him honorary A.M. degrees, the former in 1781, and the latter in 1787. An honorary M.D. was awarded by Harvard in 1810 and an LL.D. in 1817. He served also as president of the Society of the Cincinnati, president of the Bible Society of Massachusetts and a member of the Academy of Arts and Sciences.

In 1808 he delivered the anniversary oration before the Massachusetts Medical Society entitled "Pneumonic Inflammation." He died on March 1, 1825, at the age of seventy-three.

Josiah Bartlett (1759-1820) was born in Charlestown, Massachusetts, on August 11, 1759, the son of a sea captain, George Bartlett, who came from Slocum Regis in Devonshire. At the age of fourteen he was placed under the guidance of Dr. Isaac Foster, a Charlestown practicing physician. Just prior to the start of the Revolution, Bartlett received practical medical instruction from Dr. Foster. When the preceptor was appointed chief surgeon to the General Hospital at Cambridge, the apprentice, then sixteen years old, received an appointment as surgeon's mate which he kept until 1780, during which year Dr. Bartlett attended the course of lectures on anatomy by Dr. John Warren, at Cambridge. He then participated in two voyages as surgeon to ships of war.

In 1790, he pursued a complete course of medical lectures at Cambridge and in 1791 received an M.B. from Harvard. The same University awarded him an honorary M.D. in 1809. In 1789 he was elected to the Massachusetts Medical Society and he served this organization as its recording secretary from 1792 to 1796. Bartlett, in 1810, delivered the annual oration before this society on the progress of medical science in Massachusetts. According to James Thacher: "perhaps no man contributed more time and active exertion to improve the state of the Massachusetts Medical Society, and through it, the interests of medical literature, than Dr. Bartlett."

Bartlett wrote several articles pertaining to medicine, which were published in the communications of the Medical Society and in the "New England Journal of Medicine and Surgery."

Aside from his medical organizational activities and large practice, Bartlett found time to serve his countrymen as representative, senator and councillor in the state government.

A student of early medical history, he was deeply interested in the beginnings of New England and the development of its educational and literary institutions. He brought to light much information concerning the Rev. John Harvard, minister of the Congregational Church in Charlestown, and tried to find Harvard's grave. He proved the error of Dudley, Mather, Holmes and other writers on colonial history who stated that Governor Winthrop arrived at Charlestown with fifteen hundred persons in 1630. The original town records of Charlestown proved the date to be 1629.

Josiah Bartlett died of a cerebral hemorrhage on March 5, 1820, at the age of 60.

Abijah Cheever (1760-1843) a lineal descendant of Ezekiel Cheever, who, five generations earlier, had been master of the Boston Latin School, having migrated to Boston from Canterbury, England in 1673, was born in Saugus, Massachusetts in 1760. Passing his youth as a farm hand, on the eve of the battle of Lexington, he was employed in running bullets from a mould over a fire of hickory coals for the long Queen Anne muskets of his brothers who participated in that battle. He graduated from Harvard College in 1779 and studied medicine and surgery under the tutelage of Dr. John Warren. In 1785 he received the degree of A.M. from Harvard.

His commission as surgeon in the War of Independence was granted in 1782 and reads as follows:

By his Excellency John Hancock, Esq., governor and commander-in-chief in and over the Commonwealth of Massachusetts.

To Abijah Cheever, Gentleman, Greeting, Having Heard of your skill in surgery and reposing confidence in your ability and good conduct, I do by these presents constitute and appoint you surgeon on board the ship "Tartar" fitted out by this commonwealth for the service thereof. . . .

Dated at Boston this thirteenth day of May in the year of our Lord one thousand seven hundred and eighty-two, and in the sixth year of the Independence of the United States.

Signed, JOHN HANCOCK.

Cheever's adventures in the Tartar were short lived but breathtaking. Only two voyages were made. In the first, four British merchant vessels were captured. In the second, the Tartar was set upon by the British frigate "Bellsarius," and was herself captured. A prisoner, Dr. Cheever was taken to the old prison ship in New York harbor, where he remained until after peace was proclaimed. Then he set up his office in Boston, married, and engaged in medical practice for seventeen years. After this, he went back to the town of his birthplace and remained there until his death in 1843, at the ripe old age of eighty-three.

In 1787, Cheever published a case of "Encysted Dropsy" (Dermoid Cyst of the Ovary ?) with illustrations, and presented his findings before the American Academy of Arts and Sciences.

Upper left, DR. WILLIAM CABELL (1700-1774) was a pioneer of Goochland County. He charged one to five pounds for a house call. He guaranteed cure for high fees and charged minimum rates for non-guaranteed cases. (*Courtesy of Wyndham B. Blanton, M.D.*) *Upper right*, DR. THEODORIC BLAND (1740-1790) received a European medical education, returned to Virginia in 1765, practiced medicine for seven years, and retired because of poor health. (*Courtesy of Wyndham B. Blanton, M.D.*) *Lower left*, JAMES CRAIK, M.D. (1731-1814) was the first physician called in during the last illness of George Washington. (*Reproduced from Army Medical Bulletin #25.*) *Lower right*, JAMES McCLURG, M.D. (1746-1823) served his country as a surgeon in the Virginia State Navy during the War of Independence. (*Courtesy of Wyndham B. Blanton, M.D.*)

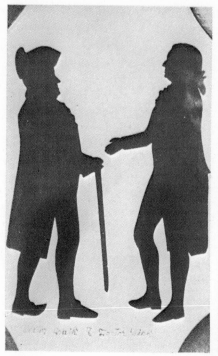

Upper left, Silhouette of DR. ELISHA CULLEN DICK (1762?-1825) and DR. JAMES CRAIK (1731-1814). (*Courtesy of Wyndham B. Blanton, M.D.*)

Upper right, DR. GUSTAVUS RICHARD BROWN (1747-1804) was an unquestioned patriot during the War of Independence. (Silhouette in the Richmond Academy of Medicine. *Courtesy of the Maryland Historical Society.*)

Right, DR. WILLIAM BAYNHAM (1749-1814) became famous for his operations for stone, cataract and tubal pregnancy. (*Courtesy of Wyndham B. Blanton, M.D.*)

GOVERNOR JOHN WINTHROP

On July 23, 1630, when Governor Winthrop sent for his wife, he stated: "...for the physick you shall need no other, but a pound of Doctor Wrights' Electuaria lenitivii, and his direction to use it, a gallon of scurvy grease to drinke a little 5; or 6; morninges together, with some saltpeter dissolved in it, and a little grated or sliced nutmete." (*Courtesy of the Massachusetts Historical Society and Harvard College.*)

Upper left, JOHN GLOVER, M.D. sailed to Scotland in 1650 and was awarded a medical degree by the University of Aberdeen. (*Courtesy of the Massachusetts Historical Society and Harvard College.*) *Upper right,* CHARLES CHAUNCY (1592-1672), although a clergyman by profession, was eminent as a physician. He disseminated among his pupils a knowledge of the medicine of the day, acquired in England, at a time when such instruction was badly needed in the New World. (*Courtesy of the Massachusetts Historical Society and Harvard College.*) *Lower left,* DR. SAMUEL SEABURY, who died in Duxbury in 1680, left an estate which included an antimonial cup, Culpepper's "Practice of Physic," French's "The Art of Distillation" and surgeon's instruments. (*Courtesy of the Massachusetts Historical Society and Harvard College.*) *Lower right,* THOMAS THACHER (1620-1678) was author of the first medical article to be printed on colonial soil. (*Courtesy of the Old South Meeting House, Boston; and Johns Hopkins Press.*)

Upper left, JOHN WARREN, M.D. (1753-1815) was first professor of anatomy and surgery at Harvard Medical School. (*Reproduced from Army Medical Bulletin No. 25.*) *Upper center*, DR. DAVID TOWNSEND (1753-1829) served the patriot army under General George Washington during the winter at Valley Forge. (*Courtesy of the Massachusetts Historical Society and Harvard College.*) *Upper right*, DR. JOSIAH BARTLETT (1759-1820) was a physician of prominence, a patriot during the War of Independence and a pioneer in bringing good medical literature to Massachusetts. (*Courtesy of the Boston Medical Library and Harvard College.*) *Lower left*, DR. NATHANIEL WALKER APPLETON (1755-1795) was elected first secretary of the Massachusetts Medical Society. (*Courtesy of the Boston Medical Library and Harvard College.*) *Lower right*, DR. JOHN BROOKS (1752-1825) served as colonel in the Continental Army and governor of the Massachusetts Medical Society. (*Courtesy of the Massachusetts Historical Society and Harvard College.*)

Left, DR. MATTHEW THORNTON (1714-1803) signed his name last on the Declaration of Independence. (From the painting in the New Hampshire Historical Society's Gallery; *Courtesy of the New Hampshire Historical Society.*) *Center,* DR. JOSIAH BARTLETT (1729-1795) was the second signer of the Declaration of Independence. (From the portrait by John Trumbull in the New Hampshire Historical Society's Gallery; *Historical New Hampshire,* October 1947; p. 2.) *Right,* DR. NATHANIEL PEABODY (1741-1823) was a member of that daring group which seized one hundred barrels of powder from Fort William and Mary in December, 1774. (*Courtesy of the New Hampshire Historical Society.*)

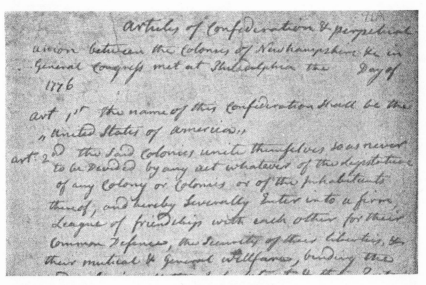

Previously Unknown Draft of the Bartlett Notes. From the New Hampshire Historical Society's Photograph of the Original Manuscript in the New Hampshire State Library. (*Historical New Hampshire,* October 1947; p. 5.)

Chapter Four

NEW HAMPSHIRE

IN 1603, MARTIN PRING explored the mouth of the Piscataqua River and issued a monograph on the New England coast from Casco Bay to Cape Cod Bay. In 1605, Samuel de Champlain discovered the Isles of Shoals and navigated along the New Hampshire coast. In 1614, Captain John Smith, in his *Description of New England*, referred to the suitable harbor at the mouth of the Piscataqua and praised the adjoining country. Under the guidance of Sir Ferdinando Gorges in 1620, the Council for New England was organized and a grant was obtained from King James I, for all the country from sea to sea between 40° and 48° N. latitude. The Council subgranted to John Mason, "the founder of New Hampshire," on March 9, 1622, the area between the Salem and Merrimac rivers (designated Mariana), and to John Mason and Sir Ferdinando Gorges jointly, on August 10, 1622, the land between the Merrimac and Kennebec rivers for 60 m. inland, under the name of the Province of Maine.

Besides these two grants, David Thomson and associates, in 1622, received title to six thousand acres near the mouth of the Piscataqua and Sir Henry Roswell and associates, on March 19, 1628, the region from three miles south of the Charles river, "or to the southward of any and every part thereof" to three miles north of the Merrimac river, "or to the northward of any and every part thereof," and extending west to the South Sea or Pacific Ocean, under the name of Massachusetts. On November 7, 1629, John Mason received that portion of the "Province of Maine" between the Merrimac and the Piscataqua, under the name of New Hampshire.

The Laconia Company, consisting of Gorges, Mason and associates, on November 17, 1629, obtained a grant of an extensive territory (termed Laconia) around the Lake of the Iroquois (Lake Champlain) together with one thousand acres at some place to be selected along the sea coast. Edward Hilton, on March 12, 1630, secured from the Council a tract on and about the lower part of Dover Neck. The Laconia Company, in November 1631, also received land on both sides of the Piscataqua river near its mouth, known as the Pescataway grant.

John Mason, on April 22, 1635, a short time before the Council surrendered its charter, obtained the New Hampshire grant which included the land between the Salem river on the south and the Piscataqua and Salmon Falls river on the north-east to a distance of sixty miles inland. Mason passed away in December, 1635, and New Hampshire, unlike the other colonies from which the United States originated, New Jersey and Delaware excepted, never was given a royal charter.

In 1623, David Thomson established Little Harbor, now within the limits of Rye. Thomson, as leader of a fishing and trading company, whose entire stock was held jointly for five years, constructed a dwelling on Odiorne's Point overlooking Little Harbor. Even though he moved to an island in Boston Harbor in 1626, it is likely he continued the business of the company at Little Harbor until the expiration of the five-year term, for it is recorded that a settlement here was assessed in 1628. The original settlement may not have been completely abandoned when colonists sent over by the Laconia Company arrived in 1630.

The basis for the Laconia Company's initial grant was invalid for it was erroneously held that the Piscataqua river took its origin from Lake Champlain. The interest of this company was primarily to establish a lucrative fur trade with the Iroquois Indians. Thomson's old house was inhabited by the colonists and nearby "Mason Hall" (the "Great House") was built in what is now Portsmouth, a name for the entire settlement that supplanted "Strawberry Banke" in 1653.

Edward Hilton and a few colonists started a colony on Dover Point, at about the time that Thomson came to Little Harbor, and in the 1630 Hilton grant notation is made that he had already built houses there. This colony was called Dover.

Reverend John Wheelwright, a prominent Antinomian, who had been expelled from Massachusetts, established Exeter in 1638 on land that he declared was purchased from the Indians. In 1638, also, Massachusetts encouraged friendly Puritans to settle Hampton on the same purchase, and about a year later, this colony organized Hampton as a town with the right to send a deputy to the General Court.

Internal conflict between Puritan and Anglican elements in Dover became prevalent. Captain John Underhill, prominent in Antinomian circles, became for a time a leader of the Puritan faction. Naturally enough Puritan Massachusetts was inimical to the Antinomians at Exeter and to the Anglicans at Strawberry Banke. Notwithstanding the fact that Exeter, in 1639, Dover, in 1640, and Strawberry Banke, not later than 1640, adopted a plantation covenant, these settlements were especially weak for there was no powerful governing tribunal. In fact, as early as 1633, appeals had been made to Massachusetts to intervene.

The grants of Massachusetts and Mariana, of course, conflicted, and under such conditions, Massachusetts discovered a new claim for its northern boundary on the basis that the charter of that colony was drafted under the impression that the Merrimac flowed east, for its entire course, whereas in reality its source was in Lake Winnepesaukee several miles north of any of the four settlements in New Hampshire. Massachusetts, naturally enough, capitalized on that part of the charter which designated the northern boundary as three English miles north of the Merrimac river, "or to the northward of any and every part thereof," and ignored the conflicting grants to Mason. Massachusetts forced its jurisdiction over Dover in 1641, Strawberry Banke (Portsmouth) soon afterwards and Exeter in 1643.

Mason's heirs vehemently protested the Massachusetts interpretation but to little avail. Although prolonged litigations eventually established Mason's rights to the land, and he succeeded in obtaining the appointment of officers who supported his claims, and decrees issued in his favor, the tenants, who contended that they had profited nothing from what his grandfather had done or that they were on lands which Wheelwright had bought from the Indians, effectually resisted the enforcement of those decrees. The contest, however, especially for the waste lands, was continued by Mason's heirs until the close of the 18th century.

From 1686 to 1689 New Hampshire was swallowed up by the Dominion of New England, which, after the first few months, was ruled by Sir Edmund Andros as governor-general. When 1689 rolled around, as there was no provincial authority in New Hampshire, a convention of the leading citizens of its four towns unsuccessfully attempted to establish one. When this failed a temporary nominal union with Massachusetts was organized which lasted until 1692. Samuel Allen, the assign of Mason, caused a royal government to be established with his son-in-law, John Usher, a lieutenant-governor. During the rest of the colonial era, New Hampshire, although separate from Massachusetts, had boundary disputes with Massachusetts and New York.

From 1676 to 1759 fear of the Indians plus the incessant boundary disputes and Mason's claims, greatly retarded colonization, but notwithstanding, at the outbreak of the War of Independence, New Hampshire had about 80,000 inhabitants, the great majority of whom supported the patriot or Whig party during that struggle. In June 1775, the once popular governor, Sir John Wentworth, was a refugee; on January 5, 1776, the fifth Provincial Congress established a provisional government; on June 15, 1776, the first Assembly elected under that government declared for independence; and on August 16, 1777 the great victory at Bennington was won by New Hampshire and Vermont troops under the command of General John Stark, whose commission originated in New Hampshire.

An even half-dozen states had ratified the Federal constitution when the New Hampshire convention was held at Exeter on February 13, 1788. The opposition to this document by the delegates from central New Hampshire was so great that after ten days discussion the leaders favoring ratification dared not risk a vote. They succeeded in obtaining an adjournment until those delegates who had been instructed to vote against it had consulted their constituents. The Federal Constitution was eventually ratified by a vote of 57 to 47.

In 1631 there arrived in Strawberry Banke some fifty men and twenty-five women on the ship "Warwick," which dropped anchor in the harbor on July 4, of that year. Included among these was Dr. Reginald Fernald (1595-1656), the first physician to settle in the province of New Hampshire. Fernald was born in Bristol, England, on July 6, 1595. It is claimed that he resigned a position in the English Navy to come to America. Not many records have come down to us regarding this pioneer. That he was held in high esteem cannot be doubted for soon after his arrival he was elected captain of the military company in the little colony. In 1643 he served as grand juror and in 1654-1655 he was elected town recorder. He also served as trial justice of the peace, recorder of deeds, surveyor, commissioner, and clerk of Portsmouth.

In May 1653, the good doctor and four other townsmen petitioned the General Court to change the name of Strawberry Banke to Portsmouth.

In January, 1655, the first coroner's inquest was held in New Hampshire by a jury of twelve men, under the direction of Dr. Fernald. The doctor certified that the jury returned the following verdict:

"Wee whose names are subscribed doe testifie how wee found Thomas Tuttell, the son of John Tuttel, by the stump of a tree which he had newly fallen upon another limb of the other tree, rebounding back and fell upon him, which was the cause of his death as wee consider. This was found the last day of the last March."

Dr. Fernald passed away in Portsmouth on October 6, 1656.

The following physicians from New Hampshire served in the Revolution:

Benjamin Adams, David Allen, —— Aubury, Abner Barker, William M. Barnett, Josiah Bartlett, Thomas Bartlett, Stephen Boardman, Joshua Brackett, Nathaniel Breed, Lawrence Brooks, Samuel Brooks, Benjamin Brown, Edmund Chadwick, Joshiah Chase, Solomon Chase, William Cogswell, John Cook, Samuel Curtiss, Ammi R. Cutter.

Amos Dakin, Levi Dearborn, Henry Dearborn, Abraham Downer, Obadiah Dunham, Abijah Durham, George Eager, George Edgar, Peter Emerson, Samuel Endicott, Ebenezer Fisk, Samuel Flagg, Nathan Foot, Abiel Foster, Calvin Frink, Thomas Frink.

Nathan Gardner, John Giddings, Joseph Gilman, John Gove, Benjamin Green, Ezra Green, Peter Green, Samuel Hale, Jacob Hall, John Hall, David Harris, Robert B. Henry, Francis Hodgkins, Samuel Holt, James Howe, Mark Howe, Mark Howze, Ivory Hovey.

Hall Jackson, Joshua H. Jackson, —— Jones, Reuben Jones, George Kezer, James Knowles, Joseph Lee, Joseph Lewis, Samuel Moore, Samuel Morey, David Morris, Moses Nichols, Enoch Noyes, Frederick Obrey, Kendall Osgood.

Benjamin Page, William Page, William Parker, William Parker, Jr., Nathaniel Peabody, Thomas Peabody, Ithurial Pell, David Peterson, Jonathan Pool, Jonas Prescott, Ezra Reed, Ebenezer Rockwood, Nathaniel Rogers, Benjamin Rowe, William Sawyer, Cheney Smith, Isaac Smith, Thomas Stearns, Ebenezer Stockton, David Taylor, Samuel Tenney, Isaac Thorn, Matthew Thornton.

Patrick Warren, Peletiah Warren, Zuriel Waterman, Samuel Wigglesworth, Elias Willard, Obadiah Williams, George Wood, James Wood, William Wood, Philemon Wright, Abijah Wright and John Young.

Conditions were so bad in Ticonderoga on September 27, 1776, that Colonel Samuel Wiggleworth wrote the Committee of Safety of New Hampshire as follows:

Ticonderoga, September 27th, 1776.

Near half this regiment is entirely incapable of any service, some dying almost every day. Col. Wyman's Regt., is in the same unhappy situation. There are no medicines of any avail in the Continental Chest; such as there are, are in their native state, unprepared; no emetics, nor cathartics; no mercurials or antimonial remedies; no opiate or elixir, tincture, or any capital remedy. It would make a heart of stone melt to hear the moans and see the distress of the sick and dying. I can scarce pass a tent but I hear men solemnly declaring that they will never engage another campaign without being assured of a better supply of medicines.

Matthew Thornton and Josiah Bartlett of New Hampshire were signers of the Declaration of Independence.

Matthew Thornton (1714-1803) signed his name last on the Declaration of Independence. Thornton was born in Ireland in 1714. At the age of three, in 1717, he migrated to this country with his father and settled in Wiscasset, Maine. The family moved to Worcester, Massachusetts and it was here he received his education and engaged in the study of medicine. He opened his office in Londonderry, New Hampshire, and built up a large practice under the tutelage of Dr. Grant of Leicester. His fame as a physician spread, and hand in hand with this, his reputation as a great patriot. In the expedition against Louisburg he served as surgeon of the New Hampshire Division, consisting of five hundred men. As the War of Independence approached, he avowed himself firmly on the side of the colonists and vehemently denounced the British. He served as a delegate to the convention which declared New Hampshire to be a sovereign state, and was elected president of this body.

When the Revolution broke out, Thornton held the rank of colonel in the militia. On June 2, 1775, his signature appeared at the bottom of an address to the citizens of New Hampshire, recommending "that a strict and inviolable regard be paid to the wise and judicious counsels of the late American Congress." He enjoyed membership in the Continental Congress from 1776 to 1778, and in the last mentioned year resigned to accept the chief justiceship of Hillsborough County. This post also was resigned two years later so that he could accept a position on the supreme court of New Hampshire. In 1783 Thornton was elected a member of the State House of Representatives, and in 1784 he became a member of the State Senate. His interest in politics never was diminished. Even at eighty, he wrote political articles for the papers. During his last days he was working on a metaphysical thesis covering the origin of sin, but this was never completed.

In 1780 he purchased a farm at Merrimac, N. H., on the banks of the Merrimac river, near Exeter. The rest of his life he sojourned there, dying in Newburyport, Massachusetts, while on a visit to his daughter, on June 24, 1803, at the age of eighty-nine.

It is said of him that "His countenance was invincibly grave, like that of Cassius, who read much and never smiled; and this trait is the more remarkable as he was distinguished for his good humoured hilarity."

A petition to which was affixed the signatures of nineteen New Hampshire physicians, from thirteen different towns, was presented to the legislature, and a bill was passed by the house, and signed, on February 16, 1791, by Josiah Bartlett, president, incorporating these physicians in an organization called the New Hampshire Medical Society. The original nineteen included Josiah Bartlett of Kingston, Joshua Brackett, Ammi R. Cutter, Hall Jackson, and John Jackson of Portsmouth, James Bracket of Lee, Moses Carr of Sommersworth, William Cogswell of Atkinson, Ezra Green of Dover, Osgood Kendall of Peterborough, Benjamin Page, William Parker, Jr., Nathaniel Peabody, and Samuel Tenney of Exeter, William Page of Charlestown, Ebenezer Rockwood of Wilton, John Rogers of Plymouth, George Sparhawk of Walpole, and Isaac Thom of Londonderry.

Matthew Thornton, of course, by the time of the founding of this Society, had already retired from practice having reached the age of seventy-seven.

The Bartlett family took its origin from ancestors who took part in the Norman conquest of England. These progenitors settled in southern England and one branch came to America. Richard Bartlett made Newbury, Massachusetts, his home in about 1635. His son Richard remained in Newbury, and this latter Richard's grandson, Stephen, married Hannah Webster, and settled in Amesbury, where Josiah was born on November 21, 1729.

Josiah Bartlett (1729-1795), while a boy, acquired a knowledge of both Latin and Greek. At sixteen he started his medical studies with his relative Dr. Ordway. He made use of all the libraries in the neighborhood, especially the excellent one belonging to Rev. Dr. Webster, a maternal relative.

In 1750, at the age of twenty-one, Josiah Bartlett started his practice in Kingston in the house of Reverend Joseph Secombe. In 1752, it is related that he was attacked by a fever, which almost cost him his life. While rapidly failing, he requested two young men who were watching him to secure some cider. Although the physician in charge had pronounced the prognosis hopeless, they brought him the cider against their better judgment, and it is reported that young Josiah improved with every gulp. In the morning a profuse diaphoresis took place and the fever receded. Following this Josiah always treated the patient—not only the disease—and did not base his practice on arbitrary rules.

It should be recalled that in 1733 and 1735 a "distemper" originated in Kingston, which eluded all the powers of the physicians, and which was termed the "Throat Distemper or Angina Maligna." This virulent epidemic spread rapidly, most children contracting it, dying. A depleting and antiphlogistic course of treatment was commonly employed for this. When in 1754 the angina again appeared in Kingston, Dr. Bartlett gave up this method of treatment and used the new remedy, Peruvian bark, very efficaciously.

Josiah Bartlett's ability and integrity became apparent and he was appointed a magistrate. In 1765 he started his political career as a representative in the Legislature, an office he continued to occupy until the Revolution. In February, 1775, Governor Wentworth relieved him of the commission he had held as justice of the peace, and commander of the militia. In September, 1775, he was appointed by the provincial congress, of which Dr. Matthew Thornton was president, to command a regiment and was chosen a delegate to the continental congress. He attended the congress and when that great moment arrived to vote for American Independence, the medical colonel's name was called first as representing the most easterly province. Bartlett was the second signer of the Declaration.

Bartlett's profound concern over the formulation of the Constitution and his deep desire that the Union of the formerly confederated states be indivisible and permanent may be readily inferred from the following letters:

The affair of a Confederation of the Colonies is now unanimously agreed on by all the members of all the Colonies: a Committee of one from each Colony are to draw up the articles of confederation or a Continental Constitution which when agreed on by the Congress will be sent to be confirmed by the Legislature of the several Colonies. As it is a very important business and some difficulties have arisen, I fear it will take some time before it will be finally settled; the affair of voting whether by Colonies as at present or otherwise is not decided and causes warm dispute.

I have been for about a week on a Committee of one member from Each Colony to form a Confederation or Charter of firm & everlasting Union of all the united Colonies. It is a matter of the greatest Consequence & requires the greatest Care in forming it: when it is agreed to by the Committee, it will be laid before the Congress & when they have agreed to it, it will be sent to Each Colony to be by them ratified & Confirmed. May God grant us wisdom to form a happy Constitution, as the happiness of America to all future Generations Depends on it.

When Josiah Bartlett travelled to Philadelphia in 1776 he was no novice in rebellion. As mentioned, he had been there previously as a member of the Continental Congress and ten years earlier, as a member of the provincial legislature of New Hampshire, had led the opposition to the famous Stamp Act. At the time of the signing Bartlett was forty-seven years old and had built up a fine practice at Kingston. Josiah Bartlett served in the Continental Congress from 1775 until 1778. In 1778 he left Philadelphia to visit his family and did not again resume his seat in Congress.

His public service to New Hampshire seems to have but begun by this change for he was soon appointed chief justice of the Court of Common Pleas (1779) and somewhat later (1782) justice of the Superior Court. In 1788 he became chief justice of the State and was a member of the convention for adopting the Confederation. In 1789 he was chosen a senator in Congress which position he declined and the next year he became president of the State of New Hampshire. Three years later he was unanimously chosen that state's first Governor. In all this notable service, Josiah Bartlett never gave up his interest in his chosen calling. He was not only a founder of the New Hampshire Medical Society in 1791, but attended its meetings and took a most active interest in its welfare. The first president of the medical society, he was elected annually for three consecutive years, following which he refused further reelection. He married Mary Bartlett, a distant relative, and had three sons, Levi, Josiah and Ezra.

The following letter illustrates the character of Josiah Bartlett: Writing to General Folsom, after the evacuation of Long Island, concerning preliminary negotiations looking toward peace, he states:

What the congress will do is at present uncertain, but I hope they will be directed by the Supreme Disposer of all events to do in this and every other affair before them that which will be most conducive to the safety and happiness of these American states.

A deeply religious man, it is said of him that like Josiah, king of Judah, "he did that which was right in the sight of the Lord . . . and turned not to the right hand or to the left."

Josiah Bartlett was always an intensely popular man. Of the votes cast for governor in 1792, he received 8,096, all but 297 of the total votes. In 1793, out of 9,854 votes, he received 7,388 or three fourths of the whole, although John Langdon and others were in the field against him. He was also one of the electors of president and vice-president in 1792.

In June, 1793, while governor of the state, he was present at a meeting of his beloved New Hampshire Medical Society, but declined a reelection to the office of President. Following this the Society entered the following upon its records:

His Excellency Governor Bartlett having signified to this society that the discharge of the arduous and important duties of his office as first magistrate of the state, with various other concerns, must necessarily engross his whole attention, and that notwithstanding he should ever aim to promote the true interest of the Society, yet it would be inconvenient for him any longer to hold the office of President; wherefore, Resolved unanimously that the united thanks of the Fellows be given to His Excellency Governor Bartlett for his very polite and friendly attention and patronage in forming and supporting the Medical Society; and they very much regret his declining to accept the office of President, and request his advice patronage and attendance at the meetings whenever he can make it convenient.

(Signed) Nath. Peabody, Vice-president.

Upon receipt of this, Bartlett returned, the same day, the following reply:

Gentlemen of the New Hampshire Medical Society:

The unexpected resolve of thanks, presented me by your committee, for the small service I have been able to afford the Medical Society I consider as an instance of polite attention and regard they mean to pay to such persons as may in any manner endeavor to promote the public happiness.

I have long wished that the practice of medicine in this state (upon which the lives and healths of our fellow-citizens depend) might be put under better regulations than it has been in times past, and have reason to hope that the incorporation of the New Hampshire Medical Society (if properly attended by the Fellows) will produce effects greatly beneficial to the community, by encouraging genius and learning in the medical science and discouraging ignorant and bold pretenders from practising an art of which they have no knowledge.

That the members of the Society may be useful to themselves and the public, and enjoy the exalted pleasure and satisfaction that arise from a consciousness that they have contributed to the health and happiness not only of their patients, but, by communicating to others the knowledge and cure of disease, to the general happiness of the human race, is the ardent wish of, Gentlemen, your very humble servant,

Josiah Bartlett.

Concord, June 19th 1793

On January 29, 1794, Josiah Bartlett resigned all public positions on account of his failing health and he died of a cerebral accident, with ensuing paralysis, on May 19, 1795, in his sixty-sixth year.

Joshua Brackett (1733-1799) was born in Greenland, New Hampshire on May 9, 1733. He engaged in study under the Reverend Rust of Stratham, and was greatly influenced by the Bible and the doctrine of the Universalist church. Joshua entered Harvard College in 1748 and graduated from this institution in 1752. He then settled in Portsmouth, and it is related that he preached eloquently and prayed extemporaneously at amazing lengths in the Universalist church, until sickness overtook him and he met Dr. Clement Jackson, Portsmouth's leading practitioner. Jackson soon observed that Brackett had been forced into the priesthood by his environment and not through natural inclination. As soon as Brackett's health was restored, Dr. Jackson took him into his office, showed him how to prepare medications and took him out on his calls. Brackett was an apt pupil and he soon opened his own office in Portsmouth. Joshua Brackett took up the study of obstetrics as a specialty and soon became famous as an obstetrician.

During the War of Independence he served on the Committee of Safety, and sat as judge of the Maritime Courts. This latter position he came by through his brother-in-law, Captain Whipple of Kittery, whose sister, Hannah, he married in May, 1761. A dowry of 300 pounds in Spanish silver dollars went with the good lady. He served in this judicial capacity until 1784 when his court was abolished.

From 1784 on, Brackett continued in medical practice. He was elected honorary and active fellow of the Massachusetts Medical Society, was one of the charter members of the New Hampshire Medical Society, its first vice-president, and then its president for six successive years (1793-1799). In 1792 he received an honorary M.D. from his alma mater. The meetings of the New Hampshire Medical Society under his guidance were held in different localities and were attended by a dozen members. It was customary at each meeting for some one to present a rare case, which was discussed until noon when dinner was served. After dinner and a pipe and a glass of punch, the members set off on horseback on their lonely rides, to far distant homes.

Dr. Brackett gave many valuable medical books to his beloved state Society which maintained a lending medical library, giving the members a chance to brush up on modern trends in medicine and surgery. He helped design a permanent seal for the Society, which was made of solid silver at a cost of 6 pounds. When he died, he gave $1,500 to Harvard toward a chair of botany and natural history, as well as his library of one hundred and forty volumes to the Society. His widow, by his request, left the Society $500, which was expended for books. A few of Brackett's books can still be seen in the New Hampshire State Library at Concord.

Suffering with heart disease, Dr. Brackett, in May 1802, travelled to the springs of Saratoga, but no relief was forthcoming. Realizing the end was near, he returned to Portsmouth, on or about July 10, 1799, and died on July 17, 1799.

Hall Jackson (1739?-1797) was born in Portsmouth in about 1739, the son of Dr. Clement and Sarah Hall Jackson. His father taught him about the medical arts, following which he visited the London hospitals to learn more about surgery. He settled in Portsmouth, and his fame became widespread. His skill at smallpox inoculation made him much sought after, and several hospitals for this procedure were placed under his management. He also was noted as an obstetrician and as an oculist. Harvard awarded him an honorary M.D. and the Massachusetts Medical Society welcomed him as an honorary member. He wrote an article entitled "Putrid Sore Throat," published in Portsmouth in 1786. On September 28, 1797, death after a carriage accident overtook him prematurely at the age of fifty-eight.

Nathaniel Peabody (1741-1823) was born in Topsfield, Massachusetts on March 1, 1741. His only education was imparted to him by his father, a distinguished physician, who also initiated him in the medical arts. He moved to Plaistow at the age of twenty-one. In 1770 he was commissioned by the royal governor a justice of the peace and quorum, and four years later he was appointed lieutenant-colonel in the militia. He accompanied that daring group which seized one hundred barrels of powder from Fort William and Mary, in Portsmouth, in December, 1774. In a later raid on the fort, fifteen light cannon were carted off. This ammunition went to the battle of Bunker Hill, where New Hampshire furnished about half the troops and nearly all the powder.

During the first years of the War of Independence, Peabody was a leading member of the legislature and chairman of the Committee of Safety. In 1778 he was adjutant-general of the state militia, and served in Rhode Island. In 1779 he was delegate to the Continental congress. In 1785 and 1790-1792, he served as senator and was major-general of the militia. Dartmouth awarded him an honorary A.M.

Sad to relate, Peabody got deeply in debt, and was committed to Exeter jail, although permitted to move around town within certain limits. He practiced medicine more or less for some twenty years.

Peabody was elected vice-president of the New Hampshire Medical Society in 1793 at Concord, and in 1794 at Exeter. He attended meetings held in Exeter in 1806 and 1807. From 1807 to 1818, his name does not appear again in the annals of the society. In 1818 a resolution was passed to cancel his dues amounting to thirty-two dollars. He passed away on June 27, 1823, at the grand old age of eighty-two.

William Cogswell (1760-1831) was born in Haverhill, Mass., in July 1760. He followed a classical curriculum for three and one-half years. At the start of the War of Independence he was fifteen and a half years old, but he promptly enlisted as a private in the company raised by his brother, Captain Thomas Cogswell. In a year he returned to study with Dr. Nathaniel Peabody, at Atkinson. On July 19, 1781, Cogswell received the position of surgeon's mate to Dr. William Eustis in the general military hospital at West Point, which position he held until the end of the war in 1783. In January, 1784, he was promoted to the rank of chief surgeon in charge of the hospital, and he held this appointment until September, 1785. He then returned to Atkinson, where he engaged in private practice until his death in 1831 at the age of seventy-one.

He was instrumental in establishing the Atkinson academy, one of the oldest literary institutions in New Hampshire.

Benjamin Page (1742-1824) was born in Dunbarton, in 1742. When the Revolution broke out he joined his relative, General John Stark, and served as surgeon from 1775 to 1787. He and Stark took part in such noteworthy engagements as Bunker Hill, Ticonderoga and Bennington. At Bennington, Page personally took command of a company whose captain was disabled, and led them on to victory with such bravery as to earn special commendation. Following the battle he again took care of the wounded, his surgical instruments being the only ones on the field. After the war he practiced in Chester and Exeter, and in Hallowell, Me., where he died at the age of eighty-two.

William Page (1749-1810) was born in Connecticut in 1749. After a limited preliminary education he moved to Charlestown at the close of the war, was appointed a militia colonel, and served in the legislature for several years, and in the senate in 1791-92. It is recorded that he was present at the second meeting of the New Hampshire Medical Society in 1791, and during the ensuing two years. He served as a councillor of the Society, and was appointed to organize the Western District Society. He passed away at the age of sixty-one in 1810.

Samuel Tenney (1748-1816) was born in Byfield Massachusetts on November 27, 1748. He graduated from Harvard college in 1772 and took up the study of medicine with Dr. Kittredge of Andover. In 1775 he moved to Exeter, but when the War of Independence erupted, he rode horseback to Boston, arriving in time to assist in caring for the wounded at Bunker Hill. Throughout the war he continued in the capacity as surgeon. For one year he assisted Dr. Eustis in a Massachusetts regiment and later in the Rhode Island Line. He was on hand at the surrenders of Burgoyne and Cornwallis. This patriot volunteered to defend Red Bank on the Delaware and did not himself, hesitate to carry a musket. In this campaign, with the aid of Peter Turner, he dressed the wounds of Count Dunop, who was mortally wounded. The Count gave over his pocketbook to the doctor because "he looked like an honest man."

When the War of Independence was completed, Tenney returned to Exeter although he did not practice much. For seven years he was elected vice-president of the New Hampshire Medical Society.

In 1791 Tenney served as a member of the convention for forming a constitution for the state. In 1793 he was appointed judge of probate for Rockingham county, and he kept his seat on the bench until 1800, when he was elected to Congress, where he served for three terms. Dr. Tenney also was active in several literary, historical, and scientific societies, to which groups he contributed various articles. The Academy of the Arts and Sciences published articles by him on the mineral waters of Saratoga, and on the theory of prismatic colors. The Massachusetts Historical Society published his essay on Exeter, and a notice of the dark day, May 19, 1780. The Massachusetts Agricultural Society was proud of his monograph on orcharding. His political essays in the newspapers, particularly those favoring the Federal Constitution, were noteworthy. He passed away in 1816, at the age of sixty-eight.

Isaac Thom (1746-1825) was the first physician of Windham, where he practiced for thirteen years and was a member of the Committee of Safety. He moved to Londonderry in 1782 and practiced there until 1795. He was justice of the peace and first postmaster in Londonderry. He died on July 13, 1825, at the age of seventy-nine.

Ezra Green (1746-1847) was born in Malden, Massachusetts on June 17, 1746. After graduating from Harvard in 1765, he settled in Dover in 1767. In June, 1775, on the Sunday after Bunker Hill, he joined the New Hampshire regiment under Colonel Reed, on Winter Hill in Charlestown, as surgeon, and served in this capacity until the winter of 1776, when he returned to Dover. After being appointed surgeon of the *Ranger*, Captain Paul Jones, this boat sailed for France on November 1, 1776 and took part in the engagement with the Drake. The Ranger returned to Portsmouth on October 1778. The doctor was married, and sailed very soon again as surgeon of the Ranger, returning in July. In 1780 and 1781, he was surgeon on the *Alexander*.

After the war he gave up practice, went into the mercantile business, and was the first post-master of Dover. This patriot lived to be more than one hundred and one years old. In 1838 he remained sole survivor of the nineteen original members of the Society.

Moses Carr (1716-1800) was born in Newbury, Mass. He opened his office in Dover in 1735 following which he went to Somersworth. He practiced in this location until his death in 1800, at the age of eighty-four. He served as judge of the court of common pleas from 1776 to 1784.

Ammi R. Cutter (1734-1819) was born in Yarmouth, Maine, in 1734. When twelve years old, he was sent on horse-back with a trusted servant, one hundred and fifty miles, to Cambridge, to be educated. He entered Harvard in 1748, and this college later awarded him an honorary M.D. John Wentworth, his classmate, was instrumental in convincing him to go to Portsmouth to take up his medical education. After serving with Dr. Clement Jackson, he was appointed surgeon to the famous Robert Rogers body of rangers, which formed a section of the army in the Indian frontier war of 1755.

In 1758 he was a surgeon at Louisburg, and after the capture, he went back to Portsmouth on a business venture. Although he was Governor Wentworth's personal physician when hostilities started, he without faltering, sided with the colonists. At the congressional reorganization of the medical department of the army, Dr. Cutter, at the request of General Whipple, left his family of ten small children and went to Fishkill to be physician-general of the Eastern department. He served in that capacity for about a year, after which he was obliged to return to look out for and educate his children. His only political office was a seat in the convention that framed the constitution of New Hampshire.

Brewster wrote in his "Rambler," concerning the epidemic of yellow-fever in Portsmouth, in 1798: "Drs. Cutter and James Brackett stood firm through the whole, and never took the fever."

Cutter was elected an honorary member of the Massachusetts Medical and Humane societies, and served as third president of the New Hampshire Medical Society, his term of office lasting from 1799 to 1812. He passed away in December, 1819, at the advanced age of eighty-five.

John Rogers (1755-1814) was born on March 27, 1755, in Leominster, Massachusetts. It is thought that he was a son of Reverend John Rogers. Graduating from Harvard in 1776, he practiced in Plymouth, and was justice of the peace there in 1804. He died on March 8, 1814, at the age of fifty-nine.

George Sparhawk (1757-1847) was born in 1757, graduated from Harvard in 1777 and settled in Walpole. He built up a large and lucrative practice. He served as state councillor in 1792 and 1793. When he passed away in 1847, he was ninety years old.

Ebenezer Rockwood (1746-?) was born in 1746. He graduated from Harvard in 1773 and took his place as surgeon in the continental army. In 1779 he accepted an invitation signed by nearly all the legal voters of Wilton to settle there. He practiced in Wilton until his demise.

Dr. Kendall Osgood (1757-1801) was born in Andover, Massachusetts, in 1757. After practicing in Atkinson from about 1785 to 1788, he settled in Peterborough. He served as surgeon on a privateer during the War of Independence. He withdrew from the New Hampshire Medical Society in 1799 and died in 1801.

The first meeting of the New Hampshire Medical Society was held on May 4, 1791, at Exeter. Ten of the nineteen charter members were present at the meeting, including John Rogers, of Plymouth, who came on horse-back to attend the meeting. Thirteen new members were admitted to the society at this time including Levi Bartlett, oldest son of the governor, Josiah.

Levi was born in Kingston in 1763, and received his preliminary education at Dummer academy. He studied medicine with his father and with the celebrated Thomas Kittredge of Andover. He then opened his office in Kingston, where he built up a lucrative practice and a fine reputation as physician and surgeon. He served as secretary of the New Hampshire Medical Society for nine years. He held the rank of colonel in the militia. He served several times in the legislature, and was a member of the council two years. He was presidential elector in 1804, chief-justice of the court of common pleas in 1807, and judge of the circuit court from 1816 to 1820.

The second meeting of the New Hampshire Medical Society was held at Concord, on June 2, 1791, at which function eighteen physicians were present. Three new members were elected, including Nathan Smith, of Cornish. Another meeting was held on June 3, 1791, at 7 A.M.

The annual meeting was called together at Dover, on June 13, 1792, with twelve members present. The code of by-laws was adopted, and provision made for instituting district societies. Dr. Joshua Brackett, the vice-president, donated his library of one hundred and twenty volumes at this meeting.

No quorum was present when the Society met on June 13, 1793, at Concord, nor on the 14th; but on the 19th twelve members were present, and two new members were admitted. A certificate of qualification to practice was issued at this time to Joshua Gee Symmes, of Newbury, Mass., signed by Hall Jackson and Levi Bartlett, censors of the Eastern District Society. Another similar certificate was issued by the censors of the Western District to Richard Hazelton. "Five Spanish mill'd dollars" was the fee enacted for each license.

The fourth meeting was called together at Exeter with eleven members present. It was voted that "the secretary, Samuel Tenney, be allowed twelve shillings for his trouble in transcribing and procuring the laws of the Society to be published." Two additional members were elected, and President Brackett presented thirteen more books.

In 1795, 1796, and 1797 the Society met without a quorum. In 1798 there was a short session, with six members present. In 1799, at Chester, five licenses were issued. Dr. Brackett declined a reelection, and Dr. Ammi Cutter was chosen president which office he held for thirteen years. Dr. Brackett presented eleven more books, and Josiah Bartlett, of Stratham, was elected a member. Josiah was the second son of Governor Bartlett, and was born in Kingston on August 29, 1768.

It is of interest to note that at the second annual meeting, held in Dover in 1792, an elaborate set of Laws and Regulations was adopted in accordance with which the State was divided into two Districts, the Counties of Rockingham and Strafford constituting the Eastern District, and the other three counties (there being then only five in the state) the Western District. Prospective fellows were proposed to the Council and if that body gave its consent, the application was read by the Secretary and at the following annual meeting the candidate was balloted for "and if two thirds of them ballot in his favor, the choice shall be valid."

Here is appended an old fee list, signed in 1806 by the physicians of Portsmouth:

FEE BILL

Established by the gentlemen practising Physic, Surgery etc. in the town of Portsmouth, N.H., June 1, 1806.

Visit in ordinary cases with advice, recipie or one dose of medicine,
    or common application $0.75
Visit by night in ordinary cases with advice, recipie or one dose of
    medicine, common application 1.50
Visits, two necessary ones, the same day with advice, recipie or one
    dose of medicine, each time 1.50
If more than two visits are absolutely required in twenty four
    hours, then charge for attendance .... (blank)

Visit and consultation, first time, with advice or recipie.......... $1.50
Visit and do, repeated in the same sickness with advice or recipie.. 0.75
Visit and bleeding at the patient's house........................ 1.00
Visit and extracting a tooth at patient's house 1.00
Visit, opening a small abscess and dressing it.................... 1.00
Visit and making a seton 1.00
Visit and reducing a simple hernia............................. 2.00
Visit and reducing compound fractures of the large bones........ 6.00
Visit and reducing simple fractures of the large bones........... 3.00
Visit and reducing dislocations of the large joints................ 4.00
Visit and amputating toes & fingers & extirpating small tumors..... 2.00
Visit and performing paracentesis & for hydrocele 5.00
Visit and introducing Catheter, first time...................... 3.00
Visit and repeating the same 1.00
Visit and dressing recent wound with one stitch................. 1.00
    and 25 cts. for each additional stitch.
Visit on board a vessel at the wharf with advice, recipie or one dose
    of medicine 1.00
Visit on board a vessel below the narrows, out in the harbor, in Kit-
    tery or New Castle Coves, with advice, recipie, or one dose of
    medicine 3.00
Visit to Kittery point, Gerrish's Island, or New Castle with advice,
    recipie or one dose of medicine........................... 3.00
Visit to Kittery foreside and neck & the Islands against the town
    with advice, recipie or one dose of medicine................ 1.50
Visit to Isle of Shoals with advice, recipie or one dose of med..... 10.00
Travel, one mile, with advice, recipie or one dose of med......... 1.00
    with 50 cts. addition for each additional mile.
In cases of midwifery and large operations, no mileage nor visits to
    be charged, when they occur nigh the town.
Cases of midwifery, easy or common.......................... 6.00
Cases of midwifery, laborious, exceeding 24 hours.............. 8.00
Amputating trepanning, hernia, couching or extracting a cataract,
    and amputating cancerous breast 30.00
Bleeding at Surgeon's house 0.50
Extracting a tooth at Surgeon's house.......................... 0.50
Using glyster syringe, in 24 hours, visit not included............. 0.50
Opening small abscess and dressing it at Surgeon's house.......... 0.50
Dressing recent wound at Surgeon's house with one stitch........ 0.50
    and 25 cts. for each additional stitch.
Dressing old wounds and sores at Surgeon's House, not less than... 0.25
Cases of gonorrhoea, simple and soon cured.................... 5.00

Cases of go. protracted a long time with gleet.................(erased)

Cases of Lues Venerea, simple and soon cured................ $5.00

Cases of Lues Venerea of long continuance.................... 10.00

Inoculating individuals with cowpox......................... 3.00

Inoculating families with cowpox, each person................. 2.00

Almshouse, each year 100.00

For each and every dose of medicine, or every half dozen of pow-
    ders, pills or boluses, after the first, twenty cents, or double
    the apothecary's price 0.20

We the subscribers, practising Physicians, Surgeons, etc., in the town of Portsmouth, N. Hampshire

Do hereby severally solemnly engage and bind ourselves upon our honour, that in no case whatever will we or either of us ask demand or charge less than the prices or fees before named or stipulated for each, every one or any of the before named services performed by us or either of us. But if in any case whatever, by reason of poverty or any other cause it may appear to be a deed of charity to give or remit a part or the whole of the before named charges then each and every one of us have a right to so do, but at the same time hold ourselves in honour bound to name the whole amount of the foregoing items as our regular charges, and then say, for certain reasons we give you in so much of the amount of the bill.

And we furthermore engage that each and every bill or account made out by us or either of us shall specify the number of visits and shall not be charged or rated in the whole or in any particular whatever, less than the foregoing prices, although charity should require a deduction from the foot thereof. And we furthermore engage that each and every one of us will annually present our bills for payment or settlement, and will endeavor to have each and every amount or bill paid or settled at least once a year.

Quarterly meetings
First Mondays of September,
December, March & June

Of the signers of this list, it will be recalled that Ammi R. Cutter and John Jackson were also incorporators of the New Hampshire Medical Society. In 1806, when this list was signed, Dr. A. R. Cutter was serving as President of the Society, Lyman Spalding as Secretary, and William Cutter as Councillor.

The following account is taken from the address of Dr. A. B. Crosby delivered before a New Hampshire Medical Society meeting at Concord in June 1870:

One of the earliest practitioners in my own neighborhood—who left a good name and an honorable record—was, tradition says, the owner of a pair of shoes. When he visited the poor his feet like those of his patient were habitually bare, the shoes being carefully concealed within the capacious saddle-bags, in part for economy's sake, but quite as much lest the feelings of his humble friends should be wounded. But when he approached, at long intervals, a patrician bed, the long cherished shoes were donned, and in these galoches of professional fortune, he was wont proudly to tread the sick room like any aristocrat, well shod.

It is related that on one of his professional trips he was consulted by a young man from Connecticut, who, bred in comfort, had come into the new country and cleared a piece of land, but his poor bare feet were bruised, torn and bleeding. "I know what will cure you," said the benevolent doctor, and, opening his saddle-bags, he gave him the long treasured shoes; and then, lest, I fancy, his resolution should fail him, he turned his face resolutely homeward.

Dissection of the human body was almost wholly unknown, and only the marked men in the profession possessed a skeleton. Nevertheless there was here and there a worthy disciple of the great Vesalius who dared public opinion sufficiently to attempt to gain a knowledge of anatomy by dissections of the human body. The first execution for a capital offence in my own county took place at Haverhill, the condemned man being a negro. The gallows was erected in an open field, and a large concourse assembled to witness the melancholy spectacle. Dr. McKinstry, of Newbury, Vt., secured the body, which was rapidly carried to a cabin on the great Ox-Bow Meadow. All the neighboring physicians were invited to be present, and were requested to bring any dissecting instrument they might deem of use. Tradition says that one brought a hand-saw, another an axe, still another a butcher's cleaver, and a fourth came armed with a large carving-knife and fork.

Meantime popular excitement at this proposed sacrilege had reached a high pitch, and it seemed for a time as though all the instruments of these pseudo anatomists must be used in self defence. A guard, however, with firearms, was stationed around the locality, and, thus protected, the dissection began. The great point to be settled was what should be done first. After long and earnest consultation, it was unanimously decided that the subject should first be skinned, and skinned it accordingly was, with neatness and dispatch. The cuticle of this unfortunate Ethiop was subsequently tanned and cut up into small pieces, as souvenirs of the occasion. Tradition says, with how much truth I know not, that an enthusiastic but impudent student cut off the ears and sent them in a letter to one of the professors in the academical department of Dartmouth College, whom he did not particularly admire.

How far these dissections were carried, or how long they were continued, I am not informed. There is, however, still living at North Haverhill, Dr. McNab, a venerable medical man, who was present and aided in this early effort to establish a "chair of anatomy."

At the annual meeting of the Board of Trustees of Dartmouth College, in August, 1796, Mr. Nathan Smith, who was then a Bachelor of Medicine, not having received the degree of M.D., made an application to the board, asking their encouragement and approbation of a plan he had devised to establish a Professorship of the Theory and Practice of Medicine in connection with Dartmouth College. After considerable discussion, the board voted to postpone their final action upon the proposition for a year, but in the meantime a resolution was passed complimentary to the character and energy of Mr. Smith, and promising such encouragement and assistance in the future as the plan might merit and the circumstances of the college admit.

The records of the college are extremely barren of details respecting the preliminary steps towards a medical establishment, and there are no means of knowing what the action of the board was the following year. It is evident, however, that some measures must have been taken in relation to the future welfare of the school, for in the year 1798 we find that "the fee for conferring the degree of Bachelor of Medicine *pro meritis* be twenty dollars." The honorary degree of Master of Arts was the same year conferred on Mr. Smith, while it remained for a subsequent board to discover that his professional attainments merited the rank and title of Doctor.

Later in the same session it was voted "That a professor be appointed, whose duty it shall be to deliver public lectures upon Anatomy, Surgery, Chemistry, Materia Medica, and the Theory and Practice of Physic, and that said professor be entitled to receive payment for instruction in those branches, as hereafter mentioned, as compensation for his services in that office." Mr. Smith was at once chosen to fulfil the laborious, and almost incredible duties of this professorship, while the compensation alluded to was for a long time held in abeyance. It may be that the trustees thought that to so self-sacrificing a man, reward of conscience would be superior to any pecuniary emolument. We also find that in this year the board adopted the following code of Medical Statutes:

1. Lectures shall begin on the first day of October, annually, and continue ten weeks, during which the professor shall deliver three lectures daily, Saturday and Sunday excepted.

2. In the lectures on the theory and practice of Physic, shall be explained the nature of diseases and method of cure.

3. The lectures on Chemistry and Materia Medica shall be accompanied by actual experiments, tending to explain and demonstrate the principles

of chemistry, and an exhibition shall be made of the principal medicines used in curing disease, with an explanation of their medicinal qualities, and effect on the human body.

4. In the lectures on Anatomy and Surgery, shall be demonstrated the parts of the human body by dissecting a recent subject, if such subject can be legally obtained; otherwise, by exhibiting anatomical preparations, which shall be attended by the performance of the principal capital operations in surgery.

5. The medical professor shall be entitled to the use of the college library and apparatus gratis.

6. The medical students shall be entitled to the use of the college library under the discretionary restrictions of the President.

7. Medical students shall be subject to the same rules of morality and decorum as Bachelors in Art residing at the college.

8. No graduate of any college shall be admitted to an examination for the degree of Bachelor of Medicine, unless he shall have studied two full years with some respectable physician or surgeon, and attended two full courses of lectures at some university.

9. No person not a graduate shall be admitted to such an examination unless he shall have studied three full years, as above, attended two full courses of lectures, and shall, upon a preparatory examination before the President and professors, be able to parse the English and Latin languages, to construe Virgil and Cicero's orations, to possess a good knowledge of common arithmetic, geometry, geography and natural and moral philosophy.

10. Examination shall be holden in public before the executive authority of the college, by the medical professor, and candidates shall read and defend a dissertation, etc.

11. Every person receiving a degree in medicine shall cause his thesis to be printed, and sixteen copies thereof to be delivered to the President, for the use of the college and trustees.

12. The fee for attending a full course of lectures shall be fifty dollars; that is, for anatomy and surgery, twenty-five dollars; for chemistry and materia medica, fifteen dollars, and for theory and practice, ten dollars.

13. The members of the two senior classes in college may attend the medical lectures by paying twenty dollars for the full course.

Besides these statutes, the trustees voted that Mr. Smith might employ assistants in any of his departments, at his own expense, and that one half part of the fees for conferring the degree of Bachelor of Medicine be his perquisite, and the other half a perquisite to the president of the college.

The first course of lectures was delivered in the fall of 1797, although Mr. Smith was not elected to his professorship until after his return from

Europe, the following year. In the year 1798, two young men were graduated with the degree of Bachelor of Medicine. The next year the trustees voted to appropriate the northeast corner room in Dartmouth Hall to the use of Professor Smith, and it was repaired and furnished for that purpose. The room was a small one, scarcely as large as a common parlor, but still it served for a lecture hall, dissecting room, chemical laboratory and library, for several years, when another room adjoining was appropriated to the same purpose.

In 1801, the degree of Doctor of Medicine was conferred upon Mr. Smith, and a committee was appointed to confer with him in relation to a salary, and concerning some proposed alterations in the Medical Department. It would seem that corporations as well as individuals are addicted to procrastination, for that committee, as well as several others subsequently appointed for the same purpose, never reported. A grant of fifty dollars per annum was voted him, from which was deducted a debt he owed the college probably for money lent to him to enable him to visit Europe.

The trustees about this time made a change in the term of study required for a degree. The new statute fixed the period of three years for academical graduates, and five years for non-graduates.

The evidence is pretty strong that the undergraduates who attended the lectures paid for the privilege rather reluctantly, for, by the request of Dr. Smith, it was voted that the treasurer collect, as part of the regular college bills, all lecture fees due from college students.

In 1802 the salary of the Professor of Medicine was fixed at fifty dollars, and an additional grant of fifty dollars, yearly, was voted for contingent expenses. These emoluments were not, however, ample enough to induce Dr. Smith to remain. Accordingly, in 1803, the board voted a yearly sum of one hundred dollars for the purpose of accommodating him with a house, and added, as an additional bonus, the use of ten acres of land as a pasture, both to be continued during his residence in Hanover and his continuance in the professorship. Notwithstanding these tempting allurements of house-rent and pasturage, Dr. Smith still indicated his intention of leaving. Thus stimulated, the board, in 1804, voted to raise his salary to two hundred dollars, at which sum it remained.

The following are official records of the New Hampshire Legislature bearing on this subject:

SENATE, June 10, 1803.

A Resolve, That Dr. Nathan Smith have and receive out of the treasury, in his capacity as professor of anatomy, surgery and chemistry, six hundred dollars for the purpose of purchasing the apparatus prayed for, the apparatus to remain the property of the state for the use of said institution; was brought up, read and concurred. Presented and approved.

HOUSE, June 6, 1807.

Voted, That Messrs. .... be a committee to consider the petition of Dr. Nathan Smith and others, for and in behalf of the New Hampshire Medical Institution, and report thereon.

HOUSE, June 10, 1807.

Committee reported that the petitioners have leave to bring in a bill. Report accepted.

HOUSE, June 13, 1809.

Voted, That Messrs. Evans, Harper, Woodbury, Cady and S.P. Webster, with such as the Senate may join, be a committee to consider the petition of Dr. Nathan Smith, praying for assistance, that he may be enabled to erect buildings near Dartmouth College, for the use of the medical school, and report thereon.

(Journal of June 14th, 1809, torn out.)

HOUSE, June 16, 1809.

Voted, That Messrs. Hough, Kimball and Olcutt, be a committee to take into consideration a bill making a grant of six thousand dollars to Dr. Nathan Smith, of Hanover, for certain purposes therein mentioned, and report the probable expense of erecting the buildings therein mentioned.

June 17. The said committee reported "That three thousand, four hundred and fifty dollars will be the probable expense of erecting and completing the proposed buildings."

Again: Voted, That Messrs. Meserve, Hough and Parrot, be a committee to take into consideration a bill making a grant of six thousand dollars to Dr. Nathan Smith, and report such alterations and amendments as they shall judge necessary.

HOUSE, June 10, 1809.

On reading the bill entitled "An Act appropriating three thousand, four hundred and fifty dollars for certain purposes therein mentioned, and on the question, "Shall the first section pass?" which is in the following words:

SECTION 1. Be it enacted by the Senate and House of Representatives in General Court convened: That the sum of three thousand, four hundred and fifty dollars be, and the same hereby is, appropriated for the purpose of erecting a building of brick, or stone, for a medical school, sixty-five feet in length, thirty-two feet in width, and two stories in height; provided the said Nathan Smith, before the said money, or any part thereof, be paid out of the treasury, convey to the state of New Hampshire, by a good and valid title, one half acre of land, contiguous to Dartmouth College, whereon to erect said building; and provided the said Nathan assigns to the state aforesaid, such parts of the anatomical museum, and chemical apparatus, as are his private property."

The yeas and nays being called thereon, stood, yeas, 102, nays 59, so the section passed.

HOUSE, June 9, 1812.

Voted, That the petition of Dr. Nathan Smith, praying for legislative aid, be referred to the committee to whom was referred so much of His Excellency's communication as relates to literature and science, and that they report thereon.

JUNE SESSION,
Tuesday, June 16, 1812.

House met according to adjournment.

The committee on the petition of Dr. Nathan Smith, reported the following statement of facts:

The legislature in 1809, appropriated the sum of three thousand, four hundred and fifty dollars for the purpose of erecting, at Hanover, a building of brick, or stone, for a medical school, to be sixty-five feet in length, thirty-two feet in width, and two stories in height, on condition that Dr. Smith, before said money, or any part thereof, be paid out of the treasury, should convey to the state of New Hampshire, by a good and valid title, one half acre of land contiguous to Dartmouth College, whereon to erect said building, and also to assign to said State such parts of the anatomical museum and chemical apparatus as were his private property.

In compliance with this condition, Dr. Smith has legally conveyed one acre, instead of half an acre, of land, and assigned said anatomical and chemical apparatus to the state. The anatomical and chemical apparatus, so assigned, are at a moderate estimate, of the value of one thousand five hundred dollars.

The committee appointed to superintend the erection of the building, in the act of 1809, to render it convenient and useful for the purposes intended, concluded to add ten feet to the length, and, to accommodate more students, to divide the two wings into three stories; this was done, however, without increasing the height of the walls. The alteration from the first plan appears to have been necessary. The full sum of three thousand, four hundred and fifty dollars has been appropriated toward the erection and completion of the building, under the direction of the committee, who received compensation for their trouble of Dr. Smith. But the amount of the appropriation was found to be insufficient to defray the expenses of finishing the building in a plain and suitable manner, in a sum of one thousand, two hundred and seventeen dollars and fourteen cents. This sum Dr. Smith has paid, or secured to be paid to the contractors.

The building, and anatomical and chemical apparatus, will be exclusively the property of the state, on the death or removal of Dr. Smith from the medical school.

The committee would further state, that ten years preceding the year 1798, Dr. Smith spent much time, and a very considerable sum of money, acquired by his practice, in attaining a more perfect knowledge of his profession and in procuring a library and other apparatus, in order to promote medical science in the state, especially knowledge in surgery; that Dr. Smith, in 1798, was appointed Professor of Medicine at Dartmouth College, and then commenced a course of public instruction in all the branches of medical science generally taught in medical schools, with a library and other apparatus, procured at his own expense, and without any salary from the college. From 1798 to 1810, Dr. Smith supported the medical school by his own indefatigable exertions, in teaching all the branches of medicine himself, except in two instances, when he procured, at his own expense, assistant instructors. During the last twelve years, through his liberal management, the advantages of medical instruction have been greatly improved, and the number of those who attended the medical school increased.

At present, the medical institution at Hanover affords to students of medicine all the means of a correct and useful education. The number of students for the last three or four years, we believe to have been greater than at any medical school in the United States, that at Philadelphia excepted. The reputation of the school is deservedly high. Its connection with Dartmouth College increases the usefulness and celebrity of that literary institution. On the whole, we do not hesitate to declare that this medical school is worthy the patronage of the legislature.

Under these circumstances, the committee submits to the consideration of the legislature, whether it would not be proper to allow Dr. Smith the sum of one thousand, two hundred and seventeen dollars and fourteen cents.

LEVI JACKSON,
For the Committee.

Yeas 58, nays 96. So the motion did not prevail.

We find nothing of interest in the records of the college proper from 1804 until 1810, when Dr. Cyrus Perkins (created a doctor upon that occasion), was elected Professor of Anatomy. Some trouble having occurred about this time between the college officers and the medical students, the following articles were added to the laws:

1. That each person, previous to becoming a member of the Medical Institution, shall be required to give satisfactory evidence that he possesses a good moral character.

2. That it be required of medical students that they conduct them-

selves respectfully towards the executive officers of the college, and if any of them should be guilty of immoral or ungentlemanly conduct, the executive may expel them, and no professor shall receive or continue to receive as his private pupil, any such expelled person, or recommend him to any other medical man or institution.

3. That the executive officers of the college be, and hereby are, authorized to visit the rooms of the medical students whenever they think proper.

In the year 1812, some important changes were made in the economy of the institution. Up to this time the degree of Bachelor of Medicine only was conferred upon recent graduates, while the degree of M.D. was only allowed in course three years after graduation. This was now changed, and the degree of Doctor of Medicine was conferred upon all medical graduates. The term of study was again changed and fixed at four years. Another of the new regulations, and perhaps the least agreeable one to the students, compelled candidates to read their theses publicly in the chapel.

The Faculty was also strengthened by the appointment of Rufus Graves, Esq., as lecturer on chemistry, making this department, for the first time, a separate branch. Col. Graves, although a good lecturer, was an unsuccessful manipulator, which caused his dismissal in 1815, three years later. During this same year we find that Mr. Reuben D. Mussey, a name thoroughly identified with the success of the school, and with medical progress in New Hampshire, was created a Doctor of Medicine.

In 1814, Dr. Smith, having been absent for a year, it was voted that the salary and emoluments pertaining to the chair of medicine, be paid to Dr. Perkins, and at a meeting the resignation of Dr. Smith was received and accepted.

When Dr. Smith entered the profession, every case of protracted fever in the valley of the Connecticut was termed typhus. Dr. Smith soon became convinced that while true typhus did prevail, there was yet a continued fever essentially different in its character, and so he came to differentiate between typhus and typhoid. Noting carefully the symptoms in these cases, making autopsies whenever a chance occurred, and observing the morbid changes thus revealed, he soon found himself master of the situation. Then he wrote an unpretentious little tract, in which he embodied his observations and his inferences. This brochure included a comprehensive description of typhoid fever and exhaustively covered not only the clinical history, but the pathology.

The following anecdote further illustrates Dr. Smith's sagacity. While residing in Cornish he had a friend who was a sea captain, and who, on his return from foreign voyages, was wont to relate to him whatever of interest in a medical way he might have chanced to observe while abroad. On one occasion he told Dr. Smith that on his previous voyage one of the sailors dislocated his hip. There being no surgeon on board, the captain unsuccessfully tried to reduce it. The man was accordingly placed in a hammock with the dislocation unreduced. During a great storm the sufferer was thrown from the hammock to the floor, striking the knee of the affected side violently. On examination, it was found that in the fall the hip had somehow been set. This interested Dr. Smith intensely, and he questioned the narrator again and again as to the exact position of the thigh, the knee and the leg, at the time of the fall.

From this apparently insignificant circumstance, Dr. Smith eventually evolved his famous method of reducing dislocations: a system as useful as it is simple, and as scientific as the principle of flexion and leverage on which it depends.

When deeply interested in an operation, Dr. Smith was accustomed to soliloquize or think aloud, without any consciousness that he was giving utterance to his thoughts. On one occasion, at Cornish, he operated on a man for a strangulated hernia, the bed being surrounded by anxious friends. On cutting through the abdominal wall he discovered a peculiar odor, and immediately his usual soliloquy began, as follows: "What! what! have I cut a gut? I have—I have cut a gut! They might as well make his coffin now as ever." After this little bit of self communion, he completed the operation with a perfectly unmoved face, utterly oblivious that he had said anything. He then called the friends into another room, and with a grave face announced to them that the case was a bad one, and that he was a little afraid that the man might die.

Oliver Wendell Holmes, who twenty years later became professor of Anatomy at Hanover, declared: "Nathan Smith filled no chair at Dartmouth; he occupied a whole settee."

Smith was not a clock watcher; his dissertations lasted three or even four hours, and were well attended by upper classmen and faculty. It is related that after attending his lecture, President Wheelock issued the following prayer at services: "O Lord, we thank Thee for the oxygen gas; we thank Thee for the hydrogen gas and for all the other gases. Also, O Lord, we thank Thee for the cerebrum, the cerebellum and the medulla oblongata."

Henry Dearborn (1751-1829) famous as General Dearborn, was the son of Dr. Simon Dearborn, a physician of Hampton, New Hampshire, and followed his father's profession, engaging in the practice of medicine in New Hampshire and Maine. Born in Hampton, New Hampshire on February 23, 1751 after receiving a local preliminary schooling he studied medicine with Dr. Hall Jackson of Plymouth, with whom he practiced for two or three years. He then opened an office for himself at Nottingham Square, in New Hampshire, where he practiced from 1772 until 1775. Nottingham Square was a little settlement in the town of Nottingham, on the turnpike road from Portsmouth to Concord. Upon the advent of the Revolution, Dearborn promptly gave up his practice and accompanied General Stark's men to the Battle of Bunker Hill.

He commanded the New Hampshire Company in Arnold's Quebec expedition and was major of the Third New Hampshire, and Adjutant at Saratoga. He was selected to carry the news of victory to Congress. He served as lieutenant colonel in the First New Hampshire from April 1, 1781 to the end of the war. When Congress proposed to make him a brigadier in 1777, he declined.

Following the war, he secured a large tract of territory, then called Monmouth, in the district of Maine, a region which is now divided into the city of Gardiner and the towns of Monmouth, Litchfield and Riverside. His wife was Mary Bartlett of Nottingham, New Hampshire. While in this district, he primarily engaged in agriculture but always practiced some medicine. Affairs of state soon called him away, however. In 1790, he was appointed major-general. He served in Congress for two terms, and was secretary of war from 1801 to 1804. He later was appointed minister to Portugal, and collector of the port of Boston.

In the War of 1812 he started his campaign successfully but met with reverses for needed reinforcements were not forthcoming. He subsequently resigned from the army and once again engaged in the practice of medicine. He died in Roxbury, Massachusetts, on June 6, 1829, at the age of seventy-eight. Fort Dearborn, the nucleus of Chicago, was named after him.

Chapter Five

NEW YORK

In JULY 1609, Samuel de Champlain discovered the lake which has been named after him. He chose to lead his Algonquian Indian allies against the Iroquois, and this ill-advised act aroused the Iroquois who, for a protracted interval, were to hold within their group the balance of power between the English and the French in the New World.

September 3, 1609, is the day that Henry Hudson, operating on behalf of the Dutch East India Company, sailed into New York Bay on the "Half Moon" in search of the "northwest passage." Hudson was of the opinion that a huge fur trade with the Iroquois could be organized and his report was favorably received in Holland. The United Netherlands, whose independence had just been obtained the prior spring, established a claim to the newly discovered country.

A shipload of goods suitable for traffic with the Indians was dispatched in 1610, and as a result of this voyage a lucrative fur trade with the Indians was established.

The West India Company, in 1621, received a twenty-four year charter and the right to a monopoly of Dutch trade with the whole American coast from Newfoundland to the Straits of Magellan. The Company was awarded the right to establish and govern colonies with very little interference on the part of the States-General.

In March 1624, the Chamber of Amsterdam sent over the "New Netherland," with the first permanent colonists: thirty families mostly Walloon, under Cornelis Jacobsen Mey, the first governor or director of the colony. This party reached Manhattan early in May. A few colonists remained in Manhattan; a small group established a temporary post (Fort Nassau) on the Delaware River; and a third detachment began the erection of a fortified settlement on the site of present Hartford, Connecticut. More than half of the settlers,

however, sailed up the Hudson to Fort Orange, and at the mouth of
Tawasentha Creek, founded a colony in the area that is now Albany.
Three more vessels brought reinforcements in 1625, and Mey was
succeeded as director by William Verhulst in that year. The colony
now had a population of over 200. In 1626, the government of the
province was fully established and power was vested primarily in a
director-general and council.

Peter Minuit, the first director-general, arrived with more colonists
in May 1626, and shortly thereafter, Manhattan Island was purchased from the Indians. Fort Amsterdam was erected at its lower
end, and the settlement here was made the seat of government.

As soon as the Charter of Privileges and Exemptions of the Company went into effect in 1629, a few of the directors of the Amsterdam Chamber hastened to take advantage of their patroon status
to secure parcels of land most favorably situated for trade. On both
sides of the entrance to Delaware Bay, Samuel Godyn, Samuel Blo-
maert and five other directors who were admitted to partnership in
the second year (1630), established a manor and colony of Swaanendael; on a parcel opposite the lower end of Manhattan Island and including Staten Island, Michael Pauw set up the manor and colony of
Pavonia; on both sides of the Hudson and extending in all directions
from Fort Orange (Albany), Kilian van Rensselaer organized the
manor and colony of Rensselaerwyck. The Indians made short work
of the colony of Swaanendael in 1632. Pauw, after holding on to his
colony of Pavonia for seven years, sold out to the Company.

Rennelaerwyck was actually the only colony that prospered under
the patroon system. Meanwhile the patroons claimed unrestricted
rights of trade within the boundaries of their estates, a principle that
was declared illegal by the Company. In 1632, Director-General
Minuit was recalled on the complaint that he had favored the
patroons. Wouter van Twiller, who replaced him in 1633, sought to
promote only the selfish commercial policy of the Company. As a result, by 1637, provincial affairs were in a chaotic condition.

William Kieft became Director-General late in 1637, and in 1638
the Company decided to abandon its monopoly of trade in New
Netherland and give notice that all inhabitants of the United Provinces, and of friendly countries, might trade there subject to an import duty of 10% and an export duty of 15%. The only stipulation
was that all goods were to be conveyed on Company ships. Induce-
ments were made to influence immigration from the home country,
New England and Virginia. This freedom of trade antagonized the
Indians, and the attempt by Kieft to collect a tribute from the
Algonquian tribes in the vicinity of Manhattan Island provoked them

into open hostilities. Between 1641-1645, the Indians ravaged most of the outlying settlements.

This conflict led the colonists to demand a government in which the colonists had more voice. In August 1641 Kieft convened a group of the heads of families in the neighborhood of Fort Amsterdam to consider the question of peace or war. The assembly elected a group of twelve to represent it, and this board demanded certain reforms, especially that the membership of the director-general's council should be increased from one to five by the popular election of four members. Kieft gladly promised these concessions so as to gain the board's consent for waging war; however, when things calmed down, he later denied the board's authority to exact promises from him and dissolved it.

In 1643, during another crisis, Kieft was again forced to call a second assembly of the people. A board of eight men was chosen to confer with him. This group denied his right to levy certain war taxes, and when it saw that to further object to his arbitrary measures was futile, it sent a petition, in 1644, to the States-General for his recall. This petition was granted.

Peter Stuyvesant, his successor, came to Fort Amsterdam in May 1647. Under his rule prosperity returned and between the years 1653 and 1664 the population of the province increased from 2000 to 10,000. Stuyvesant was an arbitrary man, too, however. The board of nine "tribunes," which he selected from eighteen elected individuals was treated by him with disdain. All it could do was to remonstrate to the States-General. That body suggested a representative government, which the Company refused to permit.

In March 1664, Charles II amalgamated into one province the entire territory from the west side of the Connecticut river to the east side of Delaware Bay together with all of Long Island and a few other dependencies of minor importance, and granted it to his brother James, the Duke of York, as its lord proprietor. The Duke thereupon selected Colonel Richard Nicolls as its governor and authorized him to bring this area under subjugation.

Nicolls cleverly gained the goodwill of the burgomaster of New Amsterdam and other prominent citizens by the favorable terms which he offered, and Stuyvesant was forced in a bloodless coup, to surrender, and New Netherland thus became New York.

The separation of New York from New Jersey, was accomplished by the duke's transferring the Jersey area of his province to Berkeley and Carteret. Changes from Dutch to English names included the change of Fort Orange to Fort Albany. A treaty of alliance with the Mohawks and Senecas was obtained by the English. The transition from Dutch to English institutions was effected peacefully and gradually and Dutch private interests were not violated.

The bringing of English institutions into settlements wholly or largely English was begun in 1665 by the erection of Long Island, Staten Island and Westchester into an English county under the name of Yorkshire, and by putting into operation in that county a code of laws known as the "Duke's Laws." This legal system was based largely on the laws of New England, and, although a source of popular discontent, it gave to the freeholders of each town a voice in the government of their town by allowing them to elect a board of eight overseers which chose a constable and sat as a court for the trial of small causes.

Nicolls resigned the governorship in 1668 and his successor, Francis Lovelace, continued his policy of autocratic government, arbitrary in form, but mild in practice, with a progressive attitude toward the matter of religious toleration.

In August 1673, when Holland and England were at war, a Dutch fleet surprised New York, captured the city, and restored Dutch authority and the names of New Netherland and New Amsterdam. But by the treaty of Westminster consummated in February, 1674, the Dutch title to the province was extinguished for all time, and in November 1674, the English again took possession. A new charter was issued to the Duke to perfect his title and Edmund Andros was appointed governor and instructed to establish English institutions and enforce English law in all sections.

In 1675, Andros organized a commission for Indian affairs which long rendered important service in preserving the English-Iroquois alliance. Andros was no more democratic than his predecessors and he came to have numerous enemies. Some openly charged him with improper use of the revenue. In 1681, he was called to England to answer these charges, and during his absence, the demand for a representative assembly was accompanied with a refusal to pay the customs duties and so much other insubordination that the duke appointed Colonel Thomas Dongon to succeed Andros, and instructed him to call the desired assembly.

The assembly congregated at Fort James in the City of New York on October 17, 1683, and remained in session for about three weeks, and passed fifteen acts. The first, styled a charter of liberties and privileges, required that an assembly elected by the freeholders and freemen should be called at least once every three years; vested all legislative authority in the governor, council and assembly; forbade the imposition of any taxes without the consent of the assembly; and provided for religious liberty and trial by jury. This charter of liberties and privileges was approved by the duke, but before the news of this reached its authors, the duke became King James II, and in 1686, when a frame of government for New York as a royal province was provided, the assembly was dispensed with.

The new king strengthened his control over New England and sought to erect a stronger barrier against the French. In 1688 New York and New Jersey were consolidated with the New England colonies into the Dominion of New England and placed under the authority of Sir Edmund Andros as governor-general.

When knowledge of the English revolution of 1688 reached the colonies, there was an uprising in Boston, and in April 1689, Andros, who had been returned to office, was seized and imprisoned. Francis Nicholson, the lieutenant-governor, continued to quietly run the government of New York, and a majority of the population of the province were satisfied to await the outcome of the revolution in the mother country, but in the southern portion of the province, especially in the City of New York and on Long Island, were a number of restless spirits who were encouraged by the fall of Andros to take matters into their own hands. They found a leader in a German merchant named Jacob Leisler.

Leisler refused to pay duties on a cargo of wine on the ground that the collector was a "papist," and on May 31, 1689, during a mutiny of the militia, he and other militia captains seized Fort James. In the following month Nicholson deserted his post and sailed for England, and Leisler easily gained possession of the city. To strengthen his position he called an assembly which conferred upon him the powers of a dictator. Some time after a copy of the order of the new monarchs (William and Mary) to continue all Protestants in their offices in the colonies had been received, Leisler falsely announced that he had received a commission as lieutenant-governor.

Albany defied his illegal authority until a united front against the French and their Indian allies was necessary, for in February 1690, Schenectady was surprised and burned. Two other French attacks had at the same time been directed against New England, and to meet the dangerous situation Leisler performed the one statesmanlike act of his public career, notable in American history as the first step toward the union of the colonies. At his call, delegates from Massachusetts, Plymouth, Connecticut and Maryland met in New York City with delegates from New York on May 11, 1690, to consider concerted action against the enemy. The expedition which was sent out was doomed to failure.

Leisler proclaimed the new monarchs of Great Britain and declared that his only desire was to protect the province and the Protestant religion until the arrival of a governor appointed by them. When he ascertained that he had been ignored and that under the new governor, Colonel Henry Sloughter, his enemies, van Cortlandt and Bayard, had again been appointed to the council, he became infuriated. When Major Richard Ingoldsby arrived with two companies of the king's soldiers and demanded possession of the fort, Leisler refused although he stated that he would be glad to turn it over to Sloughter. On March 17, 1691, Leisler's force fired on the king's soldiers, killing two and wounding several. On March 19, Governor Sloughter arrived and the revolt terminated in the arrest of Leisler and his chief followers. Leisler and Jacob Milborne, his son-in-law, were convicted of treason, and were executed on May 16, 1691.

Governor Sloughter, as his commission directed, re-established in 1691 the assembly which James II had abolished in 1686, and throughout the remainder of the colonial era, the history of the province relates chiefly to the rise of popular government and the defence of the northern frontier.

The *New York Gazette*, established in 1725 by William Bradford as a semi-official organ of the administration, was New York's first newspaper. In 1733 a popular organ, the *New York Weekly Journal*, was established under John Peter Zenger (1697-1746), and in 1735, both the freedom of the press and a great advance toward judicial independence resulted from the renowned Zenger libel suit.

Protecting the northern frontier weighed heavily on New York, but by its problems the growth of the union of the colonies was promoted. From the destruction of Schenectady to the Peace of Ryswick (1697) hostilities between the French and the English in the New World took the form of occasional raids across the frontier, chiefly by the Indian allies.

The main effort of the French, however, was, by diplomacy, to destroy the English-Iroquois alliance. This concord had as its motivating force the fact that the Iroquois were afraid of the French. The Indians, however, complained of the weakness of the English caused by the disunity among them. Governor Fletcher, therefore, in 1694, summoned a second intercolonial conference, including representatives of New York, Massachusetts, Connecticut and New Jersey. At the assembly, Fletcher loudly proclaimed the need for unity among the English colonists.

The Peace of Ryswick brought calm for a few years; the Peace of Utrecht (1713) lasted longer. French priests, none-the-less, indoctrinated the Iroquois during this period and purchased their goodwill with presents. Because of the success of French diplomacy, the English were kept constantly in a dither about their security. The

English in 1701 influenced the chiefs to deed their lands (800 miles by 400 miles) to the King of England. The English to counteract French influence, distributed presents. It appears that the fifth columnist activities of the French at the end of the 17th century and the early part of the 18th century would have been crowned by success were it not for the tireless efforts of Peter Schuyler (1657-1724) whose personal influence was, for years, dominant among all the Iroquois except the Senecas.

After the Iroquois declared themselves neutral, Schuyler influenced many of them to join troops from New York, New Jersey and Connecticut in the unsuccessful expeditions of 1709 and 1711 against the French at Montreal. The English, because of the fact that they could furnish goods for the Indian trade much cheaper than their rivals, were in a better position than the French. When Governor Burnet saw that this advantage was being lost by trade between Albany and Montreal he convinced the assembly of the need for an act (1720) prohibiting the practice. To further augment his wise policy, Burnet, in 1722, established a trading post at Oswego. This post was fortified in 1727, and placed the Iroquois in the good position of being middlemen in a profitable fur trade with the "Far Indians."

During King George's War, New York contributed 3000 pounds and some cannon toward New England's famous expedition against Louisburg. But protection of the home was neglected, and while the assembly was wrangling with Governor Clinton for the control of expenditures, the French and their Indians were burning farm houses, attacking Saratoga (November 16, 1745), and greatly endangering the English-Iroquois alliance. Even after the Peace of Aix-la-Chapelle (1748), the Iroquois complained bitterly of the fraudulent land speculators, and in 1753 the chiefs of the Mohawks threatened to declare the covenant chain broken. A reconciliation was effected, however, by Colonel William Johnson (1715-1774), who had long been superintendent of Indian affairs.

To satisfy the Iroquois, the home government called to meet at Albany the most important assembly of the colonial deputies that had yet gathered. Twenty-five members representing seven colonies, met in June 1754, and, besides negotiating successfully with the Iroquois, it adopted with some modifications, a plan of colonial union prepared by Benjamin Franklin. The plan was not approved by New York or any of the other colonies. In the first year of the war (1755), expeditions were sent against Fort Duquesne (on the site of Pittsburgh) and Fort Niagara and Crown Point on the New York frontier. None of these objectives were taken, however.

On September 8, 1755, Major-General William Johnson, in command of the expedition against Crown Point, defeated a French and Indian force under Baron Dieskau in the battle of Lake George. As Johnson thought it unsafe to pursue the routed army, his victory had no other effect than the erection here of the useless defences of Fort William Henry, but as it was the only success in a year of gloom, parliament rewarded him with a grant of 5000 pounds and the title of a baronet.

In August 1756 Montcalm took Oswego from the English and destroyed it, and in 1757 he captured Fort William Henry; but in the latter year the elder Pitt assumed control of affairs in England, and his aggressive, clearsighted policy turned the tide of war in England's favor. Ticonderoga, Crown Point and Niagara were seized from the French and New York was freed.

England's decision to force the colonies to pay the expenses of the war by the stamp tax thoroughly antagonized commercial New York, which already was writhing under the Navigation Acts and burdened with a war debt of its own exceeding 300,000 pounds. In the events which followed the Stamp Act, personal rivalry and greed were subordinated to political principles. The court party became the Loyalist party, standing for law as against rebellion, monarchy and the union of the empire as against republicanism. The popular party became the patriot party, determined to stand on its rights at any cost.

The Stamp Act was repealed in March 1766, but the Townshead Acts, imposing duties on glass, paper, lead, painters' colors and tea, followed closely. These enactments were followed in New York by fresh outbursts of the Sons of Liberty and, as in the other colonies, by an association of nearly all the merchants, the members pledging themselves not to import anything from England until the duties were repealed. The New York Assembly refused to provide certain supplies for the British troops quartered in the city and parliament in 1767, angrily forbade it to do any other business until it complied.

It was under these highly strained circumstances that the Loyalists, in the elections of 1768 and 1769, gained control of the assembly and in the latter year passed an act granting the soldier's supplies. When, in 1770, all the duties except those on tea were repealed, the conservative merchants wished to permit the importation of all goods from England except tea. The Sons of Liberty strongly opposed this, but the conservatives won and went over to the Loyalists. The moderate Loyalists joined in the election of delegates to the first Continental Congress; but the great body of Loyalists in New York strongly disapproved of the "dangerous and extravagant" measures adopted by that body, and the assembly, in January 1775, refused to approve its acts or choose delegates to the second Continental Congress.

The patriots met this refusal by calling a provincial convention to choose the delegates. Scarcely had they done this when news of the encounter at Lexington produced a strong reaction in their favor, and in May 1775 they called a Provincial Congress which seized the powers of the Assembly.

In June 1776, when a vote on the Declaration of Independence was pending in the Continental Congress, the New York Provincial Congress refused to instruct its delegates as to what to do. A newly elected Provincial Congress, influenced by a Loyalist plot against the life of Washington, adopted the Declaration when it met, on July 9, 1776.

British military policy throughout the War of Independence was to hold New York City at all costs, and use it as a base to establish a line of fortified posts along the Hudson by means of which communication might be maintained with another base on Lake Champlain. Such a scheme, if successfully carried out, would have driven a wedge into the line of colonial defence and cut off communication between New England and the southern colonies.

A few days after the fight at Lexington and Concord, Connecticut authorized an expedition under Ethan Allen which surprised and captured Ticonderoga and Crown Point. In the following year (1776) the British began their offensive operations for the control of the Hudson; an army under Sir William Howe was to Capture New York City and get control over the lower Hudson, while another army under Sir Guy Carleton was to retake Crown Point and Ticonderoga and get control of the upper Hudson. Howe's army of British and Loyalists vastly superior in equipment and numbers to Washington's untrained militia, landed in July on Staten Island and late in August defeated Washington at the battle of Long Island within the present limits of Brooklyn borough. In the following month Washington withdrew from New York City which the British entered and held until the close of the war.

The last episode of the war as far as New York was concerned was the discovery of Benedict Arnold's attempt in 1780 to betray West Point and other colonial posts on the Hudson to the British. On November 25, 1783, the British forces finally evacuated New York City, but the British posts on Lakes Erie and Ontario were not evacuated until some years later.

New York ratified the Articles of Confederation in 1778. Under George Clinton, governor in 1777-1795, New York state jealously guarded its commercial interests. The Confederation Congress appealed to it in vain for the right to collect duties at its port; and there was determined opposition to the new Federal constitution. In support of the constitution, however, there arose the Federalist party under the able leadership of Alexander Hamilton. When a majority of the constitutional convention of 1787 had approved of the new constitution, Hamilton alone of the three New York delegates remained to sign it; and when, after its ratification by eight states, the New York convention met at Poughkeepsie (June 17, 1788) to consider ratification, two-thirds of the members were opposed to it. But others were won over by the news that it had been ratified by New Hampshire and Virginia and by the logic of Hamilton. On July 26, 1788, the Constitution was ratified.

The present author is greatly indebted to Claude E. Heaton's excellent work in the preparation of this chapter.

Not a great deal is known about the very early history of medicine in New York State. We do know that William Hays, Peter Vreucht, Jacob Hendrickson, Varvanger, Isaac Jansen, Jacob Mallenancy, and John Pau all practiced medicine in New York from 1647 to 1652.

As a physician and a member of the governor's council, Johannes La Montagne, a Huguenot who had graduated from Leyden and come to New York in 1637, was held in great esteem. In 1641 he joined the expedition sent out to defend Fort Good Hope.

Annetje Jansen (Anneke Jan), aside from owning a large portion of what is now New York City, was famous as a midwife. Her daughter, Sarah, married Dr. Kierstedt, a practitioner of medicine in this city from 1638 to 1661. Dr. Kierstedt came to this country with another surgeon, Gerritt Schult on the same boat as William Kieft, director-general of the West India Company, in March 1638.

The following quotation is from the Dutch Records of February 2, 1652 (reference is here made to the aforementioned Dr. Johannes La Montagne):

"On the petition of the chirurgeons of New Amsterdam that none but they alone be allowed to shave; the director and council understand that shaving alone doth not appertain exclusively to chirurgery, but is an appendix thereunto; that no man can be prevented operating on himself, nor to do another the friendly act provided it be through courtesy, and not for gain which is hereby forbidden." It was then further ordered that "ship-barbers shall not be allowed to dress any wounds nor administer any potions on shore without the previous knowledge and special consent of the petitioners or at best of Doctor La Montagne."

New York passed the first law employing the doctor in the detection of crime. In December, 1657, the following city ordinance was enacted:

To all Chirurgeons of the City that when they are called to dress a wound they shall ask the patient who wounded him and that information thereof be given to the Schout (i.e., sheriff).

The previously mentioned Duke of York's Code of 1665 included the following regulation:

Chirurgeons, Midwives, Physicians—That no person or persons whatever employed about the bodys of men, women, or children for the preservation of life or health, as chirurgeons, midwives, physicians, or others, presume to put forth or exercise any act contrary to the known approved rule of art in each mystery or occupation, or exercise any force, violence, or cruelty upon or towards the body of any, whether young or old, without the advice and counsel of such as are skilful in the same art, (if such may be had,) or at least of some of the wisest and gravest then present, and consent of the patient, or patients; if they be *mentis compotes*, much less contrary to such advice and consent, upon which law, nevertheless, is not intended to discourage any from all lawful use of their skill, but rather to encourage and direct them in the right use thereof, and to inhibit and restrain the presumptuous arrogance of such as through confidence of their own skill or any other sinister respects, dare boldly attempt to exercise any violence upon or towards the body of young or old, one or another, to the prejudice or hazard of the life or limb of man, woman, or child.

Parenthetically it should be stated that this law is essentially the same as one enacted in Massachusetts in 1649.

An act to regulate the practice of physick and surgery in the City of New York was passed on June 10, 1760:

Whereas many ignorant and unskilful persons in physick and surgery, in order to gain a subsistence, do take upon themselves to administer physick and practice surgery in the city of New York, to the endangering of the lives and limbs of their patients, and many poor and ignorant persons inhabiting the said city, who have been persuaded to become their patients, have been great sufferers thereby; for preventing such abuses for the future—

1. *Be it enacted by his honor the lieutenant-governor, the council, and the general assembly, and it is hereby enacted by the authorities of the same,* That from and after the publication of this act no person whatsoever shall practice as a physician or surgeon in the said city of New York before he shall first have been examined in physick and surgery, and approved of and admitted by one of His Majesty's council, the judges

of the supreme court, the King's attorney-general and the mayor of the city of New York for the time being, or by any three or more of them, taking to their assistance for such examinations such proper person or persons as they in their discretion shall think fit.

A graduate of Harvard College and the University of Utrecht in both medicine and theology, Samuel Megapolensis became pastor of a church in New York. He was one of the Dutch commissioners who transacted negotiations with the English which led to New Amsterdam becoming New York in 1664.

Jacob D. Commor practiced surgery in New York in 1660. Later he moved to the Swedish colony called New Castle on the Delaware. Jan du Parck and J. Hughes are listed as New York practitioners in 1661. In the same year the Fort Albany resident surgeon was the Frenchman, De Huise.

The Hollander, Abraham Staats, practiced in Fort Orange. In 1664 his wife and two sons were burned to death after the Indians, with whom he was making treaties, set fire to his house. A surviving son studied medicine in Holland and returned to New York City to practice until his death in 1716.

Gysbert van Imbroeck and Gerardus Beekman were prominent physicians toward the end of the seventeenth century. Doctor and Latin Professor, Alexander D. Curtis left New York when it was surrendered to the English. A Frenchman, Giles Geodineau, described as physician and surgeon, received letters of denization in 1680. In 1689, the Scotchman Lockhart was resident surgeon at Fort Albany.

Seven physicians and about thirty chirurgeons or barber-chirurgeons were given "small burgher rights" of New York City from 1695 to 1770. These rights were identical to those dispensed to chimney sweeps, butchers, bakers, cordwainers, perriwig makers, vintners and gentlemen-attorneys-at-law. Most medical men tied up with an autocratic group of merchants, officials and landed gentry, for the masses of the poor, the indentured colonists and the negro slaves, could not support a physician.

In 1677, Jonas Wood was licensed to practice by the General Court of Assizes of Huntington, Long Island:

"Upon Intimation of divers Considerable Cures in Chirurgery done on severall persons by Mr. *Jonas Wood* of *Huntington,* and the great good hee is capable of doeng in that art, but that hee is not willing publickely to practice it without some particular licence or Allowance from Authority as the Law directs. There being likewise no other Chirurgeon in these parts. The Crt have recd full satisfaction of the abilityes of ye sd Mr. *Wood* in that faculty, They do allow of his practice in Chirurgery of which all persons concerned may take notice accordingly."

Fourteen years later, John Stuard, who was well aware of the fact that he could not make a living from the practice of medicine alone, with eighty-one citizens, petitioned the Proprietors and Freeholders of Hempstead, Long Island, as follows:

> The request of John Stuard humbly showeth, that in as much as it has pleased God to make me a master of a family, I finding it a necessity to settle myself, I am willing to settle among you, to follow the trade of a cooper, as also to practice the art of surgery. I do therefore request that you be pleased to give me a right of 18 or 20 acres of land that is tillable, a little east of the Blue Point, near the Plain Edge. It is the bit of that hollow, called the Bloody Hollow, for which I shall be very thankful, and also ready and willing to serve you in either of the arts aforesaid, so far as I have understanding.

Lacking hospitalization, the municipality of New York paid physicians on a per annum basis for treating the poor. In 1687 and 1689, Dr. Johannes Kerfbyle received five pounds for his services to the poor, for a one year period. (This is the same Dr. Kerfbyle who in 1690 performed an autopsy on Governor Sloughter to see if he had been poisoned.) By 1713, the fee had risen to eight pounds which Jacob Provost received. In 1714 the mayor and a committee from Common Council discussed the possibility of constructing an almshouse, but decided in favor of paying for the care of the poor in private houses. It is recorded that one ailing Andrew Roulson, blacksmith, was sent to live with Elizabeth Burgher, keeper of the poor house, in 1714, at municipal expense. In the same year, Samuel Garrett, obviously in bad physical condition, was sent to the poor house by the mayor, who directed the churchwardens to remunerate Elizabeth Burgher for his keep until he could again work for a living. In 1725, John Ross, mariner, received aid under similar circumstances.

At times, the sick poor were permitted to stay in their own homes and were given subsidy by the churchwardens. Mary Holt was given three shillings and sixpence per week for "the Maintenance of her and her Children during her sickness and until she shall be able to work for her livelihood." On August 23, 1715, the churchwardens were ordered to pay Elizabeth Davis "Three Pounds Current Money of New York Towards paying her Doctor and defraying her Charges in the Cutting of her Brest. She being an Object of Charity." In 1729, Dr. Jacob Moene was awarded three pounds "for Setting and Curing the broken Leg of A poor Saylor Named John who was an Object of Charity."

Application at times was made to the city to seek redress for medical attention and shelter given a stranger. Thus in 1746, Benjamin Taylor complained to the churchwardens that he had "Suffered Very much by having one George Reynolds a Stranger" come to his house the preceding March and after staying a night or two take sick with "the Numb-Palsey . . . which Bereaved him of his Sences & Rendred him altogether Helpless." The petitioner asked recompense of eleven pounds, sixteen shillings and two pence which was for "Sundrys Bot for him and geting Watchers; to 1 Feather Bed Rotted & Totally Ruined; to Mine and my Wifes Attendance, House Room, Fire-Wood, candles and Washing."

The petitioner also enclosed a bill for professional services and medicines administered to the patient by William Brownejohn:

1746		pounds–shillings–pence	
Mar:	15—To Phlebotomy	2	6
	To a Blistering Plaster	2	0
	To a Cordial Mixture	3	6
	To 2 Emp^rs & Dresings	2	0
	16—To a Cordial Mixture	3	6
	17—To 2 Plasters & Dressing	2	0
	25—To a Cath(artic) powder	2	0
	28—To an Enema	2	6
Ap:	1—To an Enema D°..................	2	6
		1 2	6

If a person from another province, through illness, tended to become a public charge, the attempt was made to ship him back to his native city. In 1722, the churchwardens were instructed to pay Abraham Price, a blacksmith, thirty shillings: "to carry out of this Province one Thomas Turner lately a Servant of his toward Kent County in Pensilvania the place from whence he came being seized with the Palsie and an Object of Charity."

John Bard, (1716-1799) for two scientific achievements, deserves mention at this time. He was a partner in one of the first systematic dissections in the United States for the purpose of instruction and he was the first American to report a case of extrauterine pregnancy. His father was Peter Bard, who fled from France on the revocation of the edict of Nantes, travelled to London, and then to Delaware in 1703 on an unsuccessful mercantile venture, following which he settled in Burlington, New Jersey. He was appointed judge of the supreme court and a member of the governor's council, dying at an early age and leaving his widow, a daughter of an English physician named Marmion, with a family of seven children and lean finances.

John Bard, her third son, was born in Burlington on February 1, 1716. He went to Philadelphia where he received the rudiments of a classical education, partly at the hands of an erudite and polished Scotch gentleman, Annan by name, an accomplished teacher of Latin. At the age of fifteen John became apprentice to Mr. Kearsley, an English surgeon who treated his pupils with great severity and subjected them to most menial employments to which John would have scarcely submitted, as he said, were it not for the fear of disappointing his mother and because of his affection for Mrs. Kearsley, who showed him the greatest kindness. For seven tedious years he stayed with the doctor, stealing his hours of study from sleep, after the family had gone to bed and before they got up in the morning. An early intimacy with Benjamin Franklin brightened Bard's leisure hours and stimulated his mind. They were members of the same club and corresponded and kept up their friendship throughout life.

Dr. Bard settled to practice first in Philadelphia where he married a Miss Valleau, a niece of Mrs. Kearsley, like himself a descendant of a refugee and equally destitute of the goods of this world. Of this union was born Samuel Bard who will be discussed later. After practicing six or seven years in Philadelphia, Dr. Bard was induced by Franklin to move to New York in the year 1746, to take the place of Dr. Dubois and Dr. Dupie, who had died there of yellow fever.

His appearance, cheerfulness and kind disposition, which made him so different from his preceptor, plus his professional skill, won for him a large practice among the better classes. Bard avidly devoured his contemporary medical literature and also the English authors and customarily pleased his friends with erudite quotations from famous men of letters.

As a friend of famous Dr. Peter Middleton, a founder of the medical department of King's College, Bard assisted him in the first recorded dissection: "As early, however, as 1750, the body of Hermannus Carroll, executed for murder was dissected in this city by two of the most eminent physicians of that day, Drs. John Bard and Peter Middleton, and the blood vessels injected for the instruction of the youth then engaged in the study of medicine."

Although Dr. Bard retired from practice in 1778 and settled on a farm at Hyde Park, on the Hudson, the Revolution eradicated most of his wealth and he returned to New York at the peace of 1783 to resume practice.

In a letter to Dr. John Fothergill of London, dated December 25,

1759, he communicated "A case of an extra-uterine foetus," that was read to "a society of physicians in London," on March 24, 1760, and was published subsequently in volume two of "Medical Observations and Inquiries" (1763). This first case of extrauterine pregnancy to be reported concerned a 28 year old woman in the New World who went through her second pregnancy with little difficulty. At the end of nine months she had a few labor pains, but no delivery ensued. Nothwithstanding a large right-sided abdominal tumor she had another healthy child by a normal labor, but, five days after delivery, pain and fever began and at the end of nine weeks of treatment by fomentations, fluctuation in the tumor could be detected. Dr. Bard made the diagnosis of extrauterine pregnancy, and in the presence of Dr. Huck, an army physician, opened the abdomen by a long incision and delivered a macerated full-term foetus amid much purulent debris. The patient who was then nursing her child made a good recovery.

Several papers on yellow fever from Dr. Bard's pen are to be found in the files of the "American Medical and Philosophical Register," and posthumously there appeared in the same publication an essay on the nature and cause of malignant pleurisy that had been delivered before "A weekly society of gentlemen in New York," in January, 1749. Here we have a reference to one of the earliest medical societies in the country. It was patterned after Dr. Fothergill's London society apparently and, according to Peter Middleton, was in existence twenty years later. When the Medical Society of the State of New York was organized in 1788, he was unanimously elected first president.

Dr. Bard, at the age of eighty, delivered an address before the state medical society calling attention to the presence of yellow fever in the city. He advised diaphoresis in treating this dread disease—which method of therapy met with some success. In 1798 he gave up practice and retired to Hyde Park where he died on March 30, 1799, at the age of 83.

Peter Middleton (?—1781), was born in Scotland and studied at St. Andrew's University. He migrated to New York, where he became one of the most eminent medical men in the middle of the eighteenth century. In 1767 he aided in establishing the medical department of Kings College (Columbia University) in New York, in which he was the first professor of pathology and physiology, from 1767 to 1776, and of chemistry and materia medica from 1770 to 1776. Columbia conferred on him an Honorary M.D. in 1768. He was a governor of Kings College from 1770 to 1780. He published a letter on "Croup" in volume nine of the "Medical Repository" and

"Historical Inquiries into the Ancient and Present Systems of Medicine" (1769). He died of cancer of the pylorus in New York City in the year 1781.

Peter Middleton spoke of the poor house as "a public receptacle for poor Invalids...undeserving of the Name of an Hospital" and as to the medical treatment, it was doubtful whether it was "a Reproach to the Community, or a Benefit to the Patient."

At the site of the present City Hall, a Workhouse and House of Correction was completed in 1736. One of the rooms of the Almshouse was converted into an infirmary, which was the forerunner of Bellevue Hospital. In 1739, a building for contagious diseases was opened. It is said that John van Beuren, who was a graduate of Leyden, received one hundred pounds a year for taking charge of the infirmary. In 1762, Dr. John Bard received seven pounds from the Common Council for delivering and attending an inmate of the poor house.

On November 25, 1763, Dr. Samuel Clossy started a private series of lectures on anatomy and pathology. On November 28, 1763, the *New York Gazette* carried the following story:

Tom, a negro man slave, condemned the last Assizes for attempting a Rape on Mary Ryan, a Child, was executed at Fresh Water. The Mob was so incensed, after he was turned off, that the Officers could not stand their Ground from the Snowballs, Stones, &c. thrown at him; thus, were obliged to leave him to their Brutality: After they cut him down, they dragged his Body through some of the streets; when the great good Conduct of a single Gentleman soon put a stop to their Inhumanity, by seizing the Corpse, and ordering it to be interred, judiciously Knowing the Law was fulfilled by the Execution, and consequently that the Publick ought to be therewith contented. But it is said the Body has since been taken up, and likely to become a Raw Head and Bloody Bones, by our Tribe of Dissectors, for the better Instruction of our young Practitioners.

Dr. Clossy wanted to give an anatomy course at the proposed medical school to be established at King's College. On May 16, 1764, John Watts, governor of the college, sent the following letter to General Robert Monckton:

I shall not fail to make use of your name with the Governors of the College in favour of Dr. Clossy whenever it is seasonable to do it, at present it is not, there is no opening for Anatomical Lectures, the Students are so few & the funds so overcharged, besides we have so many of the Faculty allready destroying his Majesty's good subjects, that in the humour people are, they had rather one half were hanged that are allready practicing than breed a New Swarm in addition to the old, you'll say 'tis the way to have abler practitioners, it will help them no doubt, but bad enough (of Conscience) are the best we breed here. Another Obsticle stands in the way too, Sir James (Jay) who is their Mendicant at Home & has been very successful, propos'd a Branch of this kind of Education, but I don't find it relished at all, & tho' it might not serve him, it might disserve another, by throwing his Name & pretentions in the way, however we shall not be unmindful of the Doctor (Clossy) when any Nail will go.

The early medical history of New York was influenced by no factor more important than the kaleidoscopic passage of epidemic diseases on the colonial scene. In 1655, during the month of August, the Dutch have left a record of "a general epidemic." During the summer of 1659 a "painful and long, lingering sickness" devastated the colonists.

It would not be out of place at this juncture to mention the writer whose published contributions in the eighteenth century are of the greatest permanent value to medicine, and particularly to the history of epidemics. This learned gentleman, not a physician, but a useful and versatile man was Noah Webster (1758-1843), who graduated from Yale in 1778 (M.A.), and Princeton in 1795.

Yale awarded him an LL.D. in 1823. Thus he was a doctor of laws although not of medicine. He was the first epidemiologist that this country produced. In 1796 Webster published "A Collection of Papers on the Subject of Bilious Fevers Prevalent in the United States for a Few Years Past." Three years later, a two-volume work entitled "A Brief History of Epidemic and Pestilential Diseases" appeared. This work is of great value because it records direct observations of epidemic diseases in this country. Webster wrote several papers on various medical subjects. In the "Medical Repository" (2 s. vol. II), he published a critique of Erasmus Darwin's "Theory of Fever." In this article, Webster gives a logical and lucid presentation of that modern theory associated with Traube's name which explains febrile elevation of temperature by the retention of heat within the body.

Webster was admitted to the bar in 1781, and in 1788 settled in New York as a journalist. He was a co-founder of Amherst College, Massachusetts, and lived in Amherst in 1812. His other writings included the well-known "Spelling Book" (1783-5); "Dissertation on the English Language" (1789); "A Compendious Dictionary of the English Language" (1806); "American Dictionary of the English

Language" (1828); "Rights of Neutrals" (1802); "A Collection of Papers on Political, Literary and Moral Subjects," and "A Brief History of the United States" (1823).

Noah Webster lists a scourge, "autumnal bilious fever," as afflicting the colonists in 1668. This probably yellow fever epidemic was so virulent that Governor Dongan proclaimed a day of fast. In September 1668, the aforementioned Samuel Megapolensis declared: "The Lord begins to deal in judgement with his people. He has visited us with dysentery, which is even now increasing in virulence. Many have died of it, and many are lying sick. It appears as if God were punishing this land for its sins."

In January 1684, Stephanus Cortlandt declared that "hardly a day passes but someone is buried."

On October 16, 1689, following the outbreak of smallpox in New York City, the following proclamation was made:

William Lynes Master of ye ship Anne & Catherine arriving here from Nevis with a parcell of negroes whereof some have ye small pocks Ordered that all which are sound in Body may be landed cleaning themselves sufficiently & those which are sick to be Landed a Mile or thereabouts from the City & to Permit none to come to them but ye doctors Chirurgeons & attenders.

Early in 1702, smallpox broke out in New York, and by September of this year, a violent (yellow fever) epidemic swept the province. To counteract this menace, a proclamation was put forth ordering the quick burial of victims of this disease, and prohibiting the distilling of rum and the burning of oyster shells and lime—the supposed etiologic agents of the epidemic. Divine supplication via a weekly day of fast and humiliation was likewise resorted to. On September 29, 1702, a Common Council meeting, but poorly attended, was held, for "Almighty God hath for our Manifold sins Immorality and profaneness been pleased to Visit us att this time with great sickness and Mortality whereby great numbers of the Citizens of this Corporation are Dead and Many at this time lye in A Languishing Condition."

The next day George Keith preached "at the Weekly Fast, which was appointed by the Government, by reason of the great Mortality that was then at New York, where above Five Hundred died in the Space of a few weeks; and that every Week, about Seventy died."

On June 20, 1718, the State Assembly considered a law to prohibit the landing of any person "sick of the Smallpox, Measeals, or any other pestilential or infectious Distemper," and to prevent the spreading of the same, in the City of New York, but no actual quarantine was enacted until May 3, 1755.

In May, 1725, the churchwardens were ordered to "Visit Lena Spriggs and her children who lie very ill of the Bloody Flux (as is said) and if they find it true to remove them to Some Convenient Place out of the Town to Prevent Infection." A smallpox patient was landed from a ship from Madiero and the Council after an investigation, adopted quarantine measures.

Inoculation against smallpox was a subject of violent debate at this time. Even such a progressive man as Cadwallader Colden opposed inoculation, but in March, 1725, the *New York Gazette* quoted a Philadelphia writer to the effect that inoculation for smallpox is being favorably considered in that city and a case was cited to show "how groundless all those extravagant Reports are, that have been spread through the Province (of New York) to the contrary."

Naturally fear of epidemics greatly hampered trade and business. To protect business interests, on June 12, 1731, the Common Council declared:

Whereas some Evil disposed Persons for their own private Lucre and gain, have Industriously Spread A Report about the Country that the Small Pox prevails within this City, whereby to deter the Country People from Coming to Markett and to Negotiate their Other Lawfull Occasions. These are therefore to Certifie and declare that the Said Report is Fake and Groundless, and that by A Strict search and Enquiry made of all the Physicians, Surgeons and Apothecaries as could Conveniently be gott together throughout the same, We find there are but two Persons in this City who have that disease (the Small Pox) who are almost well thereof and out of Danger and that the Provident and Early care that has been taken to prevent Infection has hitherto had its desired Effect; and that all possible Caution is and will be taken to prevent the spreading of Contagion and Or'd this, be forthwith Printed in the *New York Gazette*.

Two months later, on August 23, 1731, the *New York Gazette* publicly recognized the extent of the current epidemic which had been introduced the preceding May, when "Captain Fred" brought diseased negroes from Jamaica. By August 28, the New York State Assembly decided to postpone all further business because the house had grown "very thin, and more likely to grow thinner than fuller, by Reason that the Small-pox are very rief in the City of New York, a Distemper which at least 9 of the Members never had." On September 30, Rip van Dam again adjourned the assembly for the same reason, and such adjournments were repeated later, both by him and the newly arrived governor, William Crosby, until August 9, 1732.

The following description is extracted from a letter from New York dated August 20, 1731:

.... the melancholy Scene of little Business, and less Money. The Markets begin to grow thin; the Small-pox raging very violently in Town, which, in a measure hinders the Country People from supplying this Place with Provisions. I have not yet heard that any Persons have gone out of Town for Fear of it. The last week they began to inoculate; which Practice i have reason to believe will very much be followed: The Distemper has been a long time very favourable, but now begins to be of the Confluent Kind and very Mortal.

Although James Alexander wrote to Colden in December, 1731, that "Inoculation takes mightily upon Long Island," the latter remained firm in his convictions. As late as April 27, 1732, he wrote his father "that the Smallpox" had been "inoculat in Some at New York with success" but he was "not inclinable to use that operation." Peter de Lancey, writing to Colden on June 25, 1738, said that his wife who had just been inoculated would have written "but was affraid the infection mought by her letters be carried up."

The severity of the smallpox epidemic of 1731 can be deduced from the fact that trade was at a virtual impasse and contributions were asked for the relief of the poor. The ferryman asked the Common Council for a lowering of the annual rent because his business was reduced to nothing and his family was in distress. Accordingly his rent was reduced to fifty pounds. On November 2, 1731, van Dam stated in a letter, that since the taking of the census for this year "near eight hundreds are lost by the small pox, and daily more dying." From August 23 to November 15, 478 whites and 71 blacks, or 549 in all were buried according to the weekly figures published in the New York Gazette:

New-York, November 15

Buried in this City LaST Week, viz. Church of England 4, Dutch Church 4, And Blacks 2. In all this week 10.

In the Month of AuguSt laSt the Small-Pox began to Spread in this City, and for Some Weeks was very favourable, and few died of the DiStemper, but as Soon as we obServed the Burials to increaSe, which was from the 23d of AuguSt, in our Gazette, No. 305. we began to incert weekly, the Number both of Whites and Blacks that were buried this City, by which Account we find, that from the 23d of AuguSt to this InStant,. which is two Months and 3 weeks, there was buried in the Several burying Places of this City, as follows, viz:

Church of England	229,
Dutch Church,	212,
French Church	15,
Lutheran Church	1,
Presbyterians	16,
Quakers	2,
BaptiSts	1,
Jews	2,
Whites in all	478.
Blacks in all	71,
Whites and blacks, In all	549.

From the *New York Gazette*, 1731.

As late as December 29, van Dam, in a letter to the lords of trade, stated that the province is "still mightily afflicted with the Small pox tho' not so mortal as when I had the honour by my former to acquaint Your Lord pps herewith."

Bedloe's Island was established as a quarantine station on June 27, 1738: The direct impetus that led to this was the fearful news "that the Small Pox was pritty Rief at South Carolina, and that a purple or Spotted fever began to Spread there." The Council appointed Dr. Roeliff Kiersted as "Doctor and Physician to go on board such vessels as shall come into this Port Harbour or Bay." As late as in 1744, Dr. Kiersted was still fulfilling his duties of enforcement.

Governor Clinton allied himself on the side of the anti-inoculation group. On June 9, 1747, he proclaimed an edict strictly prohibiting and forbidding "all and every of the Doctors, Physicians, Surgeons, and Practitioners of Physick, and all and every other person within this Province, to inoculate for the smallpox any person or persons within the City or County of New York, on pain of being prosecuted to the utmost rigor of the law."

The following document is again calculated to allay public fears:

We whose names are hereunto subscribed, being Practitioners in Physick in the said City of New York, Do hereby certifie, and make known to all to whom these Presents shall come or may concern, That the Fever that this city was lately visited with, is very greately abated and that there are but few persons at present Sick in this City. And we do further certifie That we do not know of any Person or Persons whatsoever in this City, that has the Distemper called *Small Pox*. In Witness whereof we have here unto subscribed our Names this 10th day of October, 1745.

Archibald Fisher,
Isaac Dubois,
William Beekman,
William Blake,
William Hewcott,
Abraham Van Vleck,

Joseph Bruning,
David Hay,
William Brownejohn,
E.B. Kimmena,
Roelef Kiersted,
John Van Buren,

Alexander Moore.

On May 3, 1755, the General Assembly enacted the following:

All Vessels having the Small Pox, Yellow fever or other Contagious Distemper on Board and all Persons Goods and Merchandizes Whatsoever coming or imported in Such Vessels and all Vessels coming from any place infected with such Distempers Shall not come into any the Ports or Harbours of this City or Nearer the same City than the Island Commonly called Bedlows Island, And shall be obliged to make their Quarantine there.

On May 6, 1755, a proclamation was issued ordering that quarantine regulations be observed. On May 25, John Bard was appointed to examine all vessels suspected of having any contagious diseases on board. We find the probable first recognition that typhus was arriving at the port about this time. Dr. John Bard's son, Dr. Samuel Bard, recalled in later years that "Just before, and what gave occasion to the appointment of the health-officer of New York, about the year 1758 or '59 a ship crowded with Germans arrived in a very sickly state and were put under my father's care. He procured accomodations for the sick at a little distance from town ... the disease he called ship or jail fever (typhus), but never yellow fever."

On February 18, 1758, Bedloe's Island was purchased for 1,000 pounds as a site for a pest house.

Among the members of the medical profession in New York at about 1741 were John Nicoll, Cadwallader Colden and Sir James Jay, who had obtained their medical degrees at Edinburgh. John Jones obtained the degree of doctor of medicine from the University of Rheims after extensive training at Edinburgh, London and Paris. Richard Bayley studied in London under John Hunter. Among the graduates from Leyden were Samuel Staats, John van Buren, Isaac Dubois, Johannes Kerfbyle, John van Brugh Tennent, Gerardus Beekman and his son William Beekman. John Dupuy studied in France as did his son John, also a physician.

New York medical writings were first published in newspapers. On February 16, 1735, the *New York Weekly Journal* printed a story about the "terrible disease in the Throat that has made such Desolations in the Country," written by Jonathan Dickinson of New Jersey.

On February 17-24, 1735, the *New York Gazette* reprinted from the *Boston Gazette* a description of "the New Distemper in the East Parts of New England," by one "Æsculapius." According to Caulfield this is the first printed description of unquestionable diphtheria to appear in America. The same issue of the *New York Gazette* published directions for compounding a medicine "for the Cure of the Sore Throat, which is being spread in these parts." The throat distemper of 1735-1740 was not as prevalent in New York City as it was in New England although Colden observed scattered cases in the Hudson Valley and it appeared on Long Island.

In 1743-44, Colden's observations on the yellow fever, which prevailed in New York during 1741 and 1742, were published in the *New York Weekly Post-Boy* (No. 49, 50, 51). This was perhaps the first publication dealing with public health in New York. The author argued that even if yellow fever was imported from abroad it was still necessary to keep the city clean and urged that sanitary duties be placed in the hands of the corporation rather than be left to private persons.

A letter addressed to Hugh Gaine from Dr. Jacob Ogden of Jamaica, Long Island, on the Malignant Sore Throat, dated October 28, 1769, appeared in the *New York Gazette* on November 6.

The earliest work on medicine printed in New York appears to be a pamphlet reprinted by John Zenger in 1731, entitled "An abstract of the Patent granted by His Majesty King George to Benj. Odell, the Inventor of a medicine, called Dr. Bateman's Pectoral Drops; together with a Short Treatise of the Virtues of Dr. Bateman's Pectoral Drops."

The following list of New York imprints of books by colonial authors, published prior to the Revolution, is printed verbatum from Heaton's fascinating account:

Douglass, William—*An Account of the Throat Distemper*, in a Letter from Wm. Douglass of Boston, M.D. To——of New York, New York: Printed by John Peter Zenger: 1740.

Tennent, John—*An Essay on the Pleurisy*. By John Tennent. Williamsburg, Printed: New York: Re-printed and Sold by James Parker, at the New Printing-Office in Hanover-Square: 1742.

Middleton, Peter—*A Medical Discourse, or an Historical Inquiry into the Ancient and Present State of Medicine:* the Substance of which was delivered at opening the Medical School, in the City of New-York. By Peter Middleton, M.D. and Professor of the Theory of Physic in King's College. New York: 1769, by Hugh Gaine.

Bard, Samuel—*A Discourse upon the Duties of a Physician, with some Sentiments, on the Usefulness and Necessity of a Public Hospital:* delivered before the President and Governors of King's College, at the Commencement, held on the 16th of May, 1769. As Advice to those Gentlemen who then received the First Medical Degrees conferred by the University. By Samuel Bard, M.D. Professor of the Practice of Medicine in King's College. New-York: Printed by A.& J. Robertson, at the Corner of Beaver-Street, 1769.

Bard, Samuel—*An Enquiry into the Nature, Cause and Cure, of the Angina Suffocativa, or, Sore Throat Distemper, as it is commonly called by the Inhabitants of this City and Colony.* By Samuel Bard, M.D. and Professor of Medicine in King's College, New-York. New York: Printed by S. Inslee, and A. Car, at the New Printing-Office in Beaver-Street, 1771.

Jones, John—*Plain Concise Practical Remarks on the Treatment of Wounds and Fractures: to which is added, a short Appendix on Camp and Military Hospitals principally designed for the Use of young Military Surgeons, in North-America.* By John Jones, M.D. Professor of Surgery in King's College, New York: Printed by John Holt, in Water-Street, near the Coffee-House, 1775.

This was the first American book on surgery and military surgery and must have been extensively used by the young surgeons during the war but few copies have survived.

Dr. John Jones (1729-?) was born in Jamaica, Long Island, in 1729. Both his father and grandfather were medical men. After receiving his preliminary medical education from his father, he was instructed by Pott and Hunter in London, by Monro in Edinburgh, and by Petit in Paris. In 1751, he received his medical degree at Rheims.

Upon his return to New York, he quickly became acclaimed as a skillful surgeon. He was appointed army surgeon in 1755 during the French and English war and served well until the end of the conflict. At the battle of Lake George, he rendered his professional services to the Baron Dieskau, who was wounded.

Jones was appointed professor of surgery in the Medical College of New York. During the War of Independence, in spite of bouts of asthma, he rendered efficient medical services and also wrote the aforementioned widely used book.

When peace was secured, Jones moved to Philadelphia and was accepted on the staff of the Pennsylvania Hospital in 1780. He was also one of the organizers of the College of Physicians of Philadelphia.

Jones was Benjamin Franklin's personal physician during his last illness and this confidence bestowed upon him by this greatest of Americans presents an index of estimation of his ability and integrity. Jones answered Franklin's last call in 1781.

Some of the salient principles presented in Jones' Surgery are as follows:

Slight puncture wounds require no therapy. Deep and tortuous ones should be incised and enlarged. Inflammation is best counter-acted by gentle laxatives, soft cataplasms, sudorific anodynes, bleed-ing and warm baths. Opium is an essential adjunct of treatment. The appearance of gangrene signifies the need of a more nourishing diet, spiritous formentations and a more intensive use of the bark. Ab-scesses need immediate incision and drainage.

All transverse wounds are in need of interrupted suturing with a needle dipped in oil. Following this a plaster is applied over the area for two or three days.

In gunshot wounds, one should first remove the ball, and secondly control hemorrhage. A light dressing should then be applied with a retension dressing on top.

All major compound fractures require immediate amputation.

Concerning the therapy of wounds, Jones declares:

Mr. Sharp, in his excellent introduction to the Operations of Surgery, recommends nothing but dry, soft lint to recent wounds; which is gen-erally the best application through the whole course of the cure. At first it restrains the hemorrhage, with less injury than any styptic medicines; and afterwards, by absorbing the matter, which is at first thin and acri-monious, it becomes, in effect, the best digestive. During incarnation (granulation) it is the softest medicine than can be applied between the roller and tender granulations; and at the same time an easy compress on the sprouting fungus.

For these reasons I shall not recommend to you any ointments for re-cent wounds, unless some mild, soft one, to arm a pledget of tow, to cover the lint.

When a wound degenerates into so bad a state as to resist, this simple method of treatment, and loses that healthy, florid appearance, which characterizes a recent wound; it is then denominated an ulcer, which is distinguished by various names.

Jones considers cardiac, aortic, cerebellar, medullary and recepta-culum chyli wounds as fatal. Chest, abdominal, hepatic, pulmonary, intestinal and renal wounds are very serious. It is advisable to dilate the external opening of wounds and to bleed the patient profusely and frequently. Then one is to employ "emollient glysters, cooling nitrous drinks, anodynes, most rigid diet consisting solely of thin, diluting drinks, perfect quiet and a proper posture."

Most wounds during the Revolutionary War were inflicted by musket balls. Occasional bayonet wounds were encountered. Knife, club and axe wounds were inflicted by the Indians. As there was no adequate system of quickly bringing the wounded to the surgeons, many died of neglect on the battlefields, even days after being injured.

New York Hospital was the second large scale hospital to be founded in the English colonies in North America. The first mention of any project for the founding of a hospital in that city is to be found in a discourse delivered by the aforementioned Dr. Middleton in King's (now Columbia) College on November 3, 1769. He declared:

The necessity and usefulness of a public infirmary, has been so warmly and pathetically set forth, in a discourse delivered by Dr. Samuel Bard, at the commencement in May last, that his excellency, Sir Henry Moore, immediately set on foot a subscription for that purpose, to which himself and most of the gentlemen present liberally contributed. His excellency also recommended it, in the most pressing manner to the assembly of the province, as an object worthy of their attention; and the corporation of the city have given assurances of granting a very valuable and commodious lot of ground for erecting the building upon; so that there is now, almost a certain prospect of this benevolent and humane foundation soon taking place. And as it is to be on the most catholic and unexceptionable plan, it is to be hoped, that it will meet with the countenance and encouragement of every compassionate and good member of society, whatever party or denomination he may choose to be distinguished by, on other occasions.

The Dr. Bard referred to by Middleton is Samuel Bard (1742-1821), the son of John Bard, who was born in Philadelphia, where his father then practiced.

The Elder Bard moved his family to New York when Samuel was four years old. Samuel went to grammar school in New York, and at the age of fourteen years, he showed great interest in the study of medicine. Following his graduation he was taken in hand by his father, and given a fine medical education. Miss Jane Colden, daughter of the lieutenant-governor of the province and a correspondent of Linnaeus, instilled in Samuel a great interest in botany. Coldenia received its name from Linnaeus in her honor. Miss Colden taught Bard the rudiments of botany and he aided her studies by drawing and coloring plants and flowers.

Bard departed for Europe in 1760. After being captured by a French privateer, he was incarcerated in the castle at Bayonne for five months. After attaining his freedom in the spring of 1761 he at once departed for London. Through the intervention of Dr. Fothergill, young Bard was accepted on the staff of St. Thomas' Hospital as assistant to Dr. Alexander Russell. He maintained this position until he left for Edinburgh. In 1765, after publishing his inaugural essay entitled *de viribus opii*, he was graduated from this institution with the highest honors including the coveted Hope Prize offered for the best herbarium of the indigenous vegetables of Scotland.

Samuel Bard returned to New York in 1765. In 1770, he married his cousin, Mary Bard and opened for practice with his father. While in Edinburgh, Samuel had corresponded with his father and informed him of the need in New York for a medical college. Three years after returning home, he, with the aid of Dr. Clossy, Dr. Jones, Dr. Middleton, Dr. Smith and Dr. Tennent, established a medical school in 1768, which was attached to King's College. At the age of twenty-eight, Bard was appointed professor of the theory and practice of physic. His speech during the first commencement in 1769 was so convincing that a large sum was raised for the benefit of the school. The Governor himself headed the list of donors. Dr. Bard served the medical department of King's College for forty years, the last twenty of which he acted as trustee and dean of the faculty of physic.

Upon the advent of the War of Independence, Dr. Bard's unpopular political views led him to retire to Shrewsbury, New Jersey. At this location, he engaged in the manufacture of salt. As this venture was not crowned with success he went back to New York during the British occupation and almost at once got back the fine practice he had forsaken. It is said that by the end of the war he had become financially independent. That Dr. Bard's character was above reproach, notwithstanding his odius political views, is excellently demonstrated by the fact that he became the family physician of General Washington during the latter's residence in New York.

Following the war, when it looked as if the attempts to revive the medical school had failed, the trustees of Columbia College annexed the faculty of physic to that institution (1792). Dr. Bard was reappointed professor of the theory and practice of medicine, and was selected to be dean of the faculty.

Samuel Bard fought hard for the establishment of the city library, and the New York Dispensary.

In 1795, he took Dr. David Hosack into partnership, and three years later he retired into the country and left Hosack as successor to his practice. In 1811 Bard was elected an associate fellow of the College of Physicians of Philadelphia. In 1816 Princeton awarded him a Doctor of Laws degree.

Dr. Bard's first article following his doctorate thesis concerned itself with the effects of opium. Up until this essay, the mode of operation of opium and its various effects upon the body were poorly comprehended. In 1771, he published, as intimated previously, "An inquiry into the Nature, Cause and Cure of the Angina Suffocativa, or Throat Distemper, as it is Commonly Called by the Inhabitants of this City and Colony." The contents of this work have been termed wise and accurate, his style classical and simple, and the description of diphtheria in skin, mucous membrane and larynx, correct and beautiful. "He knew the different forms of the disease even better than Dr. Douglass, of Boston, had distinguished them."

Dr. Bard loved obstetrics and built up a fine reputation in this branch. In 1807 he published "A Compendium of the Theory and Practice of Midwifery," intended chiefly for the use of midwives and young practitioners. The work was published in three large editions in its duodecimo form; and in two greatly enlarged and improved printings in octavo. When death overtook him, Samuel Bard was in process of preparing for the press a sixth edition.

In 1811 Bard published "A Guide for Young Shepherds," which was without doubt the most scientific work on sheep breeding then available. He wrote articles for the "American Medical and Philosophical Register," and "The Transactions of the College of Physicians of Philadelphia." Bard published "A Discourse of Medical Education" in New York in 1819.

As his last years rolled by, Bard became more and more afflicted with severe attacks of what is described as "esophageal stricture." He died at the age of seventy nine after a few hours illness of "pleurisy," at Hyde Park, New York, on May 25, 1821.

Peter Middleton, John Jones, and Samuel Bard petitioned Dr. Cadwallader Colden (who had become Lieutenant-Governor) in 1770 for a charter of incorporation for the New York Hospital. On July 12, 1771, such a document incorporating a number of prominent inhabitants of New York as "The Society of the Hospital in the City of New York in America," was granted. A board of governors was named, consisting of twenty-six of the incorporators, and the first meeting of the infant institution was held on July 25, 1771.

Passing mention of Dr. Fothergill, of London, as one of the incorporators, should not be omitted, for he, by being one of the most generous benefactors of the Pennsylvania Hospital, and the New York Hospital, thus prominently connected himself with the founding of the two first hospitals in North America. Dr. Fothergill never missed an opportunity to lend a helping hand to any young American medical man who studied medicine abroad.

Dr. Fothergill and Sir William Duncan, through tireless efforts, secured much money in London for the use of the new Hospital, and in 1772 the New York Legislature granted it an annual allowance of eight hundred pounds for twenty years.

Committees visited the various wards in New York City to solicit subscriptions. Ministers sought aid from their congregations. In 1774 the Governors of the New York Hospital asked householders to allow persons in the employ of the Hospital to sweep their chimneys and to donate to the Hospital what the expense would otherwise have been to them. Dr. Douglass, a theater manager, presented a benefit to raise funds for the Hospital. The Earl of Sterling presented the Governors with twelve Delaware lottery tickets, but unfortunately no award was drawn by any of them.

In 1773 the Board of Governors bought a lot from Mrs. Barclay and Mr. Rutgers for the erection of the Hospital. July 27, 1773, was the memorable day on which the cornerstone was laid. Prior to the completion of the buildings, however, tragedy overwhelmed the project in the form of fire which ravaged the structures on February 28, 1775.

The plans for the construction of these buildings had been procured by Dr. Jones during a trip to Europe in 1772. The only information available as to the nature of these plans is in his previously mentioned book on military surgery. Dr. Jones first mentions the unspeakable conditions in the wards of the Hôtel Dieu in Paris:

In Paris it is supposed that one-third of all who die there die in hospitals. The Hôtel Dieu—a vast building, situated in the middle of that great city—receives about twenty-two thousand persons annually, one-fifth of which number die every year. It is impossible for any man of humanity to walk through the long wards of this crowded hospital without a mixture of horror and commiseration at the sad spectacle of misery which presents itself. The beds are placed in triple rows, with four and six patients in each bed; and I have more than once in the morning rounds, found the dead lying with the living; for, notwithstanding the great assiduity and tenderness of the nurses, some of whom are women of family, who take the veil and piously devote themselves to that office, yet it is almost impossible, from the vast number of patients, to bestow timely assistance upon every individual.

He then goes on to say:

It is to be hoped that the Hospital lately built in the city of New York will have fewer objections to its plan than any hospital hitherto constructed. The principal wards, which are to contain no more than eighty beds, are thirty-six feet in length, twenty-four feet wide and eighteen high. They are all well ventilated, not only from the opposite disposition of the windows, but by proper openings in the side walls, and the doors open into a long passage or gallery, thoroughly ventilated from north to south.

The original estimates for the building called for an expenditure of about seventeen thousand dollars. The structure was to be built of stone.

Although the fire on February 28, 1775, created much havoc, the work of reconstruction was so vigorously pushed that the New York Provincial Congress took possession of the Hospital for barracks on April 2, 1776, at which time a moat was dug about the Hospital twelve feet wide and seven feet deep for defensive purposes.

Beekman, in his "Centenary Address," declares that the honor of performing the first surgical operation in the Hospital, goes to Dr. Samuel Drowne, who did an arm amputation. Drowne, at the time (July, 1776) was a surgeon's mate in the general hospital of the Continental Army. Referring to this amputation, Dr. Drowne later wrote that "one ball came into ye hospital yard, struck the ground at a little distance from us, and bounded through ye board fence."

It appears that the buildings were not used for a protracted period as barracks but were soon employed for their original purpose, for Drowne declares that the amputation was executed "at the new City Hospital, which had been fitted for the wounded." When the Americans evacuated New York in August 1776, the British converted the Hospital buildings into barracks for the Hessians.

Throughout the war and the following years, the Society of the Hospital in New York held yearly meetings for the election of officers, although the buildings were not employed for hospital purposes by the Society until January, 1791.

In March, 1785, the Society opened the doors of the hospital to Scotch emigrants who remained until June of that year. In the winter of 1785, Dr. Bailey (Bayley) was permitted to use several rooms for dissecting purposes.

Richard Bailey (1745-1811) was born at Fairfield, Connecticut, in 1745, of French-English descent. After apprenticing himself to Dr. Charlton of New York, and marrying his daughter, he sailed to London. He became friendly with William Hunter and was allowed to work in his dissecting-room. After returning to New York, Bailey practiced with Dr. Charlton. It was during this period that he began to make his observations concerning the fatal form of "croup" that was then prevalent. He published his views on this disease in "Richter's Surgical Repository."

In 1781, Bailey published his letter to Dr. William Hunter on "Angina Trachealis." His "History of the Yellow Fever in New York in 1795," attempts to differentiate between contagion and infection.

In 1776, Bailey left to spend a winter in London. His poor financial status led him to secure the position of surgeon on board a British man o' war coming to America. Finding himself with the troops on Rhode Island after the English occupation, and hearing that his wife was ill in New York, he resigned and hastened to her side. He barely arrived in time to see her die.

Bailey's painstaking attention to anatomy and pathology was denounced by many less scientific physicians as mere experimentation on sick soldiers. Unaffected by these rebuffs, Bailey none-the-less presented lectures to students in an unoccupied house while his son-in-law, Wright Post, lectured on anatomy (1778). The people in the vicinity became incensed at the "sacrilege" committed during dissection. An aroused populace represented by the famous "Doctor's Mob" broke into the building and destroyed Bailey's rare collection of morbid anatomy. The specimens were tossed into carts, hauled away and buried.

When Columbia College constituted a medical faculty in 1792, Bailey was appointed professor of anatomy, and Wright Post professor of surgery. In 1793, the two exchanged their positions.

Bailey was an excellent lithotomist. In 1782 he successfully amputated an arm at the shoulder-joint, this being the first time that this procedure was employed in the United States.

Bailey was constantly irked by the tardiness of his fellow townsmen in permitting social reforms. Bailey and a few colleagues succeeded in establishing the New York Dispensary after much hard work. During the yellow fever epidemic, he worked day and night and vehemently proclaimed that the fever was "a murderer of our own creating," due, at least in part, to a filthy harbor. He observed that yellow fever was worse when the West India ships came in the summer and fought earnestly for adequate quarantine laws.

In 1811, after discovering ship fever (typhus) on an Irish immigrant ship, he ordered the passengers to go on shore to the tents and rooms provided but to leave their baggage on board. The following morning he found the well and the sick with all baggage huddled together in one big room where they had passed the night. Considerably perturbed by this, he remained to direct matters but he was soon seized with intense pain in the stomach and head. He went home to bed in the afternoon and passed away seven days later.

In April, 1790, the Governors consulted Drs. Samuel Bard and Malachi Treat to get their opinion as to what should be done toward employing the Hospital for treating the afflicted. A committee was selected to meet with the group interested in the recently established New York Dispensary so as to ascertain by what means the two organizations might best cooperate in their respective tasks. On January 3, 1791, the hospital was officially reopened with a group of eighteen patients.

Patients were admitted promiscuously and grouped together regardless of their ailment or sanity. The Governors defined the groups that they accepted for treatment to the State Legislature as follows: Those in need of medical or chirurgical treatment, maniacs and women. The students at Columbia College received clinical instruction from its wards. The Governors appropriated two hundred pounds for the establishment of a library.

The Governors originally congregated in various coffee-houses or taverns, and at times at the City Hall. Their meeting of May 17, 1791, however, and all subsequent ones, were held within the confines of the Hospital.

It is of interest to note that the land in back of the Hospital was selected as a suitable secluded spot on which to fight a duel. It is recorded that in 1799, one of the house-surgeons was reprimanded for practicing outside the Hospital and absenting himself too often from the premises. He promptly challenged Dr. Hosack to a duel "at Hobuck." Dr. Hosack handed the challenge over to the Board of Governors, following which the surgeon posted a denunciation of Hosack in the Coffee-House and demanded an apology. The Board of Governors' dismissed him from the Hospital.

Practically all obstetrical care in colonial days was administered by midwives:

On July 16, 1716, a New York City ordinance was passed concerning the activity of midwives:

It is ordained that no woman within this corporation shall exercise the employment of midwife until she have taken oath before the mayor, recorder, or an alderman, (the terms of which are prescribed,) to the following effect: That she will be diligent and ready to help any woman in labor, whether poor or rich; that in time of necessity she will not cause or suffer any woman to name or put any other father to the child, but only him which is the very true father, thereof, indeed, according to the utmost of her power; that she will not suffer any woman to pretend to be delivered of a child who is not in deed, neither to claim any other woman's child for her own; that she will not suffer any woman's child to be murdered or hurt; and as often as she shall see any peril, or jeopardy, either in the mother or child, she will call in other midwives for counsel; that she will not administer any medicine to produce miscarriage: that she will not enforce a woman to give more for her services than is right: that she will not collude to keep secret the birth of a child; will be of good behaviour; will not conceal the births of bastards, &c.

The need for such regulations is probably a good criterion for judging the illicit practices of midwifery during this period.

The *New York Gazette* for January, 1769, carries an ad of a Mrs. Fisher, near Whitehall, who proffered her services as midwife.

Men occasionally appear to have engaged in obstetrical practice. The *New York Gazette* (December 16, 1751) refers to Doctor Peter Billings as "an experienced physician and man-midwife." William Douglass refers to the same gentleman as a notorious quack who dispensed sure cures for venereal diseases and who sold alleged prophylactic medications for yellow fever and the West Indian dry gripes.

Doctor Guischard, in 1760 or thereabouts, advertised that he is a surgeon from Paris and an expert in delivering women.

The *New York Post-Boy* (August 5, 1745) presented the following notice: "Last night, Sunday, July 21st, died in the prime of life to the almost universal regret and sorrow of the City, Mr. John Dupuy, M.D., and man midwife, in which loss it may be truly said, as of Goliath's sword, 'there was none like unto him.'"

Tennent became the first professor of obstetrics in colonial America, and he was placed on the staff of King's College in 1767.

Provision was made for delivery of the destitute in the Almshouse by an official midwife. In difficult cases, physicians were consulted, as was Dr. John Bard on one occasion.

Dr. Colden wrote to William Douglass of Boston as follows: "I wish that a certain number of Men would enter into a Voluntary Society for the advancing of Knowledge." In 1764, Colden issued the same suggestion to Benjamin Franklin who responded by stating that such a society already existed in Philadelphia. Franklin in 1763 had written a pamphlet entitled *A Proposal for Promoting Useful Knowledge Among the British Plantations in America* in which he stated that "The first drudgery of settling new colonies, which confined the attention of people to mere necessaries, is now pretty well over." He thereupon pointed out the great need for Americans to cultivate the arts and sciences, including medicine, more assiduously.

The proof that a medical society had been organized in New York during the first half of the eighteenth century rests on the fact that a manuscript notebook which belonged to Dr. John Bard bearing the date 1749 has been uncovered which lists as the first paper: "An Essay on the Nature of Ye Malignant Pleurisy that Proved so Remarkably Fatal to the Inhabitants of Huntington, L. I., and some other places on Long Island, in the winter of the year 1749, drawn up at the request of a Weekly Society of Gentlemen in New York, and addressed to them at one of their meetings."

In 1769, Dr. Peter Middleton in his first lecture at the opening of King's College medical department, demonstrated the need and value of medical societies. He states: "And permit me to add, as one of the many instances of the utility of these societies, that whatever merit there is in the present institution, it was first planned and concluded upon in a medical society now subsisting in this place, and may it long subsist."

In 1789 New York enacted a law "that when any offender shall be convicted of murder, arson or burglary, for which he shall be sentenced to suffer death, the court may at their discretion add to the judgement that the body of such offender shall be delivered to the surgeons for dissection." On April 30, 1790 Congress passed an Act giving federal judges the discretion of adding dissection to the sentence of convicted murderers.

The following petition addressed to the Provincial Congress of New York for the purpose of securing a position as physician may be taken as a sample of numerous similar ones presented at the period. In many cases the applicant was appointed solely on the basis of his petition.

John Hammell to the Provincial Congress, Gentlemen:
Having served an apprenticeship of seven years to Englebert Kemmena, practitioner of physic and surgeon to the city of New York; in which capacity being desirous of joining the forces now raising in this Province for the maintenance of our rights and privileges, beg leave to lay myself before the Honorable House for Its approbation a Recommendation of my character, and abilities, which desirous to support, I have here enclosed, wishing to have the honour of being your humble servant.
                                                    John Hammell.
New York, Tuesday afternoon, 4th July, 1775.

John Hammell, of the city of New York, having studied Physick and Surgery by me with the strictest attention full seven years, during which time he hath conducted himself with the greatest honesty, and sobriety, and convinced of his being capable of practising, do commend him to any person that may occasion assistance of the faculty.

Englebert Kemmena.

New York, July 3rd, 1775.

Smith's "History of New York," written shortly before the Revolution, stated:

Few physicians among us are eminent for their skill. Quacks abound like locusts in Egypt, and too many have recommended themselves to a full and profitable practice and subsistence. This is the less to be wondered at, as the profession is under no kind of regulation. Loud as the call is, to our shame be it remembered we have no law to protect the lives of the King's subjects from the malpractice of pretenders. Any man at his pleasure sets up for physician, apothecary, and chirurgeon. No candidates are either examined or licensed, or even sworn to fair practice.

James J. Walsh gives a number of extracts and advertisements from current newspapers supporting Smith's statement.

The General Assembly of New York on June 10, 1760, enacted the following law regulating the practice of medicine in the city of New York:

Whereas many ignorant and unskilful persons in physick and surgery, in order to gain a subsistence, do take upon themselves to administer physick and practice surgery in the city of New York, to the endangering of the lives and limbs of their patients, and many poor and ignorant persons inhabiting the said city, who have been persuaded to become their patients, have been great sufferers thereby; for preventing such abuses for the future—

I. *Be it enacted by his honor the lieutenant-governor, the council, and the general assembly, and it is hereby enacted by the authority of the same.* That from and after the publication of this act no one whatsoever shall practice as a physician or surgeon in the said city of New York before he shall first have been examined in physick and surgery, and approved of and admitted by one of His Majesty's council, the judges of the supreme court, the King's attorney-general, and the mayor of the city of New York for the time being, or by any three or more of them, taking to their assistance for such examinations such proper person or persons as they in their discretion shall think fit. And if any candidate, after due examination of his learning and skill in physick and surgery as aforesaid, shall be approved and admitted to practice as a physician and surgeon, or both, the said examiners, or any three or more of them, shall give, under their hands and seals, to the person so admitted as aforesaid, a testimonial of his examination and admission, and in the form following, to wit:

To all to whom these presents shall come or may concern:

Know ye, that we, whose names are hereunto subscribed, in pursuance of an act of the Lieutenant-Governor, and Council, and the General Assembly, made and published at New York, the tenth day of June, in the year of our Lord one thousand seven hundred and sixty, entitled "An act to regulate the practice of physick and surgery in the city of New York," have duly examined————physician (or) surgeon, or physician and surgeon, (as the case may be,) and, having approved of his skill, have admitted him as a physician (or) surgeon, (or) physician and surgeon, to practice in the said faculty or faculties throughout this province of New York. In testimony whereof we have affixed our seals to this instrument, at New York, this —— day of ————, anno Domini one thousand——.

II. *And be it further enacted by the authority aforesaid,* That if any person shall practise in the city of New York as a physician or surgeon, or both as a physician and surgeon, without such testimonial as aforesaid, he shall, for every such offence, forfeit the sum of five pounds, one-half thereof to the use of the person or persons who shall sue for the same and the other money to the church-wardens and vestrymen of the said city for the use of the poor thereof, the said forfeiture to be recovered with costs before the mayor, recorder or any one of the aldermen of the said city, who are hereby empowered in a summary way to hear, try, and determine any suit brought for such forfeiture, and to give judgement and to award execution thereupon: *Provided,* That this act shall not extend to any person or persons administering physick or practising surgery within the said city, before the publication thereof, or to any person having his Majesty's commission and employed in his service as a physician and surgeon.

The New York State Legislature passed an act in 1792 to the effect that after its passage

.... no one should practise physic or surgery within said city before he should have both attended the practice of some reputable physician for two years, if a graduate of a college, or for three years if not a graduate, and been examined, admitted, and approved by the Governor, Chancellor, Judges of the Supreme Court, Attorney-General, Mayor, and Recorder, or any two of them, taking to their aid three respectable physicians with whom the candidate had not lived to acquire medical information. (In addition to the penalty of seven pounds for practising without a testimonial of qualification, payable, half to the person suing for it and half to the use of the poor, it was also provided that) no person so practising could bring an action to recover for services or medicines. Persons practising before the passage of the Act, persons rendering gratuitous aid in emergencies, practitioners of neighboring states or counties called into consultation on a particular case, and persons having the degree of doctor of medicine from any college or university of the United States having authority to confer it were all exempt from the provisions of the Act.

This law for a period of five years was applicable only to New York City and county, following which it became a general law for the entire State. In 1797 a law was enacted that:

.... no persons practising physic or surgery at the time of the passage of the Act should continue to so practice without satisfactory proof to the Chancellor, a judge of the Supreme Court, a master in chancery, or a judge of the Court of Common Pleas, that he had practised for two years next October 1st, aforesaid, or had studied that time with a reputable physician or surgeon, and had filed a certificate to that effect with the County Clerk. (It was further provided that) No other person should practice physic or surgery without a certificate from one or more physicians or surgeons that he had studied medicine for four years under the preceptors signing the same, and that he was qualified to practise.

In the history of medicine in colonial New York, William Almon and Nicholas Romayne should not be forgotten:

William James Almon (1754-1817) was born in New York in 1754. In 1771, he became apprentice to Andrew Anderson, physician and surgeon of New York. During the War of Independence his sympathies were with the Royalists and he served as a surgeon in the British army during the Battle of Bunker Hill. When Boston was evacuated in 1776, he was transferred to Halifax, Nova Scotia, with Lord Howe's forces. After a short stay in this city, he accompanied the troops to New York. He remained in active service for several years and in 1779, Lord Townsend appointed him assistant surgeon to the 4th Battalion of Royal Artillery.

Prior to the cessation of hostilities, Almon returned to Halifax and was appointed surgeon of artillery and ordinance in which capacity he served for a protracted period. All in all, he practiced medicine in the city upwards of thirty years. He also held appointments as justice of the peace for Halifax and surgeon-general of the militia. He was held in high esteem and built up a large practice.

His absent-mindedness became legendary and gave the doctor no end of embarrassment. At one time he found himself in a bedroom with a woman who was not his wife. Once, while making a house call on Richard Bulkeley, he unconsciously toyed with a gold watch and chain which was lying around and then proceeded to slip it into his pocket. His wife found it in his clothing that evening while the town crier was loudly proclaiming its disappearance.

In 1785 Almon married Rebecca Byles, a daughter of the Rev. Dr. Mather Byles, and raised a number of children. One son, Dr. William Bruce Almon, succeeded to his practice.

Almon passed away in 1817 during a visit to Bath, England.

Nicholas Romayne (1756-1817) was a founder of the College of Physicians and Surgeons of New York. He was a man of strong beliefs and vigorous action. These characteristics led him to be unpopular with many of his colleagues. He was born in New York in September 1756, and received his preliminary education in Hackensack, New Jersey. He went abroad and studied medicine at Edinburgh at about the start of the Revolution. Following his graduation, he sojourned for two years in Paris, London and Leyden.

The following has been said about him:

"His return from Europe to New York excited considerable conversation both here and in Philadelphia; he was reported to have improved his opportunities with singular diligence. In London and Edinburgh he went through the course of study required by the university statutes and published a dissertation in Latin 'De Generatione Puris' which he composed himself 'without the aid of a "grinder," or hired translator'."

Romayne was appointed trustee of the new medical board formed in New York after the war. This gave him an opportunity to fulfill his mission as a teacher. Thacher says: "His superior attainments in literature and medicine elevated him with high notions and filled him with contemptuous ones of some who had been less fortunate in education." Unfortunately, this initial post-war faculty of professors accomplished little and Romayne resigned from their group. However, he became a successful private teacher of medicine. He taught anatomy, practice of physic, chemistry and botany all with good facility and his students came from near and far.

Then he sailed to Europe again to keep in touch with new trends in medicine. During this visit he became the first American to be honored by appointment to the Royal College of Physicians of Edinburgh. He was convicted of complicity in Blount's conspiracy of 1797 and was imprisoned for some time as a result.

The act of 1806 was passed for incorporating medical societies. Romayne was called from his retirement and elected first president of the Medical Society of the City and County of New York. The following year he became delegate to the State Medical Society in

Albany, and was later chosen president of this body. When the regents of the university acted under the provisions of the Act for providing a College of Physicians and Surgeons, Romayne became the leading figure in the organizing of this body. In 1807 he was selected as its first president. In 1808, he published an address before the students of the New York College of Physicians and Surgeons on "The Ethnology of the Red Man in America."

Nicholas Romayne died in New York on July 20, 1817.

Chapter Six

CONNECTICUT

IN 1633 THE FIRST settlement by Europeans in Connecticut was made at the site of Hartford by a group of Dutch colonists from New Netherland. In 1633, also, a trading post was set up on the Connecticut River, near Windsor, by a group from the Plymouth Colony, and John Oldham (1600-1636) of Massachusetts, after exploring the valley, reported favorably on its location and resources. Oldham's story inspired the inhabitants of three Massachusetts towns (Dorchester, Watertown and New Town), to forsake Massachusetts and settle in the Connecticut Valley.

The former Watertown residents established Wethersfield in the winter of 1634-1635; New Town (now Cambridge) colonists settled in Windsor in the summer of 1635; and the Dorchester group founded Hartford in the autumn of the same year. It should be recalled that these early colonists had come to Massachusetts in the Puritan migration of 1630. Their migration to Connecticut, led primarily by Thomas Hooker, Roger Ludlow (c. 1590-1665) and John Haymes (d. 1654), was precipitated because of their discontent with the autocratic character of the government.

Notwithstanding, the plan of government which they framed in 1639, known as the Fundamental Orders of Connecticut, certainly does not radically depart from the institutions of Massachusetts. A general court was set up with supreme civil authority. It was made up of deputies from the towns, and a governor and magistrates chosen at a session of the court attended by all freemen of the towns. There was also no separation of the executive, legislative and judicial functions, and the governor was no more than a presiding officer.

The most original feature of the Fundamental Orders was the omission of a religious test for citizenship, although a precedent for this is to be found in the Plymouth Colony. The union of church and state was presumed in the preamble, and in 1659, a property qualification (the possession of an estate of 30 pounds) for suffrage was imposed by the general court.

In the meantime, in 1638, a group of Puritans who had arrived in Massachusetts the preceding year sailed from Boston for the Connecticut coast and there established New Haven. The leaders in this migration were John Davenport (1597-1670) and Theophilus Eaton, and the rank and file consisted of the English middle class.

Shortly after their settlement, these colonists compiled a "plantation covenant" which made the Scriptures the supreme guide in civil as well as religious affairs. In June 1639, a more clarified declaration of political principles was set up in which the regulations of the Bible were established as the main criterion in regulating the church, the choice of magistrates, the making and repeal of laws, the dividing of inheritances, and all other matters of public import. It was definitely stated that only churchmen could become free burgesses and colonial officials; that the free burgesses should appoint twelve men who should choose seven others, and that these should organize the church and the civil government.

In 1643 the New Haven Colony expanded to include Milford, Guilford and Stamford. These three towns had equal rights with New Haven; their local governments were recognized and two courts for jurisdiction over the entire area were established: a magistrates' court to try important cases and hear appeals from "plantation" courts, and a general court with legislative powers, the highest court of appeals. Two other townships were later added to the colony: Southold, on Long Island, and Branford, Conn.

Except in the case of the six citizens of Milford, the religious test for citizenship was continued, and in 1644 the general court decided that the "judicial laws of God as they were declared by Moses" should constitute a rule for all courts "till they be branched out into particulars hereafter." The nature of the government thus established is clearly evidenced in the list of strict enactments and decisions. The New Haven Blue Laws included the prohibition of trial by jury, the death penalty for adultery and for conspiracy against the jurisdiction, the strict prohibition of Sabbath violations and heavy fines for "concealing or entertaining Quaker or other blasphemous hereticks."

In 1635 a third Puritan settlement was made at the mouth of the Connecticut River, under the auspices of an English company whose leading members were William Fiennes, Lord Say and Sele (1582-1662) and Robert Greville, Lord Brooke (1608-1643). The colony was named Saybrook to commemorate the names of these founders. In 1639, George Fenwick (d. 1657), a member of the company, arrived but because immigration from England rapidly fell off following the Puritan Revolution, he sold the colony to Connecticut in 1644.

The colonization at Saybrook and the sale by Fenwick are important considerations because of their relation to a fictitious land title. The Say and Sele Company secured in 1631 from Robert Rich, earl of Warwick (1587-1658), a quit claim to his interest in the territory lying between the Narragansett river and Pacific Ocean. No one knows how Warwick had obtained a right to this territory. No extant document demonstrates such ownership and no title has ever been brought forth. But the Connecticut authorities, in their zeal to establish a legal claim to the country and to thwart the efforts of the Hamilton family to assert its claims to the territory derived from a proven grant of the Plymouth Company to James, marquess of Hamilton (1606-1649) in 1635, concocted the story that the Plymouth Company had made such a grant to Warwick, and that consequently his quit claim conferred jurisdiction upon the Say and Sele Company; but even in this event the legality of the act is open to serious question for Fenwick had never obtained confirmation to make such a sale.

In 1622, a royal charter was secured which effected a union of the New Haven Colony with the older colony. This charter stated that Connecticut extended from Massachusetts south to the sea, and from Narragansett bay west to the South Sea (Pacific Ocean). The New Haven colonists not being told in advance about the charter, naturally protested against such an amalgamation. However, when there was threat of absorption of a part of the Connecticut territory by New York, the people of New Haven assented to the union in 1665.

The royal charter was unquestionably liberal. It called for the establishment of a corporation under the name of the "Governor and Company of the English Colony of Connecticut in New England in America," sanctioned the system of government already existing, provided that all acts of the general court be held valid upon being issued under the seal of the colony, and made no mention of royal or parliamentary control over legislation or the dispensing of justice. Therefore, under the charter, Connecticut's government rapidly became independent and self-reliant.

Notwithstanding the fact that the influences that effected Connecticut were essentially similar to those which moulded the rest of New England, the colony developed certain distinctive characteristics. Its policy "was to avoid notoriety and public attitudes; to secure privileges without attracting needless notice; to act as intensely and vigorously as possible when action seemed necessary and promising; but to say as little as possible, and evade as much as possible when open resistance was evident folly."

In the seventeenth century the relations of Connecticut with the surrounding colonies were downright quarrelsome. Connecticut fought with Massachusetts concerning the boundary between the two colonies. After the short war with the Pequot Indians in 1637, a similar quarrel ensued concerning Connecticut's right to the Pequot lands. In the New England Confederation (established in 1643) the friction between Massachusetts and Connecticut went on unabated. Arguments with Rhode Island were precipitated by the conflict between that colony's charter and the Connecticut charter regarding the western boundary of Rhode Island; and the encroachment of outlying Connecticut settlements on Dutch territory, and the attempt to extend the boundaries of New York to the Connecticut River, gave rise to other disputes. These questions of boundary were a source of continuous discord, the last of them not being settled until 1881. The attempts of Governors Joseph Dudley (1647-1720) of Massachusetts, and Thomas Dongan (1634-1715) of New York, to unite Connecticut with their colonies also aroused hostility.

Connecticut's contacts with England were similar to those of the other New England colonies. The worst relations took place during the administration of the New England colonies by Sir Edmund Andros, who in pursuance of the later Stuart policy both in England and in her American colonies, visited Hartford on October 31, 1687, to execute *quo warranto* proceedings against the charter of 1662. It is said that during a discussion at night over the surrender of the charter someone blew out the candles, made off with the charter, and, according to tradition, hid it in a large oak tree. Andros, failing to get the charter, dissolved the existing government. After the Revolution of 1688, however, government under the charter was resumed, and the crown lawyers decided that the charter had not been invalidated by the *quo warranto* proceedings.

Connecticut occupied a front seat in the War of Independence. While heated argumentation was going on concerning the Stamp Act, the general court instructed the colony's agent in London to demand that colonists be given the exclusive rights to tax themselves and to have the privilege of trial by jury. The patriots in Connecticut were so influential that Loyalists from other colonies were exiled there because it was felt that they could influence no one in Connecticut. The copper mines at Simsbury were converted into a military prison. Only among the nonconforming sects was there any sympathy for the British cause.

In 1774 Connecticut began to make preparations for war. On

April 28, 1775, the expedition against Ticonderoga and Crown Point was resolved upon by some of the leading members of the Connecticut assembly, and although they had acted in their private capacity, funds were obtained from the colonial treasury to raise the force which on May 8, 1775, was put under the command of Ethan Allen.

Connecticut volunteers were among the first to go to Boston after the battle of Lexington and more than one-half of Washington's army at New York in 1776 was composed of Connecticut soldiers. Yet, if we exclude the isolated British movements against Stonington in 1775, Danbury in 1777, New Haven in 1779 and New London in 1781, no battles were fought in Connecticut territory.

In 1776 the government of Connecticut was reorganized as a state, the charter of 1662 being adopted by the general court as "the Civil Constitution of this State, under the sole authority of the people thereof, independent of any King or Prince whatever." In the formation of the general government the policy of the state was national. In 1782, Connecticut acquiesced to the loss of western lands. Connecticut favored the levy of taxes on imports by federal authority. In 1786 it relinquished claims to all western lands, except the Western Reserve. At the constitutional convention of 1787 the present system of national representation in Congress was proposed by the Connecticut delegates as a compromise between the plans presented by Virginia and New Jersey.

Bradford, in his "History of the Plimoth Plantation," records that in the spring of 1634, the Connecticut Indians were stricken with

... ye small poxe, and died most miserably; for a sorer disease cannot befall them; they fear it more than ye plague; for usually they that have this disease have them in abundance, and for wante of bedding & lining and other helps, they fall into a lamentable condition, as they lye on their hard matts, ye poxe breaking and mattering, and running one into another, their skin cleaving (by reason thereof) to the matts they lye on; when they turne them, a whole side will flea off at once, (as it were,) and they will be all of a gore blood, most fearfull to behold; and then being very sore, what with could and other distempers, they dye like rotten sheep. The condition of this people was so lamentable, and they fell downe so generally of this disease, as they were (in ye end) not able to help on another; no, not to make a fire, nor to fetch a little water to drinke, nor any to burie ye dead; but would strivie as long as they could, and when they could procure no other means to make fire, they would burne ye wooden trayes & dishes they ate their meate in, and their very bowes & arrowes; & some would crawle out on all foure to gett a little water, and some times dye by ye way, & not be able to gett in againe.

But those of ye English house, (though at first they were afraid of ye infection,) yet seeing their woefull and sadd condition, and hearing their pitiful cries and lamentations, they had compastion of them, and dayly fetched them wood & water, and made them fires, gott them victualls whilst they lived, and buried them when they dyed. For very few of them escaped, notwithstanding they did what they could for them, to ye haszard of them selvs. The sachem him selfe now dyed, & almost all his friends and kinred. But by ye marvelous goodness & providens of God not one of ye English was so much as sicke, or in ye least measure tainted with this disease, though they dayly did offices for them for many weeks togeather. And this mercie which they shewed them was kindly taken, and thankfully acknowledged of all ye Indeans that knew or heard of ye same; and their mrs here did much comend & reward them for ye same.

This vicious disease went its evil way through colonial history decimating the non-immune Indians and causing a high mortality among the relatively immune whites.

Relative to the history of smallpox, on November 30, 1767, an advertisement appeared in the *Connecticut Courant*, which well illustrates how inoculation hospitals were operated:

Dr. Uriah Rogers, Jr. of Norwalk County of Fairfield takes this method to acquaint the publick, & particularly such as are desirous of taking the Small Pox by way of Inoculation, that having had Considerable Experience in that Branch of Practice and carried on the same last season with great Success; he has lately erected a convenient Hospital for that purpose just within the jurisdiction Line of the Province of New York about nine miles distant from N.Y. Harbor, where he intends to carry said Branch of Practice from the first of October next to the first of May next. And that all such as are disposed to favour him with their custom may depend upon being well provided with all necessary accomodations, Provisions, & the best Attendance at the moderate Expense of Four Pounds Lawful Money to Each Patient. That after the first sett or Class he purposes to give no Occasion for waiting to go in Particular Setts but to admit Parties singly, just as it suits them. As he has another Good House provided near said Hospital, where his family are to live, and where all that come after the first Sett that go into the Hospital are to remain with his Family until they are sufficiently Prepared & Inoculated & Until it is apparent that they have taken the infection.

Waves of epidemic disease ran rampant over New England, and Connecticut was no exception. The Connecticut General Assembly in 1663, consummated the following edict for the purpose of preventing infection from filtering in from New York;

"This court understanding that the hand of God is gone against the people at New Netherland, by pestilential infections, do therefore prohibit all persons coming from any of those infectious places into this colony."

In 1666, by court decree, the entire problem of maritime quarantine was placed in the hands of local authorities. As the years passed on, quarantine measures became stricter and stricter, but waves of epidemic disease continued unabated.

In 1659 a wave of "Cynanche Trachealis" (diphtheria) ravaged Connecticut, and in 1662, when the epidemic waned, the Legislature ordered a day of Thanksgiving. The diphtheria epidemic of 1775 was particularly severe in Middletown, Connecticut. In 1740-41, a severe epidemic of measles swept Connecticut. In 1784 scarlet fever wreaked havoc in Connecticut. In 1697-98, a severe influenza epidemic hit Fairfield, Connecticut, destroying seventy out of one thousand inhabitants in three months.

In 1745, an epidemic of dysentery confined to one street in Stamford, Connecticut, wiped out 70 out of a group of several hundred. In 1749, a generally distributed dysentery spread over Connecticut. One hundred and thirty died in Waterbury alone. Twenty died in Cornwall. Hartford and Woodbury had its victims. Dysentery spread through New Haven and Hartford in the winter of 1750-51.

Regarding epidemic pleurisy, in October 1712, Webster says there spread

.... a mortal sickness in the town of Waterbury, in Connecticut, which raged for eleven months. It was so general that nurses could scarcely be found to tend the sick. What the disease was, I am not informed; but not improbably it was that species of putrid pleurisy, which has so often made dreadful havoc in America.

In 1750, Bethel, Connecticut, had a febrile epidemic, probably malarial in nature, which took a toll of from thirty to forty citizens. In November 1760, and succeeding months, Bethel was hit by "an inflammatory fever."

In 1794, 1795 and 1796, the "bilious plague" appeared in Connecticut. It is probable that this diagnosis often referred to yellow fever. The first recorded instance of yellow fever in the colonies was by Winthrop in his "History of New England" in 1647. It was frequently called the "Barbadoes Distemper."

The following laws were passed in colonial Connecticut relative to the practice of medicine:

(1) 1722: "An Act to prevent the small-pox being spread in this colony by pedlars, hawkers, petty chapmen."

(2) 1722: Physicians and Chirurgeons to be exempt from performing military duty (part of bill regulating the militia).

(3) 1722: Physicians and Chirurgeons to be taxed and rated as others.

(4) 1728: An act amending the act of 1711.

(5) 1729: An act providing in all cases of contagious sickness.

(6) 1732: An act providing in case of infectious diseases.

(7) 1752: An act additive to the act of 1729, requiring that all goods coming from infected places be aired before exposure for sale.

(8) 1756: An act additive to the foregoing providing for vessels coming from infected ports.

(9) 1760: An act additive to the same, regulating inoculation.

(10) 1761: An act additive to the same concerning inoculation.

(11) 1769: An act revising the original act of 1729, with all its additives.

(12) 1773: An act for the suppression of mountebanks.

As far as is known the first physician to engage in medical practice in Connecticut is Thomas Pell (1613-1669), who was born in Sussex, England, and who came to the Colonies in the ship *Hopewell*, in 1635, when twenty-two years old. On the ship's list, he was registered both as a tailor and a surgeon. Pell served as surgeon to the fort at Saybrook. In 1637 he practiced at New Haven and later at Fairfield, dying at the latter place in 1669.

In the library of Trinity College at Hartford, Connecticut, there is an almanac which was once the property of Jasper Gunn. A number of amusing medical notes are jotted on its pages. The following note was made by Charles J. Hoadly, and is pasted on one of its pages:

"Jasper Gunn (1606-1670) came over in the ship *Defence* in 1635, aged 29. He was made a freeman of Massachusetts in May, 1636, and settled in Roxbury, where he was a member of the church, April 25, 1641, with his wife, Mary, and had two children baptized there. He removed to Hartford about 1646, where he bought lands, and was one of the townsmen for the north side in 1655-56. In 1649 the General Court of Connecticut freed him from training, watching, and warding during his practice of physic."

In addition to practicing medicine Gunn was a dealer in metalware. His accounts include charges for repairing kettles and skillets as well as for administering to the sick. Gunn died in 1670.

The first governor of Connecticut, John Winthrop, Jr. (1606-1676), became famous throughout New England for his medical prowess. This statesman and physician was born at Groton, Suffolk,

England, on February 12, 1606. He took up law and was admitted to the bar of the Inner Temple. However, wanderlust drove him seaward as secretary to Captain Best of the warship, *Repulse*, in the fleet under the Duke of Buckingham. When this fleet failed to relieve the French Protestants of La Rochelle, Winthrop spent the next fourteen or fifteen months in European travel, visiting, during that time, Italy, Constantinople and Holland.

In 1631, Winthrop the younger followed his father to this country and shortly thereafter was made an assistant in the Massachusetts Colony. Winthrop never stayed long in one place. In a year he led a company of twelve to Agawam (now Ipswich), where a settlement was made and where he met Giles Firmin. A year later he went back to England and received a commission to be governor of the river Connecticut, for one year. On coming back to America he directed the construction of a fort at Saybrook, Connecticut, and lived there part of that time. Then making no effort to have the commission renewed, he returned to Ipswich, from whence he moved to Salem, established a salt works, made another trip to England, and finally, receiving Fisher's Island as a grant from the general court of Massachusetts, went there in the fall of 1646.

In the spring of 1647, he removed to Pequot (now New London) for eight years, after which he settled in New Haven. After being elected governor of Connecticut, in 1657, he had to move to Hartford.

In 1647, Winthrop was commissioned to execute justice "according to our laws" and was elected an assistant of Connecticut. After serving as governor for a one year term, since there was a law preventing reelection, he became deputy governor. This law being repealed the next year, Winthrop served continuously as governor from 1659 until his death in 1676, although on three occasions he sought to be relieved of this office.

Winthrop was well read and addicted to scientific studies. His father's journal refers to the fact that he had a library of more than 1,000 volumes. "The scarcity of physicians in the colonies and Winthrop's willingness to give advice free of charge—so far as his studies enabled him to do so," caused him to be much consulted. Letters came from all sections of New England, seeking his professional advice. Cotton Mather declared: "Wherever he came, still the diseased flocked about him, as if the Healing Angel of Bethesia had appeared in the place."

Winthrop prescribed rubila, jalap, powdered coral, nitre, iron, sulphur, calomel, horse-radish, rhubarb, guaiacum, unicorn horn, elder, the anodyne mithradate, elecampane, wormwood, anise and an electuary of centipedes. The Royal Society of England, on January 1, 1662, shortly after its incorporation, elected him to membership. During his year and a half sojourn in England at that time, he was most active in the society's proceedings, and read a large number of papers.

In 1631, he married his cousin, Martha Jones, but she passed away in Ipswich, Massachusetts, in 1634. In 1635 he married Elizabeth, daughter of Edmund Reade of Wickford, County Essex, and step-daughter of the famous Hugh Peters. She died at Hartford in 1672. By his second wife Winthrop had two sons and five daughters. The sons, Fitz John (Governor of Connecticut, 1696-1707) and Wait Still (Chief Justice of Massachusetts) were well versed in the healing art.

Winthrop died on April 5, 1676, and is buried at Boston, in the King's Chapel Burying Ground.

In the Massachusetts Historical Society's Collection are included several letters written to Winthrop by colonists on medical matters.

Theophilus Eaton writes a letter to him, as follows:

My wife with thankfulness acknowledges the good she hath found by following your directions, but doth much desire your presence here, as soone as the season, & your occasions will permitt, both in refference to my daughter Hopkins, and my daughter Hannah, who hath ben exercised these 4 or 5 days with vapours rising (as we conceive) out of her stomach into her head, hindering both her sleepe & appetite to meate, and apt to putt her into fainting fitts, whether from winde, or the mother, or from what other cause I cannot informe.

Daughter Hopkins profited from Winthrop's advice as is seen from a subsequent letter:

Besides other things you left for her, the 9th of this month, she tooke the first potion of purging physick, which I heare wrought well... My daughter Hopkins hath kept her bed since she took physick, and my wife is in some doubt whether she should give her any more of it til she have your advice.

John Endicott received the following letter from Winthrop:

Worthie Sir—I ame sorie to heare of your affliction in this visitation of God; though you know that whom he loveth he chastiseth. Let that comfort you, etc.

I have snt you all I have, or what I can gett; viz Syrup of Violetts, Sirrup of Roses, Spirits of Mint, Spirits of Annis, as you may see written upon the severall vials, I have sent you Mrs. Beggarly her vnicorns horne,

& Beza stone I had of Mr. Humfry, who is sorry also for your exercise. I have sent you a Be(z)oar stone, & mugwart & organie, if you should have need of it. They are both good in this case of your wife, & also I have sent you some Galingall root. Mrs. Beggarly knows the vse of it. If the fitt of the mother come verie violently, as you write, there is nothing better to suppresse the rising of it than sneezing; a little pouder of tobacco taken in her nose, I think is better than Hellebore. If I knew how or which way in this case to do her good, I would, with all my heart, and would now have come to you, but I ame altogether vnskillfull in theise cases of women.

The following two letters were written by Williame Leete:

Our youngest childe, about 9 weeks old, ever since it was 3 or 4 days old, hath appeared full of red spots or pimples, somewhat like to measles, & seemed allwayes to be bigg, and to hang ouer on the eyebrowes & lids; but now of late the eye lidds have swelled & looked very red, burneing exceedingly, & now at last they are swelled up that the sight is vtterly closed in, that he could not see, nor for suerall dayes, not yet doth, & the verges of the lids, where they close, have a white seame, like the white heads of wheales wherein is matter; it is somewhat extraordinary such as none of our women can tell that they have ever seene the like.

Guilford June 22 1638.

Sir, you were pleased to furnish my wife with more cordiall powders by John Crane for Graciana (his daughter) but no directions within or amongst them can we find; but truly one of the most needful directions is how to make her willing & apt to take it, for though it seemes very pleasant of itself yet is she grown so marvelous aukward & averse from takeing it in beer. Wherefore I would entreat you to prescribe to vs the varyety of wayes in which it may be giuen so effectually; wee doubt els it may doe much lesse good, being giuen by force only.

The following letter written by Edward Cooke, of London, to Winthrop, was dated July 20, 1640. It introduced a Mr. Birde, who wanted to settle among the colonists as a physician:

The occasion of this letter, is in behalfe of a learned Gentleman of my acquaintance, Mr. Birde, who I vnderstand hath written to your selfe to bee entertayned of the people in your parts as a phisition, & well knowinge his sufficiencies in the practise of physick, my request to you if, that you would bee pleased to further him in his desires, which if you shall please to doe, I am assured you will not repent thereof; & I shall take this your kindeness as an especiall favour to myself.

Endorsed by Winthrop: "Mr. Cooke for Mr. Birde."

John Davenport appears to have consulted Winthrop regularly. He was very much concerned about the ocular condition which afflicted Brother Herryman, and he corresponded with Winthrop concerning it. The pastor recognized the results afforded by the drug he received

for it opened the liddes gradually little by little, and gave him ease. But, upon the opening of his eyeliddes, they find that in the eye, where the sight was, is a mattery substance which brother Peck thinckes flowed out of it (per-adventure it is the chrystaline humor); he saith it is rugged, or like white raggs undissolved, which yet he thinckes may be easily dissolved; and from the ball of the eye groweth a carnous substance, which covereth the neather eye lid all over, and at the end of it, in the corner of the eye, by his nose, is a tumor of a pretty bigness. Hereby, his eye seems to be as 2 eyes, to them that looketh upon it; yet sister Herryman saith she can see his eye under that excrescence. The excrescence is red, & so is the eye. On the 5th day last he tooke the powder, which worked very well, but most upwards, which sister thinckes increased the swelling about his eyes. Brother Peck thinckes that his eye hath no sense (in) it, nor can they yet say whether the sight is wholly lost, or not, till that white mattery substance be taken away which is before it.

A later letter infers that the patient's eye responded to the therapy.

Rubila was one of Winthrop's most famous panaceas. He recommended its use early in illness. Rubila consisted of "four grains of diaphoretic antimony with twenty grains of nitre, with a little salt of tin." This formula was kept as a family secret for three generations. Deacon Childs, of Watertown, swore by the drug:

"My wife would entreate you send to her a parcell of your physick, divided into portions for young and ould. She has many occasions to make use thereof to the help of many." The following year he writes again stating that his wife is critically ill and "often wisheth she had a ption of yor physick by sch she and others have found good. Is psuaded should doe again had she off it."

Roger Williams, afflicted with cold and fever, asked for the powder together with directions for use. "I have books that prescribe powders but yours is probatum in this Country."

Winthrop the Younger had quite a reputation as a pediatrician. In 1652, one Sam Stone wrote to him as follows:

Worthie Sir

I am bold to write a few lines about our child. he is 23 weeks old, hath been somewhat ill 3 or 4 weeks, unquiet, his eyes looking yellow, having a cough, especially when he takes his vistuals. wee thought he might have been breeding teeth: but about a week past we peceived yt. he had the yellow Jaundise. By Mrs. Hooker her advice we gave him Barbaric barke boyled in beer, wth saffron, twice a day, for two dayes together. & one time saffron alone. Also lice 2 or 3 times & Turmerick twice. we hoped yt. the Jaundise had been cured: because he was some-times more chearefull & had a better appetite, but the last Saterdaie at night he was very unquiet heavie & could not sleep & upon the Sabbath seemed to looke somewhat swart in the face. In the afternoone we gave him about 3 quarters of a grain of your purging powder, which we had of Mrs. haynes which caused him to vomit twice or thrice, & to purge downwards thrice. he slept well the night after & in the morning was somewhat unquiet again as before, wringing & winding back. his cough seems to increase, as if he had much fleagme. he seems to be sick at times but without any convulsion or starting fits. when be began to be ill, he was costive in his bodie, but now is in good temper. he doth burne often but a little sometimes.

I pray Sir send me word whether he may not take some more of that pouder & what quantity. If you thinke it conveient to prescribe anything I pray speake to Mr. Blinman I know he will pcure some Indian to bring your note & I will please him for his journey. I am much indebted to you for your kind entertainment of me when I was wth you: we remember our service to yourselfe & Mrs. winthrop, & our respect to Mr. Lake wth our love to Mr. Blinman & hoping yt we shall see you in our pts shortly I rest

Your servant in

SAM: STONE

Hartford ffebr. 28, 1652

In the same year Winthrop wrote the following letter to one Mr. Odell who had asked for his professional advice:

Pequot Novemb: 27, 1652

Sr

I received your letter about 2 daies since wherin you desire directions concerning your child, wch indeed is very uncertaine to doe in the ab-sence of the pty, it being difficult to find out the true cause & seat of the originall of such disease by the most diligent & curious observation, when the patient is dayly present: for though by your description I iudge it to be a palsy, yet the cause of that diseas is often very differing for in Some it is through too much drinesse in some too much moisture in some the cause is in the Nerves of the third coniugation of the braine sometymes in other nerves, in others it hath its originall in ye marrow of the back bone: This seems to be that kind wch we call Hemiplegia where one halfe of the spinall marrow is affected or (wch is often in others, and makes me doubt it may be so in this child, by reason of the suddainnesse wherewth she was stroken) it may come fro a light apoplexye (a stronger Apoplexye is comoly present death) This lighter kind of Apoplexy strikes suddainly & leaves comoly one side wthout sence or motion, and after continueth it wholy paraliticall: it may also come fro from thick flegme stopping the influence and distribution of ye vitall spiritts in the nerves, wch may also cause that suddaine apoplecticall stupor. The cure depends upon the knowledge of the right cause, and not only that but the constant and due application of such things as may conduce thereto, wch is difficult to doe at a distance. I am not provided of things alwaies ready for such cures yt are usuall to be had ready made in other places at the Apothecaries, and am forced to prepare things myselfe in such cases when any neighbours doe want helpe and therfore am not able to send you many things that might be usefull, and I suppose it would be uselesse to prescribe you such receipt as phisitians comend in these cases wch I know it is not probable any of them to be had wth you, if the child were nere me I might doe mine indeaveur to provide such things as I could heave make my selfe and see to the due administration therough otherwise I account it an hopelesse to direct for the cure of so dangerous a disease wherein the best meanes often faile of helpe: some generall things that may be helpfull in all kinds of those disease I shall mention—there is a coldnesse comoly accopanes this disease, whatever other cause be, therfore warmeth by aplication of hares or ffox ffurre (wch is also specificall to paralitical disteprs) or in want therof Racoones or lamb or swanes or such can be had: also artificall meanes of heat by hott clothes, hott trenchers or brickes wraped up in cloths aplied to the place most benumned also oyntments of hott chimicall oyles as of rosmary tyme Origanu also oyle of castor mixed with a greater quantity of oyle of wormes & fox grease, or for want of these wth fox grease alone: or wch is counted very efficatious the Balsam of Guido if you have any (it is any ordinary knowne oyntmet) though at present I have none of it but have sent you an other oyntment instead wherof wth wch or wth any of the other if they be to be had anoynt the whole backe bone as hott as can be indured & that side that is affected twice a day covering it presently wth hott clothes, also the aplying of cupping glasses to the heads of the muskles, they might be such glasses as have very narrow mouths and must be aplied wthout scarification, & wth a great & quick flame but must not continue as long as in other cases, but be often reiterated and a plaister of Colophony frankincense & rosin wth the pouder of Bayberries, these mixed wth as much melisett plaister all melted together & made into a plaister, and aplied to the places after the cupping glasses, also some bathes wherein the decoction of Betony

Rosmary sage in a quantity of sweete sacke or muskadell but better the spiritts of those herbes, & other hot herbes mixed wth it: but speciall care must be in the using of a bath least it overcome the patient or too much relax the nerves by being too long in it or too hott aplied: I use in such cases a bath of minerall spiritts wch I find both safe & effectuall in many cases coming neere the virtue of the naturall bathes wch must be used immediately after it is prepared, therfore I never prepare it but as it is used, nor cannot contrive a way to supply you wth it so farre of: I comend also to be used inwardly the decoction of Guaicu & Sassaparilla also some drops of spirit of rosmary in bere if it may be had, or in want of it Rosemary boyled in broth & so taken often, a vomitt in some kind of such disease is usefull but not in every kind, an Issue on the contrary arme or legge as the nature of the disease apeares if most upward in the legge if most downward in the arme may be usefull: but if she be of a very spare bode it will not be good: this is what I ca for present advise. So wth loving salutations to yourselfe & wife wth Mr. Howell Mr— (Ford) & thous I rest

Your loving freind
J. WINTHROP

Concerning all the sickness prevalent in New Haven, in 1660, John Davenport wrote: "Some have greate paine in theyre heades and stomacks, some, violent evacuations upward and downward, some burning etc. My wife also, having spent your supply is destitute of Rubila, which some have desired but returned empty."

Even in 1682 in the letters between Wait Still Winthrop and his brother Fitz John, mention is still made of rubila and its remarkable curative power. "Remember that rubila be taken at the beginning of any illness."

Surely no greater therapeutic claims could be made for streptomycin, penicillin or the sulfa drugs. The use of antimony by Winthrop as a panacea harks back to an old European custom. In Paracelsus' day, antimonial preparations were highly thought of for casting morbid materials out of the body. In 1634, John Evans wrote a book enthusiastically praising the antimonial cup which consisted of an alloy of tin and antimony. Wine placed within the cup and gently heated would become slightly impregnated, the tartar of wine acting on the film of the oxide of antimony, which formed the inner surface of the cup, making a sort of tartar emetic. Evans, a manufacturer of antimonial cups, notes in his preface, "What the Lord has sanctified, and communicated for the health of many, ought not be concealed for the envie and displeasure of a few: . . . To you therefore belongeth the medicinal Gem ... accept then this excellent Jewel as a singular gift of God."

A correspondence dated March 15, 1637, from Matthew Craddock, Governor of the London Company, to John Winthrop Sr., contains the earliest colonial reference to the cup. That its therapeutic prominence had not waned by 1680 is shown by the fact that a cup valued at five shillings was in the effects of Dr. Samuel Seabury of Duxbury.

Beinfield, after examining a list of cures accredited to the cup, concludes by stating that there was nothing it could not effectively benefit. He lists the following as a few of its virtues.

1. It keepeth the body from repletion and fulness of humours.
2. It helpeth all evil effects of the stomach.
3. It cureth all intermitting agues and burning fevers.
4. It helpeth the swimming in the head, Madness and Frenzie.
5. It cureth the greensickness, and helpeth all obstructions.
6. It prevents the Stone, the Gout, and Sciatica, and all other aches.
7. It is good against all contagious and infectious diseases.
8. It cureth worms and maketh complexion faire.
9. It emptieth the stomach of ill humours: the Liver of Choler: the spleen of meloncholy: the pectoral parts of hurtfull humours: The head and throat of flegme and rheume, and all distillations.
10. It cureth wounds and stoppeth blood.
11. It cleanseth, and healeth ulcerous sores and fistulaes.
12. It consumeth rotten and putrified dead flesh.
13. It purifieth the sight.

While it is impossible to say how extensively the cup was used in the colonies, we do know the wide use of antimony, its main constituent, is attested to by the wide circulation of Winthrop's drug, rubila, which had a similar composition.

The general court of Connecticut issued its first medical license to one Thomas Lord (?-1662) in 1652. By this authority he practiced in Hartford and the adjoining towns. A school-master, by profession, he was granted an annual salary of 15 pounds for looking after the sick and suffering members of the colony. Dr. Lord's schedule of fees, as mutually agreed upon with the General Assembly, was as follows:

Thomas Lord, having ingaged to this Courte to continue his abode in Hartford for the next ensuing years, and to improve his best skill amongst the inhabitants of the Townes uppon the River, within this jurisdiction, both for setting of bones and otherwise, as at all times, occassions and neccessityes may or shall require. This Courte doth graunt that hee shall bee paid by the County the sum of fifteene pounds for the said ensuing years, and they doe declare that for every visitt or journeye that hee shall take or make, being sent for, to any howse in Hartford, twelve pence is reasonable; to any howse in Windsor, five shillings; to any howse in Wethersfield, three shillings; to any howse in Farmington, six shillings; to any howse in Mattabesek, eight shillings; (hee having promised that he will require no more;) and that hee shall bee freed, for the time aforesaid from watching, warding and training; but not from finding armes, according to law.

Dr. Lord died in Wethersfield in 1662, 10 years after his licensure.

The general court granted a medical license to Daniel Porter (?-1690) in 1654, together with a small yearly salary. Although Dr. Porter resided at Farmington, he also was required to attend patients in Windsor, Hartford, Wethersfield and Middletown. The general court established a definite schedule of fees for Porter from which we may gather what was considered a reasonable charge at that time. Porter gathered fame as a bone-setter, and his reputation gathered momentum for many years. In 1670, the general court increased his salary, and suggested that he take under his wing suitable students. After serving as general practitioner of the colony for well nigh 35 years, he died in 1690.

His students probably included Thomas Hooker of Farmington, and Samuel Mather of Windham, both sons of local clergymen. We find, accordingly, that in 1864, the general court permitted Thomas Hooker to practice the art of physic, and directed the secretary to furnish him with a license. The same was granted to Samuel Mather. Hooker and Mather were for many years resorted to, by those who wished to obtain a license from the colonial government. In other cases, the authority to practice physic and chirurgery was procured through the agency of distinguished clergymen.

Gershom Bulkley (1635?-1713) was a noted clerical physician who had a large consulting practice in all parts of Connecticut. It is believed that he was born in Concord, Massachusetts in about 1635. His father was the celebrated divine, Rev. Peter Bulkley, who was expelled from England because of his non-conformity and who settled in Concord, Massachusetts.

Raised in excellent surroundings, Gershom graduated from Harvard College in 1655 and studied for the ministry. Where or from whom he received his medical instruction is not known. He gave up his first church in New London after four years because of his opposition to the half-way covenant. On June 1, 1666, he received a call to the church in Wethersfield, where he labored for eleven years, resigning early in 1677, probably because of weakness of his voice.

The rest of his life was devoted entirely to the practice of medicine, in the town of Glastonbury. During King Phillip's War he was appointed surgeon over a force of 350 men under Major Treat and he was wounded in the thigh in a surprise attack near Wachusett Mountain. For this zealous service, he was not only well compensated, but also received the "hearty thanks" from the Colony's Council of War for his "good services to the country during this present war."

His account books which remain give testimony to his extensive practice, although he does not appear to have been licensed until 1686 when the Connecticut court by nature of being "acquainted with the ability, skill and knowledge of Gershom Bulkley in the art of physic and chirurgery, did grant him full and free liberty and license to practice as there shall be occasion, and he shall be agreeable." A similar license was granted to Charles Bulkley of Wethersfield in 1688.

His laboratory was well equipped and his zeal for chemical experimentation made him famous as a chemist. In matters of medical jurisprudence, Gershom Bulkley was considered an authority: When Mary Brown, of Wallingford, was tried for the murder of her son, since it was well known that she had periods of insanity, the court and the jury were in a quandary to ascertain what course to follow. To extricate themselves from this embarrassing position, the court ordered the jurors to consult the most learned men in the colony. They at once consulted Dr. Bulkley, whose character as a minister, whose skill as a physician and whose judgment as a magistrate, were all held in high esteem. He summed up the case: "If she were not *compos mentis* at the time of the fact it is no felony, and consequently no wilful or malicious murder, and if she be known to be a lunatic, though she have her lucid intervals, there had need be very good and satisfactory proof that she was *compos mentis* at the time of the fact committed, for the law favors life." This sound legal opinion was far in advance of the age, and unquestionably averted the doom of the defendant.

In his will, he left to his grandson, Richard Treat, all his books and manuscripts, whether in English, Latin, or Dutch, which in any way concern medicine and chemistry, which books, with all his vessels and instruments, whether of glass, brass, copper, iron or stone, were his, provided he hold and pursue his inclination to the study of medicine, but "if by death or otherwise he be diverted and depart from it," he gave them to the next of his kinsmen who would apply himself to that study.

A mass of manuscripts also survives giving many of the remedies he employed. From an inscription upon his "obscure and modest grave-stone" in the church-yard at Wethersfield it appears that he was regarded as a man of rare abilities and extraordinary industry, excellent in learning, master of many languages, exquisite in his skill in divinity, physic and law, and of a most exemplary and Christian life. Some of his political pamphlets have been handed down to us. He is said to have had few superiors in his time. He married Sarah, daughter of President Charles Chauncey of Harvard, on October 26, 1659, and had by her six children, one of whom, John, was a clerical physician in Colchester, highly thought of in his day. Another son, Charles, also practiced medicine at Wethersfield, but he died early in life. The father died at the age of 78, and was buried in Wethersfield, in 1713.

Regarding autopsies in early colonial Connecticut, the Connecticut General Court on March 11, 1662-63, voted to remunerate Bray (or Bryon) Rossiter for "opening Kellies child" and other professional services. Rossiter was famous in his day and Trinity College at Hartford possesses his copy of the Vesalius commentary on the Hippocratic Aphorisms. In 1662 he travelled from Guilford to Hartford to perform the aforementioned autopsy on the body of Elizabeth Kelly, whose parents believed had died from a hex put upon her by an old woman named Ayres.

Dr. James Laborie of Stratford, upon demonstrating to the General Assembly that he had engaged in the practice of physic for many years, under the conduct and direction of his father, who was a well-known physician, was granted a license by the legislature. Incidentally, the elder doctor Laborie had his bill collecting problems. He was called across the river to Milford, by one Mr. Lyron, whose wife was suffering from a nervous dysfunction. Laborie responded promptly and had three men row him across the river. In a few weeks he sent Mr. Lyron a bill exceeding 50 pounds. Mr. Lyron demanded an itemization on the ground that the charges were excessive, and as the case was brought to court, the doctor was required to make out an itemized bill:

"Lewis Lyron Dr. to James Laborie of Stratford, the 13th day of December, 1706, for his wife—My journey through the ice in a canoe with three men to put me over, 12s. The same night administered to his wife hysteric cordial, comp. diaretic and hysteric drink, 1 pound 6s." For several days the hysteric cordial was diligently used and several pounds were charged for the same. In about ten days the remedy was changed, and four doses of sal. polychrestes were administered at the expense of 1 pound. The doctor also charged his friend for "my pills Royal" and "my polychrestes," and the "elixir vitae of mine," enough to show that he held them in high estimation. For bleeding the arm, the charge was only 1s., for bleeding the foot, 2s., and for a blister to the shoulder, the cost was 9s.

The total amount of the doctor's bill was 59 pounds and 2s; and to recover this sum an action was brought into the court:

"At a County Court held in Fairfield, March 9th, 1708., James Laborie of Stratford, physician plt cont^r. Lewis Lyron of Milford, defend't in an action of debt due by book, which is to the damage of the said James Laborie the sum of one hundred pounds current money of the colony of Connecticut. In this action the jury find for the plt., ye defend't to pay 62 pounds 18s. and 6d. cash, and cost of the court—the court accepts the jury's verdict and give judgment accordingly. Bill of cost allowed 1 pound 3s. 10d. cash—the defend't and Col. Matthew Sherwood acknowledge themselves bound to the treasury of the country in a Recognizance of 70 pounds cash, that the defend't shall prosecute his appeal to effect, and answer all damages in case he make not his plea good."

The defendant, in preparing his case, sought the opinion of Dr. John Clark and other physicians of Boston, and also of Dr. John Fiske of Milford. From the former gentlemen the following document was received:

We the subscribers being requested to give our opinion of Dr. Laborie's account, upon due consideration, are of the opinion that the prices of medicines in that account are extravagantly overcharged, and to the best of our judgment, considerably above 30 pounds more than any honest practitioner would have charged.
Boston, April 10, 1708.

> JOHN CLARK,
> JOHN CUTTER,
> OLIVER NOYES,
> ABIJAH SAVAGE.

Dr. Fiske rendered the following opinion:

We think the bill to be very unreasonable and extravagant in these respects—first, he has set a certain price to an uncertain quantity, of which he makes Mr. Lyron the debtor. He charges Mr. Lyron £34 of which he tells neither the quantity nor the specific quality, save only he says cataplasm, which is no more than to say poultice—we may suppose it to be made of flax seed, or hysteric, which is no more than something for the mother—we may think it to be motherwort or something like—or diuretic, which may be pumpkin seeds or parsley roots. Considering the time, either he must be extravagant in his doses or his prices, for we think it not possible for any patient to use such quantity of medicine in so short a time—wherefore we are verily of opinion that Doctor Laborie does wrong himself and Mr. Lyron both, in that he over-charges Mr. Lyron £34 for these particular articles, and we think it unreasonable for a physician to charge his patients at pleasure, without any demonstration as to the quantity or worth, of what he makes them debtor for, and how Doctor Laborie will make out the rest of his bill to be reasonable, he must find the way himself if he can."

JOHN FISKE, PRAC. PHYSIC.

May, 1708.

That an out-of-court settlement was arranged by the parties to the controversy, without obtaining the opinion of the general court, is evident from the following:

To the honorable court of assistants, now sitting at New Haven:— For as much as we have agreed upon the case, before your court, we pray you would please, not to call the action to an hearing.

Your most obedient servants,
JAMES LABORIE,
LEWIS LYRON.

In 1695, the general court of Connecticut licensed one Nathaniel Wade, a Bostonian and Cambridge graduate, to practice physic and surgery, and expressed the desire that the blessing of God might accompany his endeavors. This was done after he had filed the following petition:

The petition of Nathaniel Wade humbly sheweth, that being admitted an inhabitant of New Haven—having been educated at the college in Cambridge, under special advantages of knowledge in the faculty of medicine and chirurgery, for some time used in those sciences in the colony of Massachusetts, and for the space of a year and a half within this government, account it both my duty and prudence to beg your honorable allowance for serving the good people under your care as there may be opportunity in the exercise of these faculties and your honorable license being granted, shall oblige your humble petitioner always to pray that God will make your walls salvation and your gates praise.

Filed with the petition was a letter from Rev. Chauncy of Stratford:

I have been advantaged to have acquaintance with the aforesaid Mr. Wade and can give testimony, that he hath had great opportunity by his abode with men of skill in Massachusetts, so he hath made considerable proficiency in physic and chirurgery—and may, if the honorable court shall please to license his practice, be an instrument of great good in these ends of the colony where men of skill are so scarce.

These documents were enclosed in a letter from the Rev. Pierpont of New Haven, who declared he had "received letters from Dr. Oliver, Mr. Brattle and Mr. Stodard of Northampton, which furnished a good account of not only his education, manners, pious inclinations, but also of his manifest and known capacity in the mysteries of medicine and chirurgery." He adds "we have had satisfactory experience at New Haven, and, according to my observation, for his time, he is so accomplished that we have great reason of both satisfaction and thankfulness." Pierpont added a postscript to his letter urging the general court to repeal the law forbidding the distillation of grain spirits, on the ground that "rye was a drug in the market and spirits very scarce."

The previously mentioned John Fiske of Milford applied for a license in 1694:

That whereas relating to physic and chirurgery, the laws of our sovereign lord the king, the security of the practitioner, and the safety of the public renders it requisite and necessary, that those who practice on the bodies of their neighbors, where life and limbs are concerned, should be persons approved therein, and licensed thereto; and whereas I have now by the providence of God, the bounds of my habitation within this your colony, where I am engaged in and obliged to practice the above said art.—Therefore, I petition for a license to practice therein.

From Wrentham, a certificate was appended to the effect that John Fiske had "..... for many years, and with good success, practiced in the arts of physic and chirurgery, and had made many notable cures, and had generally been accounted one of good skill and understanding in many maladies and their remedies, of which some of us have had experience."
21st *Feb.* 1694.

In 1705, Norwalk citizens wrote the following on behalf of one John Copp:

If any petition shall be presented in behalf of John Copp, schoolmaster, of our town, to be an approved physician, these lines are to assure your honors, that it will be well accepted and approved by most people among us. We judge him to be a safe and conscientious man, and have experienced considerable good by his administration among us.

In 1712, Obidiah Hosford of Hebron applied for a license to practice. The testimonials which he presented to the General Assembly were from Gershom Bulkley (Glastenbury, May 7, 1712) and from Samuel Mather (Windsor, May 10, 1712). The former knew both personally and from reports, that he "hath practiced for years, but as for his learning, skill and success in said art and practice of physic, I know nothing." Dr. Mather certified that he was aware of his practice and reputation and that in lieu of his reading and experience, he was acceptable as a physician.

Interesting is the case of William Blogget, of Plainfield, whose petition for licensure in 1721 was denied:

Whereas Wm. Blogget of Plainfield, hath practiced physic in the colony of Connecticut, sundry years—We, the subscribers, would inform the General Assembly, that he hath had good success in his practice, and hath done much good, through God's blessing, to many distressed sick people—sundry of us having much improved him, also that he is accounted a skillful physician as well by doctors, as by those who have improved him. (Signed by numerous residents of Plainfield and Canterbury).

Blogget's personal declaration stated that he

.... had for many years studied the art and method of physic, had made divers experiments, by the blessing of God, with good success, to the satisfaction of those who have been benefited and blessed thereby, besides the judgment and approbation of divers able doctors in the neighboring governments, doth therefore pray the Hon. Assembly to grant the suppliant a license or commission to practice physic, as is usual in such cases.

This rejection of a physician who was highly esteemed and of good personal character, it is well to note, was on the basis that he was an illiterate man and therefore not up to the educational standards of the profession.

One Dr. Jonathan Bull, of Hartford, pursued his medical study seven years, with a doctor in Boston. He then came back to his home town and started practice. He applied to the general court for a license when only twenty-eight years old (in 1723), and his application was granted since he was endorsed by Drs. Mather and Hooker. Dr. Bull built up a fine nation-wide reputation and he was much sought after by those in need of medical skill. Among his pupils were the first Dr. Wells of Berlin, Dr. Hart and Dr. Rogers of Danbury.

In 1720, Benjamin Hall of Wallingford, applied for medical

licensure from the General Assembly and his application was favorably acted upon.

In 1723, the infant college of Yale awarded what is probably its most unusual M.D. degree. Daniel Turner, the recipient of this honorary degree, was an English medical man of considerable talent, having written a large number of medical books. He was most anxious to divorce himself from the London Barber-Surgeon Guild in favor of membership in the Royal College of Physicians. He attained this end but was tormented by the quips of his confreres concerning the fact that his name was not adorned by the doctorate. To remedy this condition, Turner turned to Jeremiah Dummer, agent for the Connecticut Colony, who advised him to seek an honorary M.D. degree from Yale, in return for a donation of books. Turner promptly sent the following letter dated September 24, 1722:

To the truly cultured gentlemen, the President and College of the Academy of Yale in the colony of Connecticut in the province of New England, Daniel Turner, licentiate of the Royal College of Physicians of London, gives greeting.

Most Learned Sirs:

I have recently received a letter from your friend, who deserves exceeding well of you, Mr. Jeremiah Dummer, in which he gave me an account of your academy, founded not many years ago, by Mr. Yale. I am indeed glad to hear that good literature and the liberal arts and sciences are flourishing amongst you where for almost the lapse of a century they have lain hidden, or rather in their place have reigned crude indifference and ignorance. But the good gentleman complained to me of the still infantile state of your library and along with some other professors of medicine and also of natural philosophy, persuasively urged me to contribute my help to this object: therefore in order, as far as in me lies, to adorn the Republic of Letters wherever established, I am sending to you, most honoured sirs, some books long since published by myself, along with the System of the Art of Surgery in two volumes, just off the press: in addition to these I have robbed my own library of a book very valuable beyond all others and now, as I know, not procurable elsewhere, the Great Anatomy of our Cowper, that with it I might adorn yours. Receive them I beg of you as a testimony of my friendship for your university and believe the doner to be ever, as far as lies in his power, most illustrious sirs,

Your sincere friend,

D. Turner.

Postscript.

If your worships consider me worthy of the doctoral degree of Yale Academy and have the diploma sent to me, I shall receive it not only as a sign of your gratitude, but I shall consider it an honour as much as though it had been conferred by another university, though of greater note.

Farewell most learned sirs
and may your academy flourish.

London, Sept. 24, 1722.
  At the Museum in
Devonshire Square outside the
Episcopal gate in the district
commonly called
  Bishopsgate without.

The college officials promptly accepted the books and at the following commencement, on September 11, 1723, awarded the sought-after Doctorate of Medicine to Daniel Turner. Unfortunately, the M.D. was facetiously interpreted as meaning *multum donavit*, and was never recognized by the Royal College of Physicians.

The following commendation of one Uriah Rogers appeared in 1733:

Whereas Uriah Rogers of Norwalk, late an apprentice of Jonathan Bull, physician of Hartford, hath desired the subscribers to certify others of his practice in physic since his living in Norwalk—These are therefore to signify his practice has been full and large—his success very good—his behaviour grave, modest and obliging, and he seems to be well acquainted both with distempers and medicine. If he applies to the Gen. Assembly for a license to practice we believe he will answer such a character.

JOHN COPP,
DAN'L CHAPMAN.

Samuel Porter, of Farmington, applied for and received a license to practice medicine in Connecticut in 1733.

We have seen how the early Connecticut colonial physicians received their authority to practice medicine and surgery. Prior to 1740, once licensed by the General Assembly, Connecticut physicians were, as a rule, tax exempt and freed from military and other personal duties. After 1740, physicians were taxed the same as anybody else. Of course, many practitioners did not bother obtaining authorization by the Legislature.

It was no uncommon thing for a novice to enter upon the study of medicine under the guidance of some neighboring physician, to continue as his apprentice until he felt competent to practice alone, and then, with a certificate of his good character and satisfactory attainments, to become a medical practitioner on his own. To illustrate this latter process:

This may certify whom it may concern that I yᵉ subscriber for two years time have given Thomas Thompson at Farmington sundry directions in yᵉ mysteries of physic and chirurgery and doe find that yᵉ said Thompson hath made a considerable progress in said arts and withal finding him to be very careful in his practice and administrations—doe judge him to be a man as likely to do good in said mysteries as any man I know of that is not advantaged with college learning.
Farmington, March yᵉ 29th, 1703.
THOMAS HASTINGS, licensed phisician, &c.

This may certify that I the subscriber do judge the above said Thom. Thompson has a considerable insight in the art of physic and chirurgery and has for many years practiced the said art and with good success in his administrations.
Farmington, May the 12th, 1721.
SAMUEL PORTER, allowed chirurgeon.

Jared Eliot (1685-1763) was widely accepted as the most famous physician of his day in Connecticut. He sojourned in every county of the state, and made many professional visits to Newport and Boston.

He was born in Guilford, Connecticut, on November 7, 1685, the son of Rev. Joseph Eliot, well-known minister, physician and politician. Jared's grandfather, John Eliot, famous as the "Apostle to the Indians," arrived at Boston, Massachusetts, in 1631. He converted Indians by the score and denounced the use of tobacco. John's wife was greatly respected because "of her knowledge of physic and chirurgery." Jared married Hannah, daughter of Samuel and Elizabeth Smithson. Elizabeth Smithson was a famous midwife in Guilford. Thus from his father, Joseph, his grandmother, Ann, and from his mother-in-law, Jared Eliot undoubtedly received many useful hints in the practice of medicine. Yale graduated Jared in 1706 and Harvard awarded him an honorary A.M. in 1709. About 1756-7 he was unanimously elected a member of the Royal Society of London. From 1730 until his death he was a trustee at Yale.

His printed sermons demonstrate that Jared Eliot deserves fame as much as a scientist and physician as he does as a minister. His essays upon agriculture prove him to be a scientific agriculturist. So valuable were they that they were printed in a volume in 1760. He explained how to drain lands and render them productive, how to raise mulberry trees and supply the colony with silk and how to manage and improve on agricultural development. In 1762 his "Essay on the Invention, or Art of Making Very Good, if not the Best Iron from Black Sea Sand," was published. Because of this the Royal Society of London granted him a valuable gold medal inscribed for "Producing Malleable Iron from the American Black Sand," which then, and now, is plentiful on the shore of Long Island Sound at Clinton.

Jared Eliot had nine sons and two daughters. Three of the sons graduated from Yale and two of them became physicians. One of Jared Eliot's letters adequately exhibits the scientific spirit of this colonial man of letters:

The last week, in this place, a man at his work was troubled with a fly that attempted, and, notwithstanding all his endeavors to avoid it, entered his ear and went so deep that he could not reach it. It continued for some time, and then came out of itself. He quickly found inconvenience as the spawn grew great and almost intolerable, but was there lodged; the pain and tumult in his head soon eased by thrusting into his ear a feather dipped in war oil. There came out forty maggots. This was in May, 1729.

Jared Eliot primarily devoted his life to the practice of the healing art. Toward this end he was an avid student, and he drank deeply from the well of Hippocrates, Galen and Celsus. He had a large following and since his success in the treatment of chronic ailments was great, he was called often to visit patients in every part of the colony. He was the personal friend and correspondent of Berkeley and Franklin, and the instructor of several medical students. It is related that in forty years he preached every Sunday and devoted at least some part of every week to the practice of medicine. He died at Killingworth in 1763.

Benjamin Gale (1715-1790) was the son of John and Mary Gale, and was born in Jamaica, Long Island, in 1715. He graduated from Yale in 1733. He spent all of his professional life in Killingworth (now Clinton), Connecticut, where he had studied medicine with Jared Eliot, whose daughter, Hannah, he married. He was held in such high esteem by his townsmen that they elected him to the General Assembly of Connecticut for thirty-two sessions, and would have continued him in that position, but he declined. In 1765 the London Society of Arts elected him a corresponding member, perhaps because of his invention of an improved drill plough.

He wrote on numerous subjects, including "Historical Memoirs, Relating to the Practice of Inoculation for the Smallpox in the British American Provinces, particularly in New England." He contributed a paper on the "Bite of Rattlesnakes" in 1763. President Stiles wrote

Upper left, D<small>R</small>. G<small>ERARDUS</small> B<small>EEKMAN</small> was a prominent New York physician toward the end of the seventeenth century. (*Courtesy of The New York Academy of Medicine*.) *Upper right*, D<small>R</small>. J<small>OHN</small> B<small>ARD</small> (1716-1799) was a partner in one of the first systematic dissections in the United States for the purpose of instruction. He was the first American to report a case of extrauterine pregnancy. (*Courtesy of The New York Academy of Medicine*.) *Lower left*, N<small>OAH</small> W<small>EBSTER</small> (1758-1843). The published contributions of this non-medical man comprise the most important and lasting American medical articles of the eighteenth century. (*Courtesy of The New York Academy of Medicine*.) *Lower right*, D<small>R</small>. C<small>HARLES</small> M<small>C</small>K<small>NIGHT</small>, one of the few New York physicians who played an active role in the War of Independence. (From C. E. Heaton: Medicine in New York During the English Colonial Period; *Bulletin of the History of Medicine;* Vol. XVII, No. 1; p. 27.)

A
DISCOURSE
UPON THE
DUTIES OF A PHYSICIAN,
WITH SOME SENTIMENTS,

ON THE

USEFULNESS AND NECESSITY

OF A

PUBLIC HOSPITAL:

DELIVERED BEFORE THE

PRESIDENT AND GOVERNORS

OF

KING's COLLEGE,

AT THE COMMENCEMENT,

Held on the 16th of MAY, 1769.

As Advice to thofe GENTLEMEN who then
received the Firft MEDICAL DEGREES
conferred by that UNIVERSITY.

By SAMUEL BARD, M.D.
Profeffor of the Practice of Medicine in KINO'S COLLEGE.

NEW-YORK:
Printed by A. & J. ROBERTSON, at the Corner of
BEAVER-STREET, M,DCC,LXIX.

A DISCOURSE UPON THE DUTIES OF A PHYSICIAN by Samuel Bard (From
C. E. Heaton; Medicine in New York During the English Colonial Period;
Bulletin of the History of Medicine; Vol. XVII, No. 1; p. 31.)

AN INTERRUPTED DISSECTION

(From C. E. Heaton; Medicine in New York During the English Colonial
Period; *Bulletin of the History of Medicine*; Vol. XVII, No. 1; p. 18.)

Upper left, DR. CADWALLADER COLDEN. Drs. Peter Middleton, John Jones and Samuel Bard. petitioned Dr. Cadwallader Colden (who had become Lieutenant-Governor) in 1770 for a charter of incorporation for the New York Hospital. (*Courtesy of The New York Academy of Medicine.*) *Upper right*, DR. JOHN VAN BUREN was a Leyden graduate who practiced in New York. (*Courtesy of The New York Academy of Medicine.*) *Lower left*, JOHN JONES, M.D. wrote the first American book on surgery and military surgery. (*Courtesy of the New York Academy of Medicine.*) *Lower right*, SAMUEL BARD, M.D., LL.D. (1742-1821), in 1768, was one of the founders of the medical school attached to King's College. (*Courtesy of The New York Academy of Medicine.*)

THE POOR-HOUSE ERECTED IN 1735, ON THE SITE OF THE PRESENT
CITY HALL.

THE NEW YORK HOSPITAL

Left, New York's First Hospital (From C. E. Heaton: Medicine in New York During the English Colonial Period; *Bulletin of the History of Medicine;* Vol. XVII, No. 1; p. 15.)

Right, The New York Hospital. (*Reproduced from Army Medical Bulletin #25.*)

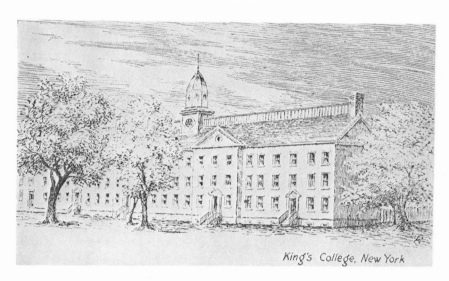

King's College, New York

KING'S COLLEGE, NEW YORK

(*Reproduced from Army Medical Bulletin #25.*)

Above, DAVID HOSACK, M.D., LL.D. succeeded to the practice of Samuel Bard in 1798. (*Courtesy of The New York Academy of Medicine.*) *Upper right*, DR. RICHARD BAILEY (1745-1811) was appointed to the professorship of anatomy of the medical faculty at Columbia in 1792. In 1793 he became professor of surgery and gave up the anatomical chair. (*Courtesy of The New York Academy of Medicine.*)

Right, DR. NICHOLAS ROMAYNE (1756-1817) was a founder of the College of Physicians and Surgeons of New York. (*Courtesy of The New York Academy of Medicine.*)

Upper left, JOHN WINTHROP, JR. (1606-1676) of Connecticut became famous throughout New England for his medical prowess. (*Courtesy James Brewster, State Librarian,
Connecticut State Library.*) *Upper right*, DR. OLIVER WOLCOTT (?-1797) signed the
Declaration of Independence. He was not only one of the great patriots of Connecticut, but a governor, son of a governor and father of a governor. (*Reproduced
from Army Medical Bulletin #25.*) *Lower left*, DR. ÆNEAS MUNSON (1734-1826)
was an organizer of the Connecticut Medical Society and an authority on materia
medica and the natural sciences. (*Courtesy of Yale University Art Gallery.*) *Lower
right*, DR. LEMUEL HOPKINS (1750-1801) was a prominent consultant and authority
on tuberculosis as well as a satirist and poet of note. (*Courtesy of Yale University
Art Gallery.*)

Upper left, DR. GUSTAVUS BROWN (1689-1765), said to have been stranded on Maryland shores, lived to become a successful practitioner and a man of means. (*Courtesy of the Maryland Historical Society.*) *Upper right,* DR. CHARLES FREDERICK WIESENTHAL (1726-1789), Prussia's gift to early Maryland medicine, comprehended the great need for regulating medical practice and headed a movement which led directly to the formation of a medical society on November 27, 1788. (*From Cordell's Medical Annals of Maryland 1799-1899; courtesy of the Maryland Historical Society.*) *Lower left,* DR. JOHN ARCHER (1741-1810) attended the Philadelphia College of Medicine (which later became the Medical School of the University of Pennsylvania) and received his Bachelor of Medicine degree on June 21, 1768. (*From the Maryland Historical Society picture collection.*) *Lower right,* JOHN CRAWFORD, M.D. was one of the first physicians to employ vaccination in America and he was a pioneer in the study of the etiology of disease. (*Courtesy of the Maryland Historical Society.*)

of him: "He was a man of integrity and uprightness, and of great skill in the medical profession, and a successful practitioner."

Rev. Phineas Fiske (?-1738), a contemporary of Jared Eliot, was a son of Dr. John Fiske of Milford, and he became famous both as a minister and as a physician. Graduating from Yale in 1704, he was appointed tutor of that institution, and following the demise of Rector Pearson, the lower classes were especially under his care. He was associated with Yale for six years, and was highly esteemed as an instructor. He was then licensed as a minister and afterwards was ordained pastor, with the Rev. Jeremiah Hobart at Haddam. How early he studied medicine is not known. It is likely that he picked up numerous hints as to the practice of medicine from his father, even before he turned his attention to divinity. He set up practice at Haddam, where he remained until his death in 1738. He was renowned for his therapy in epilepsy and insanity. Dr. Moses Bartlett (?-1766), his son-in-law and disciple, practiced medicine for over thirty years in Portland, Connecticut, where he also assumed ministerial duties. He died in 1766.

In 1699 John Bulkley of Colchester graduated from Harvard, and in 1702, he was ordained in Colchester. During his college days he exhibited great interest in law, medicine and theology, and was included by Dr. Chauncy in his list of the most talented men which New England had produced. Peters declared: "Colchester has to boast of Rev. John Bulkley for its first minister, whose grandfather, Peter Bulkley, possessed a gentleman's estate in Bedfordshire, which he sold and spent the produce among his servants in Massachusetts." John Bulkley became highly esteemed and became the spokesman of the *sober dissenters* in Connecticut. He published a clever if fabulous article for the purpose of demonstrating that the colonists had a just title to their lands. His son John became famous as a lawyer and physician and was appointed to a judgeship on the supreme court when still young.

Let us consider, for a brief interval, the attire of these early colonial physicians. Most of them were clergymen and consequently wore on professional calls their customary wigs and cocked hats. Even non-clerical physicians, who were anxious to enhance their dignity, wore the garb of the clergy. Jonathan Williams (1708-1738), for instance, a graduate of Yale (1722) who pursued the practice of medicine at Wethersfield until he died in 1738, and who was but thirty years old at the time of his death, left as part of his estate: Hat and bands, 2 pounds 12s; Wig, 1 pound 10s.; Best coat, 10 pounds; and leather breeches, 3 pounds 5s. His library, incidentally, consisted of the Modern Physician, by Philip Woodhouse, the Principles of

Medicine, by Thomas Morgany, The History of Oliver Cromwell, and a copy of Euclid.

The following account of the "drinking doctors" of early Connecticut is taken from Dr. Summer's excellent monograph:

Dr. James Hurlburt (1717–?) of Berlin was born in 1717. At the beginning of his professional career he was distinguished for industry and talents, and soon acquired the reputation of being a learned man and a skillful physician. Students applied to him for instruction, patients for relief, and neighboring physicians for counsel. Respected for his learning, and admired for his genius, the doctor might have pursued a course of unvarying prosperity, but the brilliancy of his morning sun was obscured by the clouds of noonday, and by the thick darkness of evening. He adopted the practice of drinking ardent spirits, at first moderately and occasionally, but his moderation was soon converted into excess, and his occasional potations became frequent and immoderate, and the doctor became a slave to vicious indulgence. He was no longer the pleasant associate of other physicians—no longer the gentleman whom all were glad to meet, nor the esteemed physician whom men of prudence would wish to consult; but a sot in his appearance, a vagabond in his habits, he lived to disgrace himself and inflict a stigma upon his profession. Dr. Woodward informs us that he would not in his later years, prescribe for any patient until the square bottle of rum was placed under his entire and exclusive control. He used, at the same time, enormous quantities of opium—rum for excitement, and opium to steady the effects of the rum.

For many of his last years all the avails of his practice were expended in the purchase of opium, but he was rarely intoxicated, and when so much under the influence of alcohol as not to be able to stand, his mind would appear to be clear, and his judgment unimpaired. When in the attire of a vagrant, he walked about supported by his staff, lame, filthy and miserable; if his attention was engaged to any subject of learning, he would exhibit such resources of information, such powers of logic, such judicious and sensible remarks as would astonish all his auditors, and particularly surprise strangers.

The doctor's usual place of residence was at Berlin, near the line of the Hartford and New Haven railroad, but he tasted his last dram and uttered his last groan at the house of some friend in Wethersfield, where he was buried. There was neither monument nor beacon placed over his grave to tell the visitor how he rose to a station of eminence, and how he sunk to the condition of poverty and contempt.

The most famous disciple of Dr. Hurlburt was one Dr. Bird (1733-1805) of Litchfield. He, too, was a man of uncommon talent, who paid as much reverence to Boerhaave and the brandy bottle, as had ever been exhibited by his learned but eccentric teacher, but he was more prudent in his financial arrangements and maintained to the last his position in society. "He was," says Dr. Buel, "a remarkable man and the vigor of his mind was what I think may be called prodigious." His son John, a member of Congress from the State of New York, was a man of great and original genius, eccentric and imaginative, not so much distinguished for sound common sense as his father, but in my limited opportunities I have known of no instances of what I thought superior original powers of mind, to those of the Birds, father and son.

An opinion was once prevalent in Connecticut (and Hurlburt and Bird may have given it currency) that those physicians who used ardent spirits freely, were the very best doctors, if their services could be secured before it was too late in the day—in other words, that a certain amount of stimulation sharpened the intellect, and enabled them to prescribe for the various forms of disease with extraordinary skill and success. This idea, which fortunately for the cause of good morals, has become obsolete, probably originated at a time when physicians under the excitement of ardent spirits, discoursed most fluently respecting medical theories, and most confidently concerning the great success of their own practice. The oratory of a physician under this artificial excitement might have been more impressive than the dry discourse of his sober mood, but it was a mere delusion to infer that his practice was more safe or more effectual.

Dr. Bird, however, appears to have formed a high estimate of the remedial powers of brandy. In his old age his eyes became red and inflamed, and a friend suggested to him that he would not advise a patient in his situation the same course of living. Bird replied, "I can do without my eyes but I cannot live without brandy." He was probably admonished by the sad career of Hurlburt to make some provisions for the future. He was moreover disposed to encourage others to adopt the same precautions. One occasion, having met Dr. Catlin in consultation and disposed of the case of the patient, Bird observed to his friend, "Catlin, you are devilish poor, and ought not to be so. I have laid by something for a rainy day, and it is not too late to retrieve your circumstances—charge more, take care of your money, and in five years you will be as well off as I am." Catlin's pungent reply was, "No, Bird, five years of rascality won't do it."

Dr. Bird was born at Bethlem in 1733, and died at Litchfield at the age of 72. He and his preceptor may be regarded as uncommon specimens of the drinking doctors of Connecticut.

Norman Morrison (1706-1761) was a native of Scotland and was educated at the University of Edinburgh. After finishing his medical course, he departed from Glasgow to this country in 1736. Cullen, at that time, was 24 years old, and shortly afterwards commenced his brilliant career of instruction. Doctor Morrison believed firmly in the dignity of his profession and held the opinion that the practice of medicine should be divorced from pharmacy. He personally encouraged the establishment of an independent apothecary where he practiced, and by so doing he proved himself in advance of his day.

When Morrison first arrived, he purchased a house and a lot on Main Street, a few rods north of the Suffield Court House. Temple Street was subsequently opened through his grounds, and the Market and City Hall stand on its eastern borders. Dr. Morrison was at all times regarded as a learned physician, and many young men of the colony flocked to him for instruction. Of his students, Alexander Wolcott of Windsor, son of the governor, and John Osborne, were the most distinguished. He married the widow of Mr. John Smith, a merchant in the London trade, and by this marriage greatly enhanced his property holdings.

Norman Morrison's reputation among his colleagues was very great and he was frequently called into consultation. It is related that when he was asked to visit a patient with an "Indian doctor," one Dr. Andrews who had acquired his skill from friendly natives on the boundary line between Farmington and Berlin, he was perplexed as to whether to make the call or refuse. After all his dignity did not permit him to be on a par with the unlearned Dr. Andrews. To give Andrews a pointed rebuff and yet at the same time not neglect the patient, he wrote a reply in Latin, stating when he would visit the patient. Andrews was forced to resort to a clergyman, who translated it into English. Andrews, who had no classical background at all, got even with Morrison by returning his answer to Dr. Morrison in the native Indian dialect.

It is sad to relate that Dr. Morrison's only son became ill with smallpox, and in accordance with the laws of that period, the authorities insisted that the young man be removed to some house remote from his family. His death ensued and the father's heart was overwhelmed with grief. The son was brought to his father's garden and buried, and there by his side, at a future day, were placed the remains of Dr. Norman Morrison.

The following inscription was copied from his monument:

Under this monument are Buried the Remains of Norman Morrison, who being born in the Western Island of Scotland and educated at Edinburgh, lived a physician inferior to none—an husband, brother, father and friend among the most excellent; in manners gentle, to those in need, liberal, kind and beneficent to all, and a Christian without deceit. He died much loved and lamented, the 9th of April, 1761, in yᵉ 55th *year of his age.*

Bold Wolcott urg'd all the important cause,
With steady hand the solemn scene he draws;
Undaunted firmness with his wisdom join'd,
Nor Kings nor Worlds could warp his stedfast mind.

Thus Joel Barlow eulogizes Oliver Wolcott (?-1797) a physician who signed the Declaration of Independence, who was not only one of the great patriots of Connecticut, but a governor, son of a governor and father of a governor. After Oliver Wolcott graduated from Yale College in 1747 he was immediately commissioned a captain in the colonial army. After organizing a company, he marched to the defense of the Northern Frontier. After a short time he returned to Connecticut to study medicine with his brother Alexander who was practicing in Windsor.

Alexander Wolcott, who was born in 1711, graduated from Yale College in 1731 and shortly thereafter became a student of medicine in the office of Dr. Norman Morrison. As a surgeon he accompanied his father, who was second in command of the famous Louisburg Expedition.

Oliver Wolcott probably spent two or three years in preparing for practice and, in about the year 1751, he established himself in Goshen, Connecticut. Soon after this the County of Litchfield was organized and Wolcott was appointed the first High Sheriff. From this time on he discontinued the practice of medicine and confined himself to public life. He was a member of the Continental Congress in 1775 and was appointed by that body as one of the commissioners of Indian affairs of the northern department. In 1776 he once more attended the Congress at Philadelphia and was present when the Declaration was adopted and signed. After the riot in Bowling Green in which the lead statue of George the Third was hauled down and broken up, the pieces were sent to Wolcott's home in Litchfield, where they were melted into bullets. Wolcott was in the field or attending Congress much of the time during the Revolution. He was in Congress when that body retired from Philadelphia to Baltimore in December 1776. The next year he commanded a militia brigade in the Battle of Saratoga. In 1780, he was reelected and remained a member of Congress for four years. In 1796 he became Governor of Connecticut and in 1797, one year later, he passed away at his home in Litchfield.

Alexander Wolcott distinguished himself at College by his excellence in the classics and later by the energy with which he delved into the mysteries of the healing art. After completing his studies he returned to Windsor, in 1740, to engage in the practice of medicine. His library was quantitatively and qualitatively excellent and contained many Latin folios, such as the works of Bonetus, Sennertus, Morgagni, and the first edition of the great work of Sydenham. Dr. Wolcott was wont to read these ponderous tomes of Latin and Greek. Unfortunately one of his sons, to whom these priceless volumes were left, regarded them primarily as waste paper, and so employed them.

Alexander Wolcott had a faithful domestic named Primus who accompanied him when he visited the sick, and aided him in preparing medicines for many years. Wolcott eventually rewarded his faithful slave with full liberty. As soon as he was free, he moved to the opposite bank of the river, and was at once recognized as a doctor, and as such was frequently employed. When asked to visit a sick child at Poquonnock, Primus made the call and used such remedies as, in his judgment, the case demanded. On his way home, he knocked at the door of his old master, who came out to inquire what was wanted: "Nothing particular, master, I called to say that I was sent for to see a child of our old neighbor—found it a very simple case, and said to the mother it was not necessary for her to send so far for a doctor, for you would have done for the child just as well as any one else." Primus' patients were mainly on the east side of the river, and he often crossed the path of Dr. Mather. It is related that on one occasion, Dr. Mather accosted him: "What, Primus, do you practice yet?" "Only in difficult cases, master," was the old negro's reply. Primus was clever and capable and built up quite a name for himself as a medical luminary.

Two of Wolcott's sons were physicians: one practiced at Windsor after the death of his father, and Simon, who resided at New London, was one of the founders of the Connecticut Medical Society. The General Assembly in 1776, when organizing an army medical staff, chose Dr. Wolcott as chairman of the committee to examine applicants.

The role of the physician in Connecticut's wars is a subject of some interest. As has been previously mentioned, during the Pequot War, Gershom Bulkley was elected surgeon of the forces raised in Connecticut to repress Indian hostilities. For his professional duties he was awarded the meager allowance of 14 shillings per week. In 1742, the English government raised an expedition against Louisburg. The Connecticut forces, under the command of General Wolcott, included Dr. Reed of Simsbury, Dr. Durand of Derby, and Dr.

Wheeler of Stratford, all of whom were appointed by the general court to accompany the expedition, as physicians.

Soon afterwards four regiments from the American colonies were sent to aid the English, in a military excursion against the Spanish West Indies, and Dr. Tudor (1733-1826) was one of the physicians who attended that ill-fated expedition. Although the resistance put up by the Spanish forces was weak, the disease-ridden area caused the Colonial and English forces to retreat. The same factors that caused the retreat also gave the doctors great opportunity to practice, and Dr. Tudor executed his tasks commendably. He returned with the expedition to England, where he was occupied for a decade as hospital surgeon, at the end of which time he retired, at half pay for life, at the age of 34. He promptly departed from England for the New World, eventually dying at East Windsor in March, 1826, at the age of 93, after receiving the pension of the British government for almost 60 years. In the intervening time, he engaged in the practice of medicine at East Windsor.

In 1755 another expedition was fitted out by the colony to resist the aggressions of the French. The medical men selected to accompany the expedition were Timothy Collins of Litchfield, Jonathan Marsh of Norwich, and Samuel Ely of Durham. The unit to which these physicians were attached was sent against Crown Point. Each surgeon was to be furnished with a complete set of instruments, and a box of medicines, at the expense of the colony, and each was to receive £7 per month.

Timothy Collins, a native of Guilford, and graduate of Yale was the first settled pastor of Litchfield, where he performed ministerial duties for thirty years. In 1752 he gave up his pastorate, was appointed justice of the peace, and devoted himself to medicine. It is noted that in certain departments of the profession, his wife had already acquired distinction. In a few years Dr. Collins resigned from the army on account of poor health, and as the French war continued, Dr. Elisha Lord was chosen surgeon and director of the hospital stores, and Philip Turner of Norwich, surgeon's mate.

The troops were under the command of Gen. Lyman, and their destination was Crown Point.

Several physicians entered the military service of the colony in the interval of time which extended from the year 1745 to 1765, but generally for short periods, and without entirely relinquishing their private practices. Some of the younger physicians remained longer in the service, and gained great distinction. Dr. Waldo, of Pomfret, returned from his military campaign as the most eminent surgeon of his district.

Philip Turner, assistant surgeon in the French War, became surgeon general of the Northern States during the War of Independence. Dr. Watrous of Colchester, when very young, entered the same service, and at the end of his military career, returned to the sphere of his professional duties, where he ranked with the most useful and most esteemed physicians of the State. It has generally been thought that these military campaigns gave an impetus to the progress of medical learning in the colony, and that the men who were thus brought together, each communicated and each gained some share of professional knowledge.

In April, 1775, five regiments were organized by the colonial government and the following physicians were appointed to serve in the several regiments:—

1st REG.—Jared Potter, surgeon.
> Levi Ives, Isaac Chalker, surgeon's mates.

2d REG.—Wm. Jepson, surgeon.
> Daniel Southmayd, John R. Watrous, sur. mates.

3d REG.—John Spalding, surgeon.
> Sam'l Cheeney, Elijah Adams, sur. mates.

4th REG.—Sam'l Wheeler, surgeon.
> Dan'l Sheldon, Abel Catlin, sur. mates.

5th REG.—John Wood, surgeon.
> Asel Fitch, Sam'l Whiting, sur. mates.

These physicians, all successful practitioners, declined the honor proferred upon them by the Legislature, thus necessitating other appointments. The General Assembly then proceeded to adopt the suggestion of the physicians of Norwich, and elected a committee of medical examiners, which extended to every section of the State, and embraced several names of distinction. The committee consisted of the following physicians:

Alexander Wolcott,	Platt Townsend,
John Dickinson,	Amos Mead,
John Watrous,	James Coggswell,
Æneas Munson,	John Clark,
Leverett Hubbard,	Elisha Lord,
Elisha Tracy,	Sam'l Lee,
Elias Carrington,	Ruben Smith,
Benjamin Gale,	Elisha Sill,
Eleazer Mather,	Seth Bird.

It was further resolved that these, or any three of them, be appointed to examine such persons within this State as may offer themselves to serve as surgeons and surgeon's mates in the continental

army, and upon full evidence of proper and sufficient qualifications
to give certificates accordingly.

In 1762 the medical men of Norwich applied to the Colonial
Legislature for the charter of a medical society. Their application
included valuable suggestions calculated to advance the general interests of the colony and the welfare of the medical profession.

TO THE HONORABLE GEN. ASSEMBLY OF THE COLONY OF CONNECTICUT.

The memorial of the subscribers, physicians in said colony, humbly
sheweth, that whereas life is the most desirable of all sublunary enjoyments, and health so invaluable a blessing that without it some degree of
life is little worth, and that the promoting medical knowledge among
physicians is the necessary and direct means to restore health, and even
preserve life, and is of great importance, as it will render the practice of
physic more safe and serviceable to the patient, and at the same time
yield more satisfaction to the profession. And whereas more than one
hundred years have already passed away since the planting of this
colony, and nothing has been done publicly to distinguish between the
honest and ingenious physician and the quack or empyrical pretender; by
reason which imposture has been but too commonly practiced to the
great injury of the people as well as to the disparagement of the profession.

We, your memorialists, therefore humbly pray your honors to take the
matter under your wise consideration, and enact that the physicians in
each county of this colony, for their mutual edification and instruction,
have liberty to meet together at such time and place as they shall appoint, once in three months, and at the first of such their meetings,
choose a committee of three approved physicians, to continue for the
space of one year, and annually to be chosen, such committee, for the
time being, to have full power to examine, and if found duly qualified,
to approve such candidates for the practice, as shall offer themselves for
examination—and if any person offering himself shall be adjudged not
qualified, and so not approved by the committee, he may apply himself
to any quarterly meeting in the same county, and be there examined,
and be determined by such meeting, and approved if they think fit, by
proper certificate. And that for the future no person or persons that are
not already deemed physicians, who shall pretend to practice without
such approbation and certificate, shall be allowed to bring or maintain an
action to recover any debt demand or other thing, for any service he shall
pretend to have done or presumed, as a physician, or otherwise enact, and

order some proper regulations for the practice of physic, as your wisdom should have thought most proper.
Norwich, 27th Sept., 1763.

SIGNED

Theophilus Rogers,	Joseph Perkins,
Joshua Downer,	Philip Turner,
Cyrel Carpenter,	Elisha Tracy,
Obidiah Kingsbury,	Moses Moriss,
Ebenezer Robinson,	John Barker,

Elisha Lord.

In the Lower House the question was put whether anything should be granted on this memorial, and passed in the negative.

Of the signing doctors, Elisha Lord had been previously appointed surgeon of the Colonial forces and employed to repel the encroachments of the French. Philip Turner, who had been an assistant surgeon of the same corps, had just returned from military service to Norwich. He was, when he signed the above memorial, 22 years old, and soon afterwards married the daughter of his preceptor, Dr. Elisha Tracy. It was not long before this capable and personable physician attained a position of eminence in the practice of medicine and surgery. Dr. Elisha Tracy was an eminent classical scholar and practical physician. Dr. Joshua Downer lived at Preston City (formerly part of Norwich) and was much respected for his medical skill. Theophilus Rogers was the son of an English physician, who, leaving part of his family in England, came to Norwich, with his son, then a young lad, whom he educated and trained for the duties of his own profession. His prominence among the signers of the petition is according to the respect in which he was held.

Dr. Joseph Perkins was a prominent physician in the colony. At the age of 36, he signed this petition. He was well educated and made an enviable record as a practicing physician. John Barker and Obidiah Kingsbury were respected physicians in the neighboring town of Franklin. It seems a shame that a petition embracing such rational suggestions, and such worthy signatures, was not endorsed by the Legislature. Although the plan was ideally suited to the wants of the public and of the profession, it did not gain the approval of the Lower House. However, it was adopted at once by the physicians of New London County, and became the cornerstone of the first medical society in Connecticut.

Elisha Lord soon afterwards moved to Pomfret, where, together with Albigence Waldo and other respectable physicians, a medical society was established in Windham County.

In 1765, or thereabout, a medical society was established in Litchfield County for the purpose of causing diffusion of medical knowledge, and the improvement of medical skill by friendly communication of physicians with each other.

The following extract makes reference to this early Connecticut medical society:

Though Litchfield is the youngest county in Connecticut, yet in 1766 it set an example to the rest worthy of imitation. The province had always been greatly pestered by a generation of men called quacks, who, with a few Indian nostrums, a lancet, a glyster pipe, rhubarb, treacle water mixed with Roman bombast of *vena cava* and *vena porta*, attacked fevers, nervous disorders, and broken bones, and by the grace of perseverance, subdued nature, and helped their patients to a passage to the world of spirits before they were ready. The surgeons and physicians, who were not quacks, formed themselves into a society for the encouragement of literature, and a regular and wholesome practice. But their laudable endeavors were discountenanced by the General Assembly, who refused to comply with their solicitation for a charter, because the quacks and the people said "If the charter were granted, the learned men would become too rich by a monopoly, as they had in England." The answer to this objection, was, "Would it not be better to permit a monopoly to preserve the health and lives of the people, than to suffer quacks to kill them and ruin the province?"

In 1789 Dr. Porter of Fairfield County, who resided in New Fairfield, was the presiding officer of the Litchfield society meeting at North Canaan and he demonstrated great interest in the prosperity of the organization. He was, moreover, admirably qualified to preside at such reunions of the medical faculty, himself enjoying and diffusing pleasure to others.

Other remnants of the Litchfield society may be discovered in the personal history of its members. Dr. Benjamin Welch of Norfolk, another prominent member of the society, started his practice a few years before the State Medical Society was incorporated, and was examined and licensed by the commissioners of the Litchfield County Medical Society. For many years, Dr. Welch was the most renowned medical light of Norfolk, and was for thirty years a member of the State Legislature.

Dr. Daniel Sheldon should also be mentioned as a pioneer in the Litchfield County Society. Although laid low by a severe pulmonary affection when young, he persevered in carrying out his medical pursuits until his health was entirely restored. Interest in his own case directed him to a careful study of pulmonary complaints, and he became a respected authority on this subject. It is related that Dr. Sheldon imputed his own recovery mainly to exercise obtained while riding horseback. He lived to a ripe old age.

Leonard Hopkins (1750-1801) was another famous member of the Litchfield Society. He was an eminent consulting physician, renowned for his skill in treating tuberculosis, a satirist and poet of some repute in his day. His story is well summarized by Dr. W. R. Steiner.

Born in Salem Society (now Naugatuck), Connecticut, on June 19, 1750, the second son of Stephen Hopkins, Jr., and Patience, his second wife. Little is known of his youth except the fact that he was of a slender constitution and was troubled with a "cough, hoarseness, a pain in the breast and the spitting of blood." On the maternal side he was descended from a tuberculous mother and family and his body suggested a consumptive predisposition. After being given a good classical education by his father, who was a farmer in easy circumstances, he began the study of medicine under the distinguished Dr. Jared Potter, of Hallingford. Subsequently, he removed to Litchfield in the same state, and studied under Dr. Seth Bird.

Dr. Summer remarks, "He was neither contaminated by the speculation of one master nor debased by the vicious habits of the other." In 1776 he began practice in Litchfield and served for a short time during this year as a volunteer soldier in the Revolutionary Army. He employed "the cooling treatment in fevers, in the puerperal especially, and wine in fevers since called typhus"—methods which were then thought madness and some of his cases became the subject of much newspaper discussion.

He is described as possessing large features, bright staring eyes and long ungainly limbs, which gave him an uncouth figure. Add the appearance to his eccentricities of character and very brusque manners, and it is a wonder that he won the confidence and friendship of his patients. He kept at the time a "room full of pupils" and of them Dr. Elisha North of Foshen and New London probably became the most prominent.

His great specialty was tuberculosis, which is charmingly considered in two manuscript treatises on "consumption" and on "colds." They revealed a knowledge far ahead of his time and prove Hopkins to be a rival with Rush for honors in treating the great white plague. He believed this disease was curable in its early stages and sometimes in the far advanced, and lamented the fact that physicians were apt to treat this disorder with a dull formal round of inert or harmful medicines. Fresh air and good food were factors employed in his treatment of these cases. He appreciated the fact that a neglected cold might bring on this disease.

On account of his associations with a little coterie of literary men who were designated as "the Hartford Hits," his name became familiar in the household, especially in his native state, as a man of letters. This group, composed of Hopkins, Joel Barlow (Barlow later allied himself with the party of Jefferson), Timothy Dwight, David Humphreys, John Trumbull, Richard Alsop and Theodore Dwight, were strongly Federalistic in their principles and fervent in their sentiments, before the adoption of the constitution, in favor of a strong centralized government. They were ardent supporters later of Washington's administration and strove to win the adherence of others by ridiculing the Democrats and their measures in poems which had great popularity in the newspapers of that period and were subsequently published in book form. Possessed of keen dry wit, Hopkins was peculiarly well fitted for these tasks. His other literary productions are seen especially in the poems "The Hypocrite's Hope," "The Cancer Quack" and "Ethan Allen." Hopkins was an honorary member of the Massachusetts Medical Society (1790-1801); in the year 1784 he received an honorary M.A. degree from Yale. He was one of the founders of the Connecticut Medical Society.

On March 24, 1801, he was so ill that he was "bled repeatedly notwithstanding the opposition of his friends, yet lived to resume somewhat his practice." Some days after, he collapsed at a patient's house, and on April 14, 1801, he expired.

On the last day of February 1780, the members of the Litchfield County Medical Society assembled at Sharon, and Dr. James Potter was the orator of the day. His subject, "The Rise and Progress of Physic in America" was most bombastic, in accordance with the affected style of that period. It started thusly: "The great Parent of mankind—the beneficent Founder of the universe—the infinitely indulgent and all glorious Benefactor of the intellectual economy, out of the overflowing of his exuberant and divine goodness hath been pleased again to bring this society together." In the text of the address, Dr. Potter alludes to the languor and prostration of spirits, and to his not being accustomed to public speaking: "the rules of my rhetoric having been deduced from the conversation of nurses, and the oratory of my life the groans of the sick." He apologized for what he termed his "unoratorical composition."

In the year 1784, the Medical Society of New Haven was founded. Its first organization is recorded in its own archives:

We, the medical practitioners of the county of New Haven, convened in consequence of an invitation in the Connecticut Journal, from the faculty of the town of New Haven, on this 5th day of January, 1784; having made choice of Col. Leverett Hubbard, chairman, and Dr. Samuel Darling, secretary, to resolve ourselves into a society, to be called and known by the name of the Medical Society of New Haven County, pledging our honor to each other for the strict observance of all such regulations as may be adopted by the majority of said society, formed for the following purposes, viz:

"1st. To lay a proper foundation for that unanimity and friendship which are essential to the dignity and usefulness of the profession.

"2nd. To make accurate observations on the air, seasons, climates, and the various diseases incident to the inhabitants of the county; with the mode of treatment.

"3rd. For the communication of any discoveries in physic, surgery, botany or chemistry.

"4th. For the purpose of correspondence with the several medical societies in this and the neighboring states, and in Europe.

"5th. For uniting with the several medical societies in this and the adjacent states, and to make application to the Legislature, praying them to adopt such measures for the future regulation of our salutary art, as shall effectually support merit, and discountenance ignorance and presumption.

"*Voted*, That Messrs. Leverett Hubbard, Æneas Munson, Jared Potter, Hezekiah Beardsley, Samuel Mather, and Samuel Darling, be a committee to form further regulations to be laid before the next meeting."

At a subsequent meeting the following rules were adopted:

1. The time of meeting, once in three months.

2. That in all cases where counsel is requisite, we will be ready to assist each other in consultation without reserve.

3. That if any physician or surgeon, residing within this county, shall neglect or refuse, after six months, to become a member of this society, the members will utterly refuse to have any connection with him as a practitioner, unless he can give a satisfactory reason for his neglect to the society.

4. Every person who has been in practice less than a year, must submit to an examination before admission to the society.

5. The committee of correspondence to be a committee of examination. A certificate of examination, when presented, shall entitle to membership of the society.

6. Provision for the officers—president, vice president, secretary, etc.

In May 1791 the members of this society petitioned the General Assembly for an act of incorporation:

Your honors' petitioners do not presume to ask for any powers, privileges, exemptions or immunities, but they humbly pray that your honors will take their case into your wise consideration, and decree that your petitioners shall be formed into a body corporate and politic, by the name of the Medical Society of New Haven, for the purpose of collecting and preserving a collection of useful papers relative to the practice of medicine.

This petition was presented to the General Assembly in May, 1791, and granted in the lower house, with liberty to bring in a bill, but the councils of that day were opposed to all hasty legislation, and referred the subject to the General Assembly which was to be held at New Haven in October.

The signatures to this petition which appeared in the records of the Secretary of State, are as follows:

Æneas Munson,	Theodore Wadsworth.
James Potter,	Amzi Hull,
Sam'l Mather,	Elnathan Beach,
Æneas Munson, Jr.,	Jared Potter,
Levi Ives,	John Spalding,

The more prominent members of the New Haven Medical Society were Dr. Hubbard, Dr. Munson, Dr. James Potter, Dr. Jared Potter, and Dr. Beardsley. Dr. Ives describes Dr. Hubbard as follows:

Dr. Leverett Hubbard (1732-1794), commonly called Col. Hubbard, was prompt, bold and efficient in his practice, prepossessing in address, and cheerful in his disposition. He was the son of Judge Hubbard, who was also an able physician, much respected and beloved by the colonists of Connecticut, and a man of strict integrity and great decision of character. Col. Hubbard was of medium size, formed for activity, and capable of great endurance of labor. His connections and friends gave him great influence in society, and for many years the almost absolute control of the practice in this county, and to a considerable extent in the adjacent ones. Such power would tempt him at times to be overbearing, of which he was accused—yet probably he was less so than most physicians. As an apology for those physicians who manifested this spirit, it may be said that it was the fashion of the times. It was not unusual at this period, for such men as Eliot, Gale, Bird, and Hurlburt, when called to prescribe for the patient of another physician, on their first introduction, to sweep from the table into the fireplace all the medicines of another physician, and then, like Paracelsus, magnify his own powers as supernatural. Dr.

Hubbard died at the age of 62, in the year 1794, in the city of Hartford, whither he had gone on account of ill health.

Æneas Munson (1734-1826), an organizer of the Connecticut Medical Society, a clergyman and physician famed for his knowledge of materia medica and the natural sciences, was born in New Haven on June 13, 1734. He was the eldest child of Benjamin Munson, a mechanic and schoolmaster. After graduating from Yale in 1753, he taught school in Northampton, Massachusetts, and studied divinity, soon receiving a license to preach. In 1755 he acted for a short time as domestic chaplain for the Gardiner family of "Gardiner's Island." It is related that long hours of study coupled with insufficient exercise, broke his health, and that for this reason, he gave up the ministry in favor of medicine. He studied under the Rev. John Darbe, of Oyster Ponds, Long Island, and at first settled in Bedford, New York, and then in New Haven where he became a physician of great eminence.

He was among the first to attempt to incorporate the Connecticut Medical Society and he served the organization as first vice-president for two years, until, by the death of its president, he succeeded to the presidency. He filled the presidency for seven years. The degree of M.D. was conferred upon him by the society in 1794. "It is generally believed that, up to the early part of the present century (i.e., nineteenth) Dr. Munson was the ablest physician who ever practiced for a long time in New Haven. In the matter of professional learning and scientific information, he ranked with the eminent men of his country."

On account of his knowledge of mineralogy, chemistry, botany and materia medica, he enjoyed a wide reputation, which led to his selection to fill the chair of materia medica and botany in 1810, in the newly established medical institution at Yale, although he was then seventy-nine years old. He was, consequently, unable to perform the active duties of this office, which he left to his younger associate, Dr. Levi Ives.

His quaint dry humor still survives in many amusing anecdotes. Bronson relates that he was once dining with the Yale Corporation at commencement dinner when Pres. Dwight, who was a good trencherman, remarked, preparatory to some observation on diet: "You observe, gentlemen, that I eat a great deal of bread with my meat." "Yes," said the doctor instantly, "and we notice that you eat much meat with your bread."

His first wife was Susanna, eldest daughter of Stephen and Susanna Cooper Howell, whom he married on March 15, 1761. Nine children resulted from this union and all of them reached adult life. One son practiced medicine for a time. When his wife passed away on April 21, 1803, he waited nineteen months and then married Sarah, widow of Job Perit and a daughter of Benjamin and Mary Sanford, of New Haven. She survived him by three years.

Munson's death was occasioned by an enlarged prostate, and occurred on June 16, 1826, at the age of ninety-two. His writings consist of a report of two cases in "Cases and Observations by the Medical Society of New Haven County, Connecticut," 1788, pp. 26-28, 84-86; "A Letter on the Treatment most Successful in the Cure of Yellow Fever in New Haven," in 1794, and a letter on the subject of "Bilious Fevers" published by Noah Webster in New York in 1796.

Jared Potter (1742-1810), army surgeon during the Revolution and a physician of eminence in his day, was born in East Haven, Connecticut, on September 25, 1742. He was fifth in descent from John Potter, an original settler of New Haven, who signed the "Plantation Covenant." Potter, in 1760, received an A.B. from Yale College, and immediately following this he engaged in the study of medicine for the next three years, dividing the time equally between Dr. Harpin of Medford and the renowned Rev. Jared Eliot of Killingworth. Then he returned to East Haven and rapidly built up a large practice. In about 1770, he moved to New Haven, where his "business and popularity as a physician rapidly increased." The impending struggle between Great Britain and the colonies led him to remove, in 1772, to Wallingford, which was further inland.

One of the founders and incorporators of the Connecticut Medical Society in 1792, he acted as its first secretary and later, in 1804-05, as its vice president. He was also a fellow from New Haven County for eleven years and acted as a member of important committees. He declined to become a candidate for the presidency. In 1798 the society conferred upon him the honorary degree of M.D.

During the first year of the Revolution he served as surgeon to the first of the six regiments raised by order of the General Assembly of Connecticut, and in this capacity took part in the expedition against Quebec. In subsequent years he used to describe those terrible times, and the torture he endured on account of his helplessness in the midst of so much misery. At the expiration of two years' service, in July, 1776, he became surgeon to Col. William Douglas' regiment, and was present through the campaign around New York City. He was mustered out with the regiment, on December 29, 1776, and then returned home to resume practice. His health, however, was much impaired during the next two years, by what he had undergone.

He was greatly interested in politics, and was a member of the Lower House of the General Assembly for eighteen sessions (1780-1809). On one occasion he was nominated for the upper house, but was defeated. In his political views he strongly allied himself with the Jeffersonian Democracy.

At the height of his fame he was probably the most celebrated and popular physician in Connecticut. By buying the latest books on medicine, he constantly strove to be abreast of the times. This helped, also, to make him a famous medical teacher. The celebrated Dr. Hopkins, of Hartford, was his first student. His consultation practice was very extensive and carried him over most of the state, for "..... he was an excellent judge of symptoms and specially skilled in diagnosis." His therapeutic armamentarium favored the alkalies and alkaline earths. The famous "Potter's powder," as used by him, was composed of chalk, ammonium carbonate, camphor and charcoal. This mixture was usually employed in dyspeptic and other gastric complaints.

As a theologian, he was essentially a sceptic and whatever progress his students made in medical studies, they generally left his office replete with religious doubts.

He died on July 30, 1810, from the sequellae of a unique accident. As he passed a field of rye on his farm he plucked a ripe grain and, on shelling it, threw the kernels into his mouth. Unfortunately, a piece lodged in the uvula, causing "inflammatory gangrene" and ending in his early demise.

James Potter was a renowned member of the New Haven Medical Society, as well as an active participant in the Litchfield County Society.

His guiding genius was also at hand in the formation of the Connecticut Medical Society, and he was chosen its president after the resignation of Dr. Munson. Dr. Potter was frequently a member of the State Legislature and he was an eminent practitioner on the western borders of the State.

Hezekiah Beardsley (1748-1790) was the first investigator to describe congenital hypertrophic stenosis of the pylorus in infants. He was born in Stratford, Connecticut, in 1748, and became a druggist and physician. He practiced in Southington, Connecticut, as early as 1778, so far as health would permit. In 1780 he moved to Hartford. An advertisement of his firm, "Beardsley and Hopkins," is to be found in the *Connecticut Courant* for June 26, 1781, which declares that his apothecary shop is located "a few rods east of the Court House." In 1782 he removed to New Haven, where he had a similar store on Chapel street, between Church and Orange streets.

At the time of his death, in 1790, from consumption, he had taken his brother-in-law into partnership with him.

As one of the original members of the New Haven County Medical Association, he served on the committees of correspondence and examination. In April, 1788, he reported a case of "scirrhus in the pylorus of an infant,"—the first recorded case of congenital hypertrophy of the pylorus in an infant. This case-history was printed with the papers of the society, in the transactions under "Cases and Observations." In this paper Beardsley noted practically every feature of the disease we now know. He had attended the patient for three years at Southington, and when the patient died at the age of five, he performed the autopsy. He speaks of the "constant puking," which was first noted during the first week of life. Everything in the shape of food the child took was almost instantaneously rejected and very little changed. The feces were small in quantity. He comments upon the leanness and wizened old look of the child, and states he had "pronounced a scirrhosity in the pylorus months before the child's death," although he first attributed the condition to a deficiency of bile and gastric juices joined with a morbid relaxation of the stomach. Unfortunately Beardsley did not know of the child's death "until the second day after it took place. This late period, the almost intolerable stench, and the impatience of the people who had collected for the funeral, prevented so thorough an examination of the body as might otherwise have been made." At the autopsy Beardsley noted that the stomach was unusually large and distended. "The pylorus was invested with a hard compact substance or scirrhosity, which so completely obstructed the passage into the duodenum as to admit with the greatest difficulty the finest fluid."

A Connecticut medical man who left his mark on the pages of world medical history—however transitory and erroneous a mark it be—was Elisha Perkins.

Elisha Perkins (1741-1799), son of Dr. Joseph Perkins, was born in Norwich, Connecticut, on January 16, 1741. Perkins was one of those magnetic personalities who inspired great faith in the minds of the ailing. The terms, "Perkinism" and "Tractorism," were known both in America and abroad and the wonderful metallic rods which Perkins said and believed to be curative of almost every ill in men (and horses), certainly wrought great psychotherapeutic wonders.

It is related that Perkins was a handsome six-footer who had wonderful endurance and self-control. He was educated by his father. He had felt a curious magnetic power in himself in touching anyone and set about finding some combination of metals which might have the same effect in healing disease. These he "discovered" in 1796 and named them "tractors." Perkins' tractors consisted of two small rods, about three inches long, one of brass, one of steel, which had to be drawn downward for twenty minutes over the affected parts. A patient was obtained; doctors and philosophers gravely approved, and professors of three American universities said they believed in Perkinism. The tractors came to be used in Copenhagen where twelve well-known physicians reported so favorably on them that the records were printed in an octavo volume. In 1803 Benjamin Perkins, the son, established the Perkinean Institution in London with the Right Hon. Lord Rivers as president and Sir William Barker as vice-president and five thousand cases were treated.

There is reason to think that Elisha Perkins was self-deceived by his great therapeutic success. An imaginative, restless, inquiring man, he introduced, besides his rods, a remedy for dysentery and a low fever "consisting of the vegetable with the muriatic acid in the form of common vinegar saturated with muriate of soda." Believing this to be a successful antiseptic in yellow fever he went to New York during the epidemic in 1799, and after four weeks' unremitting care of the sick, he fell ill of the fever and died at the age of fifty-nine on September 6, 1799.

It was through the efforts of Dr. Haygarth of Bath, England, that the idea of any healing power resident in the tractors themselves was refuted, for he and a colleague effected many cures with tractors made of painted wood. T. G. F. Fessenden dealt Perkinism its final blow in his "Terrible Tractoration by Christopher Caustic," London, 1800.

Perhaps the large fortune made through "tractoration" hastened the act duly registered in the "Archives of the Medical Society of the State of Connecticut, 1800," "that Dr. Elisha Perkins be expelled from the society as a patentee and user of nostrums."

Chapter Seven

MARYLAND

IN 1632 CHARLES I ISSUED a charter granting almost unlimited territorial and governmental rights to George Calvert, first Lord Baltimore (1580?-1632). George Calvert passed away even prior to this document passing the great seal. Two months later, in 1632, the charter was issued to his eldest son, Cecilius. By November 1633 the *Ark* and the *Dove*, with two hundred colonists under the governorship of Leonard Calvert (c. 1582-1647), a brother of the proprietor, sailed from Gravesend. These vessels reached Maryland late in March, 1634. The colonists immediately and for all time established friendly relations with the Indians.

William Claiborne (1589?-1676?) had violently opposed the Maryland charter, and had established a trading post on Kent Island in Chesapeake Bay in 1631. When ordered to submit to the Calvert regime, he and his followers employed armed resistance, although during Claiborne's temporary absence in England, this resistance was subdued. In 1644, while civil war raged in England, he returned to Maryland and aided Richard Ingle, a pirate who audaciously declared that he was acting in the interest of parliament, in supporting a revolution which removed Governor Calvert from his office for a period of one and one half years.

The lord proprietor was again deprived of his government from 1654 to 1658 because of parliamentary instructions which were meant to effect only Virginia, but which through the influence of Claiborne and some Puritan exiles from Virginia who had settled in Maryland, were applied also to "the plantations within Chesapeake Bay." Josiah Fendall, the proprietor's own governmental appointee, attempted to overthrow proprietary government and set up a commonwealth. This insurrection was suppressed and order restored in the province which lasted from the English Restoration of 1660 to the English Revolution of 1688.

Although the proprietor was Roman Catholic, it is obvious that he was anxious to have Protestant colonists also. He guaranteed religious toleration from the beginning and so instructed his officers. The Great Toleration Act passed by the assembly in 1649 was a milestone in the history of civilization, although, of course, it only permitted religious freedom to sects of Trinitarian Christianity.

Although the charter gave the proprietor the sole right to initiate legislation, he voluntarily, without coercion, surrendered this right in 1638. By 1650 the assembly was divided into two houses. One of these consisted only of the representatives of the freemen without whose consent no bill could become a law. Yearly sessions as well as triennial elections rapidly became routine methods in Maryland. The proprietor, in 1670, tried to disenfranchise all freemen who did not have a freehold of fifty acres or a visible estate of forty pounds sterling. This step caused a crescendo of complaints against the proprietor. He was denounced as interfering with elections, as summoning only a part of the duly elected delegates, as attempting to browbeat those summoned, as abusing his veto power, and as keeping the government in the hands of Roman Catholics, and under the control of his own family.

The area now comprising the state of Delaware was certainly within the original boundaries defined by the Maryland charter. In 1682, the territory was transferred by the Duke of York to William Penn. In 1685 Lord Baltimore's valid claim to it was denied by an order in council, on the pretext that the grant was not legal because it had been inhabited by Christians prior to the Maryland charter.

Although from the words of the charter it was evident that the parallel of 40° N. was Maryland's north boundary, and although Penn's charter clearly stated that Pennsylvania extended on the south to the "beginning of the fortieth degree of Northern Latitude," a boundary controversy arose between the two provinces. After much litigation, Charles Mason and Jeremiah Dixon, two English mathematicians, established the line named for them (Mason and Dixon Line), which runs along the parallel 39° 43′ 26″. 3 N. and later became famous as the dividing line between the free states and the slave states. This was done in 1763-1767.

The opposition in 1688 succeeded in overthrowing proprietary rule, and the crown in 1692, in support of its trade policy, set up a royal government in its place. The Church of England became the established church and the people effected a powerful control of their branch of the legislature. Government was less by executive decree and more by statute law. The proprietor decided to become a Protestant and, in 1715, proprietary government was reestablished. It is unfortunate to relate that Roman Catholics were at once disenfranchised.

In 1730 large groups of Germans began to settle in the west-central part of Maryland. They not only helped develop industry, but added considerable weight to the opposition.

After the restoration of the proprietor in 1715, a conflict arose. The members of the popular branch of the legislature were of the opinion that only British statutes specifically effecting dominions should be applied to Maryland and not general English laws. Numerous and diverse disputes rapidly ensued and internal conflict in Maryland became so intense that when the final struggle between the English and French for possession in America came, Maryland did not aid England in that struggle. This fact was seized upon by the British as a reason for imposing the famous Stamp Act. The irate Maryland citizens drove the stamp distributor out, and the arguments of lawyer Daniel Dulany (1721-1797) against the act were widely quoted by speakers who demanded its repeal. As the War of Independence approached, Maryland acted as did the other leading colonies. Even a ship with tea on board was burned. Yet there was great reticence in signing the Declaration of Independence, for the fight against the proprietor had nearly been won and most of the substantial citizens wanted the continuance of the old government. It was not until the Maryland delegates to the Continental Congress found themselves almost alone in refusing to sign this document that their instructions not to vote for independence were withdrawn.

According to the records, Henry Hooper, Chirurgeon, landed in Maryland in 1637. An inquest was held on the body of a man killed by a tree. This is one of the earliest records of a post-mortem examination in America.

The archives show that in 1639, one Thomas Gerard was elected to the Maryland Assembly. He received two hundred and thirty pounds of tobacco from the Secretary of the Province "for Physick administered to Richard Lee." In 1641, Richard Purlivant, barber and chirurgeon, settled on Kent Island, but little is known of him.

One year later, Robert Ellyson, a barber surgeon of St. Mary's County, reports an autopsy performed by himself upon the body of an infant, Ann Thompson. In 1642, also, the records mention Alexius Pulton, chirurgeon, who was paid one hundred and fifty pounds of tobacco for his services in an expedition against the Susquehannah Indians, and the aforementioned Gerard, on petition of the Protestants in the Colony, was fined by the Assembly for interfering with their worship.

The Brown family furnished several noted physicians to Maryland and the other colonies:

Gustavus Brown (1689-1765) was born near Edinburgh, Scotland, on April 10, 1689. He arrived in Maryland in May, 1708, while serving as a surgeon's mate on a British vessel. While ashore a storm blew up which forced the captain to weigh anchor ahead of schedule and Brown found himself stranded on the shore with no clothes but what were on his back. He practiced medicine among the planters who soon developed a great deal of respect for their uninvited guest. In 1710, he married a wealthy woman. After building up a large practice he became homesick for his native soil and sailed with his wife for Scotland. It is said that his wife did not share his love for his homeland, so they returned to Maryland in 1734 and settled in Charles County.

Dr. Michael Wallace, of King George County, Virginia, and Dr. John Key, of St. Mary's County, Maryland, studied medicine under him and later married his daughters. His other seven daughters all married men of standing. Dr. Brown showed characteristic Scotch shrewdness by insisting that all his sons-in-law secured upon their wives the property which he presented as dower.

Wallace is responsible for the following story about the good doctor: One day, he was summoned to make a speedy professional call to someone ill in the family of one Mr. H., a wealthy citizen of King George County, Virginia. Mr. H. was famous for his ostentation in displaying his wealth and for his slowness in paying his physician. While leaving the house, Dr. Brown came upon Mr. H. himself who was lavishly entertaining some dinner guests. A servant accosted him with a large silver plate on which two silver goblets filled with gold pieces stood. The servant pompously declared: "Dr. Brown, master wishes you to take out your fee." Brown promptly and to the dismay of his host, who was forced to hide his emotions, emptied one goblet into one overcoat pocket, and the second into the other. "Tell your master," he said, "I highly appreciate his liberality." He then hastened outside, mounted his horse and departed.

He died of a sudden stroke at Rich Hill, in April 1765. In his will he refers to himself as "Practitioner in Medicines and Laird of Mainside and House Byers in Scotland."

Brown served in several public positions of trust during his career. His son, Gustavus Richard Brown, was by a second marriage.

Gustavus Brown (1744-1801), the grandson of Dr. Gustavus Brown, Sr., and the nephew of Dr. Gustavus Richard Brown, was born at Morningside near Edinburgh, Scotland, in 1744. He studied medicine at Edinburgh for seven years, and received his M.D. in 1770.

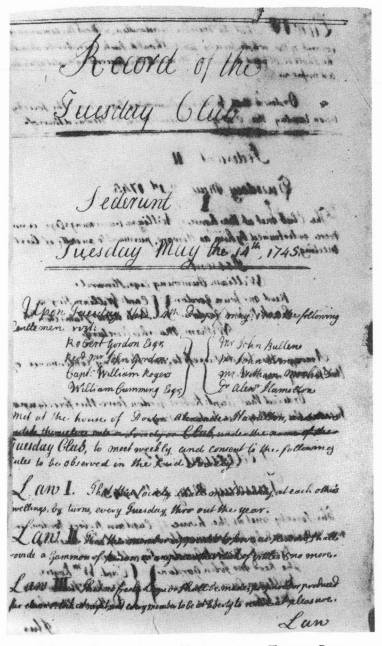

SPECIMEN PAGES FROM THE MINUTES OF THE TUESDAY CLUB

In 1745, Alexander Hamilton and Jonas Green, the editor of the Maryland Gazette, formed the Tuesday Club of Annapolis. Hamilton was secretary, spark plug and orator of this organization during the ten years that it flourished. (*Courtesy of the Maryland Historical Society.*)

The Club music
Recitative
once more shall ere take the gladsome lay, Sing Cole, the Club, & this auspicious day.
uberant themes, whence endless matter flows, Impart thy aid, while the song compose,
Symphonia Con Spirito
allegro
volti subito

Honorabilis D: Dominus Joannes (olim Oldcastellius)
Societates vulgo Tuesday Club, nuncupata Eques et propugnator
nec non ejusdem, socius, veteranus & longaevalicas.

Eques noster ferox, et vinci nescius armis,
en! qui res potuit eomin us ense geris,
Dicere difficile est quid magis egerit ille:
Quotque fugi dederis, quosque quibus que morbis —

he chusing to speak, or not to speak, as he thinks fit. — ordered that mr
Edward dorsey if he thinks fit, deliver a speech to the Club on Tuesday the 14th of october next
Ordered, that Capt Robert gordon, entertain this society upon
Tuesday the 22d of this Instant July

        Sederunt 40th
    Tuesday July 22d 1746
The Society met at the house of Capt: Robt gordon and were
                                        entertained

The first Grand Anniversary Procession.

The catalogue of graduates of Edinburgh lists him as "Brown, Gust., Brit. De Cynanche Phlogistica, 1770." He soon came to America with several of his classmates and settled in St. Mary's County, Maryland. Dr. Ireland, a former fellow student whom he took care of professionally, died in 1782 and he married his widow. The doctor settled down with her at her mansion, "Summerseat," and practiced until his death on July 3, 1801.

Dr. Brown's fame became widespread and Drs. Craik, Dick and Gustavus R. Brown, called him in at Washington's last illness. Receiving the notice at midnight, he set out on horseback at all speed for Mt. Vernon. However, when he arrived at Long Bridge, he learned of Washington's death and he turned back sadly.

Alexander Hamilton, Henry Stevenson, and Adam Thompson were prominent early Maryland physicians:

Alexander Hamilton (1712-1756) was born in Scotland, and probably received his medical degree from Glasgow where his cousin, Dr. R. Hamilton, was professor of anatomy and botany. He picked up the essentials of pharmacy in the shop of David Knox, an Edinburgh surgeon. He then went to London. His elder brother was engaged in medical practice in Annapolis, Maryland, in 1727. Alexander Hamilton acted as preceptor to Dr. Thomas Bond.

In 1745, Alexander Hamilton and Jonas Green, the editor of the *Maryland Gazette,* formed the Tuesday Club of Annapolis. Hamilton was secretary, spark plug and orator of this organization during the ten years that it flourished. The Maryland Historical Society still has possession of the minutes of this club kept by the good doctor and illustrated with his own caricatures. "Loquacious Scribble, Esq'r." aptly refers to Dr. Hamilton.

In 1807 a remarkable diary of the 1,624 mile return trip made in 1754 by Hamilton between Portsmouth, New Hampshire, and Annapolis, was published under the title, "Itinerarium." Hamilton took along letters of introduction to several eminent physicians, but in general he was depressed to find the profession in a very low state with many of the doctors, especially the New Yorkers, being mere "drunken roysterers." He witnessed several meetings of the "Physical (Medical) Club," at Boston, which was presided over by the educated Scotchman, Dr. William Douglass, who was "a cynical mortal, so full of himself that he could see no merit in anyone else." Hamilton states that at these meetings the doctors "drank punch, smoked tobacco and talked of sundry physical matters."

He purchased a copy of "Homer" in Boston which he took delight in studying, and he frequently refers to contemporary and classical literature. He subscribed to the "Physical News," a medical journal published at Edinburgh. Hamilton's manuscript was given, shortly after his return, to an Italian who visited him in Annapolis, and it was thus conveyed to Italy. It was sold in Italy and eventually made its way to the book stores of London, where it was purchased by William K. Bixby, of St. Louis, a discerning gentleman who realized its historical value and printed a small edition at his own expense for private distribution.

Hamilton passed away on May 11, 1756.

Henry Stevenson (1721-1814) was born at Londonderry, Ireland, in 1721. He studied at Oxford, England, and together with his brother, John, became a physician. Both brothers emigrated to Baltimore in about 1750. Dr. Henry Stevenson and Dr. Alexander Stenhouse married sisters and settled in Bush River Neck, Baltimore County. In 1756 Henry built a fine stone dwelling, which he named "Parnassus" but which his neighbors called "Stevenson's Folly," on the banks of Jones Falls (north of the present city of Baltimore). This mansion communicated with the town by a long trestle bridge over meadow and marshland.

In his own house he operated an inoculating hospital from 1768 to 1776, and again after the Revolution, from 1786 to 1800. In 1765 Stevenson was referred to as "the most successful inoculator in America." Besides inoculating the citizens of Baltimore, he made visits into the rural counties. Gen. James Wilkinson, later commander-in-chief of the American Army, was inoculated at his house. The standard fee for inoculation was two pistoles. Board and lodgings were billed at the rate of twenty shillings per week.

Stevenson sided with the home country during the War of Independence and fled Baltimore with his brother upon hearing of the Declaration of Independence. He served as surgeon in the British Navy from 1776 to 1786, but came back to practice in his beloved Baltimore in the last mentioned year. Here he remained until his death on March 31, 1814.

Henry Stevenson helped organize the Medical and Chirurgical Faculty of Maryland in 1799. During the yellow fever epidemic of 1797, he treated sixty-seven cases from July to October, with a mortality of less than six. He avoided venesection, used little calomel, and employed tonics copiously.

Adam Thomson (?-1767) was born in Scotland and received both his preliminary and medical education in his native land. His "Discourse on the Preparation of the Body for the Smallpox" mentions "the Famous Monro of Edinburgh" as one of his earliest medical teachers. As the eighteenth century got under way, Thomson emigrated to Prince George County, in the Province of Maryland, and engaged in medical practice. In 1748 he moved to Philadelphia and continued his practice. His fame as an inoculator was widespread throughout the colonies.

The year 1738 saw Thomson develop his method of preparing the body for smallpox. First a two week's course of treatment or "cooling regimen" preparatory to inoculation was undertaken which included a light, non-stimulating diet, the oral use of mercury and antimony, and moderate bleeding and purgation. It was Boerhaave who first noted success in employing antimony and mercury in the treatment of smallpox. Dr. Thomson's great success with his method led him to the firm conviction that "mercury under proper management is more of a specific agent against the effects of the variolous than the venereal poison." Thomson always administered mercury within the bounds of salivation and he always modified his regime in accordance with the patient's age and general health.

He states in his "Discourse:" "On every occasion for the space of twelve years where I have been called to prepare people for receiving the smallpox, either in the natural way or by inoculation—having prepared many for both—I have constantly used such a mercurial and antimonial medicine as Boerhaave has described, and I can honestly declare that I never saw one so prepared in any danger under the disease."

Adam Thomson's concept of immunity and susceptibility is of great interest considering the date of its promulgation. He declares: "It seems to me highly probable that there is a certain quantity of an infinitely subtle matter which may be called the variolous fuel, equally, intimately and universally diffused through the blood of every human creature; in some more, in others less, that lies still and quiet in the body never showing itself in any manner hitherto discovered until put in action by the variolous contagion, at which time it is totally expelled by the course of the disease."

To protect society from the quack and the poorly trained practitioner, Thomson recommended that the Legislature appoint suitable persons to judge the qualifications of one who was desirous of starting to practice medicine.

The "Discourse on the Preparation of the Body for the Smallpox" was delivered at the Academy of Philadelphia, on Wednesday, November 21, 1750. Benjamin Franklin published it and London reprinted it in 1752, and New York in 1757. It was received with acclaim in America, England and France. Thacher has this to say about this publication: "This production was highly applauded both in America and Europe, as at this period (1750) the practice of inoculation was on the decline. The author states that inoculation was so unsuccessful at Philadelphia that many were disposed to abandon the practice; wherefore, upon the suggestion of the 1392'd Aphorism of Boerhaave, he (Thomson) was led to prepare his patients by a composition of antimony and mercury, which he had constantly employed for twelve years, with uninterrupted success."

Dr. Redman, and Dr. Kearsley of Philadelphia, in the beginning opening opposed Thomson's method, but later all the colonies adopted it as standard. This American method for inoculation as it came to be called, was established routinely in the first inoculating hospitals which were established near Boston, Massachusetts, in February, 1764. Dr. William Barnett of Philadelphia was called to supervise the inoculations because of his reputation as a successful inoculator. Although using Dr. Thomson's technique, he refused to admit this fact.

The "History of the Inoculation of the Smallpox in Great Britain" by Woodville (1796. p. 341) excerpts the following from Dr. Benjamin Gale's "Dissertation on the inoculation of the Smallpox in America:" "Before the use of mercury and antimony in preparing persons for inoculation one out of one hundred of the inoculated died, but since only one out of eight hundred," and ". . . . . by last accounts 3,000 had recovered from inoculation in the new method by the use of mercury and antimony and five only had died, viz: children under five years of age."

Adam Thomson passed away in New York City on September 18, 1767. The *New York Mercury* lamented his death as follows: "On Friday morning early, died here, Adam Thomson, Esq., a physician of distinguished abilities in his profession, well versed in polite literature, and of unblemished honor and integrity as a gentleman."

Maryland physicians who served in the War of Independence include:

John Peter Ahl, James R. Alexander, Moses Allen, Thomas Andrews, William Annin, John Archer, William Baker, Colmore Beanes, William Beans, Smith Bishop, William Bordley, Thomas Bourk, Benjamin Boyd, John Boyde, John Hanson Briscoe, James Brohon, Richard Brooks, James Brown, ——— Browne, and George Budd.

Jonathan Calvert, Richard H. Courts, Thomas Craddock, ——— Craig, William Dashiell, Levin Denwood, Joseph Diggs, Richard Downing, John L. Elbert, Adam Fisher, William Gerwoud, James Gordan, Daniel Grant, James Gray, John Griffith, Joseph Hall, William Hall, Leonard Halliday, Elisha Harrison, Ezekiel Haynie, Ezekiel Haywood, John Hindman, Ephraim Howard, Thomas

Howard, John Ireland, Daniel Jenifer, Daniel Jenifer, Jr., Edward Johnson and John Johnson.

Samuel Keene, William Kilty, Samuel Knood, Robert Lemmon, Richard Lyles, William Lyon, James Manis, Thomas Marshall, Henry Maynadier, James McCallimont, James McHenry, James Morris, David Morrow, Samuel Morrow, Francis Neal, John Nelson, Thomas Parran, John Perry, John Prindell, John Pine, Zabdiel Potter, Rich Prindle and Frederick Ridgely.

Thomas Sappington, Richard Sappington, Alexander Smith, Walter Smith, William J. Smith, Henry Stevenson, Thomas Stockett, Barton Tabbs, John Tate, Barton Toby, Richard Tootle, Charles A. Warfield, Walter Warfield, Charles Wiesenthal, Robert Welch, James Wilkinson, Gerhard Wood, Charles Worthington and ——— Young.

Prussia's gift to early Maryland medicine was Charles Frederick Wiesenthal (1726-1789). He was born in this Germanic country in 1726. It is said that he was personal physician to Frederick the Great, and there is no question that he had a wide understanding of the Prussian military service. He came to Baltimore in 1755, and engaged in medical practice for thirty-four years. He was naturalized in 1771, and from the beginning, became an avid patriot. January, 1775, saw him a member of the Committee of Observation of Baltimore County. On March 2, 1776, he was commissioned surgeon-major of Smallwood's First Maryland Battalion. In 1777 he became surgeon-general of the Maryland troops, taking a keen interest in governmental medical affairs in Baltimore and establishing a hospital there.

In the back of his lot, Wiesenthal erected buildings for a medical school and dissecting room, and taught numerous students. It is recorded that in 1788, while he and his students were dissecting the body of a murderer, a mob broke up the demonstration.

Realizing the great need for a law regulating medical practice, he headed a movement for professional organization which led directly to the formation of a medical society on November 27, 1788. He served as president of this group. He died on June 1, 1789, while his only son Andrew was studying medicine in London.

It is said that Wiesenthal was the first Baltimore physician to employ a four-wheeled carriage. His carriage exhibited his crest which consisted of a horse's head bridled and bitted, with two crossed arrows beneath and inscribed with the words "Premium Virtutis."

Andrew Wiesenthal (1762-1798), the only son of Charles, was born in Baltimore in 1762. After a preliminary education, he undertook the study of medicine in his father's private school. He then took up anatomy under Shippen and attended lectures in Philadelphia.

He spent three years in London (1786-1789) as interne in St. Bartholomew's Hospital, during which period he received instruction from John Sheldon, Cruikshank, John Marshall, and Percival Pott.

He came back to Baltimore in the summer of 1789, soon after his father passed away, and began giving lectures in anatomy, physiology, pathology, operative surgery and the gravid uterus, to a class of fifteen. He and Dr. George Buchanan tried valiantly but unsuccessfully to start a medical college. However, Andrew Wiesenthal continued to give instruction in anatomy and surgery in his private school up until his death on December 2, 1798, at the age of thirty-six. One son, Thomas van Dyke Wiesenthal, who became a physician in the United States Navy, survived him.

Andrew Wiesenthal made one epic discovery which alone entitles him to lasting fame. The "London Medical and Physical Journal" for October 1799, states that he sent them a letter dated May 21, 1797, that he had ascertained that the deadly disease in fowls and turkeys, known as syngamosis, a verminous tracheo-bronchitis (popularly called "the gapes") was due to a cylindrical worm (later called "Syngamus trachealis"). This worm operates by lodging in the trachea and choking the young chicks. Andrew Wiesenthal presents an illustration of this worm of natural size and also as magnified under the microscope. Cordell claims that "this probably represents the first discovery of an organism producing an epidemic or infectious disease ever made."

Let us now consider the lives of John Archer, John Crawford, Charles Warfield, James McHenry, William Kilty, Ennalls Martin, and James Cocke:

John Archer (1741-1810) was born on May 5, 1741, near the present village of Churchville, Harford County, Maryland. He received his preliminary education at the West Nottingham Academy and Princeton College awarded him an A.B. in 1760 and an A.M. in 1763. After a brief experience in the ministry, he directed his efforts toward medicine and became a pupil of John Morgan.

He attended classes at the Philadelphia College of Medicine and the degree of Bachelor of Medicine was awarded to him on June 21, 1768. Even prior to his completion of the medical course, Archer engaged in medical practice in Newcastle County, Delaware. In July 1769, he returned to Harford County and started an active medical career that was to continue for forty years. The War of Independence saw Archer as a member of the local committee in November, 1774 and captain of a militia company in December 1774. He became a major in January, 1776. In August 1776 he took part in the convention that organized the Maryland constitution and bill of rights.

In 1776 Archer married a daughter of Thomas Harris, of the family that founded Harrisburg, Pennsylvania. Of ten children, several died in infancy, but five studied medicine. Four took their medical degrees from the University of Pennsylvania. Stevenson, the youngest child, became a congressman, chief justice of the federal court of appeals, and from 1817 to 1819 United States judge for the territory of Mississippi.

Dr. Archer taught some fifty the medical art. His disciples actually formed a medical society, the minutes of which are preserved in the library of the Medical and Chirurgical Faculty of Maryland, at Baltimore, the state medical society which Archer helped to organize in 1799. Archer served this society on the executive committee and on the examining Board. Archer was a presidential elector in 1801 and was a representative in Congress from 1801 to 1807. The "Medical Repository" of New York contains a few papers by Archer and he is given credit for having introduced "senega" as a remedy in the treatment of the croup.

Dr. Archer's health began to decline toward the end of his last term in Congress. He had a stroke and became partially paralyzed. Death resulted suddenly, probably from another cerebral hemorrhage, as he sat in his favorite chair at his home in Harford county on September 28, 1810.

John Crawford (1746-1813) was born in northern Ireland on May 3, 1746. His brother, Adair Crawford, became physician to St. Thomas' Hospital, London, and professor of chemistry at Wollwich.

He entered Trinity College, Dublin, in 1763, and later studied medicine at Leyden, which University awarded him an M.D. He served as surgeon for the East India Company on two voyages to the East Indies. He was married in 1778. Soon afterwards he was appointed surgeon to the Naval Hospital on the Island of Barbados. When the violent hurricane of 1780 ravaged the island, he distinguished himself by rendering the afflicted inhabitants both services and medicine without compensation. In 1781 poor health induced him to return to England and it was on this trip that his wife succumbed. The Dutch government appointed him surgeon-major to the colony of Demerara in South America in 1790 and in this capacity he ran a military hospital containing sixty to eighty beds.

In 1796 Crawford emigrated to Baltimore and in 1801 he was instrumental in establishing the Baltimore General Dispensary. His course of lectures on natural history presented at the College of Medicine in 1811 and 1812 was held in high esteem. His first lecture on "The Cause, Seat and Cure of Diseases" was especially noteworthy. His colleagues honored him by appointing him medical examiner, orator and member of the committee to publish the "Transactions of the Medical and Chirurgical Faculty." He served as consulting physician to the Board of Health and City Hospital and his medical articles were of a high quality.

John Crawford employed vaccination in America the same year as Dr. Waterhouse. His investigations into the etiology of disease were far in advance of his time. By 1790 he had already arrived at the idea that disease is caused by a living contagium. He pictured invisible animalculæ gaining access to the human body and instilling minute organisms which multiply to produce disease. He amalgamated and coordinated a large group of natural phenomena to prove the logic of this theory which was bitterly contested by his opponents and, for that matter, the profession at large.

Crawford had the audacity, in an era when theological dogma was universally accepted, to demonstrate that man was subjected to the same natural laws as lower animals. He promulgated the theory of universal parasitism. His logical inferences from the realm of the known to the then unknown, led him to the conclusion that whereas the disease animalculæ could not be seen by any known method, they are none-the-less not beyond the limits of man's understanding. He was certain that man would in time view them.

Crawford stated that disease seeds were similar to vegetable seeds, in that the progeny of each was like unto its parent. He applied his views to the rationale of preventing and treating disease. The disdain and hatred that Crawford's views inspired in his colleagues, forced him to publish his theories in the non-medical Baltimore Observer, of 1806 and 1807.

John Crawford passed away in Baltimore on May 9, 1813, after a short illness. His library is maintained by the University of Maryland. His writings were published in the American Medical Repository, the Baltimore Observer, the Medical and Physical Recorder (Baltimore), in Schultz's "History of Freemasonry in Maryland," and in Cordell's "Medical Annals of Maryland."

Charles Alexander Warfield's (1751-1813) birth took place in Anne Arundel County, Maryland, on December 3, 1751. It is not certain whether he graduated from the College of Medicine of Philadelphia or not. As the Revolutionary War loomed up, Warfield from the start became an ardent exponent of the cause of the colonies. In 1774 he became major of a battalion in his county and he wore a badge containing the following motto: "Liberty and Independence or Death in Pursuit of It."

October 1774 saw what might be termed the Maryland Tea Party

A

DISCOURSE

ON THE *John L. Bozman.*

PREPARATION of the BODY

FOR THE

SMALL-POX;

AND

The Manner of receiving the INFECTION.

As it was deliver'd in the Publick Hall of the ACADEMY,
before the TRUSTEES, and others, on *Wednesday*,
the 21st of *November*, 1750.

By *ADAM THOMSON*, Physician in *Philadelphia*.

*In Stibio, & Mercurio, ad magnam penetrabilitatem arte deductis, nec tamen salina
acrimonia nimium corrosivis, sed bene unitis, ut quaramus (remedium, nempe,
specificum Antivariolosum,) incitat aliquis horum aliquando successus.* APH.
HERM. BOERH. No. 1392.

Prophylaxis insitiva videtur satis certa, tutaque. Idem, Ibidem. No. 1403?

PHILADELPHIA:
Printed by B. FRANKLIN, and D. HALL. MDCCL.

Photostat of Title Page of Adam Thomson's "A Discourse on the Preparation of the
Body for the Small-Pox." Printed by Benjamin Franklin and D. Hall. (*Courtesy of the
Library of the Surgeon General's Office.*)

with the good doctor as the leader. The brig, *Peggy Stewart,* was anchored in the Annapolis harbor loaded with tea. On the nineteenth of this month Warfield organized the membership of the "Whig Club" to march down to the harbor to destroy this boat and its forbidden contents. When the irate group had reached the State House, Judge Samuel Chase, legal aide of Stewart, a Scotch merchant who was the owner of the vessel, accosted them and proceeded with fine oratory to attempt to dissuade the expedition.

Warfield listened to Chase until he could stand it no longer. He then broke into his argument and charged him with flagrant inconsistency, for the Judge had previously aroused the entire area with his patriotic speeches. Warfield declared that any member of the club who did not fulfil his mission was a coward. The party marched forward. Stewart tried to intercede by threatening the entire group with the dire vengeance of his king and government. Stewart's bold front was soon smashed by building a gallows in front of his house and giving him the choice of either swinging or else accompanying them on board while they set his ship on fire. He quickly chose the latter course. With Warfield at their head, the group went on board and fired the vessel. Soon the entire boat and cargo were aflame and completely destroyed.

Warfield became president of the College of Medicine of Maryland at Baltimore (University of Maryland) in 1812 and continued in this office until his death, which took place on January 29, 1813. In 1799, Warfield helped found the Medical and Chirurgical Faculty of Maryland and from 1803 to his death, he served on the Board of State Examiners. He acquired a fine medical reputation and a vast practice and many of the leading medical men of the next generation received instruction in his office.

James McHenry (1753-1816) was born in Ballymena, Antrim, Ireland, on November 16, 1753. His family migrated to Baltimore and James undertook a course in medicine in Philadelphia under Benjamin Rush. In 1776 he was appointed surgeon of the fifth Pennsylvania battalion and later was appointed hospital surgeon by Congress. After being taken by the British at Fort Washington he was exchanged in 1778 and appointed surgeon of the Flying Hospital.

His sagacity ended his medical career for he was appointed secretary to General Washington and in 1780 made advisor to the Marquis de Lafayette. He was elected to the Maryland Senate from 1781-86, and served in Congress from 1783 to 1786. At the constitutional convention he actively fought for the ratification of the constitution. He served as secretary of war in Washington's and Adams' cabinets and always strived to better army conditions. Fort McHenry, near Baltimore, bears his name.

He died near Baltimore on May 3, 1816.

William Kilty (1758-1821) was born in London in 1758. After completing his preliminary education at St. Omar's College in France, he began the study of medicine with Dr. Edward Johnson of Annapolis, Maryland, in April, 1778. He sojourned in Wilmington, Delaware, and was appointed surgeon's mate in the Fourth Maryland Regiment, later becoming regimental surgeon.

Unfortunately, Kilty was captured at the Battle of Camden. In the Spring of 1781 he was removed to Annapolis, where he remained for the duration, unable to secure an exchange.

After the war, this versatile doctor undertook the study of law. An act of Legislature of 1798 authorized him to compile the statutes of Maryland. He published these in 1800 in two volumes ("Kilty's Laws"). In 1800, he moved to Washington and in the following year was appointed by President Adams to be chief judge of the Circuit Court of the District of Columbia. Later he moved back to Maryland and in 1806, was selected by the governor to the chancellorship of that state. In 1818, by act of Legislature, with Harris and Watkins, he published a continuation of Kilty's Laws. He also published a "Report on the British Statutes in Force in Maryland."

He passed away at Annapolis on October 10, 1821.

Ennalls Martin (1758-1834) was born in Talbot County, Maryland, on August 23, 1758. In his youth he attended the Newark Academy in Delaware and it is said that he was proficient in Latin and Greek. In 1777 he was taken in hand by Dr. William Shippen, Jr., who was then serving as surgeon-general of the Continental Army and was assigned to the apothecary department. Martin quickly demonstrated his worth and Congress commissioned him a hospital surgeon's mate on the condition that he attend the Medical School of Philadelphia. He served at the Bethlehem Hospital. The University of Pennsylvania awarded him an M.B. degree in 1782. Shippen appointed him demonstrator of anatomy and he soon developed into a skillful dissector.

During the five years that Martin served in the armed forces he left his post only twice, once to see his father, and once to travel to Saratoga to transport the sick and wounded after the defeat of Burgoyne.

Martin started his private practice at Talbot Court House. He contributed articles to the "Medical Repository." Once Martin decided upon a course of therapeutics, nothing could alter this regime. He was known to grasp an objecting patient by the nose and ram the medicine down his throat. His patients in general feared him, and his confreres behind his back referred to him as "Abernethy of Talbot." Against great prejudice, he introduced vaccination into his town.

In 1799 he helped found the Medical and Chirurgical Faculty of Maryland. He served as orator to this body in 1807, at which time he spoke on fever, and was elected president in 1815, which office he held until 1820 when he refused reelection. The University of Maryland presented him with an honorary M.D. in 1818. "An essay on the epidemics in the winters of 1813 and 1814 in Talbot and Queen Anne's Counties, Maryland," was presented to the annual convention of the Faculty in 1815. At his death he was actually working on a dissertation on the diseases of the Eastern Shore of Maryland. Martin passed away at Easton on December 16, 1834, at the age of seventy-six, and after a medical career that lasted for over fifty-two years.

James Cocke (1780-1813) was born in about 1780 in lower Virginia. He studied under the tutelage of Sir Astley Cooper, at Guy's Hospital, London. In 1804 he received an M.D. from the University of Pennsylvania. His thesis entitled: "An attempt to ascertain the causes of the extraordinary inflammation which attacks wounded cavities and their contents," promulgated original and daring views. He defended ovariotomy in this dissertation at a time when this procedure was under fire. The demand for this monograph was so great that it was republished in 1806. In 1805, he reduced a long standing dislocation of the humerus.

In 1804, Cocke moved to Baltimore, and he became a partner of Dr. John B. Davidge in 1807. Cocke presented physiology lectures to the private class of medical students organized by Davidge. With Davidge and John Shaw he helped found the College of Medicine of Maryland, and he was a factor in developing this institution to the rank of university. He was anatomy professor from 1807 until his death in 1813. He passed away on October 25, 1813, at the very hour that he was scheduled to present the opening lecture of his anatomical course in the new building of the university.

Maryland's list of colonial enactments relating to medical matters includes the following: an act for appointing coroners in each respective county (1666); an act to prevent the spreading and infection of the smallpox, from a vessel belonging to Amos Woodward, merchant (1731); an act to oblige infected ships and other vessels coming into this province to perform quarantine (1766); an act to continue the act of 1766 (1769); and, an act to prevent infection from the ship *Chance* (1774).

Epidemics of yellow fever raged in Baltimore in 1794, 1797, 1800 and 1808.

The medical journal of October 29, 1800, carried a letter on yellow fever by Dr. Pierre Chatard of Baltimore. Cordell states: "Dr. Chatard's superior education and acquirements gave to his opinions and statements great weight." Chatard had had more than passing intimacy with yellow fever, both in Maryland and in St. Domingo. He advocated the use of the cold bath in nervous conditions complicating yellow fever. He wisely states: "I should be glad to offer you some opinions concerning the efficient cause of this destructive distemper, but the whole of this subject appears to be so obscure that it seems advisable rather to keep silence than to hazard mere conjectures."

Of the four men whose names are associated with the conquest of yellow fever: Reed, Carroll, Lazear and Agramonte, all except the last were Baltimore residents at one time or another.

Smallpox inoculation was still practiced in Maryland in 1800.

Dr. James Smith, attending physician to the County Alms-house, began to employ vaccination in Maryland, in May, 1801. He maintained a complete record of each case in the books of the institution. Baltimore physicians were invited by Smith to examine these cases and he graciously offered to furnish his colleagues with the virus. For a time Smith could not convince any of the physicians to employ vaccination, notwithstanding the fact that smallpox was rampant in Baltimore.

A complete report on his cases was published by Dr. Smith in the *Telegraph*, on December 3 and 5, 1801. He pointed out that all cases were exposed to smallpox, both by inoculation and by direct contact with sufferers of the disease. Smith's accounts were so accurate and convincing that by 1802, vaccination was formally endorsed by the Medical and Chirurgical Faculty and concrete help was afforded Dr. Smith to establish the second vaccine institute in America. Here, Dr. Smith propagated the virus and distributed it free to the poor. On February 16, 1812, thirty-eight of the most prominent members of the Faculty made the grand gesture of offering to vaccinate all who applied free of charge. This group actually offered to pay each child furnishing proof of vaccination twenty-five cents.

In 1809, there were several cases of typhus in Baltimore.

Regarding the establishment of a medical society in Maryland, it took until 1799 for a charter to be drawn up, to be passed by the legislature and to be signed by the Governor.

The act was passed on January 20, 1799 and is termed: "An act to establish and incorporate a medical and chirurgical faculty or society in the State of Maryland." The preamble reads:

Whereas, it appears to the General Assembly of Maryland that the establishment and incorporation of a Medical and Chirurgical Faculty or Society of Physicians and Surgeons in the said State will be attended with the most beneficial and salutary consequences, by promoting and disseminating medical and chirurgical knowledge throughout the State, and may in future prevent the citizens thereof from risking their lives in the hands of ignorant practitioners or pretenders to the healing art. . . .

The Act further declares that the faculty members are to further such measures as are . . . . "most conducive to the promoting and disseminating of medical and surgical knowledge, or to alleviating the calamities and miseries of their fellow citizens." The Act makes provision for the possession and disposal of property, the making of by-laws and the holding of meetings.

The first meeting was held in Annapolis on the first Monday in June, 1799. At the time, fifteen members were declared to be a quorum. The incorporators and their successors were declared to be "one community, corporation and body politic, forever, by and under the name of the Medical and Chirurgical Faculty of the State of Maryland." The names of 101 incorporators were given, representing proportionately by from three to six each, the nineteen counties into which the State was then divided as well as the cities of Annapolis and Baltimore.

Dr. Cordell states:

The names represent not only the best elements of the Maryland profession of the period, but the highest types of physicians to be found anywhere—men trained at the schools of Leyden, Paris, London, Oxford, Edinburgh, Glasgow, Aberdeen, Dublin, Philadelphia, pupils of Boerhaave, Hunter, Cullen, the Monros, Bell, Rush and others, whose names are enrolled high upon the scroll of fame; men erudite in all the knowledge of medicine as it was then taught and understood, fine classical scholars to whom Latin was almost as familiar as their native tongue.

Chapter Eight

RHODE ISLAND

REFUGEES FROM MASSACHUSETTS sojourned to Rhode Island to seek religious and political freedom. Roger Williams organized the first settlement in June 1636. Portsmouth, situated on the island of Aquidneck, was colonized by the Antinomians, William Coddington (1601-1678), John Clarke (1609-1676) and Anne Hutchinson (1591-1643), in March-April, 1638. The fascinating story of Anne Hutchinson has been recorded elsewhere. Portsmouth does not appear to have suited the fancies of Coddington and Clarke, for we find them moving and establishing a settlement at Newport on April 29 1639.

Warwick was established in January 1643 by seceders from Providence under the guidance of Samuel Gorton. Portsmouth and Newport joined together on March 12, 1640, and this was followed by the consolidation of all four settlements on May 19, 1647, under a patent of March 14, 1644, in which the entire colony was designated Providence Plantations.

The particularistic sentiment still waxed strong, however, and in 1651 this initial union split into two confederations, one, including the mainland towns, Portsmouth and Newport. In 1654, a second reunion was accomplished through the efforts of Roger Williams, and on July 8, 1663, a charter was obtained from Charles II. On March 13, 1644, the Portsmouth-Newport General Court changed the name of the island from Aquidneck to the Isle of Rhodes (hence, Rhode Island). The official designation for the province as a whole in the charter of 1663, therefore, was Rhode Island and Providence Plantations. The charter was suspended at the beginning of the Andros regime in 1686, but was restored again after the Revolution of 1689.

As the 17th century drew to its final termination, there was a gradual transition from the agricultural to the commercial stage of civilization. Newport became a metropolis not only of legitimate business, but also of piracy, privateering and smuggling. Rum, manufactured from West Indian sugar and molasses, was sent to Africa in return for shiploads of slaves who eventually were sold in the southern slave marts and in the West Indies. The Sugar Act of April 5, 1764, and the steps taken by the British government to enforce the Navigation Acts, served to undermine Rhode Island trade and arouse the citizens.

The people of Rhode Island played a prominent part in the struggle for independence. On June 9, 1772 the *Gaspee*, a British vessel which had been sent over to enforce the acts of trade and navigation, ran aground in Narragansett Bay and was burned to the water's edge by a party of men from Providence. In May 1775, Nathanael Greene, a native of Rhode Island, was made commander of the Rhode Island militia, and in August 1776, a major-general in the Continental Army. He continued in this capacity until the close of the war.

In 1776, General Howe sent a detachment under General Henry Clinton to seize Newport as a base of operations for reducing New England. This was accomplished by the British on December 5, 1776. To capture this British garrison, later increased to 6000 men, the co-operation of about 10,000 men (mostly New England militia) under Major-General John Sullivan, and a French fleet carrying 4000 French regulars under Count D'Estaing, was planned in the summer of 1778. On August 9, 1778, Sullivan crossed to the north end of Rhode Island, but as the Frenchmen were in process of disembarking on Conanicut Island, Lord Howe arrived with the British fleet. Count D'Estaing hastily re-embarked his troops and sailed out to meet Howe. For two days the hostile fleets maneuvered for positions, and then they were dispersed by a severe storm. On August 20, 1778, D'Estaing returned to the port with his fleet badly crippled, and only to announce that he was going to sail to Boston to refit. The American officers protested but in vain, and on August 28, 1778, retreated to the north end of the island. The British pursued, and the next day there was a severe engagement in which the Americans were driven from Turkey and Quaker Hills. On August 30, the Americans, learning of the approach of Lord Howe's fleet with 5000 troops under Clinton, decided to abandon the island. The British evacuated Newport on October 25, 1779, and the French fleet was stationed here from July 1780 to 1781.

Roger Williams' ideas and influence plus the peculiar conditions under which the first settlements were established have tended to differentiate the history of Rhode Island from that of the other New England states. In 1640 the General Court of Massachusetts declared that the representatives of Aquidneck were "not to be capitulated withal either for themselves or the people of the isle where they inhabit," and in 1644 and again in 1648 the application of the Narragansett settlers for admission to the New England Confederacy was refused except on condition that they should pass under the jurisdiction of either Massachusetts or Plymouth. Rhode Island was one of the first places in the world to advocate bona fide religious freedom and political individualism.

The economic transition of the later 17th century from the agricultural to the commercial régime was followed by a further transition to the manufacturing régime during the closing years of the 18th and the early years of the 19th centuries.

It was the great seaports in colonial America that became the leading medical centers. It should not be forgotten that after the ports of Boston, New York, Philadelphia and Charleston, came Newport which did not lag far behind as a port of entry. It was the second port of New England, Boston alone outranking it.

Roger Williams established his colony without benefit of a physician. Prior to near the advent of the 18th century there is no record of a physician setting up practice in the northern part of Rhode Island. Newport, perhaps because of its convenient location and climate, early attracted colonists of education and refinement, including Dr. John Clarke (?–1676), one of the orginal settlers in 1638, who had studied both theology and medicine at Leyden and who had been banished from Boston with Roger Williams. He appears to be the first doctor in Rhode Island. He also was appointed pastor of the Baptist Church (in 1644)—the first church in Rhode Island which, incidentally, still bears his name. Later he returned to England where, with the help of Roger Williams, he succeeded after twelve years in securing in 1663 the charter under which Rhode Island was governed as a colony and federal state, until 1843. He lived to the age of 67, his death occurring in Newport in 1676.

Richard Bowen, the progenitor of numerous famous Rhode Island physicians, settled in the colony in 1640.

The earliest medical license granted in Rhode Island goes back to 1641. It stated that "Dr. Robert Jeoffreys shall be authorized to exercise the function of Chirurgerie." Note the implied differentiation between the physician and the surgeon which was recognized in similar licenses granted in Virginia and Connecticut at this time— the surgeon being held distinctly inferior to the physician.

The first colonial M.D. degree was granted to Captayne John Cranston in 1664 by the colonial legislature. The act reads:

Whereas the Court hath taken notice of the great blessing of God on the good endevers of Captayne John Cranston of Newport, both in phissicke and chirurgery, to the great comfort of such as have had occation to improve his skill and practice etc. The Court doe therefore vnanimously enacte and declare that the said Captayne John Cranston is lycenced and commistioned to administer phissicke, and practice chirurgery throughout this whole Collony and is by this court styled and recorded Doctor of phissicke and chirrurgery by the authority of this the Generall Assembly of this Collony.

To the objection raised by some that this was merely a license, Professor Waite replies that as the legislature undoubtedly had the right to confer upon other bodies the power to grant degrees, it certainly could itself exercise this function. Capt. John Cranston was an outstanding example of colonial versatility. He served as Attorney General, as commissioner to the convention with the adjoining colonies, and finally as Governor of the colony. It is not known whether he had received any formal medical training.

Let us examine the records of an ancient case involving medical jurisprudence datelined Newport, 1673, and note portions of the testimony at the trial of Thomas Cornell for the murder of his mother, Mrs. Rebecca Cornell:

John Briggs' Testimony:

John Briggs of the Town of Portsmouth aged sixty-four years or thereabouts, being according to Law Sworn and Ingaged before the Councill, Testifieth, That on the twelve day of this Instant month of February in the night as this depon't lay in his bedd, he being mid dreams of Mrs. Rebecca Cornell, Sofoated and being between Sleeping and waking, as he thought, he thought he felt Something heave up the Bedcloathes twice and thought somebody had been coming to bed to him, whereupon he awaked and turned himselfe about in his Bed, and being turned he perceived a light in the room, like to the Dawning of Day and plainly saw the shape and appearance of a woman standing by his Bedside, whereat he was much affrighted, and cryd out, in the name of God what art thou. The apparition answered, I am your Sister Cornell, and twice sayd, see how I was burnt with Fire, and she plainly appeared unto him to be very much burnt about the shoulders, face and Head.

Taken before the Deputy Gov. and Councill mett the 20th day of February 1672-73 as attest John Sanford, Secretary.

John Pearce's Testimony:

John Pearce of the Town of Portsmouth aged 42 years or thereabouts being according to law engaged, Testifieth that since the Decease of

Mrs. Rebecca Cornell, this Deponent being at the House of Mrs. (or Wm.) Wood, there was Thomas Cornell and his wife, and Thomas Cornell said that his Mother in her lifetime had desired to have a good fire, and further sayd that he thought God had delivered her ends for now she had it. Taken the 7th of May 1673 in the morning before me.

Joshua Coggeshall.
Assistant.

On the strength of this unusual testimony Thomas Cornell was sent to the gallows.

John Cranston et al.

We whose names are undersubscribed being on the second inquiry after the untimely death or decease of Mrs. Rebecca Cornell of the Town of Portsmouth, desired to make a diligent search whether any wound might be found on Her. Too this affirm that we found a suspitious wound on her in the uppermost part of her stomach.

Witness our hands, ye 20th. day of February 1672-73.

Henry Greenland Chir'g'on
Simon Cooper Chir'g'on.

I do attest to the above written and declare it to be my Judgment witness my hand the day and year above written.

John Cranston Dep'ty Gov. & Practitioner
in Physick &
Chyryrgery.

The distinction between the practitioner in surgery and the practitioner in medicine is again demonstrated by these quaint old records.

Settlements were made in what is now Kent County, Rhode Island, soon after 1640, but no town was incorporated nor village laid out until 1677. The inhabitants in the earlier years, were few and just prior to the War of Independence, the total number comprised about 600.

The original colonists included the four Spencer brothers, John, Abner, Peleg, and Thomas (1679-1752), who had come from England, where they left three other brothers. Thomas Spencer, the youngest, was a seventh son, which fact alone, according to tradition, made him a physician. He received a good medical education and became the first to engage in the practice of medicine in this section of Rhode Island. He is believed to have engaged in medical practice from 1690 to 1740. Besides his medical activities, he found time to serve as a magistrate and clerk of the town. He held considerable land and became very wealthy. He was frequently called on consultation to other sections of Rhode Island. The house which he constructed still stands on the hill in back of the village.

Dr. Spencer was a Quaker and served as a preacher to this sect before he died.

In 1740 or 1742, Dr. Dutee Jerauld (1715-1800) moved from Medfield, Massachusetts, to Warwick, which is located one mile on the road from Greenwich to Apponaug. Jerauld's parents were French Huguenot refugees and he prided himself upon being an American by birth, for he came into the world soon after his parents arrived on American shores. It is thought that he learned medicine from his father, who also was a practitioner of the healing art.

Young Dr. Jerauld married the daughter of Edward Gorton of Warwick, and had five sons and four daughters. Jerauld was a plain man, short and stout, but well respected by all who knew him.

Early in his professional career, Jerauld practiced alone in an area of six to eight miles. He became particularly famous for his therapy in fevers and chronic diseases. He employed considerable common sense in conjunction with his drug therapy and never made use of radical methods. He favored medications made from indigenous roots and herbs, as infusions, syrups, or decoctions, and gave precise directions for their collection and preparation.

Jerauld particularly favored the prickly-ash, a small tree or shrub found in this area which he employed in rheumatic affections. Rumor has it that the herb was exterminated in this area because of his numerous prescriptions for it.

Jerauld's fees were small and it is probable that he died a poor man. The customary payment for his medical services consisted of farm produce.

He lived until the age of ninety, dying in 1804. He was buried on his farm. His dwelling still stands, and, although altered and enlarged, is still in use as a poor house.

Gorton Jerauld, one of his sons, followed in his father's and grandfather's footsteps, and became a physician. He practiced for a while with his father and ran a smallpox hospital in Warwick. However, he never remained in one place for any protracted period and prior to his death, he left Rhode Island.

Dr. Joseph Joslyn (1736-1780), a physician who had emigrated from Scotland, came to East Greenwich in about 1770. Although he built up a fine reputation as an excellent physician and surgeon, he unfortunately became an alcoholic and died at the age of forty-four in the year 1780. Soon after coming to East Greenwich, he married the widow of Archibald Campbell and lived in the house which she owned on the main street. Joslyn maintained a smallpox hospital near the town in which he capably and effectively managed this disease. People from all over the state came to his institution,

He also helped manage one or two other smallpox hospitals in southern Rhode Island.

During the years that Joslyn practiced in East Greenwich, one Dr. Hawkins came to this town and started to practice, but for some reason or other, he soon left the area.

From 1780, when Joslyn passed away, until 1782, no resident physician was available in East Greenwich. In the latter year, Dr. Peter Turner, who had just completed military service after serving throughout the war as surgeon to a Rhode Island regiment, came to this town to practice medicine and surgery. For over thirty years, he practiced over this entire area and brought a high grade of medical practice to this district.

Peter Turner (1751-1822) the son of Dr. William Turner of Newark, New Jersey, came into this world on September 2, 1751. In 1776 he married the daughter of Bonswell Childs of Warren, Rhode Island. His father was a practicing physician who passed away when Peter was very young. He was reared by his half-brother, Dr. Canfield, with whom he studied medicine. After completing his medical course, Peter entered the Army and served as surgeon to one of the Rhode Island regiments throughout the greater part of the war. He was present at the Battle of Red Bank and his kindness in treating the wounded of this battle was long remembered by the recipients of his humanity. Although few Americans were wounded, the British had heavy casualties and Dr. Turner, according to the highest medical ethics, rendered the injured enemy first class medical care.

With Samuel Tenney, he treated the mortally wounded Count Donop, the Hessian officer in charge of the assaulting party, and the Count during his last minutes presented his sword and spurs to him for his kindness.

After the war, largely due to the fact that his in-law, General Varnum, an eminent lawyer and officer in the continental army, lived in East Greenwich, he was induced to set up his office here. The story is told how prior to Dr. Turner's settling in East Greenwich, Dr. Isaac Senter was thinking seriously of coming to this town permanently. But Dr. Turner paid an urgent visit to him in Newport and spirited words passed between them. The record shows that Senter never came to East Greenwich.

Prior to the arrival of Dr. Turner, there had never been any fully trained surgeon in this part of Rhode Island. The citizens, for a time, had some fear in calling him, lest he perform a major surgical procedure without much provocation. However, the countryside soon learned to respect and love him and his practice soon extended for a radius of ten miles or so from East Greenwich. He frequently made calls in Exeter, South Kingston, and West Greenwich and at times in Bristol and Warren. Various patients complained of his high fees, but of course, the people had been accustomed to horribly underpay their physician.

Turner loved surgery, which he performed with dexerity, precision and skill, but he practiced a routine brand of medicine. The story is related that about four miles from East Greenwich, a boy lacerated his femoral artery with massive and exsanguinating hemorrhage ensuing. A messenger was dispatched post-haste to seek out the doctor. Turner was met just returning from Warren and, while the packet was coming to the wharf, he had a horse saddled. As soon as he landed, Turner mounted the horse and galloped away to the stricken patient whom he reached in an incredibly short time. Explaining to the grieved father that death or amputation were the only alternatives, he immediately performed the latter procedure and the boy recovered promptly and lived to a ripe old age.

Turner treated gunshot wounds, broken limbs and fractured skulls so successfully that he was greatly admired by all those who witnessed his surgical skill.

When the occasion demanded, although he was normally a person of great humanity, he kept enough of the army in him to reinforce his important orders with most vehement language.

He made his calls on horseback and was always known to maintain a rapid pace. Turner was a short, obese and heavy set man, surprisingly quick in movements, with the use of only one eye. He was given to relating humorous anecdotes with gusto and was held in high esteem by those who knew him.

His unpretentious but comfortable dwelling was surrounded by the most beautiful garden in town.

Dr. Turner's medical disciples were numerous. His nephew, Dr. William Turner of Newport, completed his medical studies in his office. Others who benefited by his instruction were his sons, Daniel, who died of yellow fever in Georgia, Henry and James, Dr. John W. Tibbitts and Dr. Thomas Tillinghast.

For several years prior to his death, Peter Turner was confined to his room and made utterly helpless by paralysis following a stroke.

He died in East Greenwich on February 14, 1822.

In 1686 a French physician, Pierre Ayrault, settled in Rhode Island, but little is known about him.

Providence in 1700 had no doctor and the population was only about 1,400. Dr. Richard Bowen, already of the third generation of doctors in his family, had settled in Seekonk (now East Providence), only two miles away, shortly before 1700 and looked after the medical needs of both communities. His sons, Thomas and Jabez, were both educated as physicians; "Jabez settled in Providence on the home-lot of Roger Williams" not far from where St. John's Church now stands, while Thomas joined his father in Seekonk. Both of them had sons and grandsons who were doctors and had the best educations obtainable at that time.

Early in the 18th century Bishop Berkeley, one of the most scholarly and highly educated men of the time, settled in Newport. He is best remembered for his empirical—almost humorous—tar-water specific:

To render Tar Water as generally useful as possible, I would draw up some rules and remarks in a small compass.

Norwegian tar being the most liquid, mixes best with water. Put a gallon of cold water to a quart of this tar, stir and work them very strongly together with a flat stick, for about four minutes. Let the vessel stand covered forty-eight hours that the tar may subside. Then pour off the clear water, and keep it close-covered, or, rather, bottled, and well-stopped, for use.

I must own myself persuaded, from what I have already seen and tried, that tar water may be drank with great safety and success in the cure or relief of most if not all diseases; in ulcers, eruptions and all foul cases; scurvies of all kinds, disorders of the lungs, stomach and bowels; in nervous cases, in all inflammatory distempers; in decays and other maladies. Nor is it of use only in the cure of sickness; it is also useful to preserve health, and guard against infection and old age; as it gives lasting spirits, and invigorates the blood. I am even induced, by the nature and analogy of things, and its wonderful success in all kinds of fevers, to think that tar water may be very useful in the plague both as a cure and as a preventive.

Bishop Berkeley played a major role in establishing the Newport Philosophical Society in 1730. This organization antedated the Philosophical Society of Philadelphia which was guilded by Benjamin Franklin. From the continent Doctors John Brett and Thomas Moffat came to Newport to mingle with Bishop Berkeley, Dr. Halliburton and others who organized the Redwood Library in 1747.

The founding of The Company of the Redwood Library marked an important forward step in the development of Rhode Island education. Ezra Stiles, who later became President of Yale College and was considered by many as "the most learned man in America," was its librarian for many years. It was he who was the sparkplug in the establishment of Rhode Island College (Brown University) in 1764.

The diary of the Redwood family contains the following:

When the establishment of a college at R.I. was first contemplated, by certain persons of the Baptist society (a people who have panted after learning in order to be able to give a reason for the faith that is in them) Mr. Redwood was applied for aid, when he offered to give a thousand pounds sterling, on condition that it would be erected on Rhode Island.

But an association of wealthy individuals in the town of Providence, chiefly of the family of the Browns offered still more, which happily fixed its location there.

The diary further states:

The medical part of them (referring to the books) was excellent; they were amply sufficient to give the medical student complete information of all that was then known in the English language on Anatomy, Surgery, Chemistry, and Botany, together with the history of drugs, and of their various preparation and uses, with the history of the progress of Physic from the time of Hippocrates. It sowed the seeds of the sciences, and rendered the inhabitants of Newport a better read and inquisitive people than any other town in the British Colonies.

"Burning Ague," a highly fatal ailment, ravaged Rhode Island in 1723, particularly in the vicinity of Providence. Webster declared: "In proportion to its patients, no disease in America was ever more mortal. It did not prevail in a large town, but in villages, and perhaps the clearing of some neighboring swamps might have been one cause of the disease."

The following account of William Hunter (1730?-1777) of Newport is based on the excellent article by Dr. E. B. Krumbhaar:

William Hunter was born during the period between 1729 and 1731, allegedly in Scotland. It is said, but not proven, that he was a cousin of the renowned William and John Hunter of Long Calderwood, in Lanarkshire. It is likewise probable but not definitely established that he was a decendant of the Hunterston Hunters. The famed brothers claimed descent from Patrick, a 17th century Hunter of Hunterston, via one of his sons, Francis. Hunterston Castle was located in West Kilbride, Ayrshire, near Southannan. A resemblance between the good colonial physician and his cousins has been noted in examining their respective portraits. The resemblance is most marked between William, the son of the colonial physician, and John Hunter.

It is said that the William Hunter now under discussion was at Culloden, where as a mere boy he was a surgeon's mate assisting the famous Peter Middleton of New York. He apparently was not effected adversely by his adventure for we see him soon engaging in the study of medicine at Edinburgh under the tutelage of the elder Monro (primus, 1697-1767). His great grandson found books at Edinburgh with his name inscribed in them, but more definite evidence of his sojourn there is not yet forthcoming.

Dr. John D. Comrie of Edinburgh reported to Dr. Krumbhaar that records do not show Hunter's name as being in Monro's class list from 1746 to 1749. Unfortunately this record was not kept from 1750 to 1767. He further says: "It can be said definitely that he did not graduate at Edinburgh, and that he was not a member of the Royal Medical Society, but he may have taken a license from the Royal College of Surgeons. His name is not in the Bibliotheca Britannica." With reference to Culloden, Doctor Comrie states that Hunter's name is not in the list of Jacobite prisoners, as was perhaps to be expected, and naturally is not in MacNaughton's "Heroes of the Forty-five," or Johnston's "Roll of Officers in the Medical Service of the British Army."

It seems probable that William Hunter studied at Leyden. and while he is not listed as a matriculant, he could have pursued special studies there without registration.

William Hunter arrived in the New World in 1752 at the age of twenty-two or twenty-three. He brought a considerable collection of books with him. This formed the foundation of a library which was the largest in New England at the time of its dispersion after his death. His son presented some of these books to the library of Brown University, where they are still to be found, although not preserved as a collection. Among the titles were: J. Allen, "Synopsis Universæ Medicinæ" (1730); Alpinus, "De Medicina Methodica" (1719) and "Medicina Aegyptiorum" (1719); C. Benedictus, "Tabidorum Theatrum" (1656); Boerhaave, "Disputatio Medica" (1702); Fr. Hoffman, "Opera" (6 vols., 1748); Mangetus, "Bibliotheca Pharmaceutica-Medica" (1703); Spigelius, "Opera quae Extant Omnia" (1645); J. J. Wepfer, "Observationes anatomicae ex Cadaveribus eorum quos Sustulit Apoplexia" (1724); Th. Willia, "Cerebri Anatome" (1666) and 80 Leyden dissertations. Besides these volumes in the inventory of Hunter's effects are mentioned "Alston's Lectures in 2 Volums (sic) 13/6, Macbride 15/9, Elabratory laid open 5/6, Persivals Essays in 2 Volumes 9/, White, on pregnant women 4/6, London Practice on Physick 1/6, Mackburg on ye Bile 3/6, Whites Cases 3/, A new dispensatory 6/9 2, old ditto 4/6, Eddenborough

Letters 3/6, Quincy's Lexicon 2/6, Clarke's observations 2/3, Family Physician 4/6, Medical consultam 3/6, Eustachu Plates 9/, Smalla's ditto 21/, Monros Anatomy 2/3, and Johnson Dictionary folio in Two Volumes."

William Hunter settled in Newport which was already a flourishing community. The basis for Newport's good situation was the charter granted by Charles II to Roger Williams and John Clarke, which granted increased civil and religious freedom above that permitted in any other province. John Brett, Thomas Moffatt and John Halliburton, physicians all, also came from England to Newport at about this time. Hunter's success was not long in developing, for after all, European graduates in medicine were none too prevalent in the colonies at that time. William Hunter was the first "male accoucheur in the colony."

The following prescription was written by Hunter: "For Mrs. Arnold ℞ Tincture: perm: Elixr—Vitriol: Sign: the Tincture half a tablespoonfull of which to be taken in a cup of Balm Tea morning, noon, and night every day Apl 24, 1777."

His ledger yields the following:

Dos Ex. Ipecac No: Bol. No. Ex. Vitre Antim; a child—Dos. ex Rhei.; Dos. Ex. Sal. Glaub.; Mist. Anod.; Bol. ex. Rhei.; Pills; Plasters; a operation hard open abscess in her throat 3/; b. to directing a proper complex bandage and tapping you 2/8/o; Ph. Tinct.: Bol. Capini; The Strong Mixture Empl. Epis.; Jallay's Solut.; Mixr Hydragog.; Bol. Ex. Opium No. VI 4/; Mixr. purg. u.a.; Decoc. ex. F. Senna; Phil. Ex. G. Gambage— case of dropsy; Child—emetic; Ph Tinct. c. Peru. & Rhei. 3/6; Ph. of Balsam; Box of Pectoral pills; A blister inter scapula 2/o/o; Child. Dos. ex Calom. No.; Nov. 6, 1763—To delivering your wife of a Dhgt—8 dollars or 2/8/o, The above made a present of; Nov. 29, 1765—To delivering ditto in dangerous labour of a son—6/o/o; Dec. 20, 1767—Delivered of a daughter dangerous labour 6/o/o; Mr. Nichols—Comptroler—yr. negro boy salivated 90/o = 4/10/o, yr. negro woman visited /3—3; Us. cured of the venereal disease /60 = 3/o/o; Sept. 1768 To curing you and yr. wife of the venereal disease /120—6/o/o; Aug. 12, 1769 Cured a second time of ditto /120—6/o/o; May 21st, 1764 Cabel Arnold Carpenter near Parson Browns—Daughter a box pills 2/6d—, a pt. of Tinctr. 1/3d—, V. twice 6/—o/9/9; 23rd, Visited 3/, 25th visited 3/, 27th visited 3/, 29th visited 3/—o/12/o; 30th R. pil & Tinct. 3/9d, 31st visited 3/, July 9th a pt. of Tinct. 4/6d—o/11/3; July 9 Visited 3/, 12th R. Tinct. 4/6d, and visited 3/, 17th ℞. Tinct. 4/6d—o/15/o—total £2/8/o; Jany. 21, 1771, Visited in the night 9/, Bol. purg. 1/6, visited 3/, 22nd visited 3/, o/16/6; 23d. Al: Decoct purg 7/6 visited 3/—; Dec. 21, 1773 Given in—£7-4-0; February 1768 Given in: April 11th Then received the above in full Wm. Hunter; 1768 Mr. Allborough, a fisherman opposite Capt. Carrs on the point in Kindal Nichols house; July 2d. To delivering your Wife in dangerous Labour 120/—£6.; Lawf. money; July 30, 1771 Fanny Demmerson an Indian at .... Cured of L.V. 60/ Hot Chases; Aug. 29, 1771, Hannah Church, a mulatto at Finsons Cured of L. Vencr. 60/. Jan. 1772 paid in part one guinea.

In 1765 and 1768, services rendered Mr. & Mrs. George Wright were itemized as follows:

		Sh	D
June	5th Mrs. Wright a box Ointment 2/6. & a Box pills 6/3d	8″	9″
	—and Visited 3/—6th Visited 3/—7th Visited 3/—	9″	
	10 Visited 3/—11th the Ointment Repeated 2/6	5″	6″
	14 the pills Repeated 6/3—and twenty powders 5/—...	11″	9″
	and Visited 3/—22d the pills as before 6/3	9″	3″
	22d and powders; again 5/—and Visited 3/—July 4th		
	Visited 3/	11″	
Septemr	15, a Box pills 9/6 and more Ointment 2/6..........	12″	—
1768	and Visited twice 6/	6″	
August	2d Visited Mr. Wright 3/—3d Drefesed his hand 3/ ...	6″	
	3d and spread plaister /6 & Ointment 1/ 4th Drugs		
	Dit. 3/	4″	6″
	6th Drugs dit 3/	3″	

That Captain Edward Wanton remained his patient, at least until 1770, is demonstrated by Hunter's letter to him about his Gout.

In 1755, Hunter advertised in the Boston *Evening Post* of January 20, 27 and February 3, that he was desirous of giving a series of lectures on anatomy and surgery.

Benjamin Waterhouse stated:

About the year 1756, Dr. William Hunter gave at Newport, R.I., the first anatomical and surgical lectures ever delivered in the twelve Colonies. They were delivered in the Court House, two seasons in succession, by cards of invitation, and to great satisfaction. His collection of instruments was much larger than any professor exhibits at this day. Doctor Hunter was a man of talents, well-educated at Edinburgh, and a gentleman of taste in the fine arts.

The proof that Hunter's lectures were actually presented lies in the existence of at least two tickets of admission printed on playing card backs. However, it is not known how many attended the lectures or for how long they were given. Thacher mentions that they were

given in 1754-1756, but the date on the above advertisement seems
to indicate that they were not begun until 1755. The lectures were
given in the Old Colony (State) House. Whereas it is a mooted
question whether these lectures were the first in anatomy in this
country, there seems to be every reason to accept the belief that they
were the *first systematic, advertised, public lectures* on the subject
known to have been delivered in this country. It will be recalled that,
after returning from Europe, Thomas Cadwalader had given lectures and demonstrations of dissections in Philadelphia in 1730. But
it is very questionable if these lectures and demonstrations approached
true systematic instruction. There is certainly no known record of
their having been publicly advertised. John Bard's and Peter Middleton's instruction and dissection, harking back to 1750, also do not
appear to have been advertised. There is no record that Thomas
Wood's proposed lectures to be given in New Brunswick as advertised in the *New York Weekly Postboy* of January 27, 1752 were
ever consummated.

William Hunter's presentations of anatomy and surgery were
rudely interrupted by military necessity. In 1755 he assumed the post
of surgeon in Colonel Harris' regiment in the unsuccessful expedition
against Crown Point led by Sir William Johnston. After the campaigns of 1756 and 1757, Hunter in March 1758, was elected by the
General Assembly physician and surgeon general to the Rhode Island
troops. He left Newport on June 29, 1758, and arrived at Lake
George on or about July 4 of this year. In an epistle from the Committee of War of Rhode Island, to Governor Hopkins, dated Newport, June 29, 1758, a letter was enclosed to Colonel Babcock which
said, "store ship is arrived, with the arms and tents for the American
troops . . . and Dr. Hunter set out this morning for Providence, on
his way to Albany. . . . " A letter from Colonel Babcock to Governor
Hopkins, Camp Lake George, July 4, 1758, states "Your letter, per
Hunter, I received."

Notwithstanding the fact that the British under Abercrombie were
vanquished by the French at Ticonderoga in Canada, as elsewhere
throughout the world, their ambitions were eventually crowned with
success. Perhaps Hunter served in both Abercrombie's and Amherst's
Canadian expeditions. His status as medical officer to the Rhode Island
troops is apparent from the following resolution of the General
Assembly:

The Genereal Assembly do vote and resolve, and it is voted & resolved that William Hunter who went & officiated as Physician and surgeon to the troops of this Colony during the last Campaign, shall be

paid his wages at and after the rate of ten pounds lawful money, per month, in bills of credit of this Colony, persuant to agreement: that for the ensuing Campaign his pay shall be one hundred & eighty pounds old tenor, shall be procured for him according to his own directions, that in case the said W.H. shd loose, or by any accident be deprived of the medicine chest he shall have liberty & credit with some proper persons, to be pitched upon to that purpose, to supply himself with what shall be found necessary for the remaining part of the Campaign; that Mr. Hunter shall have the same allowance made for him by the Colony for Chirurgical instruments, in this Campaign as he had in the last; that the Colony shall furnish all stores necessary for the accommodation of the sick, who shall be tended and taken care of by a sufficient number of men suitable for nurses, to be selected out of the companies; this assembly not approving that women should be employed for that service; that if any contingent charges should accrue to the Doctor by travelling, transporting or otherwise, it shall be paid him by the Colonies commissary, and lastly, he shall have a marquis or tend provided for him.

Following the British success in Quebec and Montreal, Hunter went back to his practice in Newport.

Ezra Stiles, a mortal enemy of Hunter and his toryism presents this picture of obstetrics in Newport in 1774:

"In conversation with Mrs. Dennis a principal Midwife of this Town, she told me, that the number of Births in this Town last year was four hundred & thirty, that there would be 440 this year, that the number of actually bearing Women was near nine hundred, and that their usual Term of bearing was from fourteen Months to two years, that is each had a Child once in 14 mo or two years, that of the 900 Women Dr. Hunter had about fifty and might deliver 30 a year; Dr. Halliburton about a dozen Women; all the other Doctors together not so many as a dozen. There are three women Midwives more all which deliver but a few, suppose 20 or 30, I should suppose Mrs. D. delivers 350 or more per annum. I suppose these comprehend Whites & Blacks; of all which there are in Town Nine Thousand Two Hundred souls. . . . Total Souls in Newport last May 7917 Whites, 1292 Blacks and Indians 9209."

Hunter, like other colonial physicians, imported his own drugs. He dealt mostly with one Mr. Witherly and Messrs. Corbyn and Co., Druggists, Holborn, and he had an apothecary compound them and sell them. Thacher declares that Hunter "was a most eminently successful practitioner, as well as an operator in surgery; he appeared at that day to be bold and rash, but the truth was, he brought with him from Europe a more exact knowledge of anatomy, and greater chirurgical skill grounded on that knowledge, than existed in the colonies at that period."

After settling in Newport, Hunter sojourned for ten years in the "old Rodman House," originally owned by Thomas Rodman (1647-1727) who came from the Barbados in 1680. Following his demise, his son Thomas lived there; following this colonial gentleman, came Hunter; then Dr. John Halliburton. Hunter afterwards moved to a house on Thames and Mary streets. Another house that Hunter occupied was erected on Washington Street.

On September 13, 1761, Hunter married Deborah Malbone (born November 23, 1744, died abroad), the youngest daughter of Godfrey Malbone (1724-1785), an Oxford graduate who, according to Thacher, became "one of the most opulent merchants and land proprietors of the country." After this marriage, Hunter became one of the "undertakers" for an addition to the church, of which his father-in-law was a vestryman in return "for which both gentlemen were given pews, subject to a tax for defraying the expenses of the church."

Colonel Malbone was one of the most nonchalant men in colonial history. While his house was being consumed by flames, he is said to have remarked: "Though we lose our home, there is no reason to lose our dinner." Of the seven children born to William and Deborah Hunter, three, William, Katharine and Godfrey Malbone, died in infancy. Three daughters died abroad: Elizabeth (1762-1859), Anne (1766-1859), wife of John Falcounet (Falconer), and another Katharine (1773-1860) wife of the Count de Cardignan. Another William, the youngest child (1774-1849), was "a lawyer of very great classical and scholastic attainments." He became a famous member of the Rhode Island bar, was elected Senator by his home state from 1811 to 1821, and was appointed Minister to Brazil.

The aforementioned Ezra Stiles, the Congregationalist minister, who became President of Yale, naturally enough loathed Hunter for his toryism. He declared:

Heard of Dr. Hunter's death in Newport. He was Souch Physician—spent about two years in attending the medical Lecture in University of Edinburgh—then came over to America 1754 circa, with nothing. Settled at Newport, where he got an Estate, turned Chhman (Churchman, i.e. Church of England), became as haughty as a Scotch Laird, high in ministerial and parliamy Measures, an inveterate Enemy to American Liberty—dressed well, was much of the Gentleman, lived high & luxuriously—could approve nothing but what was European, despised American Literature & Colleges—of polite Morals. Of natural good Sense & a taste for the belles Lettres—but not a man of any great Reading in any Branch of Learning, even that of his own Profession. He tho't he bro't knowledge eno' with him out of Scotland, at aet. 21, for a physician in America. He determined his Mode of Religion upon secular & political Motives, such as would have joyned him to a Mosque in Turkey, the House of Rimon at Damascus, or St. Peter's at Rome. Had he taken time for inquiry into his own real principles he would probably have found them the same as David Humes or some other Scotch Deist—but he was not disposed for such a self-examination; and had he known himself a Deist he would yet have been a Scotch Chhman in New Engld, from his Hatred of New Engld Presbyterians.

Hunter was a student of the arts in a practical way. When making calls on the mainland, Hunter noted some excellent chalk drawings on a barn door. After examining other good drawings on later visits, he looked up the artist who turned out to be a mere boy—one Gilbert Stuart by name. Hunter financed an art education for the budding artist. Later Gilbert Stuart—who was destined to become the great painter—visited Hunter in Newport and was asked by the Doctor if he was ready to begin painting. The boy stated that he thought that he was. Hunter thereupon ordered him to paint his dog. The original of this picture is still to be seen in Newport in the house of Mrs. William E. Glyn, a great-great-granddaughter of Doctor Hunter.

As intimated previously, Hunter was an avowed loyalist and avid supporter of British Authority. He was a subscriber in 1767 to the anti-colonial *Boston Chronicle*, and as the Revolution loomed up, he openly denounced all American patriots. On Christmas Day, 1775, Hunter and seven other Tories were hailed before General Lee to renounce Tory principles and swear fidelity to the New Country and declare readiness to take arms in its defence if requested to do so by the Continental Congress. Three of the Tories refused to take the oath and Hunter is not among them. Notwithstanding, as a physician, he was exempted from taking arms.

In July, 1776, the General Assembly demanded that Hunter subscribe to the following declaration: "Declaration or Test, to be made by suspected persons in the Colony, relative to the War with Great Britain: 'I, the subscriber, do solemnly and sincerely declare, that I believe the war, resistance, and opposition, in which the United American Colonies are now engaged, against the fleets and armies of Great Britain, is on the part of the said colonies just and necessary; and that I will not, directly nor indirectly, afford assistance of any sort or kind, whatever, to the said fleets and armies, during the continuance of the present war; but that I will heartily assist in the defence of the United Colonies.'" Hunter refused and on July 18, 1775, he was removed by the sheriff to Smithfield, R.I. In August of the same year, he was allowed to go back to Newport on account of the dangerous illness of one of his children. Three of the state magistrates were appointed to decide when he should be sent back to Smithfield.

When the British captured Newport on December 8, 1776, it was only natural for them to accept their ally with the greatest friendliness. Stiles lists Hunter as one of the members of the Newport population at that time and gives him the dubious distinction of being a "four star Tory." Hunter's happiness to be in the area controlled by England was short-lived. According to one version, he became affected with a "putrid fever," while in attendance at the Army Hospital; according to another version he acquired the same disease while attending prisoners of war on a man of war in the harbor. A brief illness terminated fatally on January 30, 1777.

The *Newport Gazette*, a Tory paper published during the British occupation, printed the following obituary in the February 7, 1777, number:

Last Friday night departed this life Dr. W^m. Hunter in whom concentrated all those virtues wh. adorn the patriot, form the husband and compose the parent. The town has sustained a loss which can not be repaired. His worthy consort is deprived of the most engaging of husbands and his children the best, the fondest of parents. The patience with which he bore the many & unprovoked insults of his countrymen in full confidence that relief would soon arrive deserves every encomium and perhaps the goodness of his disposition is not in any instance more conspicuous than in forbearing to retaliate the injuries of any whom the restoration of the authority of his sovereign had placed in his power.

Hunter was buried in Trinity churchyard with his children who had died earlier. On his tombstone is written: "In memory of Doctor William Hunter who departed this life on the 30th of January 1777 in the 47th year of his age." His widow and three beautiful daughters were highly regarded. "Among the maidens of Newport who were adored by the French officers were the Misses Hunter. The gay followers of Rochambeau sang their praises and traced their names upon the windows of their quarters."

Eliza, the eldest daughter was threatened by blindness and Mrs. Hunter took her to Europe with the other two. The four ladies never returned to America. Two miniatures still in the family possession are illustrative of the beauty of the Hunter girls. One Mr. Chipman writes in his journal: "We have heard much of Miss Hunter of R.I. who was at Dr. Lloyd's; we were prepared to expect something supernatural. We called to see her; our expectations were exceeded by the interview. She is, without exception, the most beautiful, accomplished, and elegant person (with a mind, if possible, as we were informed by her friends, superior) that I ever beheld."

Hunter's will was not probated for almost three years after his death:

In the Name of God, Amen, I William Hunter, of Newp^t in ye County of Newp^t in ye Colony of Rhode Island, Physician, being sick & Weak, but of a disposing mind & memory, do hereby make this my last Will & Testament, & dispose of such Estate, as I am Blefsed withal in the following manner to Wit, Imprimis, I Give, Bequeath, & devise, to my Dear Wife, the Income & Profits of One Third part of my Real Estate, during her Life, as also one third part of my Personal Estate, Item, all the Remainder of my Estate both Real & Personal I order to be Divided by my Ex^{rs} into five Equal parts. Two parts of which I Give, devise, & Bequeath to my Son William, His Heirs & Assigns forever, & the other Three parts, I Give, devise & Bequeath to my three Daughters, Elizabeth, Anne, & Catharine, Share & Share alike to them, their Heirs, & Assigns forever, Item, my mind & Will is, & I order that my Wife shall have & receive ye Issue & Profits of my Real Estate, till my Youngest Child Comes of Age, & that my Daughters receive their shares of my Personal Estate when they Respectively arrive at ye age of Twenty one Years, And, Lastly, I appoint my s^d wife & my Two Friends, Francis Brindley & Simon Pease Ex^{rs} of this my Last Will, dated at Newport this thirtieth day of January A D 1777 Wm. Hunter—Seal Sealed & Acknowledged as his last Will in presence of us Francis Brindley Junr Penelope Bisset A Johnston Newpo^t The aforegoing is a true Coppy of ye Original Will of William Hunter Recorded & Compared, by Me this 15th day of decb^r A D 1780 Peleg Barker Junr Council.

In January, 1780, an inventory of his personal estate was filed. 273 drugs are listed, including ammonia, aloes, antimony, arsenic, cantharides, castor, cinnamon, hyocyamus, jalop, James' powders, lunar caustic, opium, paregoric, santonin, sulphur and tartar emetic. Numerous other remedies included are of historical value only. "Sang. Draconis," of which six ounces were valued at one shilling three halfpennies, must have been a powerful psychotherapeutic, if not physical agent. "One Neagro Man Named Mark" £22.10 is included in the inventory. Another Negro, named Quarts, was worth only £13.10, considerably less than a good piece of furniture. The Notes of Hand include 129 individual items listed for amounts varying from six shillings to 2,500 pounds and totalling £7,860, 6s. and 6 pence.

The two following letters by Hunter are of interest. They are im-bued with a certain refinement and friendliness so characteristic of the man:

The Honb'le. Sir William Johnston (sic) Baronet at New London. Newport May 10, 1768. Sir: Nothing but Mrs. Hunter's being in the Straw and not well enough to be left shou'd have prevented me at this time from the pleasure of waiting upon you at New London. As you are come this way for the benefit of the Sea-Air let me persuade you to pass a few days with us on this pleasant Island surrounded by the Ocean. Here you will enjoy more of the Sea-Air than is to be found on any other spot on the Continent. The Vapours or fogs that infest us at this season of the year and that may be deemed unhealthy to the Inhabitants I will venture to say will prove salutary to you that have lived so many years at so great a distance from the Ocean. Dr. Moffatt who is capable of giving you the best advice I dare say will confirm this. I shall do every-thing in my power to make the place agreeable to you and altho there are many here that can and will entertain you with more elegance and Splendour that I can yet I am sure there are none that will give you a more hearty welcome or be more pleased to see you than Sir Your Most Obedient Humble Servant Wm. Hunter.

To the Hon. Sir W^m. Johnson. Newport, March 15, 1773. Sir: The account our worthy friend Mr. Chew gives of the state of your health affords me great pleasure. I hope you will make it your study to preserve it, by varying your scenes of life, and not confine yourself to the Inland part of the country, which cannot long agree with a constitution, that has been used to the more salutary sea-air. You will find it necessary, and I hope you will not neglect visiting, the Sea-Coast once in three or four years. You are sensible how much easier it is to prevent sickness, than it is to restore health, therefore while you are able, come down and spend the two hot summer months on this Island, and in the Fall you shall re-turn with a sufficient store of Health for years to come. There can be no doubt that, in general, temperance is the foundation of health, yet to indulge now and then has always been allowed; but if you will honour me so much as to become my guest, depend upon it, you shall be allowed to do as you please, and it shall be our study to make everything agree-able to you. Mrs. Hunter who is the daughter of Wm. (?Godfrey) Malbone, your former acquaintance and particular friend of your Uncle Sir Peter Warren, wou'd be happy in paying attention to you, and I am sure, the Jaunt, wou'd contribute to the Establishing of your health, which all your friends are so desirous to see comfirmed.—I am Sir Your very Humble Servant Wm. Hunter.

John Halliburton (1740?-1808) was the son of a Presbyterian clergyman of Haddington, Scotland and was born in that town about 1740. In about 1760, he was surgeon on board a British frigate, commanded by Lord Colville. When this vessel docked at Newport, Halliburton made the acquaintance of the Hon. Jaheel Brenton and fell in love with one of his daughters.

After completing a required term of service on the ship, he returned to Newport and married Miss Susanna Brenton in the year 1767, following which he started a successful and remunerative practice in Newport.

Like William Hunter who also practiced in Newport, Halliburton sided with England in the dispute with the Colonies. He was thus compelled during the War of Independence to abandon his practice and property and make his escape. On the pretext of visiting patients on the mainland, Dr. Halliburton secretly escaped from Newport in a barge and landed safely at Long Island, which was occupied by the British Army. He presented himself to Sir Henry Clinton, who offered him the headship of the Naval Medical Department at Halifax.

He accepted this offer and soon sailed from New York to reach Halifax in 1782. His wife and family joined him a year later. Besides his official duties, Dr. Halliburton entered into general practice and became a leader in his profession. In 1787 he was appointed a member of His Majesty's Council. Sir Brenton Halliburton, for a long time Chief Justice of Nova Scotia, was his son.

This inscription on his tombstone in St. Paul's Cemetery happily summarizes his characteristics:

"If unshaken loyalty to his king, steady attachment to his friends, active benevolence to the destitute, and humble confidence in God can perpetuate his memory, he will not be forgotten."

Concerning Hunter and Halliburton, Dr. Benjamin Waterhouse wrote: "We doubt whether Boston, New York or Philadelphia ever had, at one and the same time, two practitioners of physic and surgery, better educated and more skilful than these two gentlemen."

According to Toner, Rhode Island had only one early law regulating the spread of disease. This was "An act to prevent the spreading of small-pox and other contagious diseases in this State." Enacted in 1743, it was revised and re-enacted in 1748.

Providence, at the middle of the eighteenth century, was a small country town, lacking in those fundamentals which are prerequisite for fine living. In 1748, having but 3,452 inhabitants, it played but a minor role in the development of medical education.

Dr. David Vanderlight (?-1755), a physician and chemist of some note, hailed from Steenwyck, on the Zuyder Zee in Holland.

After receiving a degree from the University of Leyden, he set sail for the New World in about 1750. He settled in Providence in 1750 and married Mary, sister of those four influential Brown brothers ("John and Josey, Nick and Mosey") and moved into the house on South Main Street, built in 1745. This property was demolished to make way for the new Court House.

Vanderlight became the leading druggist of Providence. With his brothers-in-law, he pursued the art of tallow manufacture, "having brought with him from Europe a knowledge of the Dutch process of separating spermaceti from its oil." He died on Feb. 14, 1755, just five days after the death of his ten months old infant son and only child.

Vanderlight, who had no real estate, left a considerable personal estate for a pharmacist in a small village. His inventory, on file in the Probate Court records, reached the astounding total of 4375 pounds 14s 4d (about $22,000). The six and one-half page inventory of his belongings mentions "1 Case for an Anatomy, with bones." This suggests that perhaps Vanderlight rendered "practical instruction in Anatomy" in Providence at an early date—certainly prior to 1755, since in his will, dated June 17th, 1754, Vanderlight describes himself as a very sick man with no hope of recovery. There is no record of a course of lectures which was advertised and publicly announced. Legend has it that at his house on South Main Street, anatomical instruction was presented.

In 1772, Dr. Jonathan Easton of Newport became the first in Rhode Island to inoculate for smallpox.

Two Newport physicians of note were Dr. David Olyphant (Oliphant) and Dr. Isaac Senter. Dr. Senter particularly was the preceptor of many who later became famous.

Dr. Isaac Senter (1753-1799) was born in Londonderry, New Hampshire, in 1753. He left his medical studies in Newport, Rhode Island, to accompany a Rhode Island regiment to Cambridge. Assigned to Arnold's detachment at the age of 22, he served as surgeon for this fine aggregation. He organized hospitals before Quebec, and at Montreal. He went with the troops to Ticonderoga in the Spring of 1777.

Retiring from the army in 1779, he started to practice in Cranston, Rhode Island. Not only was he selected to membership in the General Assembly, but he also became Surgeon General of Rhode Island. He moved to Newport where he built up a fine reputation as a medical practitioner.

Isaac Senter was elected to membership in the Edinburgh and London Medical Societies and served as president of the Rhode Island chapter of the Cincinnati. Brown University gave him an M.D. in 1787 and appointed him a trustee of that institution. Yale awarded him an M.D. in 1792 and Harvard followed suit in 1793. He passed away in 1799 at the age of forty six.

As has been intimated, Senter served as surgeon on the breathtaking expedition led by Benedict Arnold through the unknown Maine wilderness, directly on Quebec. Dysentery appeared early in the expedition. Later on exhaustion, harrowing living conditions and daily wading through icy rivers began to tell on this heroic group. A "brush hut" and a "log hospital" were constructed enroute for the seriously sick. As the group progressed, Dr. Senter noted that the quantity of sickness increased, but never became excessive. Rheumatism and camp diarrhea were frequent but typhus and smallpox never developed.

Upon meeting the British General Carleton, the little army became bold and tried to bluff their opponents, but there was no artillery and Carleton kept a firm front. Senter says there was some sickness from "free eating," also "peripneumonias," "anginas," etc. Senter recorded "Wounded, one Sergeant Dixon, that his leg was amputated." He died of tetanus.

Senter relates that a hospital was prepared in a convent on the St. Charles River, one half mile from the St. Roque's Gate:

Had now orders to take possession of the Hospital for the reception of sick and wounded. This was an elegant building (a convent) situated upon St. Charles River, half a mile from St. Roque's Gate. A chapel, Nunnery, and hospital were all under one roof. The building was in every way fit for the purpose, a fine, spacious ward, capable of containing fifty patients, with one fireplace, stoves, etc. The number of sick were not very numerous. The Hospital being in an advanced part of the army, I did not think it expedient to assume a residence therein as yet, in consequence of which I was obliged to visit it daily in open view of the enemy's walls, who seldom failed to give me a few shots every time.

This hospital, although close to the firing line, was seldom fired upon and Senter moved his quarters into it. Senter states:

Smallpox appeared, five cases brought to the Hospital. Not only the smallpox, but the pleurisy, peripneumonia, with the other species of pulmonic complaints were now very prevalent in the army. However, the issue of it all generally favorable.

Inoculation was practiced and Senter himself was inoculated, but he makes no mention of being sick.

Senter asked permission to lead a company in storming the gates of the enemy fort, but Arnold replied:

Dear Sir:—

I am much obliged to you for your offer, and glad to see you so spirited, but cannot consent you should take up arms, as you will be wanted in the way of your profession. You will please to prepare dressings and repair to the main guard house at 2 oclock in the morning, with an assistant.

I am in haste, yours,
B. Arnold, Col.

Doct. Center,
27 Dec. 1775.

Senter tells of the attack:

Not more than an hour had the action continued before the wounded came tumbling in so that the grand ward was directly filled. They continued to come until the enemy rushed out at St. John's and St. Roque's Suburbs, and captured the horses and carriages which were employed in the service. Few of the wounded escaped from their hands, after the capture of the horses, etc., except those wounded slightly. Daylight had scarce made its appearance ere Colonel Arnold was brought in, supported by two soldiers, wounded in the leg with a piece of a musket ball. The ball had probably come in contact with a cannon, rock, stone, or the like, which had cleft off nigh a third. The other two-thirds entered the outer side of the leg, about midway, and in an oblique course passed between the tibia and fibula, lodged in the gastrocnemea muscle at the rise of the tendon Achilles, where upon examination I easily discovered and extracted it.

Senter and Arnold did not give up when they heard the catastrophic news of defeat and they learned that the enemy was advancing on the hospital.

We soon perceived this to be true, in consequence of which all the invalids, stragglers, and some few of the artillery that were left behind were ordered to march immediately into St. Roque Street with a couple of field pieces under command of Lieut. Captain Wool, who much distinguished himself on this occasion. He took the advantage of a turn in the street, and gave the enemy so well directed fire as to put them to flight immediately. Notwithstanding this, we were constantly expecting them out upon us, as we concluded Arnold's division, then under the command of Lieut. Col. Greene, were all killed, captured, etc. Under these circumstances we entreated Colonel Arnold for his own safety to be carried back into the country. He would neither be removed, nor suffer a man from the Hospital to retreat. He ordered his pistols loaded, with a sword on his bed, etc., adding that he was determined to kill as many as possible, if they came into his room. We were now all soldiers, even to the wounded on their beds were ordered a gun by their side. That if they did attack the Hospital to make the most vigorous defense possible. . . . The storm still continued tremendously. The prospect was gloomy on every side. The loss of the bravest of Generals, with other amiable officers smote the breast of all around with inexpressable grief.

On January 2nd Major Meigs came out on patrole informing us that Arnold's party had forced its way into the city, only to be surrounded, overpowered and captured. Capt. Hendricks, Humphrey and others were killed. Morgan, Greene, Meigs, prisoners, etc.

The remains of the decimated American army were in a sad state. Colonel Campbell wrote:

Medicines are much wanted here, and I am told that Dr. Beaumont has claimed a chest worth fifty pounds, which was the property of the Crown and ought to belong to Congress. . . . I hope you will not forget to remind the Congress of the necessity of furnishing a suitable chest for the Army that may be ordered here, a thing much neglected this campaign for our army.

The army was reinforced by New Hampshire and Massachusetts troops. Of the 1900 soldiers before Quebec, 900 were sick, mostly with smallpox. The soldiers got into the habit of inoculating themselves. When British ships appeared before this sad collection of soldiers, Senter says the whole force fled helter-skelter. Two hundred of the sickest patriots were left at the hospital. One hundred and fifty smallpox victims fled with the rest. Senter prepared a hospital for these patriots in Montreal. Arnold wrote to a Congressional Commission headed by Benjamin Franklin:

I should be glad to know your sentiments in regard to inoculation as early as possible. Will it not be best, considering the impossibility of preventing the spreading of smallpox, to inoculate five hundred or a thousand men immediately, and send them to Montreal, and as many more every five days, until the whole received it; which will prevent our army being distressed hereafter; and I make no doubt we shall have more effective men in four weeks than by endeavoring to prevent the infection spreading.

The Commission agreed with Arnold. Senter declares:

I accordingly made application to General Arnold, then commanding in the city, and obtained a fine capacious house belonging to the East India Company. It was convenient for nigh six hundred. I generally inoculated a regiment at a class, who had it so favorably as to be able to do garrison duty during the whole time. . . .

We were now between the two arms of the foe, under every embarrassment possible, no quantity of ammunition, no provisions but obtained by force. . . . Our principal fortification not tenable against an equal number if attacked by land. Our prospect was still gloomy. General Thomas caught the natural smallpox, was carried to Chamblee and died. . . . Our army, weakened by the smallpox, and finding every movement against the enemy unsuccessful, a retreat was ordered to St. John's.

The following is a list of Rhode Island physicians who took an active interest in the War of Independence:

Jonathan Arnold, James Ballasseure, John Bartlett, Nicholas Bogart, Isaack Bowen, William Bradford, John Chase, Elias Cornelius, Solomon Drowne, Jonathan Easton, Caleb Fiske, Gorton Jerauld, Joseph Joslyn, John Martin, Reuben Mason, Samuel Montgomery, Stephan Munro, Jacques Pallifer, John Parish, Joshua Perry, Jachues Pulliser, Joseph Rhodes, Ebenezer Richmond, Edward Sands, Isaac Senter, Peter Turner, James Walcott, Samuel Watson, Levi Wharton, Daniel Peck Whiple, Stephan Wigneron, John Wittredge, and John Young.

Dr. Jacques Gardette, a contemporary of Lafayette, was commissioned as a surgeon in the French navy. When the French fleet and army arrived at Newport in 1780, Gardette successfully engaged in the practice of general and dental surgery.

In October 1798, the first Board of Health was created in Newport. The act reads:

NEWPORT   October 9.

The Town-Council of this Town Yesterday adopted a System of Regulations for the Preservation of the Health of the Inhabitants, and providing for the Removal and Prevention of Nuisances.

—The Town is for that Purpose divided into five Districts, in each of which one Member of the Board of Health is to reside.—The following Gentlemen were appointed of the Board of Health.—1st District, Thomas Weaver; 2d District, Walter Nichols; 3d District, Robert Lawton, jun.; 4th District, Daniel Sheldon; 5th District, John Slocum.

One of the first orders of this Board reads as follows:

At a Meeting of the Board of Health, held at
        Council-Chamber, July 1, 1799.

It was Voted and Resolved, That the Persons who now do or may hereafter occupy the Houses and Lots, fronting that Part of Thamesstreet, extending Southward from Liberty-Tree to the House of Capt.

John Cahoone, shall on Saturday Afternoon, in every Week, cleanse and remove the Dirt, from that Part of said Street. In Front of their respective Houses or Lots, extending to the Middle of said Street; and that the Occupier of the Corner Lots, fronting said Street, as fronts the Lanes and Wharves; and that this Regulation be in Force until the First Day of November next.

By Order of the Board,
John Slocum, Secretary.

By 1800 the Providence population had increased to 7,614 from 3,452 in 1748. The leading medical luminaries were the Bowens and Drs. Drowne, Throop and Wheaton. As an aftermath of the need for better education, Rhode Island College was founded at Warren in 1764. In 1770 it was moved to Providence. The famous Brown brothers (Moses, Nicholas, John, and Joseph) not only contributed to but also personally supervised the erection of the "College Edifice," now known as University Hall, and the President's house which stood upon the Front Campus. According to old records, considerable rum was consumed during the construction project. In 1804 Nicholas Brown, Jr., whose father had passed away in 1798, presented the college a $5,000 gift as a consequence whereof Rhode Island College became officially Brown University. The charter granted the right to confer degrees in theology, law and medicine. Its first exercise of this function was in conferring an M.D. on Solomon Drowne, whose story is soon to be presented.

It was not until 1811 that a School of Medicine was opened. Even though it lacked endowment, library, laboratories and clinics, it was still better off than Dartmouth for it had three professors, each with a chair of his own. The three initial members of the faculty were Solomon Drowne, Materia Medica and Botany; William Ingalls, Anatomy and Surgery; and William Corlis Bowen, "Chymistry." There was no professor of Theory and Practice of Medicine. Dr. Ingalls hailed from Boston and was an excellent surgeon and a vigorous opponent of blood-letting. Dr. Bowen, a brilliant young man who, after completing his academic course in this country, went abroad, took his M.D. at Edinburgh and then spent some time in France and in England, where he was an intimate of Sir Astley Cooper, died in 1815 from lung trouble that developed while performing experiments with bleaching compounds in the search for new textile processes.

Solomon Drowne (1753-1834) was born in Providence, Rhode Island on March 11, 1753. His father was Solomon Drowne, who came to Providence in 1730 and became a successful and public-spirited merchant. The son graduated from Rhode Island College (Brown University) in 1773. He was graduated from the University of Pennsylvania in 1781 and he also received a medical degree from Brown in 1804, and an A.M. from Dartmouth in 1786. From 1783 until his death in 1834 he was a fellow of Brown University. He served faithfully in the War of Independence. He was highly esteemed by Lafayette, Count de Rochambeau and Count d'Estaing, and invalid soldiers were left to his care when the head of the medical staff returned to France. Drowne, on a cruise as surgeon to the privateer *Hope*, wrote a journal containing the genealogy of his family.

In 1784-1785 he visited hospitals and medical schools in Belgium, England, France and Holland. While overseas, he met Franklin, Jefferson and other noted men. He came back to Providence and in 1788 moved to Ohio. With General St. Clair he was involved in securing the treaties of Fort Harmar. He also presented the first anniversary oration on the settlement of Marietta (1789), after which he spent several years in Virginia and Pennsylvania in an attempt to regain his health.

In 1801, Drowne went to Foster, Rhode Island, and spent the remainder of his life cultivating his botanical garden, doing scientific and literary work, and practicing. He became professor of materia medica and botany at Brown University in 1811, in which capacity he served until his demise in 1834.

The Historical Introduction of the first "Pharmacopoeia of the United States of America, 1820," contained the following paragraph: "The Rhode Island Medical Society at their annual meeting, held on the first of September, 1818, concurred in the formation of a National Pharmacopoeia and appointed Solomon Drowne, M.D., their delegate." He was heartily engaged in the activities of the Rhode Island Society for the Encouragement of Domestic Industry, of which he was a founder. With his son, William Drowne, he published "The Farmer's Guide" in 1824. He served in various public offices and wrote scientific and literary articles for magazines. He gave several courses of botanical lectures and made public addresses, one of them being a "Eulogy on Washington," on February 22, 1800. He was an original member of the Rhode Island Medical Society and a member of the American Academy of Arts and Sciences.

Drowne passed away at Mount Hygeia in Foster, Rhode Island, on February 5, 1834.

Brief mention might be made of Jonathan Arnold (1741-1798), surgeon of the Revolution, who was born in Providence, Rhode Island, on December 14, 1741. After obtaining grade school education, he started to study medicine under a preceptor. When the War of Independence broke out he was a member of the General Assembly of Rhode Island. He personally actually drafted the act repudiating English rule in that colony. He was appointed a surgeon in the Continental army. When the French fleet arrived in 1780 at Providence, Arnold and Dr. Isaac Senter conferred with Dr. Craik, sent by Washington, regarding the care of the sick. He was a member of the Old Congress in 1782-84. After the war was over he resided in St. Johnsbury, Vermont, and was judge of the Orange County Court from 1782 until his death on February 2, 1798. His son, Samuel, was not only elected to Congress but was governor of the State of Rhode Island in 1831 and 1832.

In the history of medicine in early Rhode Island, a more complete summary of the life and works of Benjamin Waterhouse (1754-1846) is in order:

This many sided colonial physician was the first to employ vaccination in the United States. He was the first professor of theory and practice of medicine in Harvard Medical College. He was the first to give systematic lectures on natural history in America. He was the founder of the Botanical Gardens at Cambridge, and he started the collection of mineralogy at Harvard.

Waterhouse's publications included: "Rise, Progress and Present State of Medicine," Boston, 1786; "Dissertatio Med. de Sympathia," Ludg. Bal., 1780; "The Botanist," 1811; "Lectures on Natural History with a Discourse on the Principle of Vitality," 1790; "Circular Letter to the Surgeons in the Second Military Department of the United States Army" (on dysentery); "Whooping Cough, with Observations on the Diseases of Children," Boston, 1822; "Essay on Junius and his Letters; Life of W. Pitt, etc.," Boston 1831; "Journal of a Young Man of Massachusetts Captured at Sea by the British, May, 1812," a novel, Boston, 1816; "Oratio Inaug. Quam in Academia Harvardinia Habuit., 1783," Cantab. 1829.

Waterhouse was born in Newport, Rhode Island on March 4, 1754. Timothy Waterhouse, his father, was a tanner who moved from Portsmouth, Rhode Island, to Newport. The elder Waterhouse became a Common Pleas judge as well as a member of the Royal Council for the Colony of Rhode Island and Providence Plantations. It is interesting to recollect that his mother, Hannah Proud, was a niece of Dr. John Fothergill of London, England. Both maternal and paternal families were Quakers. Gilbert Stuart, illustrious painter, attended school with Waterhouse who early in life also entertained artistic ambitions.

When Benjamin was 16, he was apprenticed to Dr. John Halli-

burton of Newport, studying with him until he departed for Europe
in 1775. Leaving Boston in the last ship permitted by the British to
sail from that port, he arrived in England in April, 1775. Just prior
to his departure, his friend, Gilbert Stuart, painted his portrait which
is still preserved in Redwood Library at Newport. After reaching
London, he went directly to Dr. Fothergill, and after pursuing his
studies with him for a while, he went to Edinburgh to receive the
best available in medical lectures and hospital experience. While in
Edinburgh he acted as secretary for the Royal Society at its meetings.

On his return to London, Waterhouse once more was taken under
the tutelage of Dr. Fothergill, and in 1778 he went to the medical
school of the University of Leyden. After pursuing a four year curriculum, he received his degree in 1781. He attained notoriety by
enrolling himself as "a citizen of the free and United States of America," but the faculty did not permit him to put that title on its diploma.
He found opportunity, while engaging in his travels about Europe,
to meet Benjamin Franklin and John Adams, and for an interval, he
lived with John Quincy Adams. The elder Adams later joined the
young men in their quarters at Leyden while waiting for the negotiations that were taking place with England.

After receiving his degree, Waterhouse studied and practiced with
his uncle in London. It was the custom at Dr. Fothergill's abode for
groups of the more serious-minded people (philosophers, authors,
distinguished foreigners, members of the House of Lords and Commons) to gather at breakfast, to discuss the latest in scientific discoveries. It was at these get-togethers that Benjamin Waterhouse
formed many distinguished acquaintances, with whom he kept up a
correspondence for the remainder of his life.

As Dr. Fothergill was a bachelor, a wonderful opportunity was
offered young Waterhouse to set up permanent residence in London
as Fothergill's assistant and successor. But the young American was
made of stern stuff and the thought of riches and an easy life did not
prevent him from returning to his homeland, where he knew he was
needed. Waterhouse brought to America the knowledge that he had
acquired during his years of study in England and on the continent.
Perhaps he returned as the most erudite physician in the young
country.

In June, 1782, after an absence of more than seven years, Waterhouse, 28 years of age, returned to his native town and began to
practice. As plans were being organized in Boston and Cambridge
for the formation of a medical school in connection with Harvard
College, Waterhouse was invited to become professor of theory and
practice of medicine. The inauguration of the three new professor-

ships followed in 1783. Dr. Waterhouse and Dr. John Warren recognized the need for clinical material in supplementing the lectures on medicine and surgery, and in 1784 applied to the town of Boston for the use of the infirmary at the almshouse. Motives of an ungracious nature caused this application to be opposed by members of the Boston Medical Society. Thus the progress of medical education was retarded for a period of over twenty years.

Besides making him a man of great erudition, Waterhouse's long period of study in England, exposed to the influences of the greatest men of medicine and science, also had the undesirable effect of somewhat unfitting him for his tasks in the new world. He never was a financial success for he neither desired nor built up a practice. His controversial and independent spirit conflicted greatly with the attitude of his inadequately trained contemporaries. As a religious dissenter and an opponent of the aristocratic group that controlled affairs in Boston and about the university, he was not endeared to the hearts of his colleagues and fellow men.

Dr. Waterhouse was especially unpopular with his professional brethren. Strictly speaking he was not a good practitioner of medicine for "patients bored him." As a member of the sect of Friends and as a Jeffersonian Republican at a time when such political ideas were entirely hostile to the temper of the ruling faction in the State of Massachusetts, long the home of Federalism, he was a thorn in the side of many.

With the dawn of the nineteenth century, young and vigorous men, fresh from European hospitals, returned to Boston to seek egress for their medical enthusiasm and the first decade of the century was filled with acrimonious disputes with the unpopular professor of theory and practice. At the end of this time, he was deprived of his professorship, and from then on devoted himself largely to letter writing and the care and supervision of the United States medical posts on the coast of New England.

Waterhouse's most important literary productions were his writings regarding smallpox. A lecture delivered to the students of Cambridge on "Cautions to Young Persons Concerning Health" became very popular. It featured the general doctrine of chronic disease with emphasis on the evils of tobacco upon young persons with special attention on the ruinous effects of smoking cigars. He denounced demon rum with vehemence.

Dr. Waterhouse in this lecture depicted the stagnation and decline of the Harvard student of the day and asserted that "six times as much ardent spirits were expended here (in Cambridge) annually as in the days of our fathers. Unruly wine and ardent spirits have supplanted sober cider." For twenty-seven years, from 1769 to 1796, there had been but nine deaths among the students; in the following eight years, there had been sixteen deaths, mostly from consumption. Indeed, never in his twenty-three years of experience had Waterhouse seen "so many hectical habits and consumptive affections of late years." He ascribed all these diversified ills to the evil effects of smoking and drinking. His argument was potent, unsparing of the clergy, and calculated to do great good. Six editions were printed during the next fifteen or twenty years, and the lecture was translated into several foreign languages. The fame of this popular lecture always displeased Dr. Waterhouse.

Concerning his private life, Dr. Waterhouse married twice, the last time a daughter of Thomas Lee, of Cambridge. In personal appearance the eminent doctor was of medium height, compactly built and devoid of any superfluous adiposity. He was quick and alert and always ready both physically and mentally for immediate action or speech. He was always dressed with scrupulous neatness in the English medical style, wearing fine black broadcloth, and carrying a gold-headed cane.

During the winter of 1786-1787, Waterhouse presented a series of lectures on natural history at Rhode Island College in Providence, and he later repeated these at Cambridge. These lectures appear to comprise the first systematic course of instruction in the branches of mineralogy and botany. Waterhouse also helped start a botanical garden at Cambridge for the purpose of securing specimens with which to illustrate his lectures.

It has been well said that the most important medical event to occur in America prior to the discovery of anesthesia was the introduction of vaccination, and its introduction and, later, its acceptance on a scientific basis, were due largely to the efforts of Dr. Waterhouse. It was in 1799 that he received from his friend, Dr. Lettsom, a copy of Edward Jenner's "Inquiry into the Causes and Effects of the Variolae Vaccinae or Cowpox," published in 1798. This is the first recorded copy of the famous document to reach America. Waterhouse, sensing the value of Jenner's work, proceeded at once to publish in the Boston *Columbian Sentinel* of March 12, 1799, a short account of the new inoculation method. "This publication," he says, "shared the fate of most others on new discoveries. A few received it as a very important discovery, highly interesting to humanity; some doubted it; others observed that wise and prudent conduct which allows them to condemn or applaud, as the event might prove; while a greater number absolutely ridiculed it as one of those medical whims which arise today and tomorrow are no more."

Later in 1799, Dr. Waterhouse obtained from London Dr. George Pearson's book: "An Inquiry Concerning the History of the Cowpox Principally with a View to Supersede and Extinguish the Smallpox." Toward the end of 1799, at a meeting of the American Academy of Arts and Sciences held at Cambridge and presided over by President John Adams, and before an audience of many eminent literary men, Waterhouse read a paper on the new vaccination method that he had gleaned from Jenner's and Pearson's books. This communication was received with much interest by the members of the Academy.

Waterhouse evidently attempted to obtain vaccine from England immediately on receipt of the books, but it was not until June, 1800, that, after many futile attempts, he succeeded in securing vaccine virus from Dr. Haygarth of Bath, England. On July 8, employing this material, he vaccinated his oldest son, Daniel O. Waterhouse, five years of age; later, another child of three, and several other members of the family. He closely scrutinized the reactions associated with the vaccination and saw that they corresponded in every way with the accounts given by Jenner in his book. To make absolutely sure that vaccination really protected from smallpox, he made application to Dr. Aspinwall, who had a private smallpox hospital in Brookline, Massachusetts, and requested that he inoculate the persons that Dr. Waterhouse had vaccinated with the variolous matter. None of the persons so inoculated contracted smallpox. Thus Waterhouse was assured that the process of vaccination was the same in America as in England and that vaccination protected against smallpox.

In a short time, various young Americans who had been studying in England, returned to America with vaccine. Some of these men had studied with Woodville, who did not teach obeyance of Jenner's golden rule: i.e. never take the virus from a vaccine pustule, for the purpose of inoculation, after the efflorescence is formed around it. Failure to obey this warning caused vaccination to fall into disfavor. Another cause for disfavor was the fact that many persons secured contaminated rags which they saturated with pus from a vaccinated arm and cut into strips which were sold promiscuously about the country. The result was many badly infected arms, and it is probable that by 1801 all bona fide vaccine had disappeared from Boston and for that matter, the rest of the country.

Waterhouse secured new material from ten different sources in England, and it was with this, his second importation, that vaccination was introduced throughout the country. Dr. Waterhouse had been in correspondence with President Jefferson for some time regarding the matter of vaccination, and after several unsuccessful attempts, in 1801 he succeeded in sending some active virus to Monticello, with which President Jefferson had his family vaccinated; from there it was sent to Washington, and later to various points in the South. New York and Philadelphia were likewise supplied, not once but several times, as their vaccine suffered the same deterioration as had taken place in Boston and vicinity.

The pros and cons on the value of vaccination were the subject of hot debate, so Dr. Waterhouse proposed to the board of health of Boston that a public experiment be conducted by taking a number of children, vaccinating them, and later having them inoculated for smallpox. The experiment was conducted under the guidance of seven of the most esteemed doctors in Boston. In August, 1802, nineteen children were vaccinated; in November of the same year, these children were inoculated on two different occasions with variolous matter and exposed for twenty days to the contagion of smallpox at the smallpox hospital on Noddle's Island (East Boston). This experiment struck a powerful blow against the opponents of vaccination for it successfully demonstrated that not one of the previously vaccinated children contracted smallpox. Similar experiments were carried on in Milton, and a very extensive one, in which seventy-five or more persons were involved, at Randolph, Vermont. Dr. Waterhouse directed his energies without stint to strive for the adoption of the new prophylactic remedy, and he maintained with great caution the purity of his vaccine virus.

After many years of poor health Benjamin Waterhouse expired in 1846.

Chapter Nine

DELAWARE

I T WILL BE recalled that the Delaware River and Bay were first intensively explored by Henry Hudson in 1609, and by Cornelius Hendrikson in 1615 and 1616. The reports circulated by these men stimulated the incorporation of the Dutch West India Company. Thus in 1631, the first Delaware settlement was made under the auspices of this company near the site of the present Lewes. Captain David P. de Vries and the other leaders in this pioneer project were desirous of establishing a colony for the cultivation of grain and tobacco as well as to carry on the whale fishery in that region. Misfortune overtook these early settlers, however, and the colony was wiped out by the Indians. In 1624, the South Company of Sweden formed the "Australian Company," under the guidance of William Usselinx, who had also been the chief organizer of the Dutch West India Company, and obtained a charter from Gustavus Adolphus. In 1633, the rights of the company were extended to include Germans and in about 1640 the Dutch members were bought out.

Peter Minuit, working for this same company, founded a settlement at what is now Wilmington in 1638. He named his new colony Christinaham, after the infant queen Christina. Minuit purchased from the Minquas Indians an area extending indefinitely westward from the Delaware River between Bombay Hook and the mouth of the Schuylkill River and called it "New Sweden." Later, this territory was considerably enlarged.

In 1642 a new company, officially named the West India, American, or New Sweden Company, but like its predecessor popularly known as the South Company, was chartered, and a governor, Johan Printz (c. 1600-1663) was sent out by the crown. He arrived early in 1643 and subsequently established settlements on the island of Tinicum, near modern Chester, Pennsylvania, at the mouth of Salem Creek, New Jersey, and near the mouth of the Schuylkill River.

Friction soon developed between the Swedes and the Dutch, although a formal friendship was maintained because of their common antagonism toward the English. Nevertheless, in 1651, Peter Stuyvesant, governor of New Netherland, established Fort Casimir, near modern New Castle. In 1654, Printz's successor, Johan Claudius Rising, who had arrived from Sweden with a large number of colonists, succeeded in driving out the Dutch from Fort Casimir. In retaliation, Stuyvesant, in 1655, with a fleet of seven ships and seven hundred men, recaptured the fort and went on to take Fort Christina (Wilmington). As a result of this campaign, New Sweden came under the control of the Dutch. In 1656 the Dutch West India Company sold part of what had been New Sweden to the city of Amsterdam, which in the following year established a settlement called "New Amstel" at Fort Casimir (New Castle).

In 1663 the entire area of Delaware passed under the jurisdiction of the city of Amsterdam, but in 1664, together with New Netherland, it was seized by the English. For a brief interval the Dutch were again in control, but by virtue of the Treaty of Westminster, the "three counties on the Delaware" again became part of the English possessions in America, controlled by the Duke of York. His formal grant from Charles II was executed in March 1683. To prevent encroachment on his seat of government in New Castle, the northern boundary was calculated by drawing an arc of a circle, 12 miles in radius, with New Castle as the center. This accounts for the curved boundary line between Delaware and Pennsylvania.

It should be recalled that as far back as August 1680, the Duke of York had leased this territory for 10,000 years to William Penn, to whom he conveyed it in August 1682. However, religious and racial variations and economic competition between New Castle and the Pennsylvania towns, and petty political quarrels were so violent that Penn in 1691 appointed a special deputy governor for the "lower counties." However, Delaware was reunited with Pennsylvania in 1693. In fact, the governor of Pennsylvania was the chief executive of Delaware until 1776.

A long continued boundary dispute with Maryland, which colony at first claimed the whole of Delaware under Lord Baltimore's charter, was not settled until 1767, when the present line separating Delaware and Maryland was mutually accepted.

In the War of Independence only one regiment of the patriot army originated in Delaware, but this turned out to be one of the first in the service. One of its companies carried a number of game-cocks said to have been the brood of a blue hen; hence the soldiers, and later the people of the state, became known as the "Blue Hen's Chickens."

A state government was set up in 1776 which represented "the Delaware State." The term "State of Delaware" was not adopted until the constitution of 1792. The Delaware government was unusual in that in addition to the regular executive, legislative, and judicial departments, there was a privy council which to all intent controlled the governor.

Delaware was one of the five states represented at the Annapolis Convention of 1786. On December 7, 1787, Delaware was the first to ratify the Federal Constitution.

One of Delaware's earliest practicing physicians was Doctor Tyman Stidham. In 1654, this pioneer came to Delaware, and for twenty years practiced medicine with great success. The archives of the colonial government show that at his death he had built up a wealthy estate.

Dr. Henry Fisher, a physician of considerable erudition, arrived from Ireland in 1725. One of his children, Henry, became famous because of his zealous patriotism during the Revolution.

Delaware's physicians were time and again honored by being selected to positions of great public trust. Such men as the first President of the State, Dr. John McKinley, and Dr. Joshua Clayton, its last President, and Governor for two terms, who died while serving in the United States Senate, are illustrative of this fact.

John McKinley (1721-1796) was born in north Ireland on February 24, 1721. He came to the New World equipped to start at once in medical practice. McKinley became a charter member of the first Delaware Medical Society, which incidentally was the third medical society in the United States.

In the First Presbyterian Church, of which he was a trustee, and now used as the building of the Delaware Historical Society, is a large iron lantern with glass panels which bears the following inscription:

"The lantern of Dr. John McKinley, of Wilmington, Delaware." This lantern, carried by Fortin, his devoted Negro servant, lighted the path of this physician during his nocturnal visits to the sick.

In 1757, the colonial government appointed him sheriff of New Castle County, and he kept this office for three years. In 1759 he was selected chief burgess of the small borough of Wilmington, which position he maintained without interruption for fifteen years. In 1777 he was elected the first governor of Delaware, or "President" of the State. Dr. McKinley steadfastly opposed English oppression, and became an ardent outspoken patriot. At all times McKinley fearlessly spoke his mind and violently opposed taxation without representation. In September 1777, following the Battle of Brandywine, a detachment of British soldiers appeared in Wilmington, looted the governor's house, and took him prisoner. After one year of captivity he returned once more to his home on the northwest corner of Third and French streets and resumed his practice and other duties. The public library in New York contains a sworn statement by Dr. McKinley, as to damage done his property by British soldiers, but it does not seem likely that he received remuneration for his loss.

Dr. McKinley passed away in Wilmington at the age of seventy-five on August 31, 1796.

Joshua Clayton (1744-1798) was born at Dover, Delaware, on July 20, 1744. He was the son of John and Grace Clayton, and a lineal descendant of Joshua Clayton, who came over with William Penn in 1682.

Joshua Clayton developed into one of the leading Delaware physicians. When the War of Independence broke out, thinking that he was living on the Maryland side of the state line, he helped organize the Bohemia Battalion of the Maryland regiment and was commissioned major in that battalion on January 6, 1776. When the Bohemia Battalion broke up as a separate organization, Clayton joined the Continental Army and took part in the Battle of Brandywine, where, as a colonel, he acted as aide de camp to General Washington. Clayton also was a veteran of the hard winter at Valley Forge, and when the army ran out of sufficient quinine, it is said that he devised a substitute prepared from oak and poplar bark, which was used with good effect throughout the war.

When peace was declared, Dr. Clayton was elected to the Delaware House of Representatives, and he became state treasurer in 1786. In 1789 he was elected to fill the unexpired term of President Collins. He later became Governor and in 1796 United States Senator. He served well as senator until his death from yellow fever on August 1, 1798. During the epidemic of yellow fever in Philadelphia in 1798, Dr. Clayton was frequently called in as consultant by Dr. Benjamin Rush and other leading physicians, and it was from contact with his patients that he contracted this fatal disease.

Joshua Clayton left three sons: Richard, Dr. James Lawson, and Thomas, the last of whom became Chief Justice of Delaware and United States Senator.

Friedberg extensively quotes a colonial medical manuscript which was sponsored, if not wholly authored, by one Matthew Wilson (1734-1790), a Delaware minister and physician of note. Although originally a native of Chester County, Pennsylvania, where he was born on January 15, 1734. Wilson built his reputation in Lewes, Delaware, where he lived until his death on March 30, 1790.

Dr. Francis Alison, a prominent minister and patron of learning, who was rector of the University of Pennsylvania, was his preceptor. While there is no indication that Dr. Wilson had a medical degree, it is established that his medical studies were pursued under the direction of the Reverend Dr. McDowell.

In 1754 Dr. Wilson was licensed to preach and in 1756, he was ordained as pastor at Lewes, Delaware and Cool Spring, Maryland. A few years later a third congregation was added at Indian River. While engaging in his numerous ecclesiastical duties, Wilson found time to practice medicine, to render instruction in Hebrew, Latin, and Greek, to take an active interest in sciences, and to concern himself greatly with the grave political questions that preceded the Revolution.

Thacher says of Wilson: "The joint functions of minister of the Gospel and physician were sustained and discharged by him with an ability and popularity which evinced he was a man of extraordinary talents, attainments, and energy. His ardent industry and the comprehensiveness of his mind reduced every obstacle, and embraced every object of knowledge. He wrote an able compend of medicine, which was called a Therapeutic Alphabet. Commencing with the classification of Sauvages, it contained the diseases in alphabetical order, with definitions pared for the press, used by himself, and transcribed by his students, but never published."

It is from this Therapeutic Alphabet that the following representative material quoted by Friedberg is presented. The book that houses the Therapeutic Alphabet is small and thick and composed of over three hundred leaves. The fact that several persons engaged in its transcription is demonstrated by the numerous variations of penmanship, spelling, punctuation, and corrections. Even the style of writing varies greatly, in some places appearing almost modern while in others deeply imbued with the quaintness of early colonial days. Several of the articles bear the signature of M. Wilson. "The Preface by the Editors," makes mention that Wilson himself wrote the articles on the principal diseases, but the definitions of the lesser complaints were generally translated by his pupils from Vogellius, Cullen, Linnæus, Brooks, and Sauvages. This practice of employing an editor-in-chief and an editorial board in the production of a comprehensive medical work is modern indeed!

Two title pages are present in this volume, the second being separated from the first by the preface, præcognita and prognostics. The two title pages are essentially the same with the exception that at the lower part of the second occurs the statement that "it is now transcribed from M.W., D.D. Notes, &c., by Thomas B. Chraghead & other students. A.D., 1787, January, 29." This date implies that the contents of the manuscript are based upon experience gained over the years from 1756 to 1787. It is unfortunate that the desire to publish this work was not carried out, for, had it been presented, it would have been the first book on the practice of medicine published by an American author. Wilson's work gives a vivid insight into the status of colonial medicine.

The following representative passages from Wilson's work are now quoted:

The title page reads as follows:

> *Multum in parvo*
> *being a new*
> *Therapeutic—Alphabet or*
> *A Pocket-Dictionary, of*
> *Medicine, Midwifery, & Surgery;*
> *extracted from*
> *Short Medical Notes on about*
> *Nine Hundred Diseases, in both*
> *their Technical and English names;*
> *with many new and old successful Remedies*
> *important Precognita, Crises & Presages;*
> *Containing a concise yet full History &*
> *Theory of all the Principal Diseases, with a———vulgar*
> *and Medical Recipes adapted to the Middle States of N.*
> *America.*
> *By Matthew Wilson D.D. Presbyter &*
> *Physician at Lewes, about 29 years.*
> *"Nullius addictus jurare in Verba Magistri." Hor.*
> *To every candid Reader.*

As America, in any Northern Latitude, is more than ten Degrees colder than the same Latitudes in the Old World; so in experience it is very certain that the Diseases, even of the same Name are very different; The Physical Writers, therefore, in Europe do often lead young American Physicians into fatal Mistakes.—To prevent this & be of some use to my Country was the Design of permitting the present Publication, in this rough unpolish'd Dress.

M. WILSON.

THE THROAT DISORDER IN AMERICA.

This dire contagious, putrid & nervous Disease began in N. England A.D. 1735 & gradually moved on Westward, thro' most Part of North America. Children & young People were more generally affected, yet some Old Persons have died of it.—It prevails most among the Poor and Scorbutic, who feed much on Pork & live in wet & low Grounds.—In Some Families it spreads like the Plague—Others at the same Season take it without Opportunity of Contag(ion)—Some have it very mildly & none die, & yet I have heard of 4 Children dying in one House in a Few Days.—It will often keep in a Neighbour(hood) for some years—Some have it more than once. Some seem to have it long hatching, before it breaks out as appearing by the Languishing Scorbutic Habit, Corrosive Humors &c.

Symptoms.—The common attending Fevers (but seldom Nausea or Vomiting) putrid Heat, but moist & seldom parch'd.—A frequent irregular Pulse—Countenance dejected—Lowness of Spirits—The Tongue much furr'd, wc continues to the Tonsils & Throat.—When milder the Tonsils only swelled, wt white spots, at most ½ an Inch Diameter—thrown off from Time to Time in Cream colour'd sloughs—When these come off the Tonsils appear deeply pitted & corroded—The Sloughs soon renew again—Sometimes the Throat is swollen internally & Externally, and frequently mortify—But generally the Swelling does not endanger Suffocation—Sometimes they imposthumate—The last Symptoms are Oppression great of the upper Part of the Chest difficult breathing, a deep hollow hoarse Cough—livid Countenance—Then Death.—N. Some walk about till near Dying, their Danger not apprehended by their Friends—Some die the 4 or 5 day—others the fourteenth—The putrefaction is so great that nature cannot excite a Fever, when they die suddenly of a Mortification.

Cure: It was long at first fatally treated as an Angina, with the usual Evacuations—And it is still fatal when Physicians are unacquainted with the manner of treating this uncommon Malady.—All Evacuants in general are Fatal—Bleeding—Blistering—Purging—Sweating hasten fatal Mortifications. And what is surprising tho' so putrid Cold-Air, & Jesuits Barks are pernicious.—All Flesh Meats, Fish, & Spirits are very hurtful. At last it was discovered by Dr. Douglas of Boston that the only Way to cure it is by confining the Sick to Bed in a gently moderate Warmth for many Days—Giving very small Doses of Snakeroot, but not to sweat, but only a gentle Diaphoresis with Sage Tea, for some time after all the Symptoms Disappeared.

N. All greasy Applications are hurtful.

N. Gargles are useful of Sumack Burries, Snakeroot &c a little Allom dissolved in it.—Gargle before Swallowing.—

N. Wash ye sores wt Tinct. of Myrrh & Alloes wt Honey.

N. Externally Poultices of Rue & bitter Herbs. Sal Ammon wt. sharp Vinegar.

N. Some have had Sores in other Parts, even ye Privates, & less in the Tonsils, & were relieved in the same Way.

N. Wine freely to a Glass every few Hours has cured some very low in Nervous Fevers—

See Putrid Fevers, Typhus, Scarlatina, Biliosa &c.

Acataposis:—Is a deprav'd swallowing. Vide Angina.

Ageustia or Agehustia:—Is a diminished or deprav'd taste. Vide gastritis.

Angina—Quinsy:—Is a pain, Tumor, inflammation of the Fauces, with a continual, inflammatory nervous or putrid Fever; attended with a difficulty of Breathing or Swallowing or fear of Suffocating. Vid. Cynanche.

There are five species enumerated. The Best Rule is to treat according to the Fever. If inflammatory: Bleed the Arms & under the Tongue, blow Allum often in the Throat—Purge wt Glysters, Give Nitre, Steams of hot Venegar—, Puke wt White Vitriol, Anodynes etc. See under Quinsy ye Theory. If Putrid, Dont Bleed, but Puke & Suit the symptoms. Contrayerva is good, blow Allum, Poultis wt Jews Ears, or Rue or Horehound Leaves, & a little Milk, Stew'd with Salt & Vinegar. Internally Vin Antimon, Camphor, Bathe wt Saponacious Liniment, Gargle wt Tincture of Myrrh or Acid Elix; Use Barks & Snake-root with Wine, Exercise, Milk in Decoction of Alder.

Gentle Sudorifics, Check Purging, Some Syringe the Throat with Acet. Egyptiacum &c. If nervous & Suffocative the Mucus is thickened to a membrane, (Endemic here), it is cured wt Mercury by thinning the Mucus, by its accrimony with Anyodynes, Sudorifics; Salivation does it no harm. Bathe with Volatiles, Saponacious Balsams &c. Convulsiva—Vide Angone cujus est species. See Sore Throat.

Angone:—Is a Spasmodic, sharp choaking of the Fauces without an inflammation. Vide Asthma.

Cure; By a Dose of Opium, Camphor, Volatile & Traumatic Balsam mixt together. Repeat if needfull, this Cured an Epidemic (at Indian River) after great numbers had died. This scarcely failed, only blowing Allum Powder in the Throat &c.

Anosmia:—Is a defect of Smelling. See Nervosi Morbi.

Antipathia:—Is a particular Aversion to an Object of Sight, Smell, or Taste, so as to be thrown into grievous Symptoms by them, as Col. Robertdeau at a cat & Mrs. Boyd at the smell of Tar & mySelf at Cod Fish.

The Cure is commonly Death.

Aphonia:—Is a deprav'd Voice and the same wt Paraphonia. This may be from many Causes. If from Cold see Catarrhus. If from a Fright see Hysteria. If from Lues Venerea, see Scorbutis. If from any other Cause, remove the Cause. But if from ill-configuration of the Parts, it seems incurable.

Aphthae;—Thrush:—Are little whitish Ulcers affecting all parts within the Mouth & sometimes the Pudendum.

The Cure:—Vomit Infants wt the vinum Antimonii gut. 5-12 in Breast Milk. Vide Erysipelas from which it differs only by the Weather.

Juice of Horehound mixt with Honey & give a little often. Give also Cathartics, Alternatives, Antiseptics, Astringents inwardly. Externally wash with Juice of Green Persimmon & Loaf Sugar, or rusty Nails and Vinegar, or with Horse Radish Root Juice or Strong Tea of Oak Moss wt a little Honey, and Allum to wash the sores &c. Vide Mouth Sore. N.B.: Onion Juice cures it by sending it to the Skin in dangerous cases.

HISTORY & THEORY OF THE THRUSH.

Aphthae:—for which there is no English Name, unless Sore Mouth or Thrush, is a frequent and fatal Disease, especially among Infants, & pregnant Women in this Place, tho' little considered or understood. These are small, round, superficial Ulcers, on the inside of the Mouth, which Boerhaave found on Accute inquiry to be the Exculcerations of the Excretory Ducts of the Glands, which separate Salivery Humours & convey them to the Mouth, Now this Fluid rendered too thick and Viscid stops up the Extremities & Causes them to inflame, in all parts where ever these Excretory Ducts should discharge themselves as the Lips, Gums, Cheeks, Tongue, Palate, Fauces, Uvula, Throat, Stomach, & Intestines. In low and Marshy Ground, & in hot & rainy Seasons, Infants & Old People are most affected by the Aphthae.

THE PROLEGOMENA OR CAUSES.

Continual putrid Fever, wt a Diarrhea, or Dysentery, perpetual Nausea, Vomiting, loss of appetite, Febrile Anxiety, Pain at the Pit of the Stomack, often returning; great Weakness; considerable Evacuations; Stupor, & Heaviness, but perpetual Drowsiness & pain about the Stomack. Those that appear at first with one Pustle, and are afterwards white & Pellucid like pearls, unequal, are mild & safe. Those which first appear in the Throat like New Bacon with a white thick crust, beginning in the Stomack, & slowly Ascending to the mouth, these are Opaque because of thickness, & very dangerous. Those which appear over the whole mouth wt a hard firm thick tenacious kind of Crust, turning brown, yellow, or livid, are very often Fatal. But those which break out in the same way, & then turn black, are worst of all, & commonly take life. The sooner the Separation the better; the longer before they fall off, the more dangerous to the Patient. The Salival Juices are discharged, thro' the whole internal surface of the Mouth, in order to be mix'd with the Aliments in Mastication; there are also numberless mucous Cryptae, or Cells in the back of the Tongue, Tonsils, Velum of the Palate, Pharynx, and Gula, which excrete thick Mucus for the Lubrication of those parts. But the eruptive Aphthae happen when this Mucous Humour is inspissated, and cannot be Driven thro' the Ducts, but Adheres and blocks up the Opennings into the Mouth, as may be seen through a Microscope. Nine days are said to bring the Crisis of this Fever—but sometimes it goes much longer.

The Aphthae or Thrush are Seldom Observed in hot Countries except in some infants; for being more thin and lax, they are more disposed to perspire & Sweat. Sweats & Urine carry off the Apthae, if copious & render them mild. Hence all diets, drinks, & nursing which interrupt these are always detrimental. Van Swieten, (If I recollect the Author) Observes when Apthae don't appear, as in Hot Countries, then Miliary Spots white & red, are frequently to be seen on the Skin; and conjectures that the Humor deposited is the same. The Miliary Eruptions and Apthae attend the same Diseases & such accute Fevers as have the same disagreeable smell of Vapid Vinegar.

He remarks the miliary Eruptions or Pustules are filled with similar pelucid Liquor, perfected above the Cuticle, & after they dry up, that they scale off, & are often renew'd as in the Apthae. Both are preceded by Anxiety about the Heart, Weakness, Slight but continual dosing, & unequal intervals. If the Apthae & Miliary spots sudently disappear, there is great danger of their oppressing the Stomack & Heart. N. Then there is no hope, but by expelling the Apthae again outward to the Skin. Stupor, & Heaviness presage the Apthae; sometimes they thicken The Ductus Communis, & Pancreas, (not having the way clear into the Duodenum) by a thick Apthous Crust; there is great Anxiety, about the Precordia. But when the obstructing Crust is removed, we need not wonder that the accumulated bile, breaks loose; Hence the severest gripes in the Bowels, almost Excorriated, & hence dangerous Diarrhoeas & Dysenteries arise. Hence on giving a Purge a fatal Hypercatharsis may suddenly arise from the Acrid Bile & Pancreatic Juice, rushing into the excorriated Bowels. N. a Salivation follows the Thrush, before the Dilated Vessels can recover their former size.

Now the Stomack & Intestines being in the same State, it is no wonder that the body is exhausted like a Consumption after it by the Purging &c.

N. Apthae of the Mouth in Pregnant Ladies may cause Abortion by destroying digestion, and absorbing of the Chyle. But she needs nourishment for two bodies, of which the weaker, the Foetus, dies.

N. A Hickup at the beginning is worse than at the End of the Apthae, as denoting the Stomack lined with thick Apthae. N. Cold Applications in this Disease are Dangerous.

Cure: Whey, Vapour Baths, Weak Panada, Gargarisms, Glysters, Corroborating healing drinks, as Alder & Mallows, & Soot, M. in Tea with Milk. Jellies constantly on the Tongue &c. &c. with the Remedies first mentioned.

Apogeusis:—Is a defect of Taste. Vide Ageustia. Find the Cause and try to remove it.

Apophlegmatizantia:—Provokers of Spitting. These stimulate the Glands of the Palate, Fauces, and Salival ducts, & purge off the viscid Phlegm. They are proper in defects of Taste, Hardness of Hearing, to drive viscid humours from the Head, in Catarrh & Obstructions of the Fauces. They are preservative Agt. contagious Diseases. V. Salivantia, Tobacco chew'd or Smok'd, Chewing Hickory Bark, Ginger, Mistletoe, Mercury &c.

Arcditas:—Is a dryness of the Skin, Nostrils, Mouth & Tongue from a dissipation of the Watery Juices by the febrile Heat; while the impervious Blood distending the Vessels make the skin rough & dry. Vid. Typhus, Sore Throat &c.

Asaphia (Aphasia?):—A Defect of the Voice. Vide Aphonia, Cophosis, Multitas. See Sauvages ingenious Treatise of Mutitas.

Balbuties:—Is a Stammering & Loosing Letters in Speaking. Vide Psellotis. See kinds of it in Sauvages Chap. vi.

Battarismus:—Vide Balbuties.

Blaesitas:—A depraved Pronunciation of the Letters S. & R. Vide Traulotis.

Black Dry Tongue:—Worst Presage in Fevers owing to a Deficiency of Lymph, or when the larger Vessels, surcharged with Blood, press and stop the smaller. Hence the Tongue. Index of the Stomack, is dry and gangrenous. See putrid Fevers.

Bronchocele or Goitre:—Is a large swelling which is formed on the fore part of the Neck, between the Skin & the Wind Pipe, & sometimes hangs from the Neck like a large Bladder; It contains atheromatous, steatomatous, fleshy, or honey-like Matter. See Encysted Tumors.

Bronchotomy, the Operation:—This Operation is chiefly useful in the Angina, when the Throat is exceedingly enlarged by the Tumor of the Thyroid Gland & Part adjoining, called, Bronchocele, which pressing on the Trachea, prevents the free Course of the Air to & from the Lungs.

It is an incision made in the Aspera Arteria to admit the Air to the Lungs to preserve Life, in a violent compression of the Larynx.

Frightful Cautions have been laid down by Writers, for fear of dividing the recurrent nerves, or the great Blood Vessels. But there is scarce any danger at all; for they lie quite out of the reach of any Instrument in a tolerable cautious Hand.

The Manner is simply this; Pinch up the skin a little below the Tumor, but as near it as you can if it be low; & make an Incision quite thro' the Skin, three quarters of an Inch long. It is commonly in the 3rd or 4th Ring of the Trachea, but the Tumor will not sometimes permit you to choose the Place. Then part the lips of the Wound, make a small transverse Incision into the wind-pipe & immediately introduce a Silver Cannula, near half an Inch long, wt a couple of little Rings at the top of it, thro' which pass a Ribband to pass round the Neck to keep it fast in the Wound.

N. After the Patient is cured of the Quinsy, & can breathe by the natural passage you may wtdraw the Tube, which leaves only a Simple Wound and requires only a superficial application.

Capistrum:—A Spasm closely & immovably shutting up the Mouth. See Spasmus Maxillae inferiorii, See Opium.

Catarrhus—Catarrh:—Is perhaps the most common Disease in our County, yet the least examined or understood. When People are taken wt it, they only say they are very poorly, & have catched a bad Cold, & no further Notice is taken of it, 'till it frequently ends in dangerous Pleurisies, Peripneumonias, Consumption &c. It may be defined "An Unusual Defluction of Lymph, Serum or Mucus, from the Glands about the Head, Jaws & Throat, exciting a Cough, distressing & frequent. It is attended wt Hoarseness generally & an inflammatory Fever."

The cause is called taking Cold, tho' in fact it is more frequently by Violent Heat; however, it is generally caused by a Diminution of insensible Perspiration, the outward Skin being exposed to the Air, Whereby a Plethora arising, the great Author of Nature has provided an internal Perspiration by the Mucous Cryptae of the Skin of the Mouth, Fauces, Bronchiae, Lungs, &c. But too great quantities collected in these, by the Heat of the Parts becoming Viscous, are cast off, after they have caused much trouble & Irritation by Coughs, Sneezing, & Running at the Nose, until more be collected, which stuffs up, & often rattles in the Breast. This frequently produces wt is called the Catarrhal Fever & often produces mild Consumption, called Deffluxion on the Lungs.

Catarrhs are distinguished according to an old Verse:

"Si fluat ad pectus dicatur rheuma Catarrhus;
Ad fauces, Bronchus, ad Nares esto Coryza."

Besides an obstructed Perspiration, some other causes may produce Catarrah, as the Stoppage of usual evacuations, or Natural Secretions as of Urine &c., or as Weakening digestion as only to produce a Watry Chyle & Blood, when its fluid Parts will escape more easily by the Numerous Glands about the Head. Prognostics here are easy, if the Catarrhal Matter, is but little, & not Acrid & discharged only by the Nose, the Cure is easy. If discharged by the Throat it is more difficult. But when it is very Acrid, & falls in a copious Manner on the Lungs, especially in one advanced in Years, or who is liable to Cough, Asthma, or Consumption, it is both very difficult & dangerous.

Cure in general; Softning the Serous humours, drinking large Draughts of Hydromel warm, or Tissots Elder Flowers, Balsam Traumatic, Vomits, Blisters, Anodynes wt Camphor, Antimon, Vin., Flannel Shirts, Cough Mass, Volatiles, Issues, Smoking Tobacco.—See Peripneum. Catarrh., See the Theory of Opium. More particularly The Diet should be soft, smooth, & balsamic; most Authors agree to give a gentle Vomit at first, if the strength will permit. and if the Patient be Phlethoric or Asthmatic Bleeding may be necessary, but in no other Case. It will be necessary to give gentle Purges as

> ℞
>
> Infus. Sena.................... ℥ iij
> Mannae .... ℥ i
> Sal Glauber.................... ℥ ss
> Aq. Nux Muschatae............. ℥ ij
> M.S. Potio Mane Sumanda.

If there be Restlessness, & Anxiety, give a gentle Anodyne, with large Draughts of Rosemary or Bran Tea &c. made into Hydromel & a Stronger Purge of Rusl's Pills or of Soap & Alloes.

When the Cough is troublesome:

> ℞
>
> Conserv. Rosar,
> Syrup, Balsam,
> Syr. e. mecon................... a̅a̅℥ i
> Spt. Vitriol. Tenuis .... qs
> ad levem Aciditatem, m. cap. cochl.,
>   subinde, urgente Tussi,

or else,

> ℞
>
> Terr. japan.................... ʒ ij
> Bal. tolutan .... ʒ j
> cog. in Aq. font........ ℥ xii ad ℥ viij
>   colat, add

> Syr. e. mecon....................℥ ij
> M. cap. cochl. .... ij
> h.s. et urgente Tussi

After removing the cause, it may be necessary to thicken the Juices & restrain the Flux of sharp Acrimonious Matters.

℞

> Conserv. Rosar...................℥ i
> Bals. Cocatalli ....℥ ij
> Sperm. Citi, Terr. japonic........a͞a ℥ i
> Oliban pulv. ....℥ iss
> Syrup. Balsam., q. s. m. f. Electar.
> Dos. q. n. m.

In the meantime Cupping & Blistering & Issues may be applied to the side or part affected, according to the Symptoms. Also to divert the Defluction from falling on the Lungs, let him use freely Diuretics & Diaphoretics for some time.

℞

> Therac, Androm, Oliban.........a͞a Ɔ ss.
> Gum ammoniaci, croci...........a͞a gr. v.
> Syrup q. s. f. Bolus, to be taken three times a day.

Lime Water & Milk & Tar Water, & Tea of Pine Buds, or Pine saw dust, or grounding, & Sassafras will make good, common Drink, not much inferior to the above elegant Forms from London. See Treatise under Phthisis. See Syrup of Horehound under Tussis from a French Physician.

Catarrhus Suffocativus:—Is a very difficult Respiration, Attended wt a sudden Interception of the Senses & Motion, snoring & intermitting Pulse. See Pnigma, Bleed, Vomit, Bathe, purge, Barks of Alder, Tea of common Scotch Thistle &c. See Asthma, Angina.

Cionis:—Is a painful thickness of the Uvula & Palate. See Angina & Sore Throat.

Clamor:—Is an anxious Exaltation of the Voice; often in Mania.

Clangor:—Is a Sharp screeching Voice. See Paraphonia. See Sauvages.

Coryza:—Is an extraordinary Running of a thin Serum from ye Nose or a Catarrh of the Nostrils. See the Latin Verse under Catarrhus.

Cough:—See Tussis, Pertussis, Catarrhus. Syrup of Horehound or Sulphur & the Yolk of an Egg, or take Barbadoes Tar, Honey & ye Yolk of an Egg &c.

Cynanche:—Quinsy: Is an inflammatory & sometimes putrid Fever; attended wt pain & Redness in ye Fauces, a difficult swallowing & Breathing wt a Sense of Straightness in ye Fauces. See Angina, & Quinsy. If

Inflammatory: Bleed under Tongue, in ye Arm or Feet. Bathe Feet in warm water, blow Alum or Nitre into ye Throat often. Apply a Chin Stay of Bals. Sapon. or Camphorated Spts., purge by Mouth & wt Glysters. Blister if pain in ye Head. Gargle the Throat with Oak Oose or persimmon bark wt Ol. Vitriol & Honey, Snuff Honey. Apply Poultises of Jews Ears or Horehound, plantane & Vinegar. If putrid; Mercury is called a Specific. V. Malignant quinsy.

Dysphagia:—A difficulty of Swallowing wtout any remarkable difficulty in Breathing. Vide Angina.

Epistaxis:—Is a Profusion or Haemorrhage of blood from ye Nostrils, wt pain & heviness of ye Head, Redness of ye Face. Vid. Hemorrhagia, Haemorr. Nar. & c.

Original Epistaxis:—is a Haemorrhage from a Plethora. Symptomatic Epistaxis: are 1st from internal Causes: Febrile Haemorrhage, critical Haemorrhage, insalutary Haemorrhage, 2nd: From external Causes; common Haemorrhage, Haemorrhage by Leeches &c.

Cure: Bleed Feet, Purge, Sweat over bath of Cedar Tops, Epithem in each Nostril of Pulv. Alumen, on Lint &c.

Fauces:—Pain'd or inflamed; See Angina.

Glossagra:—Is a Rheumatism of ye Tongue and is a Species of Rheumatismus. Q. Vide.

Glossocele:—Is a spasmodic, violent & sharp Extrusion of ye Tongue.

Glossocoma:—Is a spasmodic, violent & sharp Revulsion or hauling in of ye Tongue.

Gravido:—Cold in ye Head; Is a kindred Catarrh of ye Nostrils wt a painful uneasiness & heaviness of ye Head, hoarse Voice & difficult Breathing, Vid. Catarrhus, Frigus.

Cure: Thrust roots of ye Thin Yellow rind of an Orange up each Nostril, hold ye Head over Steam of hot Infusions.

Hiccup:—Seems to be a Convulsion of ye Oesophagus drawing ye Diaphragm upwards, whilst it is suddenly seized wt a convulsive Paroxysm & drawing downwards & proceed either from Repletion or Inanition. See Singultus.

Hoarseness:—See Catarrhus, Pertussis, &c.

Himantosis:—Is a greater Length or Slenderness of ye Palate yn usual wt Pain.

Hypostaphyle:—Is a Prolapse or Production of ye Palate wn it is either relax'd, inflamed, ulcerated, incrassated, attenuated or forked. V. Scorbutus, Blow Allum or Nitre on it. Wash Acid Elixir, Honey &c.

Ischnophonia:—Is a Fault of Pronunciation in wc one Syllable can't join another quickly. V. Psellimus.

Labium Leporinum:—Hare Lip. See Lagocheilos.

Lagocheilos:—Hare Lip. Is a Deformity in whic ye Lip is divided by

Chasms or Fissures. See Lab. Leporin. The Operation should be omitted untill ye Child has some Reason to suffer it to be done. On wc see Van Swieten, Sharp. It is pretty common for ye Roof of ye Mouth to admit of Reunion. Fissures of ye Palate often close in some years. Separate ye Lip from ye upper Jaw; divide ye Frenulum wc connects it to ye Gums. If ye Dentes in Infants. Cut off ye callous Lips wt Scissors ye whole length, but take Care to make ye Wound in Straight Lines. Then bring ye two Lips of ye wound exactly together, & pass a couple of pins, one pretty near ye Top & ye other as near ye bottome, thro' middle of both edges of it, & secure ym in yt Situation by twisting a Piece of Wax'd thread, across & round ye pins 7 or 8 times. Then cut off ye points, lay a small Bolster of Plaster under ym, to prevent their Scratching. Wn only ye lower Part of ye Hare Lip can be brought into Contact, one Pin is Sufficient. The practice of bolstering ye Cheek upward does more injury to ye Patient, yn good to ye Wound. Dress superficially as often as is Necessary for Cleanliness. In 8 or 9 Days ye parts generally are found united, yn gently extract the Pins & apply dry Lint and Adhesive Plaster. This method may be useful in some Fistulae &c. Silver Pins & Steel Points suit ye Pomp of ye Great, but common Pins Answer ye End fully as well. See Cullen on Copper.

Lagostoma:—The Upper Lip divided. See Lagocheilos.

Leptophonia:—Is a fault of ye Voice which is very Weak. See Paraphonia.

Mumps:—Species of Angina. Q. Vid. Poultis wt Wormwood & Vinegar. Give them Antimonial Essence freely. Avoid Greasy things internally & externally.

Mouth Sore:—See Scorbutus, Parotis, Parulis, Apthae. Wash wt a Decoction of Hyssop, Sage, Oak Moss, mixt in honey & a little Allum, Horse Radish Root Juice & Honey. Purge wt Mullein Juice. Bathe the Head wt Rum, Glyster Saline, Tea of Black courrants. Rhubarb in Soot Tea, Syrup of Mulberries, &c.

Mutitas:—Is an Impotency in pronouncing Articulated or joined words. See Aphonia.

Nefrendis:—Is a Deformity in wc ye Teeth is out of the Head.

Noma:—Is an Ulcer wc does not consume & eat ye Afflicted Part alone, but all ye Neighboring Parts. See Cancer, Ulcus.

Odaxismus:—Is a pain of ye gums yt Infants have whilst Teething. See Dentitis.

Oesophagismus:—Is a Spasm of ye Oesophagus wc detains ye Food in ye Gullet after Swallowing it, attended wt great Pain. See Spasms.

Oxyphonia:—Is a shrill Voice, such as is commonly uttered in Wailing & Lamentation. See Paraphonia.

Ozaena:—Is a putrid Ulcer of ye Nostrils, from wc a stinking Mucus

distills. See Ulcus. Wn it is venerial, see Syphilis; if not, Tobacco Ointment or Honey of Roses wt a little red Precipitate; See Polypus.

Palate Diseased:—See Hypostophyle.

Palsy of ye Mouth:—Gargle wt Sage Juice, purge well, chew, mustard.

Palsy of ye Tongue:—See Paraglossa.

Paraglossa:—A Swoln Tongue.

Paraphonia:—A Deprav'd sound of ye Voice. Remove the Cause if possible. Chew Ginger &c. See Aphonia. See Pr. Sauvages.

Parotis:—Is a Swelling of ye Parotid Gland (See Boils, Syphilis). Inflammation of Glands behind ye Ears after an imperfect Crisis. Suppurate
wt Leeks & treat as Phlegmon, Q. Vide.

Parulis:—A Tubercle on ye Gums, giving much Pain, & of ye Inflammatory Kind. See Phlegmone.

Pertussis:—See Chin-Cough. The Whooping or Chin-Cough Is a Contagious Disease, attended wt a convulsive & Suffocating Cough; a sonorous
inspiration and Expiration; & oftentimes a Vomiting.

Cure:—Lobs Tincture ℥ i bis vel ter die in Juice of Pennyroyal ℥ ss,
M. Purge once a Week. Mistletoe & Garlic, or Wild Onion Teas freely;
Baum de Vie Pt. vij, Tinct. Canthar Pt. j. m. is also good; Glyster daily.

N.B.: After a Dose of Train Oil & Onion Juice ye Whoop no more.

N.B.: Our Epileptic Pills; Tar Water is good after it. Tea of Scots
Thistle, Electar. of Sulph., Honey & Yolk of Egg, m.

Polypus of Ye Nose:—Is an Excrescence filling ye Cavity of one or
both Nostrils, almost suffocating, or at least making Respiration difficult,
arising from ye Laminae Sangiosae Membrane. There are several Species,
Some resembling ye Hydatides of ye Liver, as in some Dropsies; Some
like Ganglions of Nerves, wc borrow their Coats from its Vessels. Those
wc are soft like Serum are form'd of Water, contained in Cysts; these are
too tender to be extracted; but should be left to harden, wc in time
ye commonly do. If ye are Viscid, tho' ye cannot be drawn out at once
by ye Roots yet at several attempts ye may be brought away in Bits.
There is another sort neither so soft as to be squiezed to Pieces, nor so
hard & brittle as to crumble, nor adhere to ye Membrane. This is ye
favourable Kind, yt suits for Extraction by ye Forceps. But there is
another Kind, & ye worst of all, wc is hard & Scirrhus, adhearing so as
to tear rather yn Separate, wc often ends in a Cancer wc See.

The Polypus sometimes grows large as to alter ye Bones of ye Face.
When ye Polypus appears in ye Throat, Surgeon Sharp advises to extract
it yt way because experience has taught, it is more easy to be Separated,
wn pulled yt Way.

Operation on the Polypus. Let ye Patient lie Supine 2 or 3 hours to
bring it further down before ye Operation. Extract it by a Pair of
Forceps, yt will take a good hold, introduc'd into ye Nostrils an inch &

half, to make more sure of its roots. Then twisting ym a little from one Side to another, continue in yt action, while you pull away very gradually ye Body of ye Polypus. If it breake, you must repeat ye Extraction so long as any remains, unless attended with a Violent Haemorrhage; wc often happens if ye Polypus is Schirrous. But be not Alarm'd ye Vessels presently collapse. Dry Lint, or Lint dipt in some Styptic will readily stop it. We prevent its future Growth by Vitriol in Toddy on Lint wn applied. The Cauteries & Setons of some are very good.

Psellimus:—Is a stammering in Speech, or a fault in pronouncing some Letters, Words, or Syllables.

Psellotis:—Is a Fault in Pronunciation, wn one Syllable or Letter is left out or taken away.

Quinsies or Sore Throat:—See Angina. Are Various but always mean a Sense of Pain in ye Throat impeding in some Degree Swallowing or Breathing or both. The first Division is respecting Tumour. A Quinsy wtout Swelling is called Catarrhus Suffocativus by Some. Wn there is a Tumour it is again very various, Aqueous, Scirrhus, Inflammatory, Convulsive, Catarrhus, Oedematous, Purulent, Cancerous, & Gangrenous. All these must be treated differently according to ye Causes & Symptoms. See ye Original Diseases Inflamatio, Oedema, Cancer, &c. Wn inflammatory it is called Cynanche, ye Breath much interupted, ye Voice much sharpen'd, ye Anxiety considerable &c. There is great danger Indeed & Death sometimes ensues in 8 hours or less.

Cure:—Bleed a large quantity immediately, apply Cupping Gourds or Glasses around ye Neck. Give a good purge immediately. Immediately blow Powder of Alum or Nitre on ye Palate, Larynx &c. & repeat as often as needful. It is a Remedy I have used for some years wt amazing Success & instances. Also take a Tea Cup of honey & as much Good Vinegar & 12 of boiling hot Sage or Alder or Rosemary Tea, & let him drink abundantly till he Sweats. Take

Crumb of Bread........................ ℥ iij
Sweat Oil or fresh Butter................. ℥ i
Milk .... q.s.

An Onion beaten, boil into a Poultis & apply hot to ye Throat & keep it hot. Wn ye inner Membrane of ye Larynx is inflamed, ye Danger is greater. Give 20 grains of Nitre in every hour in his Hydromel if he can Swallow. If a redness appear on ye Neck & Breast, ye patient oft recovers. Another sort of Quinsy, & much more common, is wn one of ye Tonsils grows red, & swelled, and painful, & ye Pain commonly extends to ye Ear on ye same Side. In a day or two ye Disease attacks ye Glands of ye other Side, ye first disappearing. These must be treated according to ye Pulse. And if ye Pulse be hard & quick Phlebotomy is necessary,

& if ye Redness, Swelling of ye Throat, & difficulty of Breathing do not abate, bleed again; If ye Pulse be natural omit Bleeding; ye Hydromel, Nitre, Powder blown & Purges or Glysters, (wt Syrrup of Black Currants called a Specific) and Nitrous Decoctions &c are Sufficient.

N. If these Disorders are neglected too long, or ye inflammation is too great, yn Suppuration ensues, wc is known if ye red Tumour last above 3 Days unabated. Then use emollient Gargles perpetually, wt Poultises, Glysters &c. In ye Cynanche & some Quinsies, to save life, Heister used safely to open one or more of ye Cartilaginous Rings, so that, even that is not dangerous. Only beware of ye Blood Vessels. Keep ye Canula in 'till ye inflammation cease. To know Wn stop ye orifice of ye Canula wt ye Finger, & if ye Patient can breathe easy, by ye Mouth, take out the Tube, & heal up ye Wound. Support wt nourishing Glysters. Embrocate wt Volatile Liniments. Give Powder of Camphor & Nitre, drink Hydromel, Gruel, Panada &c. (See Bronchotomy).

For ye Gangrenous Quinsy or putrid Sore Throat (V. Gangrena, Cancer, Typhus). Medicines not only Vegetable Acids, but Fossils too, as Spt. Sulph. Nitr., Spt. Vitriol, Spt. Sal Marine wt Honey of Red Rose &c. Constringe ye Vessels & prevent ye too great Expansion, repel ye impervious particles, in ye larger Trunks & cure or prevent putrid Gangrines, Sydenham & Swieten used these as Gargles.

The Ancients used Alum, Flax, Oris, & Stercora of Animals. The Farmers of Zealand are fam'd for curing Quinsies by touching ye Uvula often wt White Vitriol, Sal. Ammoniac, & Crude Alom, to ye great relief of ye Patient. At first I puke wt White Vitriol gr. 25. Give Salts every day. I Keep up ye Vis Vitae. I would Gargle wt Strong Oose of Persimmon Root Bark, Honey & Alom. I give ye Bark a Teaspoonful every 2 hours wt Spt. Sal Amoniac ʒ j in each Dose in Wine. I give Antimonial Wine ʒ j thrice a Day. I have Mist. Sal. Tart. Guaiacum, Camphire, Nitre & Sal Amoniac āā ʒ j in Spt. Vin. ℥ iij often wt Success. Poultis wt Rue Jews Ears. Horehound & Lees.

Quinsy Malignant: Cynanche Maligna; Cullen. History or Description; It is Contagious; Seldom Sporadic, i.e. Endemic. Affecting few People in a Season. Commonly Epidemic, attacks all Ages & Constitutions, but more commonly ye Young & infantile & infirm. It first Shews itself in a Pyrexia, Cold Shiverings, Sickness, Anxiety, Vomiting, yn Stiffness of ye Neck, Uneasy Fauces, Hoarse Voice, ye internal Fauces of a deep red & some Tumour, Deglutition is seldom painful. White Ash Colour'd Spots wc Spread & Unite in thick Slough over ye Fauces; These falling off discover Ulcerations. A Coryza of thin Acrid & foetid Matter attend; Infants purge then, Acrid, excoriating Stools. Pulse small, frequent, irregular, worst in ye Evening, Great Debility, Delirium & Coma. On ye Second Day, sometimes later, Efflorescences appear on ye Skin, patches of a red colour first on ye Face, yn over ye whole Skin, wt wc ye Fingers are stiff and swell. This usually continues 4 Days before Disquamation, but still ye Fever remains. Ulcers in ye Throat livid & black, breath foetid, Gangrenous Symptoms, Fever putrid, some die on ye 2d (?) Day, but more on ye Seventh; Putrification Continues along ye whole Alimentary Canal wt Diarrhoeas. Large Swellings of ye Lymphatic Glands of ye Neck, wc sometimes suffocate, Respiratory Organs hurt too. Wn ye Ulcers are more mild, ye Efflorescence disquamates after 3 or 4 Days. The Cure comes by gentle Sweats on or before ye Seventh Sleep & Appetite return &c.

Cures: Avoid Bleeding & Purges. Attend to Septic Tendency. Antiseptic Gargles, & Injections. Neutral Antiseptics as Cortex. Emetics both by Vomit & Nausea. Wn Tumours, Blisters, Flux, Essence, Throat Powder; Anasarcal Drink; Volatiles; See Cancer Poultises &c.

Scarify: Cup between the Shoulders & repeat it; Shun Antimon, Purges: Use gentle Emmollient Glysters; Blister ye Shoulders; Also ro und ye Throat. For ye putrescent Diathisis Cortix & Serpentaria; For ye Diarrhoea, Anodynes & Antihysteric Mixture. Throat Powders; Our Anasarcal Drinks. Bathe Neck wt Fucus & Rum, m., Haustus Cardiacus; Camphor & Volatiles. Apply ye White of an Egg & good Mustard & red Pepper to ye Pain of ye Throat. Pulv. Antispasmodic. Antiseptic Drops in ye Ears, also internally. Poultises of Lees & Rue from Ear to Ear.

N. B. A fatal Epidemic Cynanche was found by Prof. Monro & by ye New York Physicians to have a new membrane in ye larynx, of wc ye only cure was Mercurials &c.

Ramula:—Is an Encysted Tumour seated upon ye Frenum of ye Tongue, containing a thick tobaccous Matter.

Raucedo:—Hoarseness. Is a rough & obscure Voice, wc cannot be heard unless by those standing very near.

Cure:—Swallow slowly ye Juice of Horse Rhadish Root, Chew peruvian Bark & Ginger, Figs, Starch Liquorice, Oily draught, Balsamics &c. Lohoch Pectorale:

℞

  Sperm. Citi, & White Soap.................... āā 3 ij
  The Yolk of an Egg, Ol. Lin.................. 3 iss
  Syr. Althae.................................. 3 iii

M.S. Lohoch; rub ye Soles of ye Feet wt Hogs Lard before ye Fire. See Pectoralis.

Renchus:—Is a Sound uttered thro' ye Nose. See Stertor.

Rhenophonia:—A Speaking thro' ye Nose. Is a nasal Voice wc is not altogether uttered from ye Nostrils.

Rhachmos:—Is a sterterous Sound wtin ye Fauces. See Stertor.

Screatus:—Is Sonorous Evacuation of Mucus from ye Fauces.

Sternutatio:—Sneezing. Is a Convulsive Agitation of ye Membranes of ye Nose wt an impetous Inspiration of Air & presently making ye like Expulsion thro' ye Nostrils wt a Sound.

Suffocatio:—Is a Suppression of the Breathing or Respiration, from a continued contraction, or narrowness of ye Fauces or Trachea, wtout a Fever, a Symptom of Asthmas, Hysterics, Some Quinsies. Also See Dyspnoea, Orthopnoea, Ephialtes &c, &c.

Suffocatio Stridula:—A Disorder in Children called here & in Ireland ye Hives, in Scotland ye Croup, & in somes Places Chock or Stuffing. In England ye rising of ye Light (See ye Pennsylvania Journal no. 1410). It seems to be a Species of Asthma attended wt very Violent Symptoms. The Infants are seized wt a Sudden & great Difficulty of Breathing, wc is soon Mortal unless relieved. It seems to be Nervous & Spasmodic. It is probable yt may arise from a Phlegm or Mucous accumulated & hardened adhereing to ye Trachea & Bronchia, like ye membrane discover'd by Dr. Monroe (&c wc has been discovered here in a putrid contagious Quinsy, at New York, many Years since) difficulty separable from ye Larynx. For Cure I would bathe ye Throat often wt ye Saponacious Balsam. Put his Feet in hot Water; if plethoric, bleed. Puke wt Antimonial Wine. Mix a little Camphire in Sweat Oil and add Honey, wt a few Drops of wc moisten ye Throat, removes ye Mucous Membrane and removing ye Spasm wt Lobb's Tincture, or a Grain of Opium, carefully dissolved in Soot Tea ℥ viij by Spoonfuls till better. I would recommend Onion Tea, Saline Glysters & a Plaster of Turpentine & Camphor between ye Shoulders.

Thrush:—See Aphthae, Purge wt Rhubarb. Glyster 2 a day, wash ye Mouth often wt Strong Tea of sage, Hysop & Alder wt honey & Alom mixt. Melasses wt Juice of Horse Radish Root is good.

Tooth Ache:—See Odontalgia: Blow Tobacco Smoke in ye Ear of ye affected Side & put Oil of White Oak in ye Tooth made by burning ye twigs on a Cold Ax, or Pewter dish.

Tortura:—Is a bending of ye Mouth to one Side.

Traulotis:—Is a vitious Pronouncing of ye Letters S. & R. (See Blaesitos).

Chinese Cure:—℞. Pomegranate Rind wt Pepper four Seeds beat & apply as Snuff. But if from Cold Blood, ye Smell to a Composition of Sal. Ammoniac & Lime Water tied up in a rag. If from atrophy, ye drink Wine wt some Frankincense infused in it &c. Vomit, Cold Baths, Snuff ye Dew from Mallows Leaves. Drink a Decoction of Primrose. Wash ye Head wt a Decoction of Sage, Mustard Seed gr. 30 every Morning.

Vociferatio:—Is a painful & exalted Exclamation of ye Voice, to harden ye Body.

Urula Relaxed:—Blow in Alom, Nitre &c. Infusion of Mustard Seed. Decoction of Water Dock.

Otitis, The Ear-ach is, an inflammation of ye Ear. Otites, Diseases of ye Ear are internally & externally, especially ye former attended wt very Severe Pain, Head-ach & Alienations of Mind (See Delirium) a Loss of Sleep, & sometimes Convulsions &c. See Odontalgia. It occasions great Restlessness & Anxiety, Pain, Redness, Heat & Fever, like other Inflammations (wc see) proveading from Suppression of Perspiration, exposing ye Head to cold Water or Air wn Sweating. Cure in this case must be by Bleeding ye Arm or Jugulars, Cupping the Neck, giving Antimonial Wine & Hydromel, Powder of Camphor & Nitres. Formenting the Ear wt ye Steams of Warm Water Or applying ye Ear to a Jug filled wt a Decoction of Cedar Tops or Camomel &c.—Bathing ye Feet in Warm Water—And all around ye Ear wt Volatile Liniment &c &c. If it cannot be dispersed yn it will be best Suppurated by Juice of roasted Onions & a drop of Sweet Oil often applied in ye Ear.—If it break & run white & laudable Pus, wash it a little wn needful wt Honey & Rum, & dress wt. Onion Juice & Honey mixt till well.

2. A Defluxion of an Acrimoneous humour, this has not ye great heat, burning & pulsation, but is painful from Irritation. See Opium. Blow tobacco Smoke thro an inverted Pipe into ye Ear wc eases ye Pain. Then gently Syringe, wt a Decoction of wild Cherry Bark.—Mix Camphire in Sweat Oil & drop into it daily—or Syringe wt Warm Wine or drop Rosemary & Sage Juice in ye Ear often—Drink Bark & Guiacum in Decoction.

3. Ear Ach from Worms, Wn there is felt a sharp shooting Pain, a gnawing, & horrible Noise in ye Head, as wn a Flea or any insect, has made its Way to ye Drum of ye Ear.—In this Case a drop in ye Ear of Sweat Oil, or Brandy, or Juice of Wormwood, or even Warm Milk quickly destroys, or dislodges ye Insect, wn it will come out on ye Cotten, or be cautiously extracted.

4. Ear Ach from Morbific Matter translated, as in ye Decline of Malignant Fevers & generally a favourable symptom, tho' it may cause Deafness. This may be eased by ye smoak of Tobacco, Camphorated Oil & Onion Juice.

5. Tinnitus Aurium, a tingling Noise in the Ears, often attends Nervous & Malignant Fevers & is also frequently a chronic Disorder, & very troublesome, & often ending in e(n)tire Deafness, wc is seldom cured, & if relieved a while is apt to return again. See Phrenismus.

6. Deafness and Thickness of Hearing differ only in degrees. Sounds unless very loud make little impressions on them. This distressing Mallidy is seldom cured, because ye fine Organs of Hearing cannot be seen, nor their Disorders well ascertain'd, in living subjects & ye dead have no use

for it. It is however sometimes occasioned by hard Wax in the Meatus Auditorius, & other pituitous Matter. This may be relieved by gently syringing the Ears with Warm Water.

If ye Tympanum &c be too tight Sweat Oil & Camphor, or Onion Juice in ye Ears on Cotten will have a good Effect, as I have often found. But if it bee too lax & debilitated, washing ye Ear with strong Decoction of Wild Cherry Tree Bark, or black Alder Bark, or Wine wt sage & Rosemary stewed in it, may do good. Steams of Rue, Rosemary & Garlic, thro' a Funnel may be safely tried. Many have tried ye Fumes of Amber & Olibanum, & Spirit Sal Ammoniac, but it should be wt Caution. Some have applied Musk, Amber & Civit in a Dossil of Lint in ye Ears, wc seems rational to affect the sluggish Nerves—Some use Galls of Eels & Partridges & even Fumes of Sulphur, But the (se) appears to me improbable & dangerous.—Some commend ye Eggs of Ants in Onion Juice as almost infallible, but I have never ventured it. Some try Salivation by Mercurial Unction as the last probable Remedy.

Dr. Graham ye Otistis Rules by wc He pretended to cure inveterate Deafness were these (1) Bleed the Jugular ℥ xiij every 10 Days for three times.—(2) Three Emetic Boluses given one ye Day after each Bleeding. —(3) A Mixture Night & Morning (perhaps Tinctura Sacra & Amara mixt) drinking Sage, Sasafras & Fennel Seeds Tea.—(4) His Accoustic Essence in Each Ear & yn wt Force s(n)uffing it up ye Nostrils as long.— But Juice of Ground ivy, Rue, Rosemary & Garlic ℥ ii in hot Tar Water would be perhaps better.

(5) Then his Caephalic snuff wc was no better yn Powder of ye Bark of Myrtle Root, or white Hellbore & Ginger, was often to be taken, yt we must sneeze, keeping ye mouth shut, & ye Nostrils pressed together.—

(6) His Etherial Essence (not so good as camphorated Spirits) were applied to ye Ears & volatiles to ye nose for 5 minutes.

(7) His warm Drops for Deafness (perhaps Sweat Oil camphorated) 5 or 6 on Lint in each Ear.

(8) Pen(e)trating Spirits ℥ i (Juice of Horse Rhadish Root is better) on ye Tongue applied to ye Palate & keeping ye Mouth shut long after.

(9) All these were done at night & repeated next morning, three times ye first Week & only twice a Week after.

(10) Twice a Week ye Legs & Feet were beathed wt warm Water. Semicupia of Decoction of Cedar Tops had been better.

(11) He embrocated the Head sometimes wt perhaps ye Volatile Liniment.—This was a Prescription for one born Deaf but by some mischance did not fully succeed tho' it made a considerable change. N.B. I once knew a Deafness cured by putting on Cotton some drops of a hot Pickle or Allom Salt applying it in ye Ear often.

Auditus:—See Cophosis & Surditas, & the Theory under Otalgia.

Cophosis:—A difficulty or Impotency of hearing or perceiving Sounds from some Impediment wtin or wtout the Labirinth of ye Ear. See Surditas. Try Camphorated Oil, Juice of Sage &c. Electricity has succeeded in Nervous Cases. Bleeding or Blistering in inflammatory. If Ulcers inject Tinct. of Myrrh & Honey. Insects remove by Oil.

Buzzing in Ears: See Otalgia & Tinnitus Aurium.

Dullness of Hearing: See Corphosis.

Ears pain'd; See Otalgia, Surditas, Vermes.

Epiphlogisma:—Heat of some part, as if made by a burning Coal, attended wt pain. If in the Ear it is called Pyrosis.

Giddiness: See Vertigo.

Hearing (Dullness of): See Cophosis.

Hearing (Diseases of): See Otitis.

Nystagmus: is an involuntary Spasm of ye Eye or Lid.

Otophlatos: An Excretion of an ill-scented Humidity from behind ye Ears. This was one Year in Sussex, endemic & fatal among many Children, who had Agues & Fevers before. The Agues ceasing ye Children were swelled, bloated, Oedematious, & their Faces Cadaverous. Sores came behind ye Ears & several turn'd to Cancer & Gangrenes. At length we succeeded in curing it in ye same manner. See Cancer.

Otopuosis:—Is an Efflux of Pus from ye Ear, or a sordid Catarrh of ye Ear. See Otalgia.

Otorrhea: Is an Efflux of Blood from ye Ear. See Otalgia & Haemmorrhagia.

Paracusis:—Is a difficulty of hearing articulated Voices, no Words distinctly. See Cophosis, Otalgia.

Surditas:—Surdity or Deafness: Is an abolished Hearing (See a Treatise under Otalgia). Drop a Strong infusion of Allom Salt in ye Ear. Camphor dissolved in Sweat Oil. Some drop Juice of Ground Ivy.

Susurrus: Is ye perception of Sound not existing or a buzzing in the Ear & Disorder in ye Sensation of hearing. See Otalgia.

Tinnitus Aurium:—Tingling of ye Ears. See Otalgia. Put a clove of garlick dipt in Honey in ye Ear, alternately 8 or 10 nights.

Vertigo:—Is an Imagination in wc all things appear to a man to be turned wt himself. See Epilopsia.

Chinese Cure. ℞. Pomegranate Rind wt Pepper, four Seeds, beat & apply as Snuff. But if from Cold Blood, ye Smell to a Composition of Sal Ammoniac & Lime Water tied up in a Rag. If from atrophy, ye drink Wine wt some Frankincense infused in it &c. Vomit, Cold Baths, Sniff ye Dew from Mallows Leaves. Drink a decoction of Primrose. Wash ye Head wt a Decoction of Sage. Mustard Seed gr. 30 every Morning.

As has been mentioned, Delaware was the third state to recognize the importance of and to establish a State Medical Society. The Medical Society of Delaware was launched by twenty-eight physicians in 1789. The legislature by subsequent acts enabled the Society to form a Board of Medical Examiners, with authority to regulate medical practice and license practitioners. Many states later copied the Delaware laws into their own medical code.

The first president of the Delaware State Medical Society was Dr. James Tilton, whom we shall consider a little later.

The science and practice of medicine was advanced by the pursuits of the members of this Society, notably Drs. Snow, Barratt, Capelle, Tilton, Wilson, David Bush, and Edward Miller. Miller particularly contributed to the treatment of intermittent and yellow fever by means of Peruvian bark, the alkaloid of which, of course, is quinine. The reputation and correspondence abroad of Miller vied with those of Benjamin Rush. The latter referred to Dr. Miller as "second to no physician in the United States." Dr. Miller established the first medical journal of this country in New York, and in that city won acclaim as Port Physician, Professor of Practice of Physic in the University of New York, and attending physician to the New York Hospital. Miller became one of the outstanding members of the Philosophical Society of Philadelphia. He and Dr. Samuel Black were ardent advocates of vaccination.

Dr. John Vaughan, whose father was a physician, became a member of a number of famous scientific bodies. He lectured upon chemistry and natural philosophy in Delaware as early as in 1790.

Dr. Robert R. Porter (1811-1876) and Dr. Samuel H. Black became noted literary figures in early Delaware. The libraries of these physicians were said to be of the finest type.

In 1793, Delaware's Dr. Nicholas Way received in his private dwelling those unfortunates who fled in terror from the yellow fever epidemic in Philadelphia. This act of humanity and hospitality beyond the cause of duty led his fellow-citizens to soon emulate him and their houses were thrown open to the refugees. It was during the great epidemic of 1797 that Dr. Way passed away in Philadelphia. It is said that his death was probably contributed to by his great personal devotion to his patients. In 1802, Dr. John Vaughan was the only physician left in Wilmington to fight yellow fever.

Most famous physician in the early annals of Delaware medicine was Dr. James Tilton (1745-1822), Surgeon-General of the army, and first President of the State Medical Society of Delaware. He was born on June 1, 1745, in Kent County, then one of the three "lower

Upper left, Dr. CHARLES ALEXANDER WARFIELD (1751-1813) became president of the College of Medicine of Maryland. (*Courtesy of the Maryland Historical Society.*) *Upper right*, Dr. JAMES McHENRY (1753-1816) became secretary to General George Washington and aide to the Marquis de Lafayette. (*From the Maryland Historical Society picture collection.*) *Lower left*, Dr. ENNALLS MARTIN (1758-1834) was known to grasp an objecting patient by the nose and ram the medicine down his throat. (*Courtesy of the Maryland Historical Society.*) *Lower right*, Dr. JAMES SMITH (1771-1841), attending physician to the county alms-house, began to employ vaccination in Maryland in May, 1801. (*Courtesy of the Maryland Historical Society.*)

Upper left, Dr. WILLIAM HUNTER OF NEWPORT (1730?-1777). (*This and all pictures pertaining to Hunter are reproduced from E. B. Krumbhaar: Doctor William Hunter of Newport, Annals of Surgery, Vol. 101, No. 1, January 1935, pp. 506-528.*) *Upper right*, ISAAC SENTER, M.D. (1753-1799) served as surgeon on Benedict Arnold's breathtaking expedition through the Maine wilderness to Quebec. (*Courtesy of Army Medical Bulletin #25.*) *Lower left*, SOLOMON DROWNE, M.D. (1753-1834) was first professor of materia medica and botany at Brown University Medical School (*Courtesy Brown University.*) *Lower right*, WILLIAM INGALLS, M.D. was first professor of anatomy and surgery at Brown University Medical School. (*Courtesy Brown University.*)

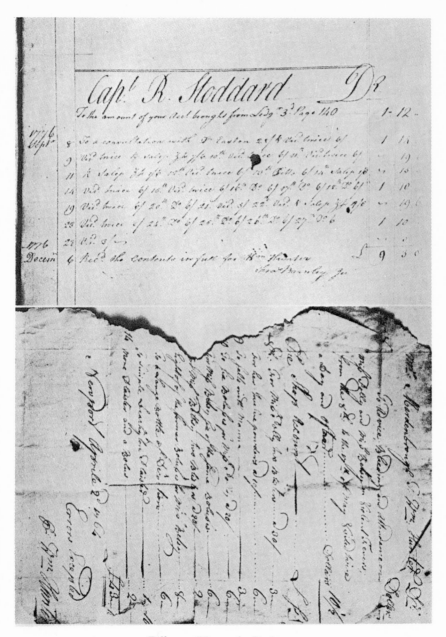

Bills to Hunter's Patients

Hunter's Letter to Captain Edward Wanton on the Care of His Gout.

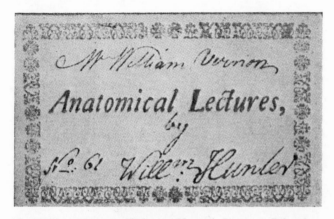

At *Rhode-Island,*

On Monday the 3d of *February* next, will begin

An Anatomical Expofition

of the Structure of the *human Body,* to which will be added, a brief Explanation of the Principles of the Animal Œconomy : the whole interfperfed with occafional Remarks and practical Obfervations, and to conclude with a Courfe of

Chirurgical Operations,

with the Application of the Bandages.

Any Gentlemen who intend to favour me with their Company, may communicate it by Letter, or perfonally with me here, and receive any farther Information from

Their humble Servant,

Newport, 3d *Jan.* 1755.   WILLIAM HUNTER.

Photostat of Advertisement of Hunter's Lectures in the Boston *Evening Post,* January 20, 1775.

Mr. William Vernon's Ticket to Hunter's Lectures, Printed on the Back of a Playing Card.

Playing Card Back of Mr. Brindley's Ticket to Hunter's Lectures.

BENJAMIN WATERHOUSE, M.D. (1754-1846)

Dr. Benjamin Waterhouse introduced vaccination into the United States. (*From the portrait by Gilbert Stuart; courtesy of the Redwood Library and Athenaeum and the Frick Art Reference Library.*)

Upper left, Title Page of Dr. James Tilton's: ECONOMICAL OBSERVATIONS ON MILITARY
HOSPITALS; AND THE PREVENTION AND CURE OF DISEASES INCIDENT TO AN ARMY. (*U. S.
Army Medical Museum. Neg. No. 68728.*) *Upper right,* JAMES TILTON, M.D. (1745-
1822), Surgeon-General of the army and first President of the Delaware State Medical
Society, was the most famous physician in the early annals of Delaware medicine.
(*U. S. Army Medical Museum. Neg. No. 49601.*) *Lower left,* DR. JOSHUA CLAYTON
1744-1798) joined the Continental Army and participated in the battle of Brandy-
wine, where, as a colonel, he acted as aide de camp to General George Washington.
(*Courtesy of State of Delaware Public Archives Commission.*) *Lower right,* DR.
JOHN HENRY LATIMER (1752-1819) was praised for his medical services during the
War of Independence by General George Washington. In 1813 he became surgeon-
general of the army. (*Courtesy of State of Delaware Public Archives Commission.*)

Obſervations

On that terrible Diſease,

Vulgarly called

The Throat Diſtemper,

With

Advices as to the

Method of Cure,

In a Letter to a Friend.

By J. Dickinſon, A. M.

Boston: Printed and Sold by S. KNEELAND and T. GREEN, in Queen Street over againſt the Priſon. 1740.

Photostat of Title Page of Jonathan Dickinson's Famous Work: Observations on that terrible Disease, The Throat Distemper. (*The Author's Collection.*)

counties" of the province. He received his preliminary education at the academy of Reverend Finley of Nottingham, formerly located in Pennsylvania, but which had been moved to Delaware. He studied medicine with Dr. Ridgely of Dover and in 1765 completed his course at the Philadelphia Medical College, graduating with the first class. He opened his office in Dover, Delaware.

In 1776 he entered the army as surgeon of the Delaware Regiment with the rank of lieutenant. Early in the war, he was sent to Dumfries, Virginia, to supervise the inoculation of Continental soldiers. He saw considerable service in Long Island, White Plains, New Jersey and Wilmington, prior to his promotion in 1777 to the grade of hospital surgeon. While holding this rank he violently objected to the grouping of purveyor and director-general into one post. He also opposed the over-crowding of hospitals for it was from this cause that he blamed his own case of typhoid. Upon the reorganization of the medical department in 1780, Tilton was appointed senior hospital physician and surgeon. Perhaps he is best known for his untiring efforts to secure army medical organization reform.

Tilton's fame as a physician was, if such is possible, surpassed by his reputation for intense patriotism. Both as soldier and an army surgeon, he served his country with skill and valor. He found the patriot army in a depleted state with its efficiency almost nil because of the great amount of sickness in the hospital, and especially because of the prevalence of typhus fever. Tilton successfully tackled the problem of caring for these poor sick souls who were underfed, packed together like sardines, and receiving a poor quality of medical treatment. While commanding hospitals at Trenton and New Windsor, he radically modified the entire hospital system by subdividing the large hospitals, and dividing the sick into small groups, each group being kept in a well ventilated individual hut.

At the close of the war, when the army medical staff was being curtailed, Washington personally insisted upon the retention of Surgeon Tilton.

Following the surrender of the British at Yorktown, in 1782, Tilton returned to practice in Dover. He was elected to Congress, where he served one term, and to the Legislature where he served several terms.

His great success in rendering hospital conditions more satisfactory may have been anticipated by his study on the subject of respiration, which was published in Wilmington, Delaware.

Tilton has this to say regarding the dysentery he encountered in the hospitals of Pennsylvania and New Jersey:

The putrid diarrhoea was generally the result of dregs of other camp and hospital diseases; and was the most intractable disorder of any we had to deal with. The patient would often be able to move about, with little or no fever, his skin remarkably dry and dusky, and constant drain from the bowels. Various attempts have been made to force the skin by warm bathing, Ipecac mixed with opium, & c., and by that means to divert the current of humours from the bowels; but all to no purpose. The only astringent I recollect to have been of any use was recommended us by Doctor Craik, one of our physicians general, noted for his great range in the materia medica. It consisted of Tinct. Huxham, and Tinct. Japon.; equal parts, of this mixture one or two teaspoonfulls were given every morning before breakfast, and again before dinner.

But while the patients remained about the hospital, nothing appeared to have more than a palliative effect. Multitudes melted away, as it were, of this miserable complaint, and died. The only expedient I ever found effective for their relief was to billet them in the country, where they could enjoy pure air and a milk diet; or to furlough them to their own homes, if within reach.

Of all the diseases of that day putrid fever was the most feared. This was a term synonymous with jail fever, camp fever and hospital fever; and included typhoid as well as typhus. While the descriptions always mention the purple spots, Tilton afterwards could not remember them, probably having seen more typhoid than typhus. Yet there was enough of typhus: in the terrible camps of the Northern Army; in the barracks on Manhattan Island; in the crowded hospitals of New Jersey and Pennsylvania; even in the smallpox hospitals of Virginia; and, above all, in the horrible prisons and prison ships of New York.

Tilton again is an excellent witness. He not only saw this disease in all its malignancy, but himself suffered from it in the hospital at Princeton. His description corresponds fairly well with the symptoms of typhoid:

The jail fever generally gives some days notice of its approach, by a languor and listlessness of the whole body, and a peculiar sensation of the head, as if it were tightened or compressed by a hook. The febrile attack is very much in the style of the Synochus, as described by Cullen. It is not very uncommon for the symptoms to run very high in the beginning, so as to warrant blood letting and an antiphlogistic course. But after some days, more or less, in different patients, the pulse begins to sink, a dry tongue, delirium, and the whole train of nervous and putrid symptoms supervene. If I ever saw the *petechiae*, so much dwelt upon by

Pringle and Munroe, I have forgotten all about them. This I am sure of, they were not regarded as essential to the disease.

Although often compelled to let blood in the commencement of this fever, we were cautious of repeating the operation; and were disposed to avoid it altogether, when not demanded by a full pulse and other pressing circumstances. . . .

When the fever is formed, mercury is of the greatest importance, so long as any signs of an inflammatory diathesis remain. This Sampsonian remedy has the power of subduing all manner of contagion and infection that we are yet acquainted with. . . .

As soon as the pulse sinks, and a dry tongue, delirium and other typhous symptoms predominate, we must have recourse to bark (Peruvian bark), wine, volatile salts, blisters, etc. A dry tongue generally warranted the use of the bark. . . .

Wine was deemed a capital remedy in every stage of typhus. In my own case, besides an obstinate delirium, I had a crust on my tongue as thick as the blade of a knife, and black soot. The skin was worn off my hips and dorsal vertebrae so as to make it necessary to patch those parts with common plaster. At the acme of my disorder, eleven surgeons and mates all gave me over, and only disputed how many hours I should live. Providence ordered otherwise. My friend, Dr. Rush, paid kind attention to me; and a benevolent lady of the neighborhood sent me several gallons of excellent wine. I drank freely of the liquid, and took, at the same time, liberally of Huxham's tincture. My tongue soon after began to moisten on the edges; and in the course of some days the whole crust fell off and left it so raw and irritable that I was obliged to hold skinned almonds in my mouth to abate the irritation.

. . . . All the cuticle scaled off from my skin; and all my hair gradually combed off from my head; so that instead of my former straight hair I had an entire new suit, that curled beautifully.

Being reduced to skin and bones I had a voracious appetite, and in a moderate space of time recovered a more than ordinary plump habit; but it was not less than nine months before I gained the usual elasticity of my muscles.

Tilton had this to say concerning syphilis: "Many a fine fellow have I brought into the hospital for slight syphilitic affections, and carried out dead of a hospital fever."

Tilton spoke thus of the camps of the Continental soldiers:

The ignorance and irregularities of our men in the new scene of life subjected them to numberless diseases. The sick flow in the regular current to the hospitals; these are overcrowded so as to produce infection, and mortality ensues too affecting to be described.

Our Revolutionary Army exemplified this misfortune in a shocking manner. The Flying Camp of 1776 melted like snow in a field; dropped like rotten sheep on their struggling route home, where they communicated the camp infection to their friends and neighbors, of whom many died.

He presented a gloomy picture of the hospital at Bethlehem:

After the Battles of Brandywine, Redbank, &c., a general hospital was established in the village of Princeton, where I was a prescribing surgeon. The sick and wounded flowing promiscuously without restraint to this hospital, it soon became infectious and was attended with great mortality. I caught the jail fever myself (typhus) and narrowly escaped with my life. After a tedious illness I got leave to return home for the recovery of my health. The enemy occupying Philadelphia at that time, it became necessary for me to make a circuitous route to the state of Delaware, through Bethlehem in Pennsylvania.

At Bethlehem there was another hospital, and I found it convenient to rest there a day or two. During my stay it was natural to inquire into the state of the hospital. The method I took was to propose a competition —not whose hospital had done the most good, but whose hospital had done the most mischief. I was requested to give an account of Princeton Hospital. I stated with all the exaggeration I could with truth, not only affecting mortality among the sick and wounded soldiers, but that the elderly men, nurses and other attendants on the hospital were liable to the infection; that I had myself narrowly escaped death; and that five other surgeons and mates had afterwards been seized.

I was answered that the malignancy and mortality of Princeton Hospital bore no comparison with theirs; that at Bethlehem not an orderly man or nurse escaped, and but a few of the surgeons; that one surgeon, Joseph Harrison, a fine young fellow, distinguished for his assiduity, had died. And, to give me some idea of the mortality of their hospital, one of the surgeons asked me if I were acquainted with that fine volunteer regiment of Virginia, commanded by Col. Gibson (Col. John Gibson of Virginia) 9th Regt.

I answered I knew it only by reputation. He then went on to say that forty of that regiment had come to their hospital and then asked me how many I supposed would ever rejoin the regiment? I guessed a third or a fourth part. He declared solemnly that not three would ever return; that one man had joined his regiment, that another was convalescent and might possibly recover, but that the only remaining one besides was in the last stage of the colliquative flux and must soon die. I was obliged to acknowledge the hospital at Bethlehem had been more fatal than that at Princeton.

Discussing the physical aspects of military hospitalization, Tilton has this to say:

Tents, I should suppose would be particularly proper in warm climates as well as in our warm summer seasons. . . . I have used common horsemans' tents, and long tents, formed like the roof of an house, prepared expressly for hospital purposes.

But in cold climates and winter seasons some better protection than tents afford may be necessary. In such cases, the best hospital I have ever contrived was upon the plan of an Indian hut. The fire was built in the midst of the ward, without any chimney, and the smoke circulating round about, passed off through an opening about four inches wide in the ridge of the roof. The common surface of the earth served for the floor. The patients laid with their heads to the wall round about, and their feet were all turned to the fire. The wards were thus completely ventilated. The smoke contributed to combat infections, without giving the least offence to the patients; for it always rose above their heads, before it spread abroad in the ward. And more patients could be crowded with impunity into such wards, than in any others I have seen tried. This was the expedient I employed in the hard winter of 79-80, when the army was hutted near Morris Town, and I was well satisfied with the experiment.

He then presents the ground plan of this hospital and goes on to say:

"It should be noted also that the walls of this hut were built of rough logs, without hewing; that the chinks were daubed with mortar made of common clay and water only; that the middle or main ward, 31½ by 19½ feet in the clear, was assigned to febrile patients; and the smaller end wards, 31½ by 16 feet clear, were occupied by the wounded and other cases of typical infection."

He states that "the bedding of a sick soldier in the American hospitals, in houses as well as in tents, consisted of a bunk or cradle, a sack or bed tick of coarse linen filled with straw, and one or more blankets."

In Dr. Tilton's hospital, the central ward, with twelve beds, had a little less than fifty square feet of floor space per patient. An end ward, with eight beds, had seventy-two square feet of space per patient—a reasonable amount for that time. There are no reports of any considerable amount of sickness in camp or in the army generally during the winter.

Tilton recognized the great mortality caused by the infectious diseases. He said:

My brethren of the faculty will probably think it an interesting fact that more surgeons died in the American service in proportion to their number, than officers of the Line; a strong evidence that infection is more dangerous in military life, than the weapons of war; and should be a powerful excitement, with all concerned, from motives of self preservation, as well as honorable duty, to use all possible care and diligence in warding off that greatest of all evils, the *plague of infection*.

Tilton recognized the value of Baron Steuben's work as Inspector General:

The regular muster of clothing is of immense consequence to our army. Before the introduction of this measure, our army was kept bare and naked, by multitudes of soldiers selling their clothes for drink, and otherwise wasting them. When Baron Steuben was appointed Inspector General, besides the muster of clothing, he introduced a number of salutary regulations, which contributed more to the health and comfort of the troops, than did the utmost efforts of all the medical staff.

Tilton's "Economical Observations on Military Hospitals" ploughed under previous ideas of military medicine and led to his appointment as physician and surgeon-general of the army during the War of 1812. By dint of great personal effort and careful supervision, Tilton greatly improved the sanitary conditions of the army and materially reduced the sick rate.

Besides being first president of the Delaware State Medical Society, he also served in this capacity for several other terms.

Toward the end of his long and faithful service as physician and surgeon-general, he developed several growths. One growth on a lower extremity necessitated amputation. It is said that during the course of this operation, Dr. Tilton supervised and directed the procedure with unparalleled fortitude.

A word as to the eccentric side of this great American. Of friendly disposition and six feet six inches tall, Tilton remained a bachelor of odd habits. He never partook of tea or coffee and prided himself upon the fact that he would not permit cups or saucers in his house. His last years were spent in a stone mansion overlooking the city of Wilmington, and it was here that he died on May 14, 1822, at the age of seventy-six.

John Henry Latimer (1752-1819) was born at Newport, Delaware, on April 24, 1752. He received an A.B. from the University of Pennsylvania in 1770 and an A.M. in 1773. His medical education was secured at Edinburgh University, but he never obtained a degree from this institution. It was in Wilmington, Delaware, that Latimer opened his office, but when war broke out he received an appointment as hospital surgeon. In 1777, he and Dr. Tilton were appointed surgeons of the flying hospital. Gen. Washington spoke highly of Latimer during the war and in 1813 he became surgeon-general of the army. He quit this post in 1815. Latimer was a charter member of the Delaware State Medical Society and at one time its president. Both in the army and out, Latimer·was always considered a man of great integrity and a first-rate physician and surgeon. Latimer forsook the practice of medicine, and in 1794, became a member of the State Legislature. He was elected United States Senator from 1795-1801. He passed away in Philadelphia, on December 19, 1819.

A list of Delaware's physicians who served in the War of Independence includes Joshua Clayton, Newport Duff, Reuben Guilder (Gilder), John Hazlett (who was mortally wounded at Princeton), John H. Latimer, Thomas MacDonough, John McKinley, John Miller, George Monroe, James Pate, John Platt and James Tilton.

Delaware's one regiment in the War of Independence and the natives of this state who fought in the War of 1812, added many famous names to the annals of medical history. Dr. Jacob Jones, more famous as Commodore Jones, commanded the U.S.S. *Wasp* in that ever-memorable battle which terminated within forty-three minutes in the capture of H.B.M.S. *Frolic*. It was when the morale of the American soldiers was at a low ebb from repeated defeats that this and other notable naval successes, acted as a transfusion to the exsanguinated patriots, both on the sea and on the land. Then, from the very mouth of defeat, the battle of Lake Champlain erupted like a volcano and forever quelled the British from attempting to gain back their lost American empire.

It was Commodore Thomas MacDonough, the son of a physician, who played the leading role in this drama. In his youth, the elder MacDonough's overpowering patriotism led him to join the army as a volunteer. When death overtook him, he bequeathed little worldly goods to his son except a name that was associated with personal integrity and love of country.

Commodore MacDonough met the combined invading English army and fleet near Plattsburgh, and off Cumberland Head on Lake Champlain. The English presented the formidable force of twelve thousand soldiers under Sir George Provost, and seventeen vessels carrying ninety-five guns and about one thousand men under Commodore Downie. With a much smaller group of only eight hundred and twenty men, with eighty-six guns and fourteen vessels (some of the latter having been constructed and launched within forty days after the felling of the trees that composed them) MacDonough and his men met the enemy and conquered. This amazing repulse and overthrow of the well trained and equipped enemy and the capture of the boats of invasion which were assigned to capture and hold a line of military posts extending along the chain of Lakes and the Hudson River, saved the young country. If the English had succeeded in their project the eastern section of the United States would have been cut off and perhaps even our prized independence would have been nullified. Thus the very saving of the life of the young republic was due in large measure to the inspiring leadership of a son of a Delaware doctor.

Chapter Ten

NEW JERSEY

THE FIRST VOYAGE of a European to what is now New Jersey was made under French authority by Giovanni da Verrazano, a Florentine navigator, in the spring of 1524. Estevan Gomez, a Portuguese sailor in the service of emperor Charles V., is said to have made notes of the Hudson and Delaware Rivers in 1525. French traders, it seems likely, soon afterwards penetrated the region along the lower Hudson. It was not until 1609, however, that Henry Hudson explored the region between Sandy Hook and Raritan Bay and sailed up the river which now bears his name. Following Hudson's explorations, Dutch traders established themselves on Manhattan Island and soon crossed the Hudson River into what are now Hudson and Bergen counties. Cornelis Jacobsen Mey explored the lower Delaware in 1614 and Cornelis Henrickson repeated this procedure in 1616.

The first group of permanent colonists came to New Amsterdam in 1624 and some of these established a settlement on the eastern bank of the Delaware and built Fort Nassau near the site of modern Gloucester City. In 1631 Samuel Godyn and Samuel Blommaert were authorized by Peter Minuit, the director general of New Netherland, to colonize near Cape May, but this never materialized. A trading hut built at Paulus Hook in 1633 was the precurser of Jersey City. West of the Hudson the trading post of Hobocanhackingh (Hoboken) was established. From these places and from New Amsterdam the Dutch expanded their influence into the Raritan Valley. While William Kieft was governor, the Indians, perturbed by the encroachments of the settlers, assumed a hostile attitude, and when a number of Tappan Indians were killed in 1643 by soldiers acting under Kieft's direction, the red men rose up in arms from the Raritan to the Connecticut, laid waste the farms, massacred the settlers and forced those who escaped to take refuge on Manhattan Island. The Dutch then employed a group of English mercenaries under Captain John Underhill, a hero of the Pequot War, and in 1644 the Indians were defeated in several engagements. A lasting peace was not attained however until August 30, 1645.

In 1638, fifty Swedes colonized the western bank of the Delaware and built Fort Christina (Wilmington). In 1643 a triangular fort, called Elfsborg, was constructed on the eastern side of the Delaware near the present Salem. In 1655, however, the Swedish settlements surrendered to Peter Stuyvesant and thus were transferred to the Dutch. On the subsequent history of New Jersey, Holland and Sweden had very little influence. The Dutch and Swedes in this area were essentially traders, and did not make many permanent settlements. Furthermore they were regarded as intruders by the English colonists of Virginia and New England.

As early as 1634 a patent had been issued to Sir Edmund Plowden designating him governor over New Albion, which was defined as a tract of land including the present states of New Jersey, Maryland, and Pennsylvania. Sir Edmund tried valiantly but did not succeed in establishing a colony. In 1784, Charles Varlo, an Englishman who had bought one-third of the grant from the heirs of Sir Edmund Plowden, came to New Jersey and sought to obtain redress in a legal proceeding in chancery. He failed in his purpose and returned to England, and never again were claims pressed by the heirs of New Albion.

In 1634 a group of Virginia colonists occupied Fort Nassau, which the Dutch had abandoned. These were promptly taken into custody by the Dutch, taken to New Amsterdam, and thence sent home. In 1641 a party of Connecticut colonists migrated southward and established a settlement on the eastern bank of the Delaware River, declaring it to be a part of the New Haven Jurisdiction . In 1642 Governor Kieft, with Swedish aid, arrested the English and sent them back to Connecticut.

The English, it will be recalled, never gave up their claim to New Jersey, which was based on the exploration of the Cabots. In March 1664, Charles II turned over to his brother James, the Duke of York, the territory between the Connecticut River and the eastern side of Delaware Bay, as well as all the islands between Cape Cod and the Hudson River. In May, under the command of Richard Nicolls, an expedition was sent out and in the following August the English took over New Amsterdam. In October Sir Robert Carr ended Dutch rule by acquiring the Delaware colonies. The few inhabitants of what is now New Jersey acquiesced to the new order. Before Nicolls had even reached the New World, the Duke of York transferred to Lord

John Berkeley, Baron of Stratton, and Sir George Carteret, the land extending eastward from the Delaware Bay and river to the Atlantic Ocean and the Hudson river, and northward from Cape May to a line drawn from the northermost branch of the Delaware, "which is 41° 40′ lat.," to the Hudson river in 41° N. lat. To this tract the name of *Novo Caesarea*, or New Jersey, was given because the same name had been applied in a patent to Carteret issued in 1650, to "a certain island and adjacent islets" near Virginia which were never settled. Berkeley's and Carteret's grant gave all the territorial rights which the royal charter had conferred upon the Duke of York.

To appeal to prospective colonists the proprietors in February 1665 published a "Concession and Agreement," in which provision was made for a governor, a governor's council, and an assembly chosen by the freemen and having the power to levy taxes. Land grants were given to persons embarking with the first governor. In the meantime Governor Nicolls of New York, entirely unaware of the grant to Berkeley and Carteret, had accepted certain Indian sales of land to settlers within New Jersey, and had confirmed their titles to tracts in what later became Elizabethtown, Middletown and Shrewsbury. When he finally learned that the Duke had parted with New Jersey he convinced him that it was a great loss, and in the effort to save what was possible, Staten Island was taken from the proprietors on the ground that one arm of the Hudson flowed along its western border.

In August 1665, Philip Carteret, a relative of Sir George, arrived in New Jersey as its first governor. In May 1668 he convoked the first assembly at Elizabethtown. At the next session, in the following November, the towns of Shrewsbury and Middletown declared that they held their grants from Governor Nicolls, and that they were consequently exempt from any quit-rents the proprietors might claim. They refused to pay their share of the public expenses; and their deputies, on refusing to take the oath of allegiance and fidelity, were expelled from the assembly. The disaffection soon spread and led to the so-called "disorganizing" assembly in 1772, which went so far as to choose James Carteret, a landgrave of Carolina and presumably a natural son of Sir George, as "President." Philip Carteret returned to England and laid the case before the proprietors; they ordered President Carteret to continue on his way to Carolina and confirmed as governor, John Berry, whom Governor Carteret had left behind as deputy. The Duke of York declared that the grants made by Nicolls were null and void; the king enjoined obedience to the proprietors, and quiet was restored.

In August 1763, a Dutch fleet appeared off Staten Island, and New

Jersey for a second time became a part of New Netherland. The settled region was called "Achter Koll," or "Back Bay," after Newark Bay, whose waters, lying behind the bay of New York, had to be crossed in order to reach Elizabethtown. The period of Dutch rule was short, and by the Treaty of Westminster, executed on February 9, 1674, the territory was restored to England.

The king's lawyers cleverly declared that the rights of the former proprietors of New York and New Jersey had been nullified by the Dutch conquest, and that by treaty, the lands had been returned to the jurisdiction of the king. On June 13, 1674, Charles II wrote a letter confirming the title and power of Carteret in the eastern half of New Jersey. No similar grant was made to Berkeley, as on the 18th of March he had sold his interest in the province to John Fenwicke, sometime major in the Parliamentary army and later a member of the Society of Friends, and Edward Byllynge (d. 1687), a Quaker merchant. On June 29, the Duke of York received a new patent similar to that of 1664, and he at once comfirmed Carteret in all his rights in that portion of Jersey north of a line drawn from Barnegat Creek to "Rankokus Kill"—a stream a little south of the site of Burlington—which included considerably more than one-half of the province. The Duke of York then appointed Sir Edmund Andros as governor of his dominions, including "all ye land from ye West side of Connecticut River to ye East side of Delaware Bay." Sir George Carteret again sent over his kinsman Philip Carteret to be governor of the eastern part of New Jersey, and the two governors arrived in October 1674 in the same ship.

A quarrel ensued as to the respective interests of Fenwicke and Byllynge in the western province, and they chose William Penn to be arbitrator. Penn decided that nine-tenths of the territory rightfully belonged to Byllynge, one-tenth to Fenwicke. Pecuniary insufficiency soon led Byllynge to assign his shares in trust for his creditors to three Quakers: William Penn, Gawen Lawrie and Nicholas Lucas, and these men later acquired control of Fenwicke's share also. In 1675 Fenwicke with his family and a group of colonists established a settlement on the eastern shore to which they gave the name of Salem. Salem was the first permanent English settlement in this section of New Jersey. Denying Fenwicke's right of jurisdiction over this area, Governor Andros of New York attempted to secure his peaceful recognition of the Duke's authority, and not being able to accomplish this, he sent a military force into this district in December 1676 and made Fenwicke a prisoner. In January, however, Fenwicke was released on his promise not to act in a public capacity until he should receive further authority.

The "quintipartite deed" defining the interests of Carteret, Penn, Lawrie, Lucas and Byllynge was executed on July 1, 1676. It demarcated a line of partition from Little Egg Harbor to a point on the Delaware River, in 41° 40′ N. lat., and assigned the province east of this line (East Jersey) to Carteret and the province west of this line (West Jersey), about five-eighths of the whole, to the Quaker associates.

"The Concessions and Agreements of the Proprietors, Freeholders and Inhabitants of West Jersey in America," was adopted in March 1677, and the document probably bears the hand of William Penn. The main powers of government were allocated to an assembly of one hundred members, chosen annually and subject to instructions from their constituents. In the intervals between sessions of the assembly, affairs were to be managed by ten commissioners chosen by that body. Religious toleration was assured in the document.

The *Kent* sailed up the Delaware in August 1677, with 230 Quaker emigrants from London and Yorkshire who established a colony which developed into modern Burlington. The affairs of this new settlement, far from being run according to "The Concessions and Agreements," were managed by commissioners named by the proprietors, and when in 1680 the Duke of York confirmed the title to the land to Byllynge and his associates, he conveyed the right to govern to Byllynge alone. Although a co-signer of "the Concessions and Agreements" Byllynge now commissioned Samuel Jennings as governor of the province, and the other proprietors acquiesced, appointing Byllynge governor and permitting Jennings to serve as his deputy.

It was in November, 1681, that Jennings called the first assembly and various basic laws were enacted to provide for a governor and council. However, in other respects, the enactments were similar to those in "the Concessions and Agreements." When Byllynge, in 1682-1683 removed Jennings from office, the assembly, after being advised by William Penn, protested the removal of this popular governor and in 1684 dispatched two agents to England to negotiate with Byllynge. George Fox and other Quakers arbitrated the dispute and decided that Byllynge had acted within his rights.

When Fenwicke was released by Andros, he attempted to establish himself as "Lord and Chief Proprietor" of West Jersey, but the Duke's officers contested his claims and in 1682 Penn effected a peaceful settlement with him.

In East Jersey, after the death of Sir George Carteret in 1680, Andros again came to the fore and claimed jurisdiction over New Jersey by the terms of his commission. He issued a proclamation in March 1680 ordering Philip Carteret and his "pretended" officers to cease exercising jurisdiction within the Duke's dominions unless he could show warrant. Carteret was infuriated and on April 30, a detachment of soldiers dragged the so-called governor of East Jersey from his bed and imprisoned him in New York for a month. He was finally released after taking an oath that he would not exercise any authority until the matter could be decided in England.

Andros appeared before the assembly of East Jersey in June 1680 in the capacity of governor and asked for various enactments which were promptly refused by the delegates. As a matter of fact, his conduct had become so objectionable that England demanded that he return to answer charges that had been proffered against him. Philip Carteret then again reassumed the governorship but his regime was again marked by great friction with the assembly.

Sir George Carteret bequeathed his province to eight trustees. Early in 1682, it was purchased by William Penn and associates for 3400 pounds and the Duke of York confirmed the sale, imparting to the new proprietors all the powers necessary for governing the province. Robert Barclay, one of the proprietors, was chosen governor for life and he sent over Thomas Rudyard as his deputy. In 1683 Rudyard was succeeded by Gawen Lawrie. The rule by the new proprietors was essentially liberal. In 1686, Perth Amboy, the newly created port of East Jersey, became its seat of government.

After the coronation of James II in 1685, this monarch showed an unyielding determination to annul the privileges of the colonies, and to unite New York, New Jersey and the New England colonies under a single government. To save their rights to the soil, the proprietors of East and West Jersey agreed to surrender their claims of jurisdiction to the crown. Andros received a new commission extending his authority over New England to include New York and the Jerseys. In August 1688, he formally annexed these provinces to the Dominion of New England. When Andros was seized by the aroused people of Boston in April 1689, following the news of the revolt in England against James II, the Jersey proprietors again stepped in but their government proved ineffectual for they were now widely disseminated in America, England and Scotland and unity of action was rendered impossible. As a matter of fact, for three years, there was little or no organized government in the Jerseys.

In 1692 Andrew Hamilton was appointed governor of both East and West Jersey, thus unifying these areas under one adminstration. In 1697, a faction opposed to Hamilton had him replaced by Jeremiah Basse. He, in turn, was removed in 1699 and Hamilton was again reappointed. Many colonists refused to recognize Hamilton's authority, for he had not received the required approval of the crown. Conditions in the Jerseys bordered on anarchy. Besides these unbearable conditions, complaints against the Jerseys as bases for illegal trade, were brought to the attention of King William. His legal staff declared that as only the king could convey powers of government, those exercised by the Jersey proprietors, derived as they were from the Duke of York, were without sufficient warrant. Many Jersey citizens actually sent petitions to England, begging to be placed under the direct control of the crown so that order might again prevail.

In April 1702 all rights of jurisdiction in both Jersey provinces were transferred to the king but the rights to the soil remained with the proprietors. The provinces of East and West Jersey were then united under a government similar to that of the other royal government of New Jersey; after that date each colony had its own governor.

East and West Jersey had no trouble in finding various bickerings to keep the religious and political cauldrons boiling and bubbling. East Jersey had been colonized primarily by New Englanders and Long Islanders of Puritan extraction. West Jersey was under Quaker influence. East Jersey naturally followed the New England precedent of making the township the main element of local government. West Jersey made the county the fundamental unit. During the period of royal government, George Whitefield became famous for his preaching in 1739 and thereafter and the College of New Jersey (now Princeton University) was chartered in 1746. Queen's College (now Rutgers) was chartered twenty years later.

In November 1775, the colonial assembly of New Jersey took place. Between May 26 and July 2, 1776, the second provincial congress met at Burlington, Trenton and New Brunswick, and this organization temporarily became the supreme governing power. This organization ordered the seizure of tory governor William Franklin (the son of Benjamin Franklin) and his deportation to Connecticut, where he was imprisoned for two years prior to his exchange with the English.

We must not forget that on December 25, 1775, George Washington with about 2500 troops crossed the Delaware and surprised the Hessians at Trenton on the 26th. In this operation 1000 prisoners and 1000 much needed pieces of arms were secured. He followed up this daring maneuver by defeating a detachment of Cornwallis' army at Princeton. Following this the American army set up winter quarters at Morristown and a portion of the British army wintered at New Brunswick.

The British, after taking Philadelphia in September 1777, and noting that their lines of communication with the ocean through the lower Delaware were cut off by Fort Mercer, dispatched three battalions of Hessians which attacked the Jersey fort on October 22, 1777. They were repulsed with heavy loss by Colonel Christopher Greene's troops at the fort.

On August 19, 1779, Major Henry Lee with four hundred soldiers, surprised the British garrison at Paulus Hook, where Jersey City now stands, with a predawn attack. Losing only twenty men, this daring escapade accounted for the death of fifty of the garrison and one hundred and sixty prisoners. During the 1779-1780 campaigns, Morristown was again Washington's headquarters.

After the War of Independence, New Jerseyites sought a more powerful federal union, partly because of the near-anarchy that had so often pervaded their colonial state and partly because New York and Pennsylvania threatened Jersey's commercial existence. The New Jersey plan which was never adopted but which demanded representation in a national congress independent of wealth or population left its impress in the provision of the Constitution for equal representation in the national Senate. The Federal Constitution was ratified by a unanimous vote in the state convention which met at Trenton on December 18, 1787.

The seventeenth century in New Jersey appears to be essentially devoid of medical history. Charles Gordon, an early inhabitant of this colony, wrote to his brother in 1685:

"If you desire to come hither yourself you may come as a Planter or Merchant, but as a Doctor of Medicine I cannot advise you; for I hear of no disease here to cure but some agues, and cutted legs and fingers, and there is no want of empirics for these already; I confess you could do more than any yet in America, being versed both in chirurgery and Pharmacie, for here are abundance of curious herbs, shrubs and trees, and no doubt medicinal ones for making of drugs, but there is little or no employment in this way."

As far as historical research has demonstrated, the seventeenth century in New Jersey produced only four physicians, and little is known as to the extent of their practice. Abraham Pierson (?—1678), doctor and clergyman, came from Yorkshire, graduated from Cambridge University in 1632, and arrived at Boston in 1639. After a sojourn at Southampton (Rhode Island), he migrated to Newark, New Jersey, where he died in 1678. Daniel Cox, a Londoner, bought most of West Jersey in 1690 and became governor of this area. He ruled his holdings, however, through a deputy, and probably never practiced medicine in the New World. William Turner, after an apprenticeship with a Rhode Island doctor named Pinqueron, engaged in the practice of medicine in Newark, New Jersey, until his death some time after 1750.

The fourth and most famous physician of this group was Jonathan Dickinson (1687-1747). This learned theologian migrated from Hatfield, Massachusetts, to New Jersey. He was appointed first president of Princeton College and clergyman of the Elizabeth, New Jersey, Presbyterian Church. The latter position he kept until his death on October 7, 1747, at the age of sixty. Erskine, of Edinburgh, said: "The British Isles have produced no such writers on Divinity in the eighteenth century as Dickinson and Edwards." Dickinson also built a fine reputation as a practitioner and student of the healing art. The letter on the Throat Distemper, which follows, demonstrates that his ability to appreciate morbid phenomena in the light of his contemporary knowledge, was excellent. The preface to the publication of this letter states:

TO THE READER

The Reverend Mr. Dickinson, when at Boston nigh two Years since, being consulted by several gentlemen (anxious for themselves and others) about a most malignant Disease, which had raged for a long time in the Place where he lives, and which had commenc'd its fatal Progress in these Parts, was desired to draw up his Observations in writing, with a View to printing the same for the publick Benefit. Upon that Occasion he wrote the following Letter; which now that we have a fresh Alarm by a Return of that astonishing Distemper among us, it is thought a proper Season to publish it for a common Good.

Several of our ablest Physicians, upon the perusal of it, have expressed their Satisfaction in the Author's Account of the various Phænomina of the Malady and his Method of Cure.—His Observations are the Result of a long Series of Practice and Experience, and seem founded in the exactest Judgment. His informations are as full and particular, as any we've seen, and studiously deliver'd in the easiest Language, to accommodate unlearned Readers.—The surprising Mortality of this Distemper is enough to attract every one's serious Attention; and in such an extraordinary Case every compassionate Friend to Mankind will be ready to impart any useful Reflections: Which is a sufficient Apology both for the Author and the Publisher.

Cambridge, Aug. 5, 1740.

Although the publication of this letter was not until 1740, the original was sent to a friend in Boston in 1738-1739. The actual text of the letter follows:

SIR:

In Compliance with your Desire, I shall now communicate to you some of those Observations I have made upon that extraordinary Disease, which has made such awful Desolations in the Country, commonly called the Throat-Distemper.

This Distemper first began in these Parts, in Febr. 173⅘. The long Continuance and universal Spread of it among us, has given me abundant Opportunity to be acquainted with it in all its Forms.

The first Assault was in a Family about ten Miles from me, which proved fatal to eight of the Children in about a Fortnight. Being called to visit the distressed Family, I found upon my arrival, one of the Children newly dead, which gave me the Advantage of a Dissection, and thereby a better Acquaintance with the Nature of the Disease, than I could otherwise have had: From which (and other like) Observations, I came pretty early into the Methods of Cure that I have not yet seen Reason to change.

There have few Distempers been ever known, that have put on a greater variety of Types, and appear'd with more different Symptoms, than this has done; which makes it necessary to be something particular in describing it, in order to set it in a just View, and to propose the Methods of Cure necessary in its several Appearances. And

1. I take this Disease to be naturally an Eruptive milliary Fever: and when it appears as such, it usually begins with a Shivering, a Chill, or with Stretching, or Yawning; which is quickly succeeded with a sore Throat, a Tumefaction of the Tonsils, Uvula and Epiglottis, and sometimes of the Jaws, and even of the whole Throat and Neck. The Fever is often acute, the Pulse quick and high and the Countenance florid. The Tonsils first, and in a little Time the whole Throat covered with a whitish Crustula, the Tongue furr'd, and the Breath fetid. Upon the 2d, 3d, or 4th Day, if proper Methods are used, the Patient is cover'd with a milliary Eruption, in some exactly resembling the Measels, in others more like the Scarlet Fever (for which Distemper it has frequently been mistaken) but in others it very much resembles the confluent Small Pox. When the Eruption is finished, the Tumefaction every where subsides, the Fever abates, and the slough in the Throat casts off and falls. The Eruption often disappears about the 6th or 7th Day; tho' it sometimes continues visible much longer. After the Eruption is over, the Cuticle scales and falls off, as in the Conclusion of the Scarlet Fever. If after the Cure of this Disease Purging be neglected, the Sick may seem to

recover Health & Strength for a while; yet they frequently in a little Time fall again into grievous Disorders; such as a great prostration of Strength, loss of Appetite, hectical Appearances, sometimes great Dissiness of Sight, and often such a weakness in the Joints as deprives them of the Use of all their Limbs; and some of them are affected with scorbutick Symptoms of almost every Kind.

When this Distemper appears in the Form now described, it is not very dangerous: I have seldom seen any die with it, unless by a sudden Looseness, that calls in the Eruptions, or by some very irregular Treatment. But there are several other very different Appearances of the Disease, which are attended with more frightful and deadly Consequences.

2. It frequently begins with a slight Indisposition, much resembling an ordinary Cold, with a listless Habit, a slow & scarce discernable Fever, some soreness of the Throat and Tumefaction of the Tonsils; and perhaps a running of the Nose, the Countenance pale, and the eyes dull and heavy. The Patient is not confin'd, nor any Danger apprehended for some Days, till the Fever gradually increases, the whole Throat, and sometimes the Roof of the Mouth and Nostrils, are covered with a cankerous Crust, which corrodes the contiguous Parts, and frequently terminates in a mortal Gangreen, if not by seasonable Applications prevented. The Stomach is sometimes, and the Lungs often, covered with the same Crustula. The former Case is discovered by a vehement Sickness of the Stomach, a perpetual vomiting; and sometimes by ejecting of black or rusty and fetid Matter, having Scales like Bran mixed with it, which is a certain Index of a fatal Mortification.... When the Lungs are thus affected, the Patient is first afflicted with a dry hollow Cough, which is quickly succeeded with an extraordinary Hoarseness and total Loss of the Voice, with the most distressing asthmatic Symptoms and difficulty of Breathing, under which the poor miserable Creature struggles, until released by a perfect Suffocation, or stoppage of the Breath. This last has been the fatal Symptom, under which the most have sunk, that have died in these parts. And indeed there have comparatively but few recovered, whose Lungs have been thus affected. All that I have seen to get over this dreadful Symptom, have fallen into a Ptyalism or Salivation, equal to a petit Flux de Bouche, and have by their perpetual Cough expectorated incredible Quantities of a tough whitish Slough from their Lungs, for a considerable Time together. And on the other Hand, I have seen large Pieces of this Crust, several Inches long and near an Inch broad, torn from the Lungs by the vehemence of the Cough, without any Signs of Digestion, or possibility of obtaining it.

Before I dismiss this Head, I must observe, that the Fever which introduces the terrible Symptoms now described, does not always make such a slow and gradual Approach: but sometimes makes a fiercer Attack: and might probably be thrown off by the Eruptions, and this Train of terrors prevented, if proper Methods were seasonably used.

3. This Distemper sometimes appears in the Form of an Erysipelas. The Face suddenly inflames and swells, the Skin appears of a darkish Red, the Eyes are closed with the Tumefaction, which also sometimes extends through the whole Neck and Chest. Blisters or other small Ulcers here and there break out upon the Tumor, which corrode the adjacent Parts; and quickly bring on a Mortification, if not by some happy Means prevented. Some that are thus affected, are at the same Time exercised with all the terrible Symptoms above described; and some with none of them. If this inflamed Tumor be not quickly dispersed, it will (I think) always prove mortal.

4. Another Appearance of this Disease is in external Ulcers: which break out frequently behind the Ears; somtimes they cover the whole Head and Forehead; sometimes they appear in the Arm-Pits, Groins, Navel, Buttocks or Seat; and sometimes in any of the extream Parts. These are covered with the same Kind of whitish Crustula, above described, which also corrodes the contiguous Parts; and quickly, if not prevented, ends in a Mortification. I have ordinarily observed, that if these outward Ulcers are speedily cured, the Throat and external Parts remain free from the above mentioned terrible Symptoms; otherwise the miserable Patient must pass thro' the whole tragical Scene of Terrors before represented, if an external Gangreen don't terminate his Agony and Life together.

5. Sometimes this Disease appears first in Bubo's under the Ears, Jaws, or Chin, or in the Arm-Pits, or Groin. These, if quickly ripened, make a considerable Discharge; which brings a salutary End to the Disease; otherwise they quickly end in a fatal Mortification; or else bring on the whole formention'd Tragedy.

6. This Disease appears sometimes in the Form of a Quinsey. The Lungs are inflamed, the Throat and especially the Epiglottis exceedingly tumefied. In a few Hours the Sick is brought to the Height of an Orthopnœa; and cannot breathe but in an erect Posture, and then with great Difficulty and Noise. This may be distinguished from an Angina, by the Crustula in the Throat, which determines it to be a Sprout from the same Root with the Symptoms described above. In this Case the Patient sometimes dies in twenty-four hours. I have not seen any one survive the third Day. But thro' the Divine Goodness these Symptoms have been more rarely seen among us, and there have been but few in this Manner snatch'd out of the World.

As the Symptoms of this Distemper are very different, so the Methods of Cure should be respectively accommodated to them, and I shall therefore consider them distinctly.

When this Distemper makes its Attack with the Symptoms of a high Fever, a florid Countenance &c., (as in the first Case described) the first Intention, to be pursued towards a Cure, is to bring out the Eruptions as soon as possible; to which End, I order the Patient to be confin'd in Bed, and put into a gentle breathing Sweat, till they appear. A Tea Made with Virginian Snake Root and English Saffron, with a few Grains of Cochineal; A Posset made with Carduus Mariæ boil'd in Milk, and turn'd with Wine, the Lapis contrayerva, or Gascoign-Powder; any or all of these, as Occasions require, answer to this Purpose, and seldom fail of Success.

One of the most dangerous Circumstances that attend this Disease, is a Looseness, that frequently happens upon the first Appearance of the Eruptions; which must be speedily restrained, and the Belly kept bound, lest the morbifick Matter, evaporated by the Pores, be recalled into the Blood, and prove suddenly fatal.—To that Purpose, I ordinarily advise Venice-Treacle, or liquid Laudanum, which commonly answer all Intentions. But if the Patient should be in a dozing Habit, that these cannot be used, or if these should fail of Success, any other Astringent may be used that is proper in a Diarrhœa.

The Ulcers in the Throat should be constantly cleansed, from the Time of their first Appearance. I have found the following Method most successful to this Purpose. Take Roman Vitriol, let it lie as near the Fire as a Man can bear his Hand, till it be thoroughly calcined and turn'd white: Put about eight Grains of this into half a Pint of Water: Lay down the Tongue with a Spatula; and gently wash off as much of the Crust as will easily separate, with a fine Ragg fastened to the End of a Probe, or Stick, and wet in this Liquor made warm. This Operation should be repeated every three or four Hours.

After the Eruptions are quite gone, the Patient should be purged two or three times, to prevent the Consequences above described; and this Rule should be observed in every Form of the Disease.

If after the Crise of this Disease, in any of its Appearances, the Sick should fall into any of the Disorders mentioned under the first Head, such as Loss of Strength, a feverish Habit, Dimness of Sight, Weakness of the Joints, &c. Repeated Purging as far as the Patient's Strength will bear, with Elixir Proprietatis given twice a Day in a Glass of generous Wine, will constantly remove these Difficulties.

When this Disease makes a more slow and leisurely approach with a lingering Fever, pale Countenance, &c. as described in the second Case; all Attempts to bring out the milliary Eruptions seem in vain. And therefore, tho' the Sick may be very much relieved by the diaphoretick Medicines above mentioned if repeatedly used during the Course of the Illness; yet these are not to be depended upon for a Cure; But a brisk

Purge should be also directed every third Day, and those Catharticks, that are mixt with Colomel or Mercurius dulcis, are most likely to be serviceable, where the Age and Strength of the Patient will bear it.

If there be an extream nauseating and vehement Sickness of the Stomach, that can't be otherwise quieted, an Emetic seems necessary; tho' I have not found Encouragement to use vomiting Physick in any other Case.

The internal Ulcers of the Throat, should be treated as above directed; but if there be a great Tumefaction of the Glands, I order externally a Plaister of Diachylon cum Gummi and de Ranis cum Mercurio mixt; and internally the following Fumigation. Take Wormwood, Penny-royal, the Tops of St. John's Wort, Camomile Flowers and Elder-Flowers, of each equal Parts; boil very strong in Water; when boil'd, add as much Brandy or Rum as of this Decoction; steam the Throat through a Tunnel, as hot as can be born, three or four Times a Day.

When the Lungs are seized with this cankerous Crustula, which is indicated by the Cough and Hoarseness above described, Mercurial Catharticks frequently repeated, seem the best of any Thing to promote Expectoration. I have also found Success in the Use of the Syrup of Red Poppies and Sperma Ceti mixt.

When this Distemper appears in the Form of an Erysipelas, I have used the following Fomentation with good Success. Take Wormwood, Mint, Elder-Flowers, Cammomile-Flowers, the Tops of St. John's Wort, Fennel-Seeds pounded, and the lesser Century, equal Parts; Infuse in good Brandy or Jamaica Rum, in a Stone-Jugg well stop'd, and kept hot by the Fire; wet a Flannel Cloth with this; and after moderately squeezing out the Liquor, apply three or four double to the Tumor, as hot as can be born, every Hour.—In this Case I repeat Purging, as above directed.

As for the external Ulcers above described (under the 4th Head) they may be always safely and speedily cured, by applying once or twice a Day a good thick Pledget of fine Tow dipt in the above described vitriolick Water. I have never known this fail in a single Instance, when reasonably used. But then it must be observed, that some of these Ulcers will require this Water much sharper with the Vitrol, than others will bear. It should be so sharp as to bring off the Slough, dry up the flow of corrosive Humours, and promote a Digestion: but it must not be made a painful Caustick. In this the Practitioner's Discretion will guide him.

I need not say any more respecting the Bubo's mentioned under the fifth Head; but that they must by all possible Means be ripen'd as quick as they can; and lanced as soon as they are digested and found to contain any Pus.

I have not yet found any effectual Remedy in the 6th and last Case described.

Upon the Disease in general I have made the following Remarks; which perhaps may be of some Use.

I have observ'd, that the more acute the Fever is on the first Seizure, the less dangerous; because there's more Hope of bringing out the Eruptions.

I have observ'd that there's more Danger of receiving Injury from a cold Air in this, than in any Eruptive Fever I have seen. The Eruptions are easily struck in; and therefore there ought to be all possible Care, that the Sick be not at all exposed to the Air, till the Eruptions are quite over and gone.

I have also observ'd that there's much greater Danger from this Disease in cold Weather, than in hot. In cold Weather it most commonly appears in the Form described under the second Head; while on the contrary, a hot Season very much forwards the Eruptions.

I have frequently observ'd that once having this Disease is no Security against a second Attack. I have known the same Person to have it four Times in one Year; the last of which prov'd mortal. I have known Numbers that have passed thro' it in the eruptive Form in the Summer Season, that have died with it the succeeding Fall or Winter: tho' I have never seen any upon whom the Eruptions could be brought out more than once.

I have ordinarily observ'd, that those who die with this Disease, have many Purple spots about them; which shews the Height of Malignity and Pestilential Quality in this terrible Distemper.

Thus, Sir, I have endeavoured in the most plain and familiar Manner to answer your Demands. I have not attempted a Philosophical Inquiry into the Nature of this Disease, nor a Rationale upon the Methods of Cure. I have meant no more than briefly to communicate to you some of my Experiences in this Distemper, which I presume is all you expect from me. If this proves of any Service, I shall have Cause of Thankfulness; If not, you'll kindly accept my willingness to serve you, and to contribute what I can towards the Relief of the afflicted and miserable.

I am, Sir
Your most humble Servant
Jonathan Dickinson.

Elizabeth Town, N. Jersey Febr. 20, $173\frac{8}{9}$

POSTSCRIPT:

Since I wrote this Letter I am inform'd by a Gentleman of the Profession, who has had very great Improvement in this Distemper, That he has found out a Method of Cure, which seldom fails of Success in all the forms of this Disease herein described, (the first, fourth and fifth only excepted, which should be treated as above directed) and that is a Decoction of the Root of the Dart Weed, or (as it is here called) the Squaw Root. He orders about an Ounce of this Root to be boiled in a Quart of Water, to which he adds when strain'd, a Jill of Rum and two Ounces of Loaf-Sugar; and boils again to the Consumption of one quarter Part. This he gives his Patients frequently to drink, and with this orders them frequently to gargle their Throats; allowing no internal Medicine but this only, during the whole Course of the Disease, excepting a Purge or two in the Conclusion. I have seen a surprising Effect of this Method in one Instance; and shall make what further Observations I can. And if this answers my present Hopes, I shall endeavour to give you further Information.

The Dart Weed Grows with a straight Stalk six or eight Foot high, is jointed every eight or ten Inches apart; and bears a large white Tassel on the Top, when in the Flower. The Root is black and bitterish.

Note that Dickinson not only gives a precise clinical description of the manifestations of the disease but also suggests varying the therapy in accordance with the clinical picture.

By 1700 the population of New Jersey was between fifteen and twenty thousand. Whereas Burlington, Newark, Elizabethtown, New Brunswick, and a few other towns were somewhat settled, New Jersey was to all purposes an essentially rural area.

One of the interesting medical characters of the early seventeen hundreds in Jersey was Joseph Brown. What little we know of this gentleman is mostly gleaned from the Autobiography of Benjamin Franklin. Franklin tells how, when seventeen years old, he left the employ of his brother in Boston and shipped secretly to New York, where he arrived in three days, "without knowledge of anybody, and very little money in my pocket." Not able to find a job there, he made up his mind to go on to Philadelphia.

He reached Amboy after a stormy voyage and set out on foot for Burlington, where he contemplated taking a boat down the Delaware. At Bordentown he spent a night at an inn kept by Dr. Brown:

I got to an Inn in the evening within eight or ten miles of Burlington, kept by one Doctor Brown. He entered into conversation with me while I took some refreshment, and finding I had read a little, became very obliging and friendly. Our acquaintance continued all the rest of his life. He had been, I imagine, an ambulatory quack Doctor, for there was no town in England, nor any country in Europe of which he could not give a very particular account. He had some letters and was ingenious, but he was an infidel, and wickedly undertook some years after, to turn the Bible into doggerel verse, as Cotton had formerly done with Virgil. By this means he set many facts in a ridiculous light, and might have done mischief with weak minds if his work had been published; but it never was. At his house I lay that night, and arrived the next morning at Burlington; but had the mortification to find that the regular boats were gone a little before, and no other expected to go before Tuesday this being Saturday.

The township book of Chesterfield includes the following items: "At a township meeting in 1738, 4 Shillings to Mr. Brown for ye cure of a poor woman; 1 pound 1s. 8d. to Joseph Brown for ye trouble he had with a man who dyed at his house."

Early in the eighteenth century, it was customary for the medical aspirant to apprentice himself for a time to some established practitioner. By so doing the embryo physician gained access to the medical man's library and learned considerable by observing and interrogating his preceptor. The method of indenture became popular, particularly among the more scientifically inclined students.

Shortly after its formation, the New Jersey Medical Society made it a regulation that "..... no student be taken an apprentice by any member (of the Society) unless he has a competent knowledge of Latin, and some initiation in the Greek." The fee for the medical training was fixed at exactly one hundred pounds (proclamation money) and no member of the society was permitted to "....take an apprentice for less than four years, of which, three shall be with his master, and the other may, with his master's consent, be spent in some school of physic in Europe or America."

Here is a sample contract made a few years prior to the formation of the New Jersey Medical Society:

This Indenture made the Seventh day of August, in the Thirty-fourth year of his Majesty's reign George the Second, and in the year of Christ One thousand Seven Hundred and Sixty, Witnesseth that Jacobus Hubbard Son of James Hubbard of Gravesend on Nassau Island and Province of New York Farmer, hath put himself & by these presents doth voluntarily and of his own free will and accord and by and with the consent of his Father and Mother put himself as an Apprentice unto William Clark of Freehold in Monmouth Co. in EAST NEW JERSEYS Doctor and Surgeon, to be taught in the said practice of a Doctor and Surgeon, and in all the several branches of Physic which the said William Clark practices within the said town herein mentioned: and with him to live after the manner of such an Apprentice to continue and serve from the day of the date hereof unto the full end of Four Years and Eight months from thence next ensuing and fully to be compleated and ended. During all which Term the said Apprentice his said Master well and faithfully shall serve, his secrets keep, his lawful commands gladly every where obey. He shall do no damage to his said Master, nor see it to be done by others without letting or giving notice to his said Master. He shall not contract matrimony within the said term. At cards, dice or any other unlawful game he shall not play, whereby his said Master may have Damage. He shall not absent himself day or night from his said Master's Service without his leave, nor hant Ale houses Taverns or play houses, but in all things as a faithful Apprentice he shall behave himself towards his said Master all during his said term. And the Said Master during the S'd term shall by the best of his Means or Methods Arts and Mysterys of a Physician and Surgeon as he now professes Teach or cause the said Apprentice to be Taught to perfection in consideration of the sum of One Hundred Pounds Lawful money of New York to him in hand paid by the said James Hubbard (in four payments) that is to say Thirty Pounds in hand down, and the remainder in Four Equal payments, One each year till the whole is paid. And the said William Clark Acknowledges himself therewith contented and the Receipt thereof. And the said Master is to provide his said Apprentice with sufficient Meat Drink Washing and Lodging and Mending his said clothes within the Said term. And the said James Hubbard is to find him in wearing apparel during said term aforesaid. At the end of Said term the Said Master shall and will give unto the said Apprentice a new set of surgeon's pocket instruments—Solomon's Dispensatory, Quences Dispensatory and Fuller on Fevers, and for the true performance of all and every of the said convenants and agreements of Either of the said parties Do bind themselves Jointly and Severally to the other by these presents. In witness whereof they have hereunto set their hands and Seals the Day and Date first written.

Sealed and Delivered in   JACOBUS HUBBARD, L. S.
   the presence of   WM. CLARK. L. S.
  Pocket interlined before signing.
JOHN^nis GERRITSON,   JAMES HUBBARD, L. S.
RICH. PREST.

Receiv'd Thirty Pounds in part of the within this Seventh day of August, 1760.

WM. CLARK.

1761 July ye 6 then Received by ye hands of Mr. James Hubbard ye sum of £ 17. 10. 0 it being ye first payment of £ 70. 0. 0.

Received p^r me WM. CLARK.

Proficient apprentices were rewarded with certificates of merit. Samuel Treat received the following medical certificate in 1765:

Medical certificate to Mr. Samuel Treat, 1765.

Philadelphia. This is to certify all whom it may concern that Mr. Saml. Treat hath served as an Apprentice to me for nearly four years, during which time he was constantly employed in the practice of Physic and Surgery under my care, not only in my private business, but in the Pennsylvania Hospital in which character he always behaved with great Fidelity and Industry. In Testimony of which, I have hereunto set my hand this first day of September One thousand Seven hundred and Sixty five.

Signed JOHN REDMAN.

We whose names are underwritten do Certify, that Mr. Samuel Treat hath diligently attended the practice of Physic and Surgery in the Pennsylvania Hospital for several years.

Signed THOS. CADWALADER,
PHINEAS BOND,
TH. BOND,
WM. SHIPPEN,
C. EVANS.

This is to Certify that Samuel Treat hath attended a course of Anatomical Lectures with the greatest diligence and assiduity.

Signed WILLIAM SHIPPEN, JR.

Indicating that the successful post-revolutionary New Jersey physician received a fairly good compensation for his professional services are the following transcripts from the account books of Dr. Moses G. Elmer, of New Providence, in Morris County.

Charges for emetics are very frequent: they were evidently considered well adopted for starting therapy. Phlebotomy and venesection, were next in order, and frequently resorted to. Anodynes followed the bleeding. "Hydrarg." was frequently employed.

The average fee for phlebotomy was 1s.; for inoculation with smallpox, 7s. 6d.; for extracting a tooth, 1s.; for a village visit, 1s.; but enough charges were made for medicines to render the total bill 7 or 8 times as much, in many instances.

Judging from the large number of widows with whom accounts were opened, there must have been a very high mortality among those patriots, who fought for liberty in "the times that tried men's souls."

JOHN SIMPSON, Dr.

Feb. 4, 1786. To visit, self, Gut Sudorific, ʒij (noct.)..... £0 4 0
" Gutt Paregor, Haust................. 0 2 9
" Phlebotomy 0 1 0

NATHANIEL ROLFF, Dr.

Dec. 5, 1792. Inoculat. Son, and Daughter Betsy......... £0 7 6

GEORGE CORY, (in the village.)   Dr.

Mar. 2, 1790. To Inoculat. self and child................£1 4 0

WILLIAM WILLCOX.   Dr.

July 2, 1789. To Visit, & Reduc. Frac. Femur. Cornelius.. £0 16 0

SEARING PARSONS,   Dr.

Nov. 19, 1785. To Visit, (Bill) £0 1 0

BENJAMIN WILLCOX,   Dr.

Dec. 23, 1792. To Inoculat. & Boarding self..............£1 2 6

The following lengthy account is for the family of Ephraim Miller. Even the early New Jersey doctor had plenty of trouble keeping "books"!

EPHRAIM MILLER,   Dr.

1786.			£	s.	d.
Oct.	9.	To Visit (noct.) and V.S. self..................	0	14	0
		" Pulv. Cream Tart. ʒij	0	2	0
	15.	" Visit pd. & Pulv. Cath.. iij d.................	0	3	0
		" Visit & Phlebotomy.......................	0	7	0
		" Pulv. Purg. iij d...........................	0	2	0
		" Gut. Cephal, ʒi.............................	0	3	9
	17.	" Visit (noct.)	0	14	0
		" Emp. Epispast. (Max) Appl. Int. Scap........	0	5	0
		" Pulv. Cream Tart. ʒij	0	2	6
		" Visit pd. & Dress Vesicat....................	0	2	0
	18.	" Visit pd. & Gut. Ant. Spasmod. ʒss...........	0	4	6
	19.	" Visit & Pill Ant. Spasmod. No. 6.............	0	12	0
	21.	" Visit & Emp. Epispast. No. ij................	0	9	6
		" Visit (noct) & attend.......................	0	14	0
		" Bol. Cathart. No. 4.........................	0	14	0
		" Dress vesicat. No. ij.......................	0	1	0
	25.	" Visit & Consult, Dr. Winans.................	0	16	0
		" Bol. Cath. No. 1............................	0	3	6
		" Emp. Epispast. (Max) Int. Scap	0	5	0
	26.	" Visit & Pulv. Cath. Rub. No. 12..............	0	18	0
		" Pil. ant. spasmod. No. 6.....................	0	6	0
	27.	" Visit & Man. & Sen. Decoct ℔ j	0	9	6
	28.	" Visit & Sal Ammon. crud. ʒij	0	7	0
		" Valerian Rad. ʒ.............................	0	3	6
Nov.	1.	" Visit & Pulv. Cath. Rub No. 12..............	0	18	0

		To	£	s.	d.
Nov.	1.	" Rad. Valerian Sylv. ʒi.....................	o	3	6
		" Emp. Epist. (Max) Int. Scap................	o	5	o
		" Pil. ant. spasmod. No. 6...................	o	6	o
	2.	" Visit	o	6	o
	4.	" Visit. Elix. Cast. Valerian ʒij.............	o	18	o
		" Neut. Camp. Mixt. ʒ6.......................	o	6	o
		" Visit & Bol. Cath. No. 4...................	1	o	o
		" Rad. Valerian Sylv. ʒj.....................	o	3	6
	5.	" Visit & Consult. Dr. Darby.................	o	16	o
		" Haust. Annod. & attend, omne Noct..........	o	5	6
		" Phlebotomy	o	1	o
		" Pulv. Purg.	o	2	o
	7.	" Visit & Emp. Epispast. (Max) ad Cap	o	14	o
		" Dress, &c	o	1	o
		" Ant'l Mixt. ʒ 8............................	o	6	o
		" Phlebotomy	o	1	o
	8.	" Visit & Emp. Epispast. (Max) Caput..........	o	14	o
		" Dress	o	1	9
		" Pulv. Cream Tart. ʒij......................	o	2	6
		" Rad. Valerian Sylv. ʒj.....................	o	3	6
		" Pill Anod. No. j	o	1	o
		" Gut. Annod. ʒss............................	o	1	6
	9.	" Visit & Dress..............................	o	7	o
		" Pulv. Cath.................................	o	2	o
	10.	" Visit & Emp. Epispast. (Max) Caput..........	o	14	o
		" Dress do	o	1	o
	11.	" Visit & Dress do...........................	o	7	o
		" Pulv. Cream Tart. ʒij......................	o	2	6
	12.	" Visit & Dress..............................	o	7	o
		" V.S. & Pil. Antipasmod, No. 2..............	o	3	o
	13.	" Visit & Dress Caput........................	o	7	o
		" Emp. Epispast. (Max) co....................	o	8	o
		" Pulv. No. ij Pulv. Jalapi..................	o	3	o
	14.	" Antimon. Mixt. ʒ 8.........................	o	6	o
		" Visit & Dress..............................	o	7	o
		" Pulv. Cream Tart. ʒij......................	o	2	6
	15.	" Visit & Emp. Epispas (Max) app. Caput.......	o	14	o
		" Dress & Pill Anti Spas. No. 2..............	o	3	o
		" Haust. Annod. ʒss..........................	o	1	6
	16.	" Phlebotomy	o	1	o
		" Visit & Emp. Epispast. (Max) app. Caput......	o	14	o
		" Pulv. Cream Tart...........................	o	2	6

		To	£	s.	d.
Nov.	16.	" Dress	o	1	o
	19.	" Visit & Emp. Epispast. app. Capt..............	o	14	o
		" Dress & Pil. annod. No. ij & Pulv. Purg........	o	4	o
	22.	" Visit & Antl. Mixt. ℥ 8.....................	o	12	o
		" Dress & Pulv. Cream Tart. ʒij..............	o	3	6
		" Pulv. Cream Tart. ʒij......................	o	2	6
	27.	" Visit & Phlebotomy........................	o	7	o
		" Pill No. j & Pulv. Purg.....................	o	3	o
		" Pill ant. spasmod. No. ij....................	o	2	o
Dec.	1.	" Visit & Emp. Epispast. (Max) app. Capt.......	o	14	o
		" Antimonl. Mixt. ℥ 8.......................	o	6	o
		" Pulv. Cream Tart. ʒij......................	o	2	6
	2.	" Visit & Emp. Epispast. (Max) app. Capt.......	o	14	o
		" V.S. & Pill No. j..........................	o	2	o
		" Pulv. Cath. Jallapi........................	o	2	o
		" Gut. Annod. ℥ss............................	o	1	9
	3.	" Visit & Emp. Epispast. (Max) app. Capt.......	o	14	6
		" Ant. Spasmod. ℥ ii.........................	o	3	6
	5.	" Visit & Phlebotomy.........................	o	7	o
		" Gut. Ant. Spasmod. ℥......................	o	5	o
		" An			
		" Dress Head................................	o	1	o
		" Visit & Pulv. Cream Tart. ʒij.................	o	8	6
		" Emp. Epispast. No. ij app. arms..............	o	3	6
		" An			
		" Dress Head................................	o	1	o
	12.	" Visit & Pil. Anod. No. j....................	o	7	o
		" V.S. & Pulv. Jallapi........................	o	3	o
		" Gut. Cephal ℥j.............................	o	5	o
		" Emp. Emplast. No. ij.......................	o	3	6
		" Do. Do. app. Head.........................	o	1	o
		" Pulv. Cream Tart. ʒij......................	o	2	6
	14.	" Visit & Phlebotomy.........................	o	7	o
		" Emp. Epast. 2 pair.........................	o	7	o
		" Pil. Anod. No. j & Pulv. Purg.................	o	3	o
	15.	" Visit & Emp. Epispast. (Max) app. Head......	o	14	o
		" Pulv. Cream Tart. ʒij......................	o	2	6
		" Tinct.—Valerian ℥j	o	5	o
	18.	" Visit & Phlebotomy, Pedes..................	o	7	o
		" Do. Arm	o	1	o
		" Emp. Epispast. (Max) Capt..................	o	8	o
		" Ant. Spasmod. ℥iss.........................	o	5	o

	To		£	s.	d.
Dec. 20.	" Visit & Emp. Epispast. No. ij................		0	9	6
	" Pil. Anod. No. j...........................		0	1	0
	" Pulv. Jallapi		0	2	0
	" Phlebotomy & Ant. Spasmod. ʒj..............		0	4	6
	" Gut. Cephal. ʒj............................		0	3	6
22.	" Visit & Emp. Epispast. No. ij................		0	9	6
	" Pulv. Cream Tart. ʒiiij....................		0	5	0
	" Dress Head................................		0	1	0
26.	" Visit & Pulv. Jallapi.......................		0	8	0
	" Emp. Epispast. (Max) Head.................		0	8	0
	" Do. do. No. ij, Legs.......................		0	3	6
	" Pil. Anod. No. 1..........................		0	1	0
28.	" Visit & Consult. Doctrs. Stat & Howard.......		0	16	0
	" Emetics & Attendance......................		0	5	6
	" Pil. Ant. Spasmodic, No. 18.................		0	9	0
	" Pil. Anod. No. j...........................		0	1	6
	" Haust Annod..............................		0	1	6
	" Pulv. Ant. Spasmod, No. 3.................		0	3	0
30.	" Visit		0	6	0
Nov. 5.	" (Mistake) Emp. Epispast. (Max) Head........		0	5	0
Dec. 23.	" Do. Visit & Emp. Epispast, No. ij............		0	9	6
Nov. 8.	" Gum Camph. ʒij				

£39 1 6

Rec'd payment in full
of Ephraim Miller.

DIRECTIONS FOR MR. —— MILLER.

Once in a few days let blood be taken from the Arm, in Case the Pain continues in his Head, this must be done as his strength will allow.

The Blister on the Head must be continued, and the Seton *till all* the Symptoms are removed, the Seton especially should be continued many months.

His Diet should be temperate & easy of Digestion.

Common cheese whey for daily Drink, and for a Change a whey made with Cr. Tart.

An Anodyne once in a while if occasion requires, perhaps every Night, or every third Night.

Calomel grs. 6, once in 3 or 4 evenings, with an Anodyne the same evening, to be purged off the next morning.

Rosemary or Valerian Tea may be Drank at Bed Time if it appears necessary.

℞ Tart. Emetic, Grs. 6—Opium, Grs. 6, Spts. L. Comp. Coch. j—Water ½ pint—make palatable with Sugar.—On the days he takes no purge give one table-Spoonful 4 Times in 24 hours.

Wickes explains that these "directions" were evidently penned by Dr. Darbe, and should have been dated Nov. 5, 1786, as on that day Dr. Elmer made a note of the consultation, and soon after exhibited the Antimonial Mixture. On the back, in Dr. Elmer's handwriting, it states:

Dec. 5th, 1786.

Recipe—Ephraim Miller, John Darbe, M.D.
It will be proper that the Calomel be continued and purged off so as not to affect his Jaws.
The Seton in the neck, should be dressed with digestives to promote the Discharge if needful.
It may be advisable to keep Blisters constantly running behind the ears—and if some should be applied to his Arms and Legs interchangeably, as they heal up, it may not be amiss.
Care should be taken, that his Diet should not be too gross.
For the Dizziness in the Head, he may take Sp. Lav.—com—ana, 30 Drops 4 or 5 times a day. Pill: Rusti, in Case of Costiveness will be very good, even if he has not any difficulty that way—it may still be good to take 2 or 3 daily—the Bigness of Small Pea.
If the Case requires let him be put into warm Bath.

This, also, should have had the signature of John Darbe, M.D. It is fortunately, dated; and addressed to "Dr. Elmer," after being folded.
Mr. Miller recovered from this severe attack of disease and paid his bill. He died the "12 or 13 February, 1791," a little over four years after this occurred. "Aug. 5, 1791, a daughter of the Widow Miller; Ephraim Miller's wife as was died, aged about ten years." "Sept. 24th, 1792, Widow Miller died, Ephraim Miller's Widow. Whose death is much lamented by the respectable of her acquaintance." Dr. Elmer made but few entries against them after 1786.
Benjamin Force ran up a much bigger bill even than did Mr. Miller:

BENJAMIN FORCE,   Dr.

1784.			£	s.	d.
Dec. 25.	To Visit & Pulv. Cath. Jallapi iij		0	4	0
27.	" Do. Do. Do.		0	4	0
30.	" Magnesia, ℥ss		0	1	0

	1785.	To	£	s.	d.
Jan.	1.	" Ingred. ad Tinct. Stomac. Pulv. Cort. ʒj......	o	8	o
	22.	" Do. do. do...............................	o	8	o
Feb.	9.	" Do. do. do...............................	o	8	o
	14.	" Visit (noct) self.......................	o	6	o
		" Sperm Cæti opt. ʒj......................	o	3	o
		" Elixir. Paregor, ʒss....................	o	1	o
	15.	" Visit & Phlebotomy......................	o	2	6
		" Sperm Cæti Opt. ʒj......................	o	3	6
	16.	" Visit & Phlebotomy......................	o	2	6
		" Pulv. Febrif. Compt. No. 8..............	o	8	o
		" Mattl. ad Alter. Decoc. ℔ij.............	o	5	o
	19.	" Visit	o	1	6
		" Julep. Compt. iii Sp. Lavd. ʒ 6.........	o	7	o
		" Sperm Cæti Opt. ʒj......................	o	3	6
		" Pil. Annod. No. j......................	o	2	o
	20.	" Visit	o	1	6
		" Mattl. ad L. Decoct. ℔j................	o	5	o
Mar.	9.	" Visit	o	1	6
		" Emp. R................................	o	2	o
	12.	" Visit & Pulv. Rhei iij.................	o	5	o
	13.	" Sal Cath. Glaub. ʒj....................	o	1	6
	15.	" Visit (noct)	o	6	o
		" Gut. Cephal ʒj........................	o	3	6
	16.	" Visit	o	1	6
	29.	" Pulv. Cortie ʒss.......................	o	3	o
Apr.	1.	" Elixir Asthmat. ʒij....................	o	10	o
		" Vitl. Alb.............................	o	1	o
	12.	" Visit & Pulv. Hydrarg. ʒj..............	o	6	6
		" Consult. Dr. Elmer....................	o	16	o
	20.	" Salin. Mixt. iij Sp. L. ʒ 6...........	o	6	o
	25.	" Visit (noct)	o	6	6
		" Sudorif. Purg. Mixt. ʒ 6..............	o	6	o
	27.	" Visit & Consult Dr. Jones.............	o	17	6
	28.	" Visit pd..............................	o	1	o
	30.	" Phlebotomy ......Dick.................	o	1	o
		" Sperm Cæti Opt. ʒj....................	o	3	6
Aug.	3.	" Visit ....self....................	o	1	6
		" Haust. Purg........do.................	o	1	9
		" Emetic ....Scarifin..................	o	1	6
	5.	" Pil. Ant. Hyst. No. 4.................	o	4	o

			£	s.	d.
1786.		To			
Aug.	31.	" 2 Visits & Pulv. Diuret. No. 12..............	0	15	0
		" Elixir Asthmat. ℥ss.........................	0	2	6
Sept.	3.	" Visit	0	1	6
	4.	" Do. & Pulv. Diuret. No. 12..................	0	13	6
		" Pulv. Hydrarg. No. j......................	0	5	0
		" Gut. Asthmat. ℥ij.........................	0	10	0
	6.	" Visit	0	1	6
	7.	" Visit & Gum Camph. ℥ss....................	0	3	0
		" Empl. Mercl. ℥j............................	0	1	0
	8.	" Visit (noct)	0	6	0
		" Mattl. ad. Sudorif. Decoct. ℔j...............	0	3	6
	8.	" Visit & Pulv. Diuret. No. 12................	0	13	6
		" Pulv. Hydrarg. No. ij......................	0	10	0
		" Ingred. ad. Tinct. Stomac. iij Pulv. Cort. ℥j...	0	8	0
	10.	" Visit pd. & Dress Leg......................	0	2	0
	11.	" Do. do....................................	0	2	0
	13.	" Visit pd....................................	0	1	0
	17.	" Visit & Elix. Asthmat. ℥ss..................	0	4	0
		" Mattl. ad Diuret. Decoct. ℔ij...............	0	5	0
		" Visit	0	1	6
		" Ingred. ad Decoct. Al. ter ℔ij..............	0	5	0
	21.	" Visit pd....................................	0	1	0
	26.	" Visit & Pulv. Diuret. No. 12.................	0	13	6
		" Elix. Asthmat. ℥j..........................	0	5	0
Oct.	1.	" Visit	0	1	6
	9.	" Mattl. ad Tinct. Stomac iij P. Cort. ℥j........	0	8	0
	19.	" Visit pd....................................	0	1	0
	28.	" Visit & Puncturn...........................	0	5	6
	29.	" Elix. ad Hemorrh. ℥ij......................	0	5	0
	30.	" Extract Tooth..............................	0	1	0
		" Visit	0	1	6
Novr.	1.	" Do	0	1	6
	2.	" Visit & Pulv. Diuret. No. 12................	0	13	6
		" Visit & Pulv. Hydrarg. No. j...............	0	11	0
	4.	" Visit & Pulv. Hydrarg.....................	0	6	6
	6.	" Consult. Dr. Darby........................	0	16	0
	7.	" Visit & Scarifn. Leg........................	0	3	6
	8.	" Do. do. do................................	0	3	6
	9.	" Visit & Pulv. Hydrarg. No. j................	0	6	6
		" Scarifn. Leg...............................	0	2	0
	10.	" Visit & Scarifin. do........................	0	3	6

		To	£	s.	d.
Novr.	11.	" Do. do. do...............................	o	3	6
		" Dress	o	2	o
		" Pulv. Diuret. No. 12.....................	o	12	o
	12.	" Visit & Dress Leg Ung. Digest ʒj...........	o	9	o
	13.	" Do do. do...............................	o	5	6
	14.	" Visit Inustn. Tumor......................	o	3	6
	15.	" Dress Leg................................	o	4	o
	16.	" Visit & Dress Leg........................	o	5	6
		" Visit, Inustn. (Cauterizing) & Dress Leg......	o	5	6
		" Pulv. Hydrarg. No. j.....................	o	5	o
	17.	" Visit & Dress Leg........................	o	5	6
		" Visit, Mattl. Ad. Stomac iij Cort. Peruv. ʒj....	o	9	6
		" Dress Leg................................	o	4	o
	20.	" Visit, Inust. & Dress Leg..................	o	7	6
	21.	" Visit do. do..............................	o	5	6
	22.	" Do. do. do...............................	o	5	6
	23.	" Visit, Inustn. do. do......................	o	7	6
		" Pulv. Diuret. No. 16......................	o	16	o
	24.	" Visit & Dress............................	o	5	6
	25.	" Do do...................................	o	5	6
	26.	" Visit & Dress............................	o	5	6
		" Pulv. Hydrarg. No. j.....................	o	5	o
	27.	" Visit & Dress............................	o	5	6
	28.	" Do do...................................	o	5	6
		" Ungt. Digest. ʒss.........................	o	1	9
	29.	" Visit & Dress............................	o	5	6
		" Pulv. Hydrarg. No. j.....................	o	5	o
		" Ungt. Digest. ʒss.........................	o	1	9
		" Gut. Annod. ʒss..........................	o	1	6
	30.	" Visit & Dress............................	o	5	6
Dec.	1.	" Visit & do. do............................	o	5	6
	2.	" Do do. do...............................	o	5	6
		" Pulv. Hydrarg. No. j.....................	o	5	o
	3.	" Visit & Dress, Ungt. Digest. ʒss.............	o	7	3
	5.	" Visit Do. Do............................	o	5	6
	6.	" 2 Visits do. do...........................	o	11	o
		" Pulv. Hydrarg. No. j.....................	o	5	o
	8.	" Visit & Dress do.........................	o	5	6
	11.	" Do. do. & Haust. Annod..................	o	7	o
	12.	" Visit, Pulv. Hydrarg. (noct)...............	o	11	o
		" Dress Leg. Ungt. Digest. ʒss...............	o	5	9
	13.	" Visit & Dress Leg........................	o	5	6

		To	£	s.	d.
Dec.	15.	" Visit	0	1	6
	16.	" Visit, do. do...........................	0	5	6
		" Ungt. Digest. ʒj...........................	0	3	6
		" Pulv. Hydrarg. No. j......................	0	5	0
		" Visit & Dress Leg.......................	0	5	6
		" Unguent. Digest. ʒss.....................	0	1	9
	19.	" Visit & Dress Leg.......................	0	5	6
		" Ungt. Digest. ʒj & Pulv. Hydrarg. No. ij......	0	13	6
	22.	" Gut. Annod. ʒj..........................	0	3	6
	26.	" Visit & Dress Leg. Ungt. Digest. ʒj..........	0	5	0
		" Pulv. Hydrarg. No. j.....................	0	5	0
	28.	" Visit & Dress Leg (noct)..................	0	16	0
		" Pulv. Hydrarg. No. j.....................	0	5	0
	31.	" Ungt. Digest. ʒj..........................	0	3	6
1787.					
Jan.	1.	" Do. do. do...............................	0	3	0
	2.	" Visit & Pulv. Hydrarg. No. 1...............	0	6	6
		" Gut. Annod. ʒj..........................	0	3	6
		" Dress Leg...............................	0	4	0
	5.	" Visit & Dress Leg.........................	0	5	6
	6.	" Visit & Pulv. Hydrarg. (noct)..............	0	11	0
	10.	" Visit & Pulv. Diuret No. 10...............	0	11	6
		" Pulv. Hydrarg. No. j......................	0	5	0
		" Dress Leg...............................	0	4	0
	14.	" Visit & Dress Leg.........................	0	3	6
		" Ungt. Digest. ʒj..........................	0	3	6
	15.	" Visit	0	1	6
	17.	" Visit & Dress Leg.........................	0	3	6
		" Pulv. Hydrarg. No. j......................	0	5	0
		" Sal. Cath. ʒi..............................	0	1	6
	26.	" Visit, Scarif. & Dress Leg..................	0	5	6
		" Ungt. Digest. ʒj..........................	0	3	6
	30.	" Visit & Dress Leg.........................	0	3	6
		" Pulv. Hydrarg. No. j......................	0	5	0
Feb.	3.	" Visit & Attend. (noct)....................	0	10	0
		" Pulv. Sudorific. No. j.....................	0	1	6
		" Pil. Annod. No. j.........................	0	1	6
		" Visit & Pil. No. ij........................	0	4	6
		" Pil. Saponai Laxat. No. 30.................	0	10	0
	5.	" Visit	0	1	6
	11.	" Visit & Pulv. Hydrarg. No. j...............	0	6	0

		To		£	s.	d.
Feb.	23.	" Visit & do. do. do............................		o	6	6
	25.	" Visit		o	1	6
	26.	" Visit & Consult. Dr. P. Elmer.................		o	16	6
		" Visit & Pulv. Hydrarg. No. iij...............		o	9	o
		" Attendance 7s. 6d...........................		o	7	6
	27.	" Visit		o	1	6
	28.	" Visit & Pulv. Hydrarg. No. iij...............		o	9	o
Mar.	6.	" Visit		o	1	6
	15.	" Visit & Pulv. Hydrarg. No. iij...............		o	9	o
	17.	" Visit & Pulv. Hydrarg. No. ij................		o	6	6
	20.	" Visit pd.....................................		o	1	6
	22.	" Pulv. Diuret. No. 8..........................		o	8	o
	29.	" Visit & Pulv. Hydrarg. No. iij...............		o	9	o
		" Pulv. Diuret. No. 8..........................		o	8	o
Apl.	2.	" Visit (noct).................................		o	6	o
		" Elix. Paregor. ℨj............................		o	1	9
	7.	" Visit & Scarif. Penis........................		o	3	6
		" Mattl. ad Carminative Decoct. ℔j............		o	3	6
		" Gut. Pareg. ℨj..............................		o	1	9
	9.	" Visit & Scarif. Penis........................		o	3	6
	10.	" Visit & Attend'ce............................		o	3	6
		" Scarifn. Testicles		o	2	o
	11.	" Visit & Punctn. do...........................		o	3	6
	12.	" Visit do. do. & Attend.......................		o	5	6
	13.	" Visit & Elix. Purg. ℨss......................		o	3	3
		" Scarif. Penis & Test........................		o	2	o
	14.	" 2 Visits, Punct. Test. & Penis...............		o	7	o
		" Pil. ant. Cath. iij No. ij......self..........		o	5	o
		" Mattl. ad Carmin Decoct. ℔ij...............		o	3	6
	15.	" Visit & Consult. Dr. P. Elmer................		o	9	o
		" Attend		o	4	o
	16.	" Visit & Attend'ce............................		o	3	6
	17.	" Do		o	1	6
	18.	" Visit & Dress Test...........................		o	5	6
		" Ungt. Digest. ℨij...........................		o	7	o
		" Diuret. Cart. iij. Elix. Vit. ℨ8...............		o	9	o
		" Visit & Dress Test...........................		o	5	6
		" Elix. Asthmat. ℨj...........................		o	5	o
	19.	" Visit & Dress Test...........................		o	5	6
Apl.	18.	" Pulv. Diuret. ℨss............................		o	6	o
	20.	" Visit & Dress Test...........................		o	5	6
	21.	" Visit & do. do..............................		o	5	6

		To		£	s.	d.
Apl.	22.	" Visit & Dress Test		0	5	6
	23.	" Visit & Dress Test		0	5	6
		" Visit & Dress do		0	5	6
		" Gut. Cephal. ʒj		0	5	0
	24.	" Visit & Dress Test		0	5	6
	25.	" Visit & do. do		0	5	6
	26.	" Visit & do. do		0	5	6
	27.	" Do. do. do		0	5	6
		" Elix Asthmat. ʒj		0	5	0
	28.	" Visit & Dress Test		0	5	6
	29.	" Visit & Dress do		0	5	6
May	1.	" Visit & do. do		0	5	6
	3.	" Visit & Inust, Dress Leg		0	4	6
		" Dress Test		0	4	0
	4.	" Visit & Dress Leg		0	3	6
		" Dress Test		0	4	0
	5.	" Visit & Dress Leg. & Test		0	6	6
		" Visit & Elixir Asthmat. ʒj		0	6	6
	6.	" Visit & Dress Leg & Test		0	5	6
	7.	" Visit & Dress Test		0	3	6
	8.	" Visit & Dress Leg & Test		0	5	6
	9.	" Visit & Dress do. do		0	5	6
	10.	" Do. do. do. do		0	5	6
	11.	" Do. do. do. do		0	5	6
	12.	" Visit & Dress Leg & Test		0	5	6
	13.	" Visit & do. do. do		0	5	6
	14.	" Do. do. do. do		0	5	6
		" Visit & Dress Test		0	3	6
		" Haust. Annod		0	1	9
	15.	" Visit & Dress Leg & Test		0	5	6
	16.	" Do. do. do. do		0	5	6
		" Gut. ʒss		0	3	6
	17.	" Visit & Dress Leg & Test		0	5	6
	18.	" Visit & do. do. do		0	5	6
		" Diuret. Max V, ʒ6		0	6	0
	19.	" Visit & Dress Leg		0	3	6
	20.	" Do do do		0	3	6
	21.	" Visit & Dress Leg & Test		0	5	6
	22.	" Visit pd. & Dress Leg		0	3	6
	23.	" Visit & Dress Leg		0	3	6
	24.	" Visit pd. & do. do		0	3	6
		" Pulv. Cream Tart. ʒij		0	2	6

		To	£	s.	d.
May	25.	" Visit & Dress Leg..........................	0	3	6
	26.	" Do. Do. Do..............................	0	3	6
	27.	" Visit & Dress Leg & Scarifn.................	0	4	6
	29.	" Visit & Scarifn. Do......................	0	2	6
	30.	" Visit & Pulv. Cream Tart. ℥ij.................	0	4	0
		" Visit & Dress Leg Ung. Mercl. ℥j & Box.......	0	5	6
		" Pulv. Diuret No. 8..........................	0	8	0
June	1.	" Visit, Dress Leg & Test.....................	0	4	6
	3.	" Visit Do. Do.............................	0	3	6
	4.	" Visit & Dress Leg..........................	0	3	6

Benjn. Force's Account is Paid.

Wickes observes that the total amount of Force's bill was £66 8s. 0d. (probably Yorke money) and that the therapy extended from December 25, 1784, to June 4, 1787. As the charge for 71 Visits at 1s. 6d. is only £5 6s, the rest of the bill was for drugs and other services.

Of the consulting physicians named in these accounts, Dr. Staats was of New York; Dr. Darbe, of Parsippany; Dayton, Sr. and Jr., of Springfield; Winans, of Elizabethtown; Howard, of New Brunswick; Jones, of Morristown, and Elmer, of Westfield.

In 1786 John Simpson seems to have had the same disease that Mr. Force had, as the same parts were affected. Dr. Winans was consulted in the case:

Apl. 22, 1786. To Visit & Consult Dr. Winans........ 0 12 6

This case was treated from April 17, 1786 to May 9, 1786. Dr. Winans favored the "HYDRARG" treatment, as that was employed immediately after consultation.

John Clark, Jun'r, in 1784-5 is charged in the sum of one pound, thirteen shillings, and is credited:

May 29. *By Congregation* 0 17 6

Since the Church helped its poor sick members, the doctor had few patients on the free list.

There are no deaths recorded on Dr. Elmer's books, no intimations as to the results of treatment in any case, and no diagnoses listed.

SAMUEL PARSONS, Dr.

			£	s.	d.
1787.					
Jany.	1.	To Visit & Attendce. (omne noct.).............	0	8	0
		" Cort. Peruv. ℥ij......................	0	12	0
		" Rad. Virgin. ℥j......................	0	3	0
		" Gum Camp. ℥ss......................	0	2	6

		To		£	s.	d.
Jany.	1.	" Scarifn. Fomens		0	2	0
		" Consult Dr. Elmer		0	8	0
	2.	" Visit		0	1	0
		" Pulv. Cort. ʒj		0	6	0
	3.	" Ungt. Digest. ʒij		0	7	0
	5.	" Visit & Dress Arm (noct)		0	3	6
		" Do. & Cort. Peruv. ʒiij Dress		0	12	0
	6.	" Visit & Dress Arm (noct)		0	3	6
		" Visit & Dress Præcip, Pulv. Cort. No. ij		0	3	0
		" Do. (noct) Dress & Pulv. Cort. ʒij		0	13	0
	7.	" Visit Dress Ungt. Digest ʒij		0	7	0
		" Visit, Dress Arm (noct)		0	3	0
	8.	" Visit, do		0	2	0
	9.	" Visit, Excisn. Thumb		0	3	0
	11.	" Do. & Dress		0	3	0
		" Do. Dress. Præcipt, Ungt. Digest ʒj		0	5	6
	13.	" Visit, Dress, Pulv. Cort. ʒij		0	10	0
	14.	" Do. & Dress		0	2	0
	15.	" Do. do		0	2	0
	16.	" Do. do		0	2	0
		" Do. do. Exicisn. Finger		0	3	0
	17.	" Visit & Dress		0	2	0
	18.	" Do. do		0	2	0
	19.	" Do. do		0	2	0
	20.	" Do. do		0	2	0
	24.	" Do. do		0	2	0
	25.	" Do. do		0	2	0
	27.	" Dress Hand		0	1	0
	29.	" Do. do		0	1	0
	30.	" Visit pd. Dress do		0	2	0
		" do. do		0	1	0
		" Dress, Præcipt. rub		0	2	0
Feby.	4.	" Visit & Dress, Præcipt. rub		0	2	6
	6.	" Dress, Precip		0	2	0
	10.	" Do. do		0	2	0
	12.	" Do. do		0	1	6
	13.	" Do. do		0	1	6
Mar.	30.	" Pulv. Catht. Jallapi		0	1	6
May	7.	" V.S.		0	1	0
				£7	17	0

Paid by note of hand.

Mr. Parsons evidently recovered.

And now we come to the story of the founding of the first colony-wide medical society in the colonies:

The following advertisement appeared in the *New York Mercury* in June, 1766:

A considerable number of the Practitioners of Physick and Surgery, in East New Jersey, having agreed to form a society for their mutual improvement, the advancement of the profession and promotion of the public good, and desirous of extending as much as possible the usefulness of their schemes, and of cultivating the utmost harmony and friendship with their brethren, hereby request and invite every gentleman of the profession in the province, that may approve of their design, to attend their first meeting, which will be held at Mr. Duff's, in the city of New Brunswick, on Wednesday, the twenty-third of July, at which time and place the Constitution and Regulations of the society are to be settled and subscribed. East New Jersey, June 27th, 1766.

Fourteen doctors attended the meeting held at New Brunswick and set up the "Instruments of the Association and Constitutions of the New Jersey Medical Society." These pioneers of the New Jersey Medical Society chose the Rev. Mr. McKean, President; Doctor Chris. Manlove, Secretary; and Doctor John Cochran, Treasurer. They discussed "the mode of charging for medical and surgical services", and elected a committee to draw up a "Table of Fees and Rates." In accordance with the seventh article of the Constitution, four subgroups called the Elizabethtown, Bound Brook, Princetown, and Morristown Inferior Medical Societies were organized.

The following resolutions concerning credit were adopted:

Resolved, That long credit is both an injury to the practitioner and the people.

Resolved, Therefore, that credit above a year is a discouragement to the profession.

Resolved, That each member of this society will not credit any person (those families where they are constantly employed excepted) above three months, after his or her recovery;

That all strangers ought to pay ready money for any medical services.

Resolved, That cures of all foul diseases should be paid for immediately.

The Instruments of Association and Constitutions of the New Jersey Medical Society were adopted by the infant New Jersey Medical Society on July 23, 1766. This document guarantees that this Society will do all in its power to discourage and discountenance all quacks, mountebanks, imposters, or other ignorant pretenders to medicine;

and will on no account support or patronize any but those who have been regularly initiated into medicine, either at some University, or under the direction of some able master or masters, or who, by the study of the theory and of the practice of the art, have otherwise qualified themselves to the satisfaction of this Society for the exercise of their profession.

On July 23, 1766, a table of medical fees and rates was tabulated by the Society in New Brunswick:

PREAMBLE

The New Jersey Medical Society, considering the state of medical practice in this Government, and apprehending, that as they have separated themselves to a profession that not only deprives them of many comforts and indulgences, which persons in other offices of life enjoy, by being at the call of any one, day or night; but also exposes them to many disagreeable scenes and often to great dangers from contagious diseases, &c.; besides the great expense of education and the many painful years to be employed in preparatory studies, as well as that of the science itself, they are in an especial manner entitled to a just and equitable reward for their services, at least to live by this their useful profession. And observing that their fees or rewards are not regularly settled by law or custom, and that many inconveniences arise from such defect and the consequent vague and indeterminate mode of practitioners charging for their services, and conceiving that it will be both for the interest of the people and practitioner to establish one general and uniform mode, have unanimously agreed to the following table, in which they have affixed such reasonable rates to most of those articles that can be ascertained in an art that admits of such a diversification of forms and circumstances, as they hope will be universally satisfactory, and such as they sincerely think are consistent with equity, and by no means higher than the usual charges heretofore generally made. And this scheme they have adopted for the sake of justice and order, to prevent unnecessary disputes and differences between them and their employers, and as far as the usage of regular and principled practitioners will in that way extend to obviate the impositions of quacks and illiterate medicators. And they do hereby bind and oblige themselves at all times hereafter to keep their accounts according to the rates therein settled and ascertained, till the Legislature shall interpose, or some other happier method be devised for determining a matter so interesting both to the public and the profession.

A TABLE OF FEES AND RATES.

*For sundry articles and services in medicine and surgery, as agreed
on and established by the New Jersey Medical Society, at their
general meeting in New Brunswick, July 23d, 1766.*

PROCLAMATION MONEY

		£	s.	d.
Visits in Towns:	Visiting in towns, whereby the physician and surgeon can readily attend the patient without riding, to be charged for according to the duration of the ailment and degree of attendance, viz.: In slight cases whereby a visit or two may be wanted..............	0	05	0
Per Week:	In other cases requiring longer and daily care and attendance: for each week's attendance and in proportion for lesser or more time, exclusive of medicines.................	0	10	0
Visits in the Country:	Visits in the country under half a mile to be charged for as in towns, viz., per week, &c.	0	10	0
Above half a mile & not more than 1½:	Every visit above half a mile and not exceeding a mile and a half....................	0	1	6
Above 1½ & not more than 15:	Every visit above one and a half miles and not exceeding fifteen miles, for each mile additional	0	1	0
Above fifteen & not more than 25:	Every visit above fifteen miles and not exceeding twenty five miles, for each mile above fifteen and under twenty-five......	0	1	6
Above 25:	Every visit above twenty-five miles, for each mile above twenty-five.................	0	2	0
	Every visit in the night, exclusive of other things	0	5	0
Consultations:	Consultation Fees, viz.: Every first visit and opinion by the consulted physician or surgeon, exclusive of traveling fees..........	0	15	0
	Every succeeding visit and advice by do. &c.	0	7	6

		£	s.	d.
Surgical operations and services:	Fees for surgical operations and services, exclusive of visits and traveling charges, viz.:			
	Phlebotomy	0	1	6
	Extracting a tooth......................	0	1	6
	Cutting an issue........................	0	2	0
	Cupping with scarification...............	0	2	0
Wounds:	As first dressing of all large or deep incised or contused wounds, including ung'ts, &c., except in very extraordinary cases, where the surgeon shall consult the Society, who will adjudge the proper charge in such particular cases...........................	0	7	6
	Succeeding dressing of do., each time.......	0	2	0
Sinuses and Abscesses:	Opening large sinuses or abscesses, and first dressing	0	7	6
	Succeeding dressing of do., each...........	0	3	0
Inflammations:	Advice for large inflammations and abscesses, when attended twice a day, per week, and proportionably for a greater or less time..	0	10	0
	Do. when attended once a day, per week, &c.	0	5	0
Ulcers:	Dressing all malignant, putrid or phagedæme ulcers, each dressing....................	0	2	0
	Dressing small cutaneous or superficial wounds, small and healing ulcers and small abscesses, each dressing.................	0	1	0
	Opening small abscesses and sinuses.........	0	2	0
	Drawing off the urine by the catheter, each time	0	7	6
	Administering a clyster....................	0	3	9
Trepan:	Operation of the trepan...................	3	00	0
	Dressing each time.......................	0	3	9
Couching &c.:	Couching or extracting the cataract.........	3	00	0
	Cutting the Iris.........................	3	00	0
	Fistula Lachrymalis.......................	1	10	0
	Each dressing do.........................	0	1	6
	Bronchotomy	1	10	0
	Extirpation of the Tonsils................	1	00	0
	Extraction of the polypus of the nose.......	1	00	0
	Operation for the Hare-lip................	1	10	0

	£	s.	d.
Operation for the Wry-neck..............	1	10	0
Each dressing in the five preceeding cases...	0	1	6

Amputations:

	£	s.	d.
Amputations of the breast.................	3	00	0
Ditto of the Fore and back arm............	3	00	0
Ditto of the leg or thigh.................	3	00	0
Each dressing for the first 14 days after the preceding amputations..................	0	5	0
Each succeeding dressing.................	0	2	6
Amputation of the fingers or toes, each......	0	15	0
Each dressing do.........................	0	2	0
Suture of the tendons and Gastroraphy, each.	1	00	0
Each dressing do.........................	0	2	6
Bubonocele Epiplocele and Hernia Femoralis, each	3	00	0
Each dressing do.........................	0	5	0
Exomphalos and Hernia Ventralis..........	1	10	0
Each dressing............................	0	2	6
Hydrocle Radical operation...............	3	00	0
Ditto palliative by puncture..............	1	10	0
Castration, each Testicle.................	3	00	0
Each dressing do.........................	0	5	0
Phymosis and paraphymosis................	0	7	6
Each dressing............................	0	2	0
Paracentisis	1	10	0
Fistula in ano, deep, sinuous and of long standing	3	00	0
Do. small and recent......................	2	00	0
Each dressing in such Fistulas..............	0	3	0
Empyema	1	00	0
Each dressing do.........................	0	2	0
Extirpation of large encysted and large cancerous Tumors........................	1	10	0
Dressing do, each time....................	0	3	0
Extirpation of small encysted and small cancerous Tumors........................	0	15	0
Each dressing do.........................	0	5	0
Cutting for the stone in the bladder.........	5	00	0
Each dressing do.........................	0	5	0
Cutting for the stone in the urethra.........	1	10	0
Each dressing do.........................	0	2	0
Assistant Surgeon's fee in all operations.....			

		£	s.	d.
Midwifery, viz.:	Delivering a woman in a natural case........	1	10	0
	In a preternatural case....................	3	00	0
	In a laborious case, requiring forceps or extrication with the crotchet, &c...........	3	00	0
Inoculation:	Inoculation of the small pox, including medicine and attendance....................			
Fractures and Dislocations:	Reduction of a simple fracture, and depression of the nose, with necessary dressing during the cure.......................	1	7	0
	Luxation or fracture of the lower jaw, with do	1	00	0
	Luxation of the neck, with do..............	2	00	0
	Luxation of the Humerus, and do..........	1	10	0
	Ditto of the Cubit, and do.................	1	10	0
	Simple fracture of the Clavicle, and do......	1	10	0
	Ditto of the fore and back arm, and do......	1	10	0
	Dislocation or fracture of the wrist bones, with do...............................	1	10	0
	Dislocation of the thigh bone, with do......	2	00	0
	Ditto of the knee, with do.................	1	10	0
	Ditto or fracture of the Patella, with do.....	0	15	0
	Ditto of the ankle, with do.................	1	10	0
	Simple fracture of the thigh or leg bones, with do...............................	2	00	0
	Simple ditto of the heel, with do...........	1	10	0
	Dislocation of the fingers or toes, with do...	0	7	6
	Compound fractures of all kinds, one-third more than simple, besides the daily dressing, which is to be charged at the rate fixed for large wounds, when the fracture is of the thigh, leg or arm; but at the rate of small wounds when of the fingers or toes, &c...			
	Other surgical cases not here mentioned, either to be proposed to the Society for their decision, or to be charged as nearly to the tenor of this table as possible.			
	Rates of extemporaneous forms of medicine, exclusive of visiting and traveling fees, viz.:			
	Bolus Cathartic or emetic..................	0	2	0
	Ditto with musk........................	0	3	0
	Every other do. alterative for persons above			

		£	s.	d.
	...years of age. Every do. for persons under ... years			
	Decoction with one ounce Cort. Peruv. and proportionably with greater or less quantity	o	7	6
	Other decoctions and wines made with foreign medicaments, per pound...........	o	7	6
	Do. with indigenous or native medicines, per pound	o	3	o
	Draughts, each..........................	o	2	2
	Electary Cathartic, per ounce..............	o	7	6
	Do. Alternative, per ounce.................	o	5	o
	Elixirs and Essences, per ounce.............	o	3	9
	Emulsions	o	1	o
	Epispastic plasters for the neck, side or back.	o	3	o
	Do, for the arms, wrists or legs, each........	o	1	6
	Each dressing of the large blisters..........	o	1	o
	Each do. of the lesser....................	o	o	6
	Ingredients for nitrous decoctions, 1 pound..	o	7	6
	Ingredients foreign for other decoctions, &c., per oz................................	o	2	o
	Ditto for Glysters.......................	o	3	o
	Musk Julap.............................	o	2	6
	Julaps, per ounce.........................	o	1	o
	Linctus and Lohocs, per ounce.............	o	2	6
	Lozenges, per ounce......................	o	3	o
	Mixtures compounded of aqueous and spirituous and Saline or solid substances, per ounce	o	1	o
	Mixtures consisting solely of spirituous substances, such as Tinctures, Elixirs, Essences, &c. per oz.............................	o	3	9
Ointments, viz.:	Mere-fort, per ounce.....................	o	2	6
	Do. mit. per ounce.......................	o	2	o
Pills, viz.:	Cathart, 1 dose..........................	o	2	o
	Mercur. per dose.........................	o	1	6
	Anodyn, per dose........................	o	1	o
	Alteratives, per dose.....................	o	2	o
	Potion cathart, with manna, per ounce......	o	4	o
Powders, Cathart viz.:	Rhubarb, per dose........................	o	3	o
	All others, per dose......................	o	2	o
	Powders Emetic, per dose.................	o	2	o

	£	s.	d.
Do. Alterative, per dose...................	o	1	o
Salts Cathartic, per dose...................	o	1	6
Do. with manna, 1 ounce, per dose..........	o	3	o
Tartar Cream of, per dose.................	o	1	6
All medicines charged by the dose to persons under three years of age one-fourth less than to those above that age.			
Tinctures, per ounce.....................	o	3	o
Salivation, including medicines.............	3	00	o
Simple Gonorrhœa, includ. do..............	2	5	o
Gonorrh, attended with Chancres, or particular trouble............................	3	00	o

All other prescribed forms not here specified, to be submitted to the direction of the Society, and rated as near as possible to the tenor of this Table.

The Society reserves to themselves the right, at all times hereafter, of making all such alterations in and additions to this Table, as shall appear to them just and expedient.

ROBT. McKEAN, *President*.

Resolved and enacted, That every member of this Society, shall at all times hereafter, when he makes out a bill, charge exactly agreeable to the preceding fixed rates, without addition or diminution, and shall deliver it in this form and no other. But it is nevertheless meant and intended that every member afterwards be at liberty to abate what part of such bills he may think proper, on account of poverty, friendship, or other laudable motives, but on no other considerations whatever, under pain of expulsion.

The following newspaper extract relative to the early life of the Society shows that the road toward medical organization was not devoid of friction:

MR. GAINE.

A Number of the Practitioners of Physic and Surgery in East-Jersey having form'd themselves into a Society, for their mutual Improvement in their Profession, and other good Purposes; and as their Meetings may occasion some speculation among the Inhabitants where they reside, they have thought proper to insert in your Paper the Laws and Constitutions by which their Society is governed, as well to obviate any Misrepresentations which may arise from Prejudice or Mistake, as to convince their Employers that their Scheme is design'd to be of Publick Utility.

NARRATIVE of the RISE and ESTABLISHMENT of the NEW JERSEY MEDICAL SOCIETY.

The low State of Medicine in New Jersey, and the many Difficulties and Discouragements, alike injurious to the People and the Physician, under which it has laboured, and which still continue to oppose its Improvement in Utility to the Public, and its Advancement to its native Dignity, having for several Years passed engrossed the Attention of some Gentlemen of the Profession, and occasionally been the Subject of their Conversation, it was early last Winter, determined to attempt some Measure for rescuing the Art from that abject Condition (not to say worse) into which it seemed too fast to decline.

To this End a Legislative Interposition appeared in the first Place greatly to be desired; and in Application for that Favour was proposed; but in this it was necessary to have the Concurrence of the principal Practitioners, and as many other Persons of Weight and Influence as possible; a voluntary Association therefore of such Gentlemen of the Faculty, as might approve of the Design, was next projected; a Society of this Kind, it was thought, besides considering of a proper Application to the Legislature and promoting it most effectually, could in the mean Time take such Measures as were of immediate Importance, and from such voluntary Regulations, as would greatly conduce to the Usefulness and Honour of Medicine, and should the Legislature in their wisdom think it not expedient to interfere, might in a great Degree answer the Purposes of a more authoritative Establishment; not to mention that whether under a Law, or otherwise, a Medical Society well conducted, would naturally derive Credit on the Profession, and ever be of the highest Advantage, both to the Public, and to the several Members. With these good Views the annexed Advertisement was inserted in the Mercury.

N.B. The next General Meeting of the Society is to be held at Perth Amboy, the first Tuesday in May next.—*The New York Mercury*, No. 800, March 2, 1767.

The following newspaper announcements concerning the early meetings of the Society are of interest:

The Members of the New-Jersey Medical Society, and those Gentlemen who stand Candidates for Admission, are hereby notified, that their next stated General Meeting, will be on Tuesday the 10th of November following, at the House of Mr. William Hicks, in Prince Town, when and where all concern'd are desired to give their Attendance.

The Society beg Leave to inform the Gentlemen Practitioners in the

Western Division of this Government, that it was through mistake, the former Advertisements, respecting the forming, &c. said Society, were confin'd to the Eastern Division, it ever being the true intent and Meaning of the first Proposers thereof, as well as the Society's after formed, that the same should be general, and include the whole Government.

MOSES BLOOMFIELD, Secry.

Woodbridge, East New-Jersey, October 4, 1767.

–*The New York Mercury*, No. 832, October 12, 1767.

–*The Pennsylvania Chronicle and Universal Advertiser*, Oct. 12, 1767.

The Members of, The NEW JERSEY Medical Society, are desired to attend their general Meeting, which is to be held at Brook Farmer's, in New-Brunswick, on the 12th Day of May.

–*The Pensylvania Chronicle, and Universal Advertiser*, No. 277, April 27, May 4, 1772.

The members of the New-Jersey Medical Society are desired to take notice, that their next half-yearly meeting is appointed to be held in New-Brunswick, at the house of Mrs. Vorehise, on the second Tuesday in May next, when it is hoped the gentlemen of the faculty in general will attend. A medical dissertation will be delivered by the President before dinner.

H. STITES, Secretary.

Cranberry, April 20, 1775.

–*New York Journal*, No. 1686, April 27, 1775.

October 21, 1775.

Notice is hereby given to the Members of the New-Jersey Medical Society, that they are to meet, agreeable to their adjournment, in Princeton at the house of Mr. William Whitehead, on the second Tuesday in November next, at eleven o'clock in the morning.

H. STITES, Secretary.

–*Dunlap's Penn'a Packet*, No. 209, Oct. 23, 1775.

A Number of the members of the late New-Jersey Medical Society, desirous as well of promoting the science of medicine, as establishing some more regular system of practice in this state, propose restoring the society to its former dignity and usefulness, and will hold their first meeting for this purpose on Wednesday the 3d day of October next at the house of Mr. Bateman, in Princeton. The former members, and such other gentlemen of the faculty who are desirous of becoming members of this society, are requested to meet there at 10 o'clock in the forenoon. September 8, 1781.

> —*New Jersey Gazette*, Vol. IV., No. 194, September 12, 1781.

The Members of the late New Jersey Medical Society are requested to take notice, that at the meeting of a respectable number of members at Princeton this day, (pursuant to an advertisement in the New Jersey Gazette) it was agreed on to re-establish the Society on its former principles and constitution; and that agreeably thereto, their half yearly meeting, as usual, will be held on the first Tuesdsay in November next, at this place.

By order of the Meeting.
ISAAC SMITH, Chairman.

Princeton, October 3, 1781.

> —*The New Jersey Gazette*, Vol. IV., No. 194, September 12, 1781.

The members of the New-Jersey medical society are requested to remember, that their next general meeting will be held on the first Tuesday in May next, at Christopher Beekman's, the sign of the College, Princeton.
By order of the society.

THOMAS WIGGINS, Sec'ry.

> —*The New Jersey Gazette*, Vol. V., No. 225, April 17, 1782.

According to the Transactions of the New Jersey Medical Society, one of the original group who had set up the society, one Bern Budd from Morristown, was accused at the November 7, 1769 meeting, that he "has in sundry places misrepresented the designs of its (the society's) institution, whereby a number of the Faculty have been prejudiced against becoming members, and many persons against the Faculty in general." On May 14, 1771, Dr. Budd defended himself so convincingly that "he exculpated himself to the satisfaction of the Board; and also gave sufficient reasons for his absence from several former meetings of the society." But the minutes of November 9, 1773, affirm that "Doctor Bern Budd, a member of this society, having fallen into a most criminal deportment as a public delinquent and offender against the dignity and majesty of our most gracious King and Sovereign—the society unanimously agreed to expel from their Board the said Bern Budd, as a person really scandalous and altogether unworthy the notice of its members." A Morris County record gives evidence that in 1773 a Doctor Barnabas Budd and 3 accomplices were convicted of distributing forged bills in Morris County. Although all four were condemned to hang, Budd and' two others mustered enough influence to escape the gallows. In a list of New Jersey Surgeons Commissioned in the War of Independence, we find the name Barnardus Budd. It is likely that all three names refer to the same man. The Budd case showed that the Society, even in its infant days, had the strength to exert disciplinary action when such was indicated.

By 1764 the violent prejudices held against smallpox inoculation by laymen and physicians alike, had largely subsided, and the first public hospital for the inoculation of smallpox was opened in Boston by Doctor William Burnet, of Elizabethtown, N.J. Rush states that Burnet was invited to Philadelphia in 1759 on a similar errand. Doctor Burnet is said to have introduced smallpox inoculation in Elizabethtown. The preparatory care of persons to be inoculated with smallpox virus was well worked out and deaths were comparatively few.

Until the middle of the eighteenth century obstetrics was primarily the responsibility of women. Systematic instruction to midwives was first given in a series of lectures at the University of Edinburgh in 1726. Thirty years later, also at Edinburgh, a class of medical students received lectures and demonstrations. Dr. William Shippen, one of the Edinburgh students, became intensely interested in obstetrics, and in 1762 delivered a series of lectures on obstetrics in Philadelphia. Approximately contemporaneous with this, another Edinburgh man, John V. B. Tennent of Freehold, N.J., who had graduated Princeton in 1758, started a series of obstetrical lectures in New York. This New Jersey physician held the first chair of obstetrics in the Medical School of New York until his death in 1770.

Thomas Wood, in 1752, advertised at Brunswick a month-long course on Osteology and Myology, to be succeeded by a course in Angiology and Neurology if interest so warranted. The ad, as printed in the *New York Weekly Post-Boy* on January 27, 1752, follows:

Whereas Anatomy is allowed on all Hands to be the Foundation both of Physick and Surgery and consequently without Some knowledge of it, no Person can be duly qualified to practice either; This is therefore to inform the Publick: That a Course of Osteology and Myology, is intended to be begun, some time in February next, in the city of New Brunswick (of which Notice will be given in this Paper, as soon as a Proper Number has subscribed towards it). In which course all the human Bones will be separately examined, and their Connections and Dependencies on each other demonstrated: and all the Muscles of a human Body disected; the Origin, Insertion and Use of each, plainly shown, etc. This Course is proposed to be finished in the space of a Month, By

Thomas Wood, Surgeon.

Such gentlemen who are willing to attend this Course, are desired to subscribe their Names as soon as possible, with Mr Richard Ayscough Surgeon at New York, or said Thomas Wood, at New Brunswick, payment at the same Time Three Pounds, Proc, and engaging to pay the said Sum of Three Pounds more, when the Course is half finished. N.B. If proper encouragement is given in this Course, he proposes soon after, to go thro' a Course of Angiology and Neurology; and conclude with performing all the Operations in Surgery on a Dead Body: the use of which will appear to every person, who considers the Necessity of having (at least) Seen them performed; before he presumes to perform them himself on any living Fellow Creature.

There is no proof as to whether Wood actually gave this course or not.

No medical school was established in New Jersey until after the Revolution, when Queen's College undertook medical instruction in 1792. Modern New Jersey, incidentally, has no medical school.

An impetus to medical advance was produced after the middle of the eighteenth century by the contact of the colonial doctors with the well educated English army surgeons during the French and English War of 1758-66.

An Act To Regulate the Practice of Physic and Surgery within the Colony of New Jersey was passed on September 26, 1772:

Whereas, many ignorant and unskilful persons in Physic and Surgery, to gain a subsistance, do take upon themselves to administer Physic and practice Surgery, in the *Colony of New Jersey,* to the endangering of the Lives and Limbs of their Patients; and many of His Majesty's Subjects who have been pursuaded to become their Patients have been Suffering thereby; for the Prevention of such Abuses for the future.

BE IT ENACTED *by the Governor, Council and General Assembly and it is hereby Enacted by the Authority of the same,* That from and after the Publication of this act, no Person whatsoever shall practice as a Physician or Surgeon, within this Colony of New Jersey, before he shall have first been examined in Physic or Surgery, approved of, and admitted by any two of the Judges of the Supreme Court, for the time being, taking to their Assistance for such Examination such proper Person or Persons, as they in their Discretion shall think fit, for which Service the said Judges of the Supreme Court as aforesaid, shall be

Entitled to a Fee of *twenty shillings*, to be paid by the Person applying; and if any Candidate, after due Examination of his Learning and Skill in Physic or Surgery, as aforesaid, shall be approved and admitted to practice as a Physician or Surgeon, or both, the said Examiners, or any two or more shall give under their Hands and Seals, to the Person so admitted as aforesaid, a Testimonial of his Examination and Admission in the Form following to wit:

To all to whom these presents shall come or may concern: Know Ye, that We whose Names are hereunto subscribed, in Pursuance of an Act of the Governor, Council, and General Assembly of the Colony of *New Jersey*, made in the Twelfth Year of the Reign of our Sovereign Lord King George the Third, Entitled, *An Act to regulate the Practice of Physic and Surgery within the Colony of New Jersey*, having duly examined   of   Physician or Surgeon, or Physician and Surgeon as the case may be, And having approved of his Skill, do admit him as a Physician or Surgeon or Physician and Surgeon to practice in the said Faculty or Faculties, throughout the Colony of *New Jersey*. In Testimony whereof we have hereunto subscribed our Names and affixed our Seals to this Instrument, at   this

Day of   *Annoque Domini* 17

2. *And be it further enacted by the Authority aforesaid*, That if any Person or Persons shall practice as a Physician or Surgeon or both within the Colony of *New Jersey*, without such Testimonial as aforesaid, he shall forfeit and pay for every such Offence the Sum of *Five Pounds;* one Half thereof to the Use of any Person or Persons who shall sue for the same, and the other Half to the Use of the Poor of any City or Township where such Person shall so practise contrary to the Tenor of this Act; to be recorded in any Court where Sums of this Amount are cognizable, with Costs of Suit.

3. *Provided always*, that this Act Shall not be construed to extend to any Person or Persons administering Physic or practising Surgery before the publication hereof, within this Colony, or to any Person bearing His Majesty's Commission and employed in his Service as a Physician or Surgeon.

And provided always that nothing in this Act shall be construed to hinder any Person or Persons from bleeding, drawing Teeth, or giving Assistance to any Person, for which Services such Persons shall not be entitled to make any Charge, or recover any Reward.

Provided also, that nothing herein contained shall be construed to hinder any skillful Physician or Surgeon from any of the neighboring Colonies being sent for upon any particular Occasion, from practising on such Occasion within this Colony.

4. *And be it further enacted, by the Authority aforesaid*, That any

Person now practising Physic or Surgery, or that shall hereafter be licensed as by this Act is directed, shall deliver his Account or Bill of Particulars to all and every Patient in plain English Words, or as nearly so as the Articles will admit of; all and every of which Accounts shall be liable, whenever the Patient, his Executors or Administrators shall require, to be taxed by any one or more of the Justices of the Supreme Court, or any one or more of the Judges of the Inferior Court of Common Pleas of the County, City or Borough wherein the party complaining resides, calling to their Assistance such persons therein skilled as they may think proper.

5. *And be it further enacted by the Authority aforesaid:* That every Physician Surgeon or Mountebank Doctor who shall come into, and travel through this Colony, and erect any Stage or Stages for the sale of Drugs or Medicines of any Kind, shall for every such Offence forfeit and pay the sum of *Twenty Pounds*, Proclamation money; to be recovered in any Court where the same may be cognizable, with Costs of Suit; one Half to the Person who will prosecute the same to Effect, the other Half to the use of the Poor of any City, Borough, Township or Precinct where the Offence shall be committed.

6. *And be it further enacted by the Authority aforesaid,* That this Act, and every clause and Article herein contained, shall continue and be in Force for the Space of Five Years, and from thence until the End of the next Session of the General Assembly, and no longer.

Provincial Laws of N.J.

(This law was re-enacted by the Legislature of N.J. in 1784.)

After November 14, 1775, the Medical Society of New Jersey ceased to hold meetings for a period of six years because of the fact that the war weighed heavily on New Jersey, and because, as mentioned in the report to the society on May 7, 1782, "most of the members of this Society took an early decided part in the opposition to British tyranny and oppression, and were soon engaged either in the civil or military duties of the State."

On November 6, 1781 the society was reorganized, and on May 6, 1783 a committee was appointed to apply to the legislature for a Charter of Incorporation "to regulate and restrain the practice of physic and surgery in this State." By an Act of the General Assembly on June 2, 1790, this was secured:

AN ACT

FOR INCORPORATING A CERTAIN NUMBER OF THE PHYSICIANS AND SURGEONS OF THIS STATE, BY THE STYLE AND TITLE OF THE MEDICAL SOCIETY OF NEW JERSEY.

Preamble. Forasmuch as a number of the Physicians and Surgeons of this State, have by their petition set forth that they have long since formed themselves into a Society by the name of the Medical Society of New Jersey, and that the objects of their association have been to maintain an uninterrupted intercourse and communication of sentiments with one another, to cultivate liberality and harmony among themselves, to promote uniformity in the practice of physic on the most modern and approved systems, to correspond with and receive intelligence from the like societies abroad, and generally to improve the science of medicine and to alleviate human misery, and have prayed the aid of legislative authority to enable them more fully to carry into effect the good purposes of their Society; and the Legislature being willing and desirous that they might be enabled to make such laws and regulations for the admission and government of their own members, to preserve with safety such valuable curiosities of the animal, vegetable and mineral kingdoms as may be discovered in this country or sent them from abroad, and to record and preserve their experiments and discoveries and the success of their various investigations; therefore

SEC. 1. Be it enacted by the Council and General Assembly of this State, and it is hereby enacted by the authority of the same. That Moses Bloomfield, John Griffith, William Burnett, Ebenezer Blackley, Isaac Harris, Thomas Wiggins, Hezekiah Stites, James Newell, Isaac Smith, Jabez Canfield, Samuel Kennedy, Thomas Henderson, Jonathan Elmer, Thomas Barber, John Beatty, Elisha Newell, Benjamin Stockton, Moses Scott, Lewis Dunham, Jonathan F. Morris, John G. Wall, Hezekiah S. Woodruff, John A. Scudder, Abraham Howard, Robert Henry, James Stratten, David Greenman, Thomas Griffith, Benjamin Tallman, George W. Campbell, Edward Taylor, Lewis Morgan, John Cooper, Archibald McCalla, Thomas Montgomery, Isaac Ogden, William Canfield, Abraham Canfield, Samuel Covenhoven, Abel Johnson, Samuel Shute, Francis Bowes Sayre, Cyrus Pearson, John Reeves, Samuel Forman, William Stilwell, Paul Mercheau, Ebenezer Elmer, Hendrick Schenck, John Abraham DeNormandie; and such other persons as shall be admitted into the said Society according to the rules thereof, shall be, and they are hereby declared to be a body politic and corporate for the term of twenty-five years, and from thence to the end of the next sitting of the Legislature, and shall henceforth be called, distinguished and known by the name of the Medical Society of New Jersey, and by that name they shall have succession.

SEC. 2. And be it enacted by the authority aforesaid, that the above named Moses Bloomfield, John Griffith, William Burnett, Ebenezer Blackley, Isaac Harris, Thomas Wiggins, Hezekiah Stites, James Newell, Isaac Smith, Jabez Canfield, Samuel Kennedy, Thomas Henderson, Jonathan Elmer, Thomas Barber, John Beatty, Elisha Newell, Benjamin Stockton, Moses Scott, Lewis Dunham, Jonathan F. Morris, John G. Wall, Hezekiah S. Woodruff, John A. Scudder, Abraham Howard, Robert Henry, James Stratten, David Greenman, Thomas Griffith, Benjamin Tallman, George W. Campbell, Edward Taylor, Lewis Morgan, John Cooper, Archibald McCalla, Thomas Montgomery, Isaac Ogden, William Canfield, Abraham Canfield, Samuel Covenhoven, Abel Johnson, Samuel Shute, Francis B. Sayre, Cyrus Pearson, John Reeves, Samuel Forman, William Stilwell, Paul Mercheau, Ebenezer Elmer, Hendrick Schenck, John A. DeNormandie and their successors, be and they are hereby authorized in law to purchase, take, hold, receive and enjoy any messages, houses, buildings, lands, tenements, rents, possessions and other hereditaments in fee simple or otherwise; and also goods, chattels, legacies and donations given to the said Society in any way or manner, to the amount of five hundred pounds; and also, that they and their successors by the name of the Medical Society of New Jersey, shall and may give, grant and devise, assign, sell or otherwise dispose of all or any of their messages, houses, lands, tenements, rents, posessions and other hereditaments and all other goods, chattels and other things aforesaid as to them shall seem meet; and also, that they and their successors by the name of the Medical Society of New Jersey be, and for the term aforesaid shall be able in law and capable to sue and be sued, implead and be impleaded, answer and be answered, defend and be defended in all courts of judicature whatsoever; and further, that the members for the time being and their successors shall, and may for the term aforesaid, hereafter have and use a common seal, with such device or devices as they shall think proper, for sealing all and singular deeds, grants, conveyances, contracts, bonds, articles of agreement, assignments, powers, authorities, and all and singular their instruments of writing touching or concerning their corporation; and also, that the said members and their successors for the term aforesaid may, and as often as they shall judge expedient break, change and new make the same or any other their common seal.

SEC. 3. And be it further enacted by the authority aforesaid, that for the preservation of good order and carrying more fully into effect the good principles and objects of the said Society, there shall be in the said Society, one president who shall be the keeper of the common seal, and vice-president, who shall preside in the absence of the president; a treasurer and recording secretary, all of which officers shall be appointed by ballot, and shall continue one year from the time of entering on their respective offices, and until others are appointed in their stead, and there shall likewise be one other secretary, to be considered and called the corresponding secretary, whose office shall continue during the pleasure of the said Society.

SEC. 4. And be it further enacted by the authority aforesaid, that Moses Scott shall be, and he hereby is appointed president, Thomas Barber, vice-president, Thomas Wiggins, treasurer, and Francis Bowes Sayre, recording secretary, to hold the said respective offices and to perform and execute the duties thereunto appertaining, until the first Tuesday in November, 1790; and henceforth and for the term aforesaid, it shall and may be lawful for the members of the said Society, on the first Tuesday in November, yearly and every year, to elect by ballot a president, vice-president, secretary and treasurer, who shall continue in office until superseded by a new election, and that John Beatty be and he is hereby appointed corresponding secretary, to continue in office as prescribed in the section immediately preceding.

SEC. 5. And be it further enacted by the authority aforesaid, that the said Society, or any fifteen members when met, whereof the president or vice-president and one of the secretaries always to be a part, shall constitute a quorum to do all business relative to the Society: Provided always, that no measure entered into at any meeting of the Society where not more than seventeen members are present shall be binding, unless nine be consenting thereto; and in all other cases where more than seventeen are present, a majority of the members shall decide.

SEC. 6. And be it further enacted, that the said Society when met, shall have full power and authority from time to time and at all times hereafter, to make such laws, ordinances and constitutions for the well ordering and governing the said Society, or which shall have any tendency to promote the benevolent objects and principles of the institution, and which shall be obligatory on the members thereof, and the same to alter, diminish and reform, as to them shall seem necessary and convenient: Provided always, that such laws, ordinances and constitutions be not repugnant to the laws of this State, or of the United States.

Passed at Perth Amboy, June 2, 1790.

(Acts of the General Assembly of N.J.)

The president of this first state medical society in 1767 was William Burnet, the son of Dr. Ichabod Burnet.

Ichabod Burnet (1684-1774), was born in Southampton, Long Island in 1684. He moved with his father from Long Island to Elizabethtown in about 1700. He studied at the University of Edinburgh. In 1730 it is recorded that he lived and practiced in Lyon's Farms, but afterwards he moved to Elizabethtown.

The following is listed among the East Jersey Manuscripts, No. 40, in the New Jersey Historical Library. The names mentioned make it probable that Dr. Burnet made visits as far as Orange.

Amos Williams Dttr March ye 29, 1742.........	£	s.	d.
To one visit to see his son Dttr.....................	00	07	00
April 2 to one visit to see his son...................	00	07	00
To five ouncis of Ungd Dialthea...................	00	10	00
To twelve Dos Pill Mathea Dttr....................	00	05	00
April y 7 to one visit To his son....................	00	07	00
To Eighteen Dosis of Ant Diap....................	00	08	00
April y 11 To one visit to Joseph Rigd's............	00	06	00
Contrary credit by Medsons brought back..........			
Due to me Ichabod Burnet...................	00.	06.	00.

On the back of the account it is receipted thus:

New Jersey Sept. ye 19 day Ano Dom 1743 Then Received of Mr. Samuel Allin the Sum of one Pound fifteen shillings on the account of Mr. Amos Williams. I say Received in full of all acco from me to this day.

ICHABOD BURNET.

Ichabod Burnet is mentioned by Hatfield as one of the eminent personages of the town. He passed away on July 13, 1774, at the grand old age of ninety.

William Burnet (1730-1791), the son of Dr. Ichabod Burnet, of Elizabethtown, was born on December 20, 1730. After graduating from Princeton in 1749 he studied medicine with Dr. Staats of New York. He then settled in Newark as a practicing physician.

By the time that the War of Independence blazed forth, he was well known both as a fine physician and a great patriot. He served as chairman of the Committee of Safety. In 1776, he personally collected a group of three hundred soldiers and sent them on to New York. He became the most eminent personage in Essex County. He served as Deputy Chairman of the Newark Committee. Burnet, Captain Joseph Hedden and Samuel Hays actually governed this town for several years. Burnet became the first judge of the County Courts.

Burnet's property suffered great loss at the hands of the British. His fine library was carried off as booty by the enemy. On one occasion fifty head of cattle were looted from his farm.

On February 17, 1776, he became surgeon in the Second Essex Regiment. He was selected as one of the three commissioners for issuing State bills of credit, and making purchases of arms and ammunition in July, 1776.

He was elected to the Continental Congress for the 1780-1781 term. Early in this session, Congress subdivided the thirteen States into three military districts, and selected Burnet as a hospital surgeon and physician of the army. On March 5, 1781, Congress selected him Chief Physician and Surgeon of the Hospital Department of the Eastern District. When appointed to this post, he resigned from Congress and carried out his medical duties conscientiously until the end.

When victory was achieved, William Burnet came home to his family and interested himself in agricultural pursuits. In a short time he was appointed Presiding Judge of the Court of Common Pleas.

William Burnet was one of the original members of the Medical Society of New Jersey in 1766. He was elected President of this organization in 1767 and again in 1786. He passed away on October 7, 1791, at the age of sixty-one.

A survey of the most prominent physicians of New Jersey during the eighteenth century, and especially the Revolutionary period, would include Alexander Ross, Jonathan Elmer, Isaac Brown, John Darby, Jonathan Dayton, Nathaniel Scudder, John Cochran, John Ricker, Samuel Dick, Thomas Barber, Absalom Bainbridge, Thomas Henderson, Bodo Otto, Jr., John Lawrence, James Anderson, Ralph Assheton, John Brognard and Peter Smith.

Alexander Ross (1713-1780), was born in Scotland in 1713. He graduated from the University of Edinburgh, and came to America. He at first located at Bristol, Pennsylvania, where he studied medicine with Dr. DeNormandie. He then migrated to Burlington, and later to Mount Holly, practicing medicine in the latter place as early as 1752. Dr. Ross became one of the most eminent physicians in South Jersey. His practice took him over a wide area. He had an old black mare and kept his saddle bags stuffed with medicines. It was not unusual for Ross to make a two week trip to pay a patient a visit. Dr. Ross served as Surgeon during the War of Independence and was one of the original members of the Society of the Cincinnati.

Jonathan Elmer (1745-1817), a descendant of Edward Elmer, who came to America with the company of forty-seven that comprised the church of the Rev. Thomas Hooker in Cambridge, Mass., in 1632, and was killed by the Indians in King Philip's War in 1676, was born at Cedarville, Cumberland County, New Jersey, on November 29, 1745. He was a member of the group of ten who first received the degree of bachelor of medicine from the University of Pennsylvania on June 1, 1769. This group started their studies in Philadelphia in 1765 at the "College and Academy of Philadelphia," which institution was absorbed into the University of Pennsylvania. Jonathan Elmer's preceptor was John Morgan. After graduation, Jonathan Elmer received an M.D. degree in 1771. His diploma was signed by Benjamin Rush, William Shippen and John Morgan.

As Jonathan was frail from childhood, he turned toward the world of study and scholarship. Besides being a physician of eminence, he became learned in theology and law.

He is described as "of short stature, slender and erect; neat in his dress and stately in his address. He possessed a firm and unbending selfwill, which was perhaps intensified by his secluded habits."

Prior to the start of the War of Independence, Elmer became an outspoken exponent of the cause of liberty. Although serving as a sheriff in November, 1774, when a company of disguised men burned the tea stored at Greenwich, N.J., he pretended ignorance of the identity of the men responsible for this act of violence. In 1776 he became a delegate to the Provincial Congress. Elmer served on the committee that formulated the first New Jersey constitution and was elected to the state legislature in 1780 and in 1784.

He served in the Federal Senate from 1789 to 1791. William Maclay, a fellow Senator, refers to Jonathan Elmer in the following quotation from his journal of 1789: "I know not, in the Senate, a man if I were to choose a friend, on whom I would cast the eye of confidence as soon as on this little Doctor. He does not always vote right—and so I think of every man who differs from me, but I never saw him give a vote, but I thought I could observe his disinterestedness in his countenance. If such an one errs, it is the sin of ignorance and I think Heaven has pardons ready sealed for every one of them."

Dr. Elmer served on the Congressional Medical Committee and conscientiously visited the hospitals in his area by long journeys on horseback. It was on one of these journeys that Jonathan met his brother, Surgeon Ebenezer Elmer (1752-1843), at the military hospital at headquarters in Morristown.

Elmer was elected to membership in the New Jersey Medical Society in 1772. He was elected president of this body in 1787. He presented two "dissertations" before this organization, one entitled "On the Chemical Principles of Bodies" and the other "On the different Properties of the Air Contained in the Atmosphere."

A letter from Dr. Elmer as president of the New Jersey Medical Society, dated Trenton, 22nd January, 1788, to the president of the Massachusetts Medical Society, is preserved in the archives of the latter society. This was one of two letters submitted to the council, establishing amicable relations between the two state societies.

Dr. Elmer held the office of presiding judge in the Court of Common Pleas in Cumberland County, which he resigned in 1814, on account of his age and infirmity. He remarked to his court associates, as he left the bench for the last time, that it was forty-two years since he had become an officer of the court, and that he had outlived every person who had been a member of it, both on the bench and at the bar.

He died on September 3, 1817, in Bridgeton, at the age of seventy-one. After his death, L. H. Stockton, Esq., published a short notice of him in The Trenton Federalist, in which he declared that "in medical erudition the writer remembers his illustrious contemporary, the late Dr. Rush, frequently say that Dr. Elmer was exceeded by no physician in the United States."

Reverend Isaac Brown, (?—1787) was a descendant of John Brown, one of the first settlers of Newark. He was educated at Yale, from which institution he graduated in 1729. After preparing himself for the ministry, he went to England and was ordained by a Bishop of the Anglican Church. He became a missionary of the Society for the Propagation of the Gospel in Foreign Parts, and in 1733, he was appointed to the mission at Brookhaven, Long Island. After serving eleven years in this capacity, he was transferred to Trinity Church, Newark, which organization he served from its inception. As the War of Independence approached, he became unpopular because of his open loyalist sympathies. In 1777 he fled to New York, leaving his wife, children, servants and property in the hands "of the enemy." The last letter which he wrote to the Society, dated October 4th, 1782, depicted "the Loyalists as daily suffering for the truth's sake— driven from their homes, their property seized, plundered and sold, and themselves reduced to the most extreme poverty."

Besides being a man of God, Reverend Brown was also a medical practitioner of note. He was elected to the Medical Society of New Jersey at its second meeting in November, 1766. When Reverend McKean of St. Peter's Church in Amboy passed away, Brown desired to succeed him. However, his application for the post was denied on the grounds that the peace and harmony of the church made it necessary to refuse him. It was pointed out that his active medical practice had been a source of contention with his parishioners in Newark, because of the resentment of the bills rendered by him for medical services. As a matter of fact, the Amboy congregation had already encountered similar difficulties from Reverend McKean and avidly desired a non-medical clergyman.

Brown left New York in 1784, and went to Annapolis, Nova Scotia, where he remained until his death in 1787.

Reverend John Darby (1725-1805) was born in or around 1725. He graduated from Yale College in 1748 and was licensed to preach the Gospel in April, 1749. He spent eight years preaching on various spots in the eastern end of Long Island following which he moved to Connecticut Farms, New Jersey (1758). After serving for two years at this location, he was appointed pastor of the Presbyterian Church at Parsippany, Morris County, where he remained until his death in December 1805. During the War of Independence, Darby became one of the vehement Presbyterian "rebel parsons" of the time. A man of many attainments, he gathered fame as a physician and as a lawyer as well as a minister. His reputation as a physician and as a medical instructor led numerous pupils to seek his instruction. An honorary degree of Doctor of Medicine was conferred upon him by Dartmouth College in 1782.

Jonathan Dayton (1731-1778) was born in 1731. He left his paternal home in early manhood and settled in Elizabethtown, in the area of the town which later became the township of Springfield. In 1766 he took part in the organization of the New Jersey Medical Society and was one of the signers of the "Instruments of Association." Dayton continued to live in Springfield until his death, and built up a large practice. His professional calls were made as far away as Summit and New Providence. He passed away in the early years of the war.

His house was one of the three houses left intact by the enemy when in 1780 they burned the town. The cause of its escape from destruction is as follows: One of its rooms was employed as a warehouse for a large amount of arms and munitions of war. When the invaders entered the house for plunder, the doctor's widow demanded to see the officer of the day and forbid their further movements until they should receive further orders. The request was granted, the officer appeared and she informed him that a member of her family was lying in her house, seriously ill (her colored female servant having given birth to a child the day before), and claimed his protection as an act of humanity. The men who were standing by attempted to open the door of the magazine, when Mrs. Dayton urged her request, repeating her statement that she had a sick member of her family and entreated that the door of that room should not be opened. The officer yielded to her request and placed a guard at the door of the secret stores, who, throughout the day, protected it from plunder. The house received a hole in its north end, made by a cannon ball during battle.

Dr. Dayton's son, William W., studied medicine and practiced with his father. He died at the age of 47.

Nathaniel Scudder (1733-1781) was born on May 10, 1733. After graduating from Princeton in 1751, he took up the study of medicine. He opened for practice first at Manalapan. He then transferred to Freehold where he spent most of his life. He was one of the founders of the New Jersey Medical Society in 1766. As the Revolution approached, Scudder emerged as one of the earliest and most able champions of the patriot cause. The first large scale meeting in New Jersey to take a stand against the obnoxious acts of the British Parliament was the one held in Freehold, on June 6, 1774. At this meeting and at later ones, Dr. Scudder was a guiding spirit. This meeting elucidated the doctrine that the cause of the Bostonians was the common cause of the whole continent of North America. A resolution was passed that every Province should stand by the people of Boston, and until their odious port bill and other oppressive acts be repealed, they recommended entire stoppage of trade between the Provinces and Great Britain and the West Indies. A committee which included Dr. Scudder was formed to cooperate with other towns in carrying out any measures that might be deemed best for "the weal and safety of North America and her loyal sons."

On July 19, 1774, committees from various townships which included Scudder, met at Freehold and passed a series of resolutions which they completed expressing the hope that "some faithful record of their notification be handed down to the yet unborn descendants of Americans that nothing but the most fatal necessity could have wrested the present inestimable enjoyments from their ancestors. Let them universally inculcate upon their beloved offspring an investigation of these truths concerning both civil and religious liberty, which have been so clearly and fully stated in this generation. May they be carefully taught in their schools, and may they never rest until, through the Divine blessing upon their efforts, true freedom and liberty shall reign triumphantly over the whole globe."

On December 10, 1774, Scudder was appointed a member of the important "Committee of Observation and Inspection." On July 21, 1774, he served as a delegate at the first Provincial Congress, held in New Jersey, at New Brunswick. Scudder was also a New Jersey delegate to the Continental Congress from 1777 to 1779. He personally signed the Articles of Confederation, in defence of which he wrote a letter to Hon. John Hart, Speaker of the Assembly of New Jersey.

At the outbreak of the War of Independence, he was commis-

Sir

Trenton 22^d January 1788

The practicioners of Physic in the State of New Jersey, impressed with a sense of the advantages that would result from a general association of the faculty throughout the State, voluntarily formed themselves into a Society, some years ago, for the laudable purposes of a free communication of medical knowledge & experience, & the improvement of medical Science in general.

Notwithstanding this Society hath existed for many years, they have not yet obtained a legal establishment, nor any other legislative encouragement except a Law for regulating the Practice of Physic & Surgery in the State — By this Law, enacted about four years ago, no person who was not a practicioner at the time of passing the Law, is allowed to practice Physic or Surgery until he obtains a Certificate from two regular practicioners, that they have duly examined the candidate & find him properly qualified to practice, upon which he obtains a Licence of course from the Judges of the Supreme Court of Judicature to practice Physic & Surgery throughout the State

This Law is found to have a beneficial effect in practice, but further regulations appear necessary in order to render it more extensively useful

Photostatic copy of letter sent by Dr. Jonathan Elmer, President of the New Jersey Medical Society, to the President of the Massachusetts Medical Society. This letter is dated January 22, 1788. (*Courtesy of the Massachusetts Medical Society.*)

The medical society of New Jersey at their stated half yearly meeting in November last, having taken into consideration the disadvantages they labour under for want of a legal incorporation, & being informed that the medical Society of Boston had obtained a regular Charter of incorporation, they agreed to make application to that Society for a Copy of their Laws, with a view of applying for a similar organization in this State, apprehending that the example of a sister State might prove an inducement to our Legislature to grant us a Charter of incorporation

In consequence of this determination of our society I am directed to write to you, as President of the medical Society of Boston, for a Copy of your Laws, together with an Account of the Bye Laws & regulations which your Society have made since their incorporation, & the effects that have resulted from their institution.

In return for those favours which we are now soliciting, I am further directed by our Society, to transmit to you an Account of its rise & progress, with a Copy of the Instrument of Association, which are here inclosed

It is likewise the wish of the Medical Society of New Jersey, to form a correspondence with the medical Society of Boston, for the purpose of mutually communicating useful discoveries & improvements in Physic, & of promoting the progress of medical Literature in these United States

I am with

your unfeigned
& very great esteem

Jonath. Elmer Presidt

sioned Lieutenant Colonel of the First Regiment. In November 1776, he became Colonel of this outfit.

Through all the trials of the war, his life was spared only to be mortally wounded by an unintentional shot aimed at General David Forman with whom he was conversing. The fateful shot was fired by one of a party of refugees at Black Point, Monmouth County, on October 16, 1781. It appears that a party of refugees from Sandy Hook had landed at night at Shrewsbury and marched undiscovered to Colt's Neck, taking six prisoners. When the alarm reached the Court House, Scudder and a number of citizens started in pursuit. His last words to his family were: "There is a battle expected at Long Branch. I will go down and bind up the wounds of the poor fellows." The group rode to Black Point intending to recapture the prisoners. While firing from the bank and conversing with General Forman, the Doctor was shot dead. It seems a tragedy that Scudder did not live three more days, for if he had, he would have lived to see the surrender at Yorktown crown with success the cause he loved so much.

After Scudder's untimely death, a letter was found lying upon his table, addressed to his son Joseph, who was then studying law in Philadelphia. This long letter exhibits not only the anxieties of a father for the welfare of his son, but the spirit of a devout and loving Christian father who "with every sincere wish and prayer for (his) happiness both here and hereafter," signed himself, "Your most affectionate & careful Father." The letter was dated April 13, 1780, eighteen months before his death. It is thought that he wrote this epistle as a legacy to his son, in case of sudden death.

John Cochran (1730-1807) was born in Chester County, Pennsylvania, on September 1, 1730. He studied medicine under the tutelage of Dr. Thompson, of Lancaster. In 1758, coincident with the completion of his medical studies, the war between England and France broke out in America. As adequate hospital facilities were lacking in the Colonies, Dr. Cochran saw his chance to learn more about medicine and surgery and secured the appointment of surgeon's mate in the hospital department. He continued in this position throughout the entire war and gained much from his contacts with Dr. Munro and other eminent English physicians. It is related that while in a British vessel that was lying off Oswego during that war, a shot from the French fleet entered his operating chamber and carried away the operating table and his instruments. He left the military service with a fine reputation as a qualified physician.

Cochran then settled in Albany, New York, but soon moved to New Brunswick, New Jersey, where he continued to engage in the practice of medicine. Cochran was one of the founders of the New Jersey Medical Society in 1766. In November, 1769, he was elected President of this body as successor to Dr. Burnet.

As the Revolution hovered into the offing, Dr. Cochran became a zealous whig, and after actual hostilities broke out, he was driven from New Brunswick by the British, who burned his house. Following this alarming occurrence, his family transferred to the Manor of Livingston, on the Hudson River, which belonged to a daughter of Mrs. Cochran, by her first husband.

In 1776, Cochran promptly offered his services as a volunteer in the hospital department. In the winter of 1777, George Washington recommended him to Congress in the following words: "I would take the liberty of mentioning a gentleman whom I think highly deserving of notice, not only on account of his ability, but for the very great assistance which he has afforded us in the course of this winter, merely in the nature of a volunteer. This gentleman is Dr. John Cochran, well known to all the faculty. The place for which he is fitted, and which would be most agreeable to him, is Surgeon General of the Middle Department. In this line he served all the last war in the British Service, and has distinguished himself this winter particularly in his attention to the small-pox patients and the wounded." Congress accordingly appointed him Physician and Surgeon General in the Middle Department on April 16, 1777. In October, 1781, upon the resignation of Shippen, Congress commissioned Cochran Director General of the Hospitals of the United States, an appointment which, unlike his predecessor, was not solicited by him.

While attached to Washington's staff headquarters, Cochran was paid five dollars per day. He received news of his commission from Congress while serving with the army at New Windsor. A letter announcing his appointment was dispatched to him by Samuel Huntington, President of Congress, under the date of January 18, 1781.

When the peace treaty was ratified and the army was broken up, Washington demonstrated his personal affection for Cochran by giving him all of his head-quarters furniture.

Unquestionably Cochran's experience while in the British service served him in good stead in effecting the great improvement he made in the hospital department.

Soon after the war was terminated, the doctor and his family moved to New York, and he returned to private practice. When the new constitution was adopted, his friend President Washington, retaining, to use his own words, "a cheerful recollection of his past services," nominated him to the office of Commissioner of Loans for the State of New York. He kept this position until invalided by a stroke, after which he resigned and retired to Schenectady, New York. Doctor Cochran passed away at Schenectady, on April 6th, 1807, at the age of seventy-seven.

John Berrien Riker (1738-1794) studied for a time at Princeton, although he did not graduate from this institution. It is thought that he engaged in the study of medicine and also started his practice in New Jersey. He was elected a member of the New Jersey Medical Society in 1768, at the age of thirty. Since he was absent for the five succeeding meetings, his name was dropped from the minutes.

The battle of Long Island, in August, 1776, opened its towns to the tramp of the enemy, and the incursions of the British Light Horse, in search of "rebels," and for purposes of plunder. Dr. Riker early espoused the cause of his country, and before hostilities commenced, exerted himself to promote measures of resistance against the acts of British tyranny. The night prior to the 29th, two days after the battle, was spent by him in visiting different parts of the township, and tearing down Lord Howe's proclamation, that the people might not be misled, and induced, at this critical time, to remain and accept British protection, instead of hastening to the support of the American Arms. On the morning of the 29th, the British entered the town, and brandishing their naked swords, declared that they were in pursuit of "the ——rebel, Dr. Riker." Not finding him, they dashed on towards Hellgate; but the Doctor had escaped in a boat to Barn Island, and eluded his pursuers. He fled to New Jersey, like many of the Long Island patriots, who became exiles from their homes, to fight the battles of their Country's freedom. Dr. Riker enlisted as Surgeon, and on November 28th, 1776, was commissioned as such in the 4th Battalion, 2d Establishment, Continental Army. His familiarity with the topography of New Jersey enabled him to render valuable service on several occasions, as a guide to the army. In the expedition of Lieut. Col. Simcoe, of the Queen's American Rangers, the Doctor was taken prisoner, with several others.

When the war was over, he returned to practice medicine in his native town until his death on September 5th, 1794, at the age of fifty-seven.

Samuel Dick (1740-1812) was born at Nottingham, Prince George County, Maryland, on November 14, 1740. Samuel Finley, who later became President of Princeton College, Thomas McKean, who later became governor of Maryland, and Rev. Dr. McWhorter, of Newark, N. J., furnished him his preliminary education. He became a classical scholar of the first water. It is thought that his medical education was obtained in Scotland. At the age of nineteen, he served as surgeon's mate in the Colonial Army in the French and English

War and he was present at the surrender of Quebec. In 1770, Samuel Dick and his mother settled in Salem, N. J. The doctor lived and practiced here until his death.

In 1776 he was elected to the Provincial Congress of New Jersey, and he was one of the committee of ten appointed to draft a state constitution. On June 20, 1776, Congress commissioned him colonel in the Western Battalion of State troops of Salem County. He was appointed Surrogate of Salem County by Governor Livingston in 1780, and he served in this office for twenty-two years. On November 23, 1783, he was elected to the National Congress and he was a member of this body when the treaty was ratified acknowledging the independence of the United States. In 1783 until 1785, he was in Congress at its meetings in Annapolis, New York and Philadelphia. Dick was one of the "Grand Committee" appointed to revise the Treasury Department and he was also included on the committee selected to sit during the recess of Congress.

Throughout life, Dick remained on intimate terms with Benjamin Rush and James Craik. In 1789 Dr. Dick was again nominated to Congress, but declined to accept. The following letter from Governor Livingston is of interest:

ELIZABETHTOWN, January 25, 1789.

Dear Sir:

Be persuaded that it is not through willful neglect that I have not until now acknowledged the receipt of your letter of the 7th inst. I make it a rule to answer every letter, from the meanest creature in human shape, as soon as I have leisure to do it; and I cannot therefore be supposed inattentive to those gentlemen of distinction and gentlemen who are endeared to me by old acquaintance and the amiableness of their characters. But the conjunction of bodily indisposition, and the greater variety of public indispensible business that I have for a considerable time past met with, made it impossible for me to do myself the pleasure of discharging so agreeable an office as of answering sooner than I now do. But, my dear sir, I wish you had given me a more agreeable commission to execute, than I find I must, according to the tenor of your letter, carry into execution. Your requests, it is true, shall always with me carry with them the nature of a command, but I am sorry that your present one—"*aut volens aut nolens*" be considered mandatory, for it seems you have left me no other choice than the alternative of erasing your name from the "List of Nominations," or to write against it, "Dr. Dick declines to serve." I had particular reason to wish you to stand as candidate, and finally appear to be one of the four *elected*, because (without compliment I say it), though we have had many in Congress, who in other respects were possessed of such qualifications as men in that station ought to be endowed with, a great part of them have been totally destitute of that knowledge of mankind, and that certain politeness, which Lord Chesterfield calls *attention*, without which the greatest talents in other things will never make a man influential in such assemblies. But if it must be so that either you cannot or will not go, I must submit.

Believe me,

Your most humble Servant,

To Dr. Samuel Dick,   WILL^M LIVINGSTON."

Salem, N.J.

Thomas Barber migrated from Groton, Connecticut, to Middletown Point (Matewan), New Jersey, in about 1765. He practiced in Middletown Point the remainder of his life. On February 3, 1776, he was commissioned Surgeon, First Regiment, Monmouth State Troops. He was graduated from Yale in 1762 and received an honorary Master of Arts degree from Princeton in 1774. He died in 1806 or 1807 at about the age of eighty.

Absalom Bainbridge (1742-1807) was born in Mercer County in 1742. He graduated from Princeton College in 1762 and took up the study of medicine. He practiced in Maidenhead (now Lawrenceville), Mercer County, for six years. He moved to Princeton in 1773-4. He was elected president of the New Jersey Medical Society in 1773.

As he was a loyalist, he went to Flatbush, L. I., in 1777-8, and thence to New York. In 1778 he served in the British controlled New Jersey Volunteers.

He later became one of the earliest members of the New York Medical Society. He died in New York on June 23, 1807, at the age of sixty-five.

Thomas Henderson (1743-1824) was born in Freehold in 1743. He graduated from the College of New Jersey in 1761. He studied medicine with Dr. N. Scudder, and started practicing in his native county when he was about twenty-two years of age. He was admitted to membership of the New Jersey Medical Society at its second meeting in 1766, at the same time as his preceptor, Dr. Scudder. His wife died of tuberculosis very soon after their marriage, and when the doctor's health failed, it was feared that he had contracted this dread disease. However, after a period in a warmer climate, his health returned and he lived a long and vigorous life although it was eventually terminated by this disease.

In pre-Revolutionary days, Henderson's patriotism was unsurpassed. In 1777, he served on the Provincial Council. His military record speaks for itself: "Second Major, Col. Stewart's Battalion, 'minute men,' February 15th, 1776; Major, Col. Heard's Battalion, June 14th, 1776; Lieut. Col., Col. Forman's Battalion, Heard's Brigade; Brigade Major, Monmouth."

After the Battle of Monmouth, it was he who was the "solitary horseman," who rode up to Gen. Washington, at Freehold Court House and stood dismounted beside his horse, with his arm over its shoulder, and informed him of the retreat of Gen. Lee.

A short time after the Battle of Monmouth, an account of the depredations committed by the British, when in the county, was communicated to the *Jersey Gazette*. This was allegedly written by Col. Henderson. This account depicts the "devastation" wrought in some parts of Freehold, which "exceeds perhaps any they have made for the distance in their rout through the State. They burnt and destroyed eight dwelling houses, all on farms adjoining each other, besides barns and outhouses. The first they burnt was my own."

He was elected to Congress and served in Congress during Washington's administration. In 1794, Governor Howell, of New Jersey, went into Pennsylvania to aid in the suppression of the "Whiskey Insurrection" and Dr. Henderson, as Vice-President of Council, became acting Governor. During the remainder of his life he was constantly employed in public services, as Surrogate, Member of the Legislature, Judge of Common Pleas, and Commissioner to settle boundaries between New Jersey and Pennsylvania. However, he never entirely relinquished the practice of medicine.

Two of his bills for professional services, one dated November 12th, 1776, and the other October 10th, 1791, read as follows: "For visits & attendance Negro's £2." "Acct against ye estate of Lewis Goodard is £27. 6s. 11d."

Henderson was always polite, dignified, capable and gentlemanly. When running for any office it is said that he never sought a vote, and would not even be seen at the polls on election day.

He died on December 15, 1824.

Bodo Otto, Jr. (1748-1782) was born in Hanover, Germany, on September 14, 1748. His father, Dr. Bodo Otto, who had been educated in the finest schools in Europe, had also followed his father, Dr. Christopher Otto, into the profession. When Christopher died, the elder Otto, at the age of forty-three, emigrated to Philadelphia. Otto, senior, built up a fine reputation, especially in surgery, in the City of Brotherly Love. When the War of Independence broke out, although he was an old man ready to retire from practice, he became an avid patriot and joined the army as surgeon. During the painful winter of 1778, he was in charge of the hospital at Valley Forge.

When the war was over, Otto, senior, moved to the house of his son, Dr. John Augustus Otto, in Reading and died there in 1787.

Bodo Otto, Jr., received a good preliminary education in this country and took up medicine under the tutelage of his father. He obtained the medical degree from the University of Pennsylvania. He then settled in Gloucester County, New Jersey, a few miles from Swedesboro, and started to practice. He became an outspoken exponent of the patriot cause. He approved the doctrines promulgated by the Provincial Congress, which met at Trenton on May 23, 1775, and afterwards at Burlington and New Brunswick. On July 24, 1776, the Provincial Congress appointed him surgeon of Colonel Charles Read's battalion which was to later reinforce the flying camp. Later he served in the upper house of the Legislature. As the war progressed he became Colonel of State Troops, First Battalion, Gloucester County. While away from his farm on military duty in March, 1778, a conflict took place on this property between Colonel Mawhood's regiment and the patriots. His house and barn were destroyed in the ensuing conflagration and his wife and infant children were driven from their home. All farm products on hand were destroyed. It is said that his health was undermined by the exposure, privations and arduous duties of his army service. After a lingering illness he passed away at his home on January 29, 1782, at the age of thirty-four.

Upon his death, the following newspaper notice appeared:

Early on Sunday morning, 29th ult., at his house in Gloucester County, New Jersey, Bodo Otto, Esq., an eminent physician, sincerely esteemed by a numerous acquaintance, and whose death is universally lamented. The day following, his remains, borne by four officers, were interred at Swedesboro, attended by a large concourse of the most respectable inhabitants of the county. Eulogies of the dead are generally flattering, and meant for a compliment to surviving. friends, but on the present melancholy occasion it may be said, without violating truth, that by his decease his children are deprived of a tender parent, his wife of an affectionate husband, and the State of a most valuable member of society. Firmly attached to the liberties of America, and a zealous asserter of her independence, he early took a part in the present contest, and by the unanimous vote of the county in which he lived, he was pointed out as the intrepid Soldier and patriotic Senator. He accepted the appointment, and discharged the duties of the one with honor to himself, and of the other to the satisfaction of constituents. While applauded by all for his public conduct, the unavailing sorrow of his friends and the sighs of the distressed evince the amiableness, and will remain the best and most lasting monument of his character in private life; the former he ever received with hospitality and warmth of affection, and the benevolence of his heart taught him to feel and relieve the miseries of the latter. To him then, whose life was a constant series of good actions, death could have no terrors. He bore a lingering illness with patience, and resigned his breath to God who gave it, with the fortitude and constancy, not of a philosopher, but of a good and sincere Christian.

John Lawrence (1747-1830) was born in 1747. He completed his preliminary studied at Princeton University in 1764, and received the medical degree from the University of Pennsylvania (1768). He started practice in Monmouth County, and in 1776, it is recorded that he was a successful practitioner in Amboy. He was first and last an ardent royalist and we find that in July, 1776, he was arrested by Major Duyckink, who was sent to Amboy by order of George Washington to command the Middlesex Militia and protect the town. Lawrence and eight others were taken to Elizabethtown and held in custody. The Provincial Congress at Trenton paroled this much needed physician. However, in April, 1777, Lawrence and his father were arraigned before the Council of Safety. Lawrence fled to New York, where he engaged in the practice of medicine and commanded a company of volunteers in the defense of the city. In 1783, Lawrence came back to Jersey, where he remained for the rest of his life.

When Lawrence was arrested in Amboy, the ladies of that town rose in protest and petitioned the convention which held him under arrest to release the Doctor, lest there occur "..... fatal and melancholy consequences to themselves, their families and the inhabitants in general, if they should be deprived of the assistance of Dr. Lawrence." George Washington personally signed the following reply to Mrs. Franklin and the good ladies of Amboy: "Madam, I am ordered by Congress to acquaint you, and through you the other ladies of Amboy, that their petition in favor of Dr. John Lawrence has been received and considered. Could any application have procured a greater indulgence to Dr. Lawrence, you may be assured yours could not have failed of success. But unhappily, Madam, we are placed in a situation that motives of commiseration to individuals must give place to the safety of the public. As Dr. Lawrence has fallen under the suspicion of our generals, we are under the necessity of abiding by the steps which are taken and are Madam, Yours &c." Lawrence customarily referred to his residence in Amboy as the happiest period of his life. He loved the Amboy social circle composed of officers of the Crown, whom he felt were on a higher plane than the set in New York and Philadelphia.

Upon his return to New Jersey, Lawrence settled in Upper Freehold, in the Mulberry Hill district. He never resumed medical practice for he was a man of means. He lived the life of a gentleman and
a *bon vivant*.

Hunting foxes was his favorite pastime. The amazing hurdles made
by the doctor on his horse became legendary as did the one leap
which he did not make. On this occasion his horse stopped short
before a ditch while at full gallop, and deposited Lawrence therein.

When Dr. Lawrence was unduly plethoric, he was bled almost
every day, a total of seventeen times. His physician called in a consultant and he advised, of all things, another bleeding which was duly
performed. Lawrence none-the-less survived. At the grand old age
of eighty-three, he died in Trenton, while playing chess at a friend's
house. His tomb, in the cemetery of the Upper Freehold Baptist
Church, bears this inscription:

> Sacred To The Memory
> Of
> JOHN LAWRENCE, M. D.
> Who Departed This Life
> April 29th, A.D. 1830
> Aged 83 Years.

Lawrence kept an account book which was started in 1769, the
year after he finished medical school and which contains entries as
late as 1785. The entries definitely demonstrate that his patients were
scattered all over Monmouth County, and into Middlesex. His accounts of the patients in Amboy and Woodridge date from 1775 to
July, 1776. While in New York he treated the leading families, including those of Governor Franklin and Philip John Livingston. He
treated the family of Colonel James DeLancey and the officers of
his brigade stationed in Jamaica, Long Island, and the rector of the
Episcopal Church in Jamaica and Hempstead. There were visits at
Hell Gate and also into Westchester County.

The following account is illustrative of his fees:

f. 368.	GOVERN^R FRANKLIN	Dr.			
1776.	Amboy		£	s.	d.
Mar. 9.	Rd. Cort. Huxt. ʒiv. Ux. 6s. Rhub. 2s............			8	
	Pul. Vermif. ix.................................			9	
19.	Rd. Cort. 6s. Rhub. 2s. Pul. Vermif, ix 9s........			17	
23.	Do. 6s. Syr. Chalyb. 5s.........................			11	
26.	Do. 6s. Sper. Amar. 6s..........................			12	

			£	s.	d.
April	7.	Do. 6s		6	
	12.	Rd. Cort. &c. lbss 8s...........................		8	
	19.	Pulv. Cath. dos. xii to Honey (or horses).........	1	4	
	22.	Rd. Cort. ℔ss. 8s...............................		8	
	31.	Do. 8s. Sol. Cath. ii. 2s......................		10	
May	2.	V.X. 2s. Solut. Mann., &c. 6s...................		8	
	3.	Aq. Ophal. 3s. Rd. Cort., &c. ℔ss. 8s.............		11	
	15.	Rd. Cort. Huxt. Ux. ℔ss. 8s....................		8	
	27.	Do. 8s		8	
June		Do. 8s. to Mrs. Franklin.......................		8	
	14.	Rd. Anti-scorbut. 5s...........................		5	
	20.	Rd. Cort. repct. ℔ss. 8s.......................		8	
July	1.	Do. 8s..		8	
	15.	Do. 8s. Elix. Paregor. 5s. Laud. 3s.............		16	
			10	7	6
		Attendance	2		
			£12	7	6

N. B. The acct. contracted since our leaving Amboy and settling in New York has been paid, but not being able to procure my books during the war, this acct. has not been delivered in. June, 1784.

James Anderson (1750-1825) was born in Monmouth County, near Freehold, in 1750. He was captured by the British while serving as Captain of State Troops, First Regiment, Sussex, in 1777. During the four or five years he was imprisoned on Long Island, he was befriended by an English Surgeon who taught him the medical art. That his army record was perfectly honorable is demonstrated by the fact that Washington and Knox signed his certificate of membership in the Society of the Cincinnati on May 24, 1784. After the war, he practiced in Monmouth County where he died in 1825, at the age of seventy five.

Ralph Assheton practiced medicine in Nottingham Township, Burlington County, in 1765 and perhaps earlier. He moved during the latter part of that year. The *Pennsylvania Gazette* of September 26, 1765, contains the following interesting advertisement of the doctor's house and effects:

To be sold at public vendue, on Thursday, the 24th of October next, between the hours of three and five in the afternoon, on the premises, a house and lot of ground situated in Kingsbury, Nottingham Township, Burlington County, on the public road between Trenton Bridge and the Ferry, containing in breadth 60 feet and in depth 181 feet; the House almost new and neatly finished; the Lot inclosed with a good board fence; there is a good garden and well in the yard, and, on the lot adjoining a good new stable and coach house, belonging to the house. The purchaser may have a lease of the lot on which the stable stands, pay, viz: Thirty Shillings per annum. Half the purchase money to be paid immediately—six months credit will be given for the remainder. Any person inclining to purchase before the day of sale, may know the terms by applying to Dr. Ralph Assheton, on the premises.

N. B.—As the Doctor proposes returning to Philadelphia in a few weeks, he desires those indebted to make immediate payments, and those who have any demands to bring in their accounts for settlement.

John Baptiste Carone Brognard (1761-1823) was born in France in 1761. He undertook the study of medicine in Paris and at the age of eighteen, just prior to his graduation in medicine, he joined the French military service as a sergeant in the grenadiers. His outfit was sent to America during the War of Independence, and, since the need for physicians was great, he was assigned to surgeon's duty in the Legion of the Duke de Lauzun. He continued his professional duties until the close of the war.

Anxious to settle in the New World, Brognard desired a release from further military service. His mother sent him money to purchase his discharge. The document reads as follows:

MILITARY DISCHARGE.

We the undersigned certify to all whom it may concern that we have given a full discharge to the within named John Baptiste Brognard to go wheresoever he sees fit. Said Brognard is Sergeant in the Grenadier Company in the Corps of Foreign Volunteers of Lauzun, a native of Salino in the Province of Franche Conté in the Jurisdiction of Bessancon, aged twenty-two years, five feet, seven inches in height, oval face, aquiline nose, black eyes, chestnut hair and eye brows, a scar under his right eye and slightly marked with Small Pox.

Done at Wilmington the first day of the Month of May, 1783.

TRENTMAN.

The said Brognard has served very faithfully in the Corps since the 13th Nov. 1778, until this time and has obtained his discharge by the payment of Three Hundred Pounds which he has paid into the treasury of the Corps.

Released from military duty, Brognard at once settled in Burlington, and engaged in private medical practice. His mother in France continued to send him money until his medical practice afforded him a decent livelihood. He soon moved from Burlington to Black Horse (now Columbus), where he became famous as a physician and surgeon and where he practiced the remainder of his life.

Brognard passed away on April 17, 1823.

One of the most interesting old timers in New Jersey history was Peter Smith (1753-1816), the son of Dr. Hezekiah Smith. Peter received his education at Princeton, and, under his father's tutelage, studied the works of Dr. Rush, Dr. Brown and Culpepper. He referred to himself as an "Indian doctor," because he extensively employed Indian herb and root remedies in his practice.

In about 1780, he, his Jersey-born wife Catherine, and his small children, started an extensive series of peregrinations that took him to Virginia, the Carolinas and Georgia. He preached the gospel on the way and never missed a chance to seek knowledge from all physicians with whom he came in contact. Georgia, after a time became unbearable to him, because of his loathing of slavery. With his family, he travelled the wilderness, from Georgia, through Tennessee, to Kentucky, ending up at Ohio in about 1794. He settled in Duck Creek (near the present confines of Cincinnati), preached frequently to the local congregation, engaged in farming and practiced medicine.

In 1804, the wanderlust again assailed him and he moved to a poor farm in Donnel's Creek, Ohio, where he died on December 31, 1816. While here, he wrote his "Dispensatory." The plants mentioned in the work are described by their common names but his descriptions are so adequate that the experienced reader can identify most of them. Always intellectually honest, Peter Smith never fails to give the names of the authorities from whom he quotes the material presented.

Dr. John Beattie (1749-1826), a native of Pennsylvania, spent most of his adult years in New Jersey. After graduating from Princeton in 1769, he studied medicine under Benjamin Rush. Soon after war broke out, he joined the army and became lieutenant colonel. He was captured by the English and kept prisoner for several years. After being liberated, he became, in 1779, commissary-general of prisoners. After the war, he set up practice in Princeton but soon was called to the State Legislature and Constitutional Convention. He was elected to Congress in 1793 and two years later became secretary of the state of New Jersey. He died at the age of seventy-seven on April 30, 1826.

An insight into the status of medicine in Colonial New Jersey immediately prior to, during and immediately following the War of Independence, may be gleaned by examining colonial newspapers of this period. A voluminous collection of such material is available in *The New Jersey Archives*, an exhaustive and scholarly series of works published by the State of New Jersey under the auspices of the New Jersey Historical Society. These volumes were published in series form from before the turn of the century until recent years. The following extracts concern New Jersey practitioners and patients.

Today, when only quacks advertise their healing prowess to the public, one is amused upon reading the ads and testimonials offered by legitimate physicians in colonial times.

The following appeared in the *Pennsylvania Gazette*, No. 2008, dated June 18, 1767:

The Subscriber begs leave to inform the Public, that he has removed from Burlington to the City of Philadelphia, in Almond-street, a few Doors from the Blue Bell, on Society-Hill, where he proposes to practice all Branches of Physic and Surgery. He undertakes particularly to cure, with small Expense and Pain to the Patient, Cancers and Wens, without cutting them, the King's Evil, venereal Disorders, without Sallivation; Rupture, Strangury and Stone; and as he has had great Experience and Success in all the above Diseases, he hopes, by the divine Blessing, to be able to give Relief to any distressed Persons, afflicted with them, that shall apply to him. He takes Patients into his House, and boards and lodges them, if desired.

THOMAS WIRE.

Not a bad list of accomplishments! We note that the good doctor's home was also used as a sort of hospital and sanitarium.

That Dr. Yeldall's free advice was not entirely unappreciated may be seen from the following ad in Dunlap's *Pennsylvania Packet*, No. 187, May 22, 1775.

DOCTOR YELDALL

Has for Sale, at his Medicinal Ware-House, three doors from the Bank-Meeting House in Front-street, most kinds of medicines, both chemical and galenical. Likewise most patent medicines now in use, which may be depended on to be genuine; together with the Doctor's Family Medicines, which are well known in most parts of the continent and where any person in the country may, by sending an account of their disorder, either in writing or otherwise, have advice and medicines as the nature of their complaint may require. Those that live in the city may be waited on at their houses, and due attandance given through the cure of their disorder, and on most moderate terms. Advice is given gratis to all who chose to apply; and none will be undertaken but where there is a probability of success....

For the benefit of others, be it made public, that I, Alexander Martin, of King's woods county, New Jersey, was afflicted with a consumptive disorder for upwards of three years. I applied to every man of skill that I could, but to no purpose; and when my money and strength were gone, they desired I might go to the hospital at Philadelphia, where I continued upwards of three months, went through a course of mercury, and tried many other things in vain, and at length was discharged. I then applied to Doctor Yeldall, who, in a short time, recovered me to my perfect health.

ALEXANDER MARTIN.

John Vorhees publicly expressed his appreciation to his physician in the *New-York Journal*, No. 1716, Nov. 23, 1776 as follows:

Sir: After the discouragement I met with from a Surgeon of the first practice in your City, I have reason to thank God that I was sent to you, at whose hands I have experienced a cure of one of the worst of disorders. Our family was much surprised at finding a lump so large taken out by a plaster; especially situated as it was, between the tendons of my neck. They never before believed that the King's evil could be cured; now, happily convinced, join with me in praying for your long life. I remain your most obedient humble servant.

JOHN VAN VORHEES.

Somerset County, New Jersey, 21st May, 1775.

The following advertisement from the *New-York Journal*, No. 1682, March 30, 1775, illustrates the independence of colonial obstetrics from the practice of medicine and surgery:

Late Surgeon to his Majesty's 29th Regiment of Foot, takes this method to inform the public in general, and his friends in particular, that he has taken the house and lot nearly opposite to Thomas Latham, and now occupied by Joseph Shotwell, Jun. at Raway, in the province of New-Jersey, where he proposes to practice surgery, physick and midwifery. The experience he has had by attending the Military and the advantage of walking all his Majesty's hospitals during a thirteen years service in the above department, he flatters himself will be a sufficient recommendation to the impartial public, whose favours he is, and always will be desirous to gain and merit, by his constant assiduity and close attendance on business.

He begs leave further to acquaint the public that, after serving a regular apprenticeship to the branches of surgery and physick, he separately studied, for the term of three years, the art of midwifery under one of the most eminent practitioners in Europe; after which he attended upon the Lying-in Hospital for several years, and had daily experience in that important science. Raway, March 23d, 1775.

Relative to the colonial history of ophthamology, the following two clippings are of interest. It seems a shame that the first mentioned doctor was not an obstetrician. Dr. Walpole evidently did a neat bit of traumatic ophthalmic surgery.

January 21.

Doctor STORK

SURGEON and OCULIST to Her Royal Highness the
Princess Dowager of WALES.

Acquaints the public, that he is to continue in Philadelphia till the latter End of February next: such as are in need of his assistance may apply to him at his Lodgings near the New Meeting-house in Arch-street.

We the Subscribers are induced, not only in Gratitude to DOCTOR STORK, but likewise for the benefit of the Public to communicate the Recovery of our Sights from Blindness, by his Operations. . . . This is to certify that I Thom Roberts of Hopewell, near Trenton, being deprived of Sight for two Years, was by Dr. Stork restored to it again.—*The Pennsylvania Journal*, No. 998, January 21, 1762.

Two days after the departure of the Granville Packet, Capt. Kempthorn from Sandy Hook, he was attacked by three rebel privateers; a Sloop of 14 guns, a brig of 12, and a schooner of 10, all which after a brisk action of about an hour he forced to sheer of.—The sloop being the most powerful vessel engaged him nearest, and from appearance must have suffered very considerably, as she was obliged to bear away, and made signals of distress to her consorts, which bore away after her, and hove too a good way to leeward to give her the assistance she must have needed.—When she bore away both pumps were at work; in the course of the action, the sloop was so near the Granville, that she frequently ordered her to strike in language peculiar to American privateers, of which no other notice was taken than by plying them more hotly with their guns.—The Granville received no material damage, except in the wounds of two of the people; one of whom was Mr. Steele the first mate, who lost his eye by a piece of an iron belt weighing 13 ounces, which buried itself in the socket of his eye, and the upper part of his cheek bone, turning his eye quite over his nose; the piece was extracted and the eye replaced by the surgeon Mr. Walpole, who by reducing it, performed a very capital cure, and Mr. Steele is now in a fair way of recovery.—The piece of iron was so uncommonly large, to lodge in so mortal a place without occasioning death, that it was thought a curious present for the British Museum, where it now is with the history of the case.

N.B. The Granville only carried 12 four pounders, and 45 men.
    —*The Royal Gazette*, March 4, 1780. No. 358.

Urinary disorders, particularly calculosis, occupied the attention of colonial physicians. Naturally, all surgery in pre-anesthetic, pre-antiseptic and pre-aseptic days was attended by a high mortality. Of interest is the lithotomy on an eight year old male subject.

New York, June 29.

On Sunday last, was perform'd at Newark, the operation of Lithotomy, on a youth of about eight years of age, before several very eminent gentlemen in the practice of physick and surgery, by Mr. John Jones, one of the principal surgeons of this city. The largeness of the stone, and dexterity with which it was extracted was sufficient indications of his judgment in manual operation, and met with the cordial approbation of all the Gentlemen present. The symptoms are as favorable towards a recovery, as can be expected from the severity of so dangerous an operation.

—*The Pennsylvania Chronicle*, No. 24, June 29, July 6, 1767.

The following is an advertisement inserted by William Clark, who, it will be remembered apprenticed the aforementioned Jacobus Hubbard of Long Island in 1760.

The Calamity of Diseases being incident to every Species of Being, has employed the Time and engaged the Searches of many Men into such Things as might prove Antidotes to the Several Disorders, and to endeavour at such Applications as would totally eradicate each Distemper; and that their Attempts might be more effectual, the Animal, Mineral and Vegetable Creation have been consulted and a Union of them all rendered conducive to answer the Purpose of recovering decayed Nature, and restoring Health. Any one that is afflicted with Gravel . . . there is prepar'd by Doctor William Clark, living in Freehold, East-New-Jersey, an Oil, which has not only given Relief but by continuing of it for some Time, has so eased me of that dreadful Disorder that I am now capable of doing any Business, when that before I was not able for to go on any Ocasion of my Affairs; The Vertue and Efficacy of which Oil, in the Cure of the above mentioned Distemper, will be made evident by my own words, if questioned by any Person, upon Enquiry; Whenever I found the Disorder coming on me, I took about fifteen Drops, which gave me present Relief. Any Person that requires further Information by applying to the said William Clark, shall be informed of Persons that has made Tryal of the above Oil.

WILLIAM CLARK.

—*The N.Y. Gazette* revived in *The Weekly Post Boy*, Jan. 8, 1750.

The empirical methods of colonial prescribing are well illustrated in the following "letter to the editor" from *The Pennsylvania Gazette*, No. 1890, March 14, 1765. Of course, empiricism was very active up until the present century and is, even now, by now means completely dead.

Philadelphia, March 8, 1765.

Mr. Hall,

If you think the following worth a Place in your Paper, the Public are heartily welcome to my Endeavours to promote the Knowledge of it by a Publication.

Traveling the other Day, in Company with a reputable Farmer, he happened accidentally to inform me, that he has at Times been subject to that exruciating Disorder the Gravel, and was particularly afflicted with it some time ago, when upon a long Journèy, from His Home: Fortunately for him, in the Course of his Progress, he met with a certain Gentleman, whom he believes to be a Doctor, who, upon knowing his Case, acquainted him, that he had heard of a Remedy which had been very beneficial to Take, says he, the Saw-dust proceding from good mellow Pine, boil it in clear Spring Water, let it settle, and then strain it off; drink freely of this, and you will soon find Relief. . . . The Person, glad to alleviate his Misery, tried the Experiment, and in ten Hours after found it gave him Ease: He used the Drink three or four days, and declares his Pain quite left him, and that since that Time he has scarce felt anything of his said Disorder.

I confess the Remedy seems simple; but as I doubt not the Truth of what the Gentleman has asserted, I hope the Freedom I take on this Occasion may be excused. . . . What confirms me in the Belief of its Efficacy is, the reputed Virtues of Turpentine, the Uses of which, according to *Chambers*, "are innumerable," and is particularly "famous for clearing the urinary Passages, and as such, is prescribed for Obstructions in the Reins," &c. . . . Now, as this Substance is the well known Product of the Pine, it seems to me reasonable to think, that the Pine Dust must contain of the oily Nature, and that therefore, it may have good Effect above mentioned. If, upon Trial, it should prove as beneficial to any others, as it has done to the Person who gave me the Intelligence, my End in giving you this Trouble will be full answered. Who am

Your Friend and Customer,

CIVIS.

N.B. As they saw Abundance of Pine in the Jerseys, the Dust may be had in great Plenty: three quarts is a suitable Proportion to a Gallon of Water, and may be sweetened, to make it palatable.

Some of the claims at present expounded by laymen for prune juice are more than slightly reminiscent of the following piece on "Sugar Plumbs." Dr. Ryan got eight colonial dollars for a dozen of his plumbs!

Dr. RYAN'S
Incomparable worm-Destroying
SUGAR PLUMBS,
Necessary to be kept in all FAMILIES;

So exceedingly valued by all people who have had of them in Great Britain and Ireland, for their transcendent excellency in the destroying worms of all kinds, both in the bodies of men, women and children, by not only breaking the knots in the duodenum, or gut next the stomach, but they pass through the smallest passages of the body, and purge away those ropy and slimy humours, which are the cause of these pernicious vermin, and the source of many other disorders; they are one of the best purges in the world for gross-bodied children that are apt to breed worms, and have large bellies; their operation is mild, safe and pleasant; they wonderfully cleanse the bowels of all stiff and clammy humours which stop up the parts, and prevent the juice of food from being conveyed to the liver and made blood, which is often the case with children, and is attended with a hard belly, stinking breath, frequent fevers, rickets, and a decay of strength in the lower parts: Likewise settled aches and pains in the head, swellings, old sores, scabs, tetters, or breakingsout, will be perfectly cured, and the blood and skin restored to its original purity and smoothness; they purge by urine and bring away the gravel, and effectually cure all obstructions of the urine, or ulcers in the kidneys. They at once strike at the true cause of the scurvy, and entirely destroy it, and all scorbutic humours and effects, root and branch, so as never to return again; and what makes them more commendable is, they are full as agreeable to both taste and sight, as loaf sugar; and in their operation as innocent as new milk.

I have by these plumbs cured a great many children of whooping or chincoughts, and agues, which distempers are very common and troublesome to families, and the want of these plumbs are the ruin of many childrens constitutions.

These plumbs enrich and sweeten the whole mass of blood, carry off all gross, corrupt and putrid humours, and create a fresh and healthy complexion in such as are affected by any putrid matter.

The plumb is a great diuretic, cleansing the reins of slime: It expels wind, and is a sovereign medicine in the cholic and griping of the guts. It allays and carries off sour vapours, which occasion many disorders in the head. It opens all obstructions in the stomach, lungs, liver, reins and bladder, causes a good appetite, and helps digestion. It hath been found wonderfully successful to such persons as are going into chronical distempers, as asthmas, phthisics, or shortness of breath, dropsies and yellow jaundice. Now I hope all impartial persons are satisfied, and the medicine which works upon such humours, will almost reach any distemper. If not too far gone, since corruption and putrefaction are the forerunners of all diseases: therefore no better physic can be taken for all ages, sexes and constitutions, from infancy to an old age. These plumbs are highly serviceable to the female sex from the age of 14 to 20 years, and from 40 to 50. Each box contains one dozen of these plumbs, price Eight Dollars with directions. Sold by JAMES EMERSON, at his store in Trenton.

SIGNS of WORMS

Paleness in the face, itching of the nose, hollowness of the eyes, grating of the teeth when asleep, dulness, pains and heaviness in the head, a dry cough, and itching in the fundament, white and thick urine, unquiet sleep, often starting lost appetite, swelled belly, gnawing and biting about the stomach, frightful dreams, extreme thirsts, the body decay'd and lean, fits, often vomiting, stinking breath, &c. Also imported SALT.

—*The New Jersey Gazette*, Vol. 11, No. 68, March 31, 1779.

The prevalence of smallpox in colonial America is everywhere evident throughout colonial newspaper articles. Thieves, escaped slaves, horse thieves, etc., are constantly referred to as being pitted with smallpox.

The colonial method of smallpox inoculation is first referred to in the *New Jersey Archives* in the following clipping dated June 26, 1760. Nothing truly great in colonial science can be studied without coming across that great American, Benjamin Franklin!

Mr. Bradford,

I here inclose you a Copy of a Letter sent to Mr. HALL, last Week, containing a short Account of our present Method of treating the Small-Pox under Inoculation, which please to insert in your next Paper, for the Benefit of your Readers.

Sir,

I am obliged to you for the Pamphlet you gave me, containing plain Instructions for Inoculation in the Small-Pox, published in *London* (at the Instance of your Friend the Ingenious and public-spirited Mr. BENJAMIN FRANKLIN) by the eminent Dr. WILLIAM HEBERDEN, F.R.S. and by him sent to *America*, to be distributed gratis.

I THINK it is a very useful Performance, not only as it tends to promote the Practice of Inoculation in general, but as containing some of the best general Rules for the Preservation of our Fellow-Creatures, from the dismal and fatal Effects of that frightful distemper: And that I may add my mite towards extending so benevolent a Design, I attempt this Recommendation of it to the Public, with some few additional Directions, respecting the present new Method of treating those under Inoculation in this Country, which has been Blessed to the saving of the Lives of Thousands, within these three Years in New-Jersey.

the METHOD is THIS.

The Night before you Inoculate, give a few Grain of Calomel well levigated, with a like Quantity of Diaphoretic Antimony unwash'd, proportioning the Quantity of Calomel to the Constitution of your Patient from 4 Grains to 10 for a Grown Person, and from 1 to 3 for a Child, to be made up into a Bolus or small Pill, with a little Conserve of Roses, or any common Syrup; the next Morning give a Purge of the Pulvis Cornachini; made with equal Parts of Diaphoretic Antimony, Scammony, and Cream of Tartar; repeat the Bolus or Pill 3 Times, that is, once every other Night after Inoculation, and on the 5th Day give a Dose of Boerhave's Golden Sulphur of Antimony; about 4 grains of it with 2 or 3 Grains of Calomel, made into a small Pill, will Operate both as a Vomit and Purge at the same Time.—In the intermediate Days give 2 or 3 Papers of the following Powders, viz. Diaphoretic Antimony 10 Grains, Salt Prunel 6 Grains and Calomel One Grain, mixt together, for a grown Person and about ¼ part of a Paper for a Child. These Powders are to be continued until the Variolous or Small-Pox Fever is over, and while the Fever is high, let your Patient Drink a Cup of Whey 2 or 3 Times a Day. The Whey to be made with Cream of Tartar, instead of Rennet; and those that are of a full habit, should be Blooded once or twice within the first 8 Days and must abstain from all spiritous Liquors, as well as from Meat of all kinds, Broth, Salt, and Butter.

I MENTION the Golden Sulphur of Antimony, not because I think it has any Specific Virtue distinct from other Preparations of Antimony, that operate like it, but because some selfish Practitioners (I don't call them Physicians, for they reject all such Quackery) pretend to make a Secret of their Antimonial Panacea, to the discouragement of Inoculation; with a view either to confine the whole Practice to themselves, or else to Huckster out their Nostrum at 20 Pistoles a Piece to such as are credulous and weak enough to Pay for their pretended Discovery; which to say no worse of it, does not Discover either Generosity, Benevolence, or Humanity; when the Truth is that their whole Dependence is upon the Mercury, assisted with any Antimonial (I have lately had a preparation from Dr. SHIPPEN, which he calls Sublimated Antimony, which operates, I think with more Certainty and more Safety than any I have Used before). Purge, that will operate upwards and downwards, with safety.... At least I can Answer for myself, that my Dependence is upon the Calomel thus assisted; and I have had as great Success in Inoculations as any of my Brethren, since this Method was freely communicated to me about 2 Years ago by the skillful and candid Doctor SHIPPEN of your City, who from his great knowledge in Chymistry and his diligent and watchful Observations during a long course of Practice among you, is well known to understand the Powers of Medicine, as well as the Nature of Diseases. I therefore take the freedom to mention his Name without his leave, not only to show my Gratitude, but for the same good Reason which the great Mr. FRANKLIN gives for the like freedom he took with Dr. HEBERDEN'S; to wit, because his Name will have more weight with the Public than my own.

I MIGHT attempt to offer some Reasons in favour of this Method; by showing how or why those Medicines given in this Way are preferable to any other heretofore published; but I think the extraordinary Success with which it has been attended, is more Intelligible and more Satisfactory, to those for whose Benefit and Encouragement this Publication is intended; however it may not be amiss to mention one of the Doctors Observations upon it, which was the Time of giving the Medicines, so as that they may exert their Force upon the Blood and Humours, just at the very Time when the Disease takes Place, and by that means divert, weaken, and destroys its Power, and at the same Time by their Activity, assist Nature to throw off this Morbific or Poxey-Matter, with more Ease through the common Outlets of the Skin, &c.

I am, Your constant Customer,
AMERICANUS.

P.S. It appears by the nearest Calculation I can make, that under this Treatment, there has not Died more than one Person in 700, and in general the Distemper is very light, not above one in 100 it Full, while in the common Way of Infection, 1 dies out of 5.

If any should still Object and say, that they dare not Venture upon Inoculation because they live at a Distance from any Physicians, and have not Skill enough themselves to prepare the Medicines and proportion their Quantity's to different Constitutions.... I would advise them to apply to any of the Physicians in Philadelphia, or New-York (if nearer to them) whose Judgement they can depend upon, and I don't

doubt they may be supply'd with the Medicines properly made up into Doses, as well as Plaisters and other necessarys fit for the Purpose, with plain Directions for the use of them all, at a small Expense.
—*The Pennsylvania Journal*, No. 916, June 26, 1760.

That the colonial doctors were humanitarians and did not neglect the poor may be gathered from the next ad:

INOCULATION

George Pugh, Surgeon, lately arrived from Jamaica, acquaints the Public, that he was the first Person who introduced the Suttonion Method of Inoculation for the Small-pox in that Part of the West-Indies where he has been instrumental in almost eradicating that most loathsome Disease. He now proposes carrying on that Branch of his Profession, every Spring and Fall, in Elizabeth Town, New-Jersey, where he has opened a Commodious House for the Reception of Patients. Any Person, Family or Company desirous of being Inoculated by him at New-York, Philadelphia or elsewhere, may depend upon his strictest Care and Attendance to conduct them through the Small-pox, and upon Terms agreeable to their Circumstances, and what may justly be added, with very little Loss of Time or Hindrance. And that all Persons may have it in their Power to satisfy themselves of the Utility of his Practice, he has inserted a few of the Estates that were inoculated by him, without the loss of a Patient, in the Parish of Westmoreland, Jamaica, each Estate having not less than 400 Slaves upon an Average. Dorcas Valley, William Wittes, Esq.; Anglesea, Samuel Houghton; Paradise, John Cape; Egypt, Ditto; Prospect, H. Brickets; Amity, William Bosley; South-field, William Blake; Williamsfield, Crawl, Roaring River; Hertford Beckford, Esq.; Mount Pleasant, Jacob Ferris; Sweet-River, Friendship, Greenwich, Tho. Vassall.

With many more Estates and white People throughout the Island, too numerous to be inserted in this Advertisement.

N.B. The Poor, properly recommended, will be inoculated gratis.
—*The New York Journal or General Advertiser*, No. 1433, June 21, 1770.

John Cochran recognized some of the deficiencies of smallpox inoculation as practiced by his colleagues and proceeded to eliminate them.

INOCULATION

The Subscriber begs Leave to inform the Public, that he has opened a very convenient House in a remote tho' pleasant Situation, within three miles of New-Brunswick, for the Reception of such Persons as propose taking the Small-pox by Inoculation. The best Attendance will be given, and every Thing proper for their Accommodation shall be furnished, at a very low and easy Rate.

Many are detered from being inoculated, on Account of sore Arms, Boils and large Abscesses, often attending the common Method of treating the Disease; but more particularly from the ill Effects of the too free and indiscriminate Use of Mercury, by which many (tho' they recover the Small-pox, yet the Constitution being Injured), soon fall Victims to some other Malady.

All these Inconveniences are avoided by a particular Method of preparing the Patient, the most efficacious and the least detrimental to the Constitution, by the Manner of conveying the Infection, and by the subsequent Treatment of the Disease, without the least Confinement; the Advantages of which have been fully and clearly demonstrated in upwards of 400 Persons under the Subscribers Care in the space of a few Month's last Winter and Spring, without the Misfortune of losing any; nor has there died more than one of that Number since, which plainly shows the singular Advantages of this Method.

A sufficient Number to make it worth his While, in any Part of the Country not contiguous to a Person properly qualified. (I don't mean authorized) shall be waited on, at a short Notice, by the Publick's.

Most obedient humble servant,
JOHN COCHRAN.

New-Brunswick,
December 12, 1771

—*The New York Journal or General Advertiser*, No.
1519, February 13, 1772.

Dr. Weed is proud of his zero mortality. His N.B. is the very basis of judging clinical success. Note that spring was the season of inoculation.

Philadelphia, March 29, 1773.

DR. GEORGE WEED,

Begs leave to inform the public, that as he hath been lately engaged in inoculating for the small-pox in New-Jersey, is now returned to Philadelphia, and designs to inoculate this spring as usual, and hath already begun—And for the encouragement of those who have a desire to be inoculated for the small-pox, he can inform them, that he believeth he hath found out and prepared such medicines as the great Dr. Boerhaave hinted at in his practical aphorisms on the small-pox, which by the blessing of God has proved effectual in destroying that virulency of the pox, so as greatly to lessen the malignity of it, so that the disorder proves light and easy for the patient to undergo; and out of above eighty he hath prepared by these medicines, there were not above four or five that had any quantity of them, and they could not be said to have it bad, but all presently recovered, and, by the blessing of God, he hath had none of those he inoculated die under his hands, for which he ought to be truly thankful, and he trusts he is; and while the Lord continues thus to bless his means, he will continue to inoculate for those who apply to him, as far as he is able. We may use means, but the blessing depends upon God alone, and there is all his trust and confidence.

N.B. What greater proof can there be of the utility of medicines than the great success that attends them?
    —*The Pennsylvania Packet*, No. 75, March 29, 1773.

The following clipping offers a therapeutic measure to combat diphtheria. Note that a feather was the colonial equivalent of a throat swab:

Philadelphia, January 27.

We are inform'd, that at Corswicks in West New-Jersey divers Persons have died lately of a Distemper in the Throat, and that that Distemper prevails there. We are therefore desired to Publish the following Remedy (which has proved successful) for the advantage of those who may here-after be visited with the like Distemper. *Take some Honey and the sharp-est Vinegar, with Allom dissolv'd therein, and let the patient often Gargle it in their Throats; or if they be Children, then take a Feather and dip it into said Liquor and so wash their Throats.*
    —*The New York Weekly Journal*, Feb. 9, 1736.

The following refer to virulent measles epidemics:

Philadephia, March 11th.

The Measles begin to spread in our Town. It was brought hither from Salem in West-Jersey, where it proved very Mortal.—*The Boston News-Letter*, Numb. 18, from Monday March 15 to Monday March 22, 1713. (1714).

New York, June 28.

On the 22d arrived Gerrard in 20 days at Amboy from Barbadoes. Letters from thence say, That Island is very sickly and that a great many dye of the Sickness.—*The Boston News-Letter*, from June 28 to July 5, 1714. Numb. 533.

Cases of unintentional toadstool and other food poisonings are numerous. Rattlesnake bite was commonly also met with.

Philadelphia, July 24.

We hear from Penns-neck (in West-New-Jersey) that a few days ago, Mr. John Redstrake's Son of about 3 Years old, his Servant Boy, & Negro Woman, having eaten some Mushrooms, were all three taken with Swelling soon after they had eaten them, and kept swelling till they died, which was not long after.—*The American Weekly Mercury*, July 17-24, 1735.

New-York, June 4.

Last Week a young Woman, the Daughter of Adolph Brower, (Doubtless Femme'ie, daughter of Adolf Brouwer and Jametie Verdon, baptized in the Hackensack church 1 December, 1723.) of Hackensack was bit in three different Places by a Rattle-Snake, as she was gathering Straw berries; the injected Venom operated so speedy that she died in a few Hours.—*The Boston Weekly Post-Boy*, June 11, 1739. No. 243.

New York, April 16.

We have an Account from Morris County in the Jersies, that about a Fortnight ago a poor Man and his Son of about seven Years of Age, being burning some old Brush in a swamp, found some Roots that look'd like Parsnips, which they roasted and eat: Soon after returning home they found themselves unwell, and died both together in a few Minutes without any visible Tokens of Hurt.—*The Pennsylvania Journal*, April 19, 1753. No. 541.

New York, August 6.

We hear from Freehold, that on Thursday the 26th of last Month, one Rachel M'Koy, went out in good Health, in order to gather Huckelberries, and after being in the Woods some Time, complain'd of being out of Order, which increasing that Night, she died the next Morning; it's suppos'd she had been poison'd.—*The New York Gazette or the Weekly Post Boy*, Aug. 6, 1753.

New York, September 12.

We hear from Woodbridge, in New-Jersey, that Mr. Jonathan Kinsey, died there, very suddenly, a few Days ago, after eating freely of Mushrooms, among which it is imagined, poisonous Toadstools were intermixed. Several Misfortunes of the same Kind have recently happened in other Parts of America.—*The Pennsylvania Journal*, No. 1188, September 12, 1765.

The following group of representative advertisements give an insight into the colonial materia medica. Financial arrangements and prices, when given for pharmaceutical products, are of interest, as are also the places from where the drugs are imported. Note the money back guarantee and the colonial counterparts of the modern department store druggists.

To all Practitioners in Physick.

Imported this Spring from London, a very good Assortment of Drugs and Medicines which are to be sold at the following most reasonable Rates; also, any Part of the Utensils of a neat Apothecary's Shop, exceeding cheap. N.B. any Person who will purchase the Whole, may have them at a Cent, advance; and any One who sends an Order for any Medicines, and should not be satisfied with any of the Articles, shall have their Money returned, if said Articles are returned within a Month after their Delivery.

DR. READY MONEY, *York* Currency.

	£	s.	d.		£	s.	d.
All Compound Waters				—— Mirab. Glaub. opt.	0	3	0
per Gallon	1	0	0	Ditto 2d sort	0	2	0
Cantharides p. Pound	0	15	0	Spt. Sal. Vol. Ol. ⎫			
Conn. Cerv. Calc.	0	2	0	—— Lavend C. ⎬	0	7	0
Elect. Mithridat	0	7	0	—— Corn. Cerv. &c ⎭			
—— Theriac. Androm.	0	7	0	All Spirits and Tinctures.			
—— Diascord.	0	3	6	Fol. Semœ Alex.	0	10	0
Empl. Diachyl. S. ⎫				Syr. de Spin. C.	0	3	0
—— de Bolo ⎪				—— Violar. Lond.	0	6	0
—— de Minio ⎬	0	1	8	—— Diacodii,	0	4	6
—— Mellilot. ⎭				all other syrups.			
—— Oxycroe. ⎫				Mer. Dulc. per Ounce.	0	1	8
—— Paracels. ⎪				—— trac. alb.	0	3	0
—— Drach. cum Gumis ⎬	0	6	0	—— Rubr.	0	1	8
all other Plaisters in ⎪				Ol. Anis. Chym.	0	2	6
Proportion ⎭				—— Juniper	0	1	8
Gum. Ammoniac	0	7	6	all Chym. Oils,			
—— Arebic	0	2	0	Sal. C.C.	0	1	6
—— Assoe	0	10	0	—— Succin Ver	0	16	0
—— Camphor	0	14	0	—— Viper, per Chrachm.	0	10	0
—— Opium	1	12	0	all other Salts			
all other Gums.				Ivory Glyster Pipes, p. Dz.	0	4	6
Manna opt.	0	10	0	Box ditto	0	3	6
Second sort ditto	0	8	0	Phial Corks, per Gross	0	1	0
Sal. Cathert. Amer.	0	1	0	Large Velve Corks	0	3	6

Gallipots, Pill Boxes, Gold and Silver Leaf, Partly Gold, and Dutch Metal, Sieves &c, and all sorts of Drugs and Medicines in proportion.

Be pleased to direct to Thomas Wood, at New-Brunswick.—*The N.Y. Gazette* revived in *The Weekly Post Boy*, June 18, 1750.

Just imported in the *Nebuchadnezer*, a choice Assortment of Medicines, calculated for Practice in the Country, and are genuine, from the Hall in London; they are quite fresh, and allowed to come from the most eminent Hand, subjected to the Inspection of the Royal College of Physicians; to be sold very cheap by Charles Scham Leslie, M.D. at his House in Connecticut-Farms, a few Miles from Elizabeth-Town in the Jersies.—The said Dr. Leslie intending to deal for the Future in that Branch of Business, will always take care to have fresh Assortments from London, and to give the usual Credit; tho' now he proposes for Cash, to sell 20 per Cent. cheaper than shall appear from any Invoices or Bills of Parcels, for the same Kind of Medicines in any trading Place in America, where Practitioners are serv'd at the second-hand.—*The N. Y. Gazette* revived in *The Weekly Post Boy*, Aug. 3, 1752.

TO Be SOLD, At PUBLIC VENDUE,

At the Dwelling-House of John Van Cleeve, of Bedminister, in the County of Somerset, and Province of New-Jersey, on Tuesday the 29th of June inst. a compleat and valuable Shop of Medicines, with Mortars and sundry Instruments and other Things, very suitable for a Doctor. An Inventory may be seen of the whole on or before the Day of Sale. Reasonable Credit will be given.—*The New York Mercury*, June 14, 1762.

DR. ATWOOD,

Has removed his Store, consisting of a general Assortment of Drugs and Medicines, to the House of Joseph Riggs, Esq. in Newark, where County Practitioners and others may be supplied wholesale and retail, at as low prices as charg'd in New-York.—*New York Gazette and Weekly Mercury*, April 8, 1776.

MADEIRA WINES
Of the very best Quality.

To be sold, by the pipe, quarter cask, or five gallons, by Dr. Atwood, at the house of Joseph Riggs, Esq.; in Newark;—also, mace cinnamon, nutmegs, cloves, alspice, &c. Turlington's balsam, Bateman's drops, Haerlem oil, British oil, Anderson's pills, Hooper's pills, Lockyer's pills, James's fever powders, Hill's balsam of honey, a paste for preserving the teeth and gums, Greenough's tincture for the teeth, Boerhagg's balsam,

&c. Drugs and Medicines in general. Marble mortars of all sizes.—*New York Gazette and Weekly Mercury*, September 28, 1776.

PRACTITIONERS of PHYSICK may be supplied at moderate prices, at the printing-Office in Trenton, with the following articles: NITRE, JESUITS BARK, JALAP, RHUBARB, SENNA and MANNA—All of the first quality.—*New Jersey Gazette*, Vol. 1, No. 35, August 19, 1778.

To Be Sold By

G. DUYCKINCK,

at Morristown, New Jersey, DRUGS and MEDICINES, a compleat assortment, viz.

RHUBARB	Elixirs	Liquid Shall
Jesuit bark	Tinctures	Balsam of health
Jalap	Spirits	Daffy's elixir
Opium	Emplastrums	Francis' female elixir
Aloes	Gums	Essence of Burgamont
Borax	White Lead	Ambergrease
Salts	Red Lead	Lavender
Manna	Yellow Oker	Demons
Antimonial prepa-	Spanish brown	Verlerin
rations	Indian red and litharge	Waterdock
Mercurial ditto	Dutch Pink	Elixir Bordana
Quicksilver	Vermillion and Drop	Godfrey's Cordial
Tartar Emetic	lake	Hooper's pills
Aquas	Prussian blue	James's fever powder
Camphor	Smelter and Vergegrease	Jesuits drops
Spanish flies	Oils	Kings honey water
Calomel	Powders	Locker's pills
Cochineal	Roots	Keyfer's pills
Saffron	Refines	Fryer's balsam
Castor	Tartars	Tincture of Golden Rod
Senna	Ointments	Umber
Ising glass	Pills	White vitriol
Sago	Carraway and Anniseed	Linseed Oil and Varnish
Magnesia Alba	Pink Root	Madder and fustic
Balsams	Mercurial or itch oint-	Annetto
Causticks	ment	Logwood
Conserves		Nutgalls of Aleppo
Essences	PATENT MEDICINES	Tartar
Extracts	Anderson's pills	Press papers and allums
Electuaries	Bateman's drops	

Window glass of different sizes, viz. Best London and Bristol crown, 13 by 11, 14 by 12, 13 by 11, 15 by 13, 16 by 10, 20 by 14, 18 by 13, 15 by 18, 21 by 18, 21½ by 18½, 25½, 20 by 16, and 17 by 13.

*Hat linings; variety of brass double and single branches; painted table cloths, hair or matt cloths.

Agroll, Turkey oil stones, grain tin, bismuth, spelter, pummice stone, sandives, crocus martis, *aqua fortis, aqua regis, allum;* steel snuffers, snuff-boxes, pewter ink chest, steel pencil cases, thimbles, brass flour and pepper boxes; burning, reading and sighted glasses; barbers pinching tongs, shaving powder; *brass mortars* and *pestels;* variety of *sleeve forceps, lancets* and *lancet cases,* glister pipes, spring lancets, steel trusses single and double with foxed pad and bandages.

N.B. Those marked thus (*) and only sold by way of barter, for any kind of produce for family use. (also in the *New York Journal and the General Advertiser,* Number 1811, February 8, 1779.)
 —*The New Jersey Gazette,* Vol. 11, No. 57, Wed. January 6, 1779.

To be Sold by

WILLIAM RICHARDS

At his house in Trenton Landing,

a FRESH and good assortment of DRUGS and MEDICINES, where practitioners may be supplied as cheap as they can purchase, in Philadelphia, and in his absence at the same rate by Doctor David Cowell, in Trenton.

The best velvet corks and mustard to be sold at the above Trenton Landing.

N.B. The original store with a large and compleat assortment of the latest imported drugs and medicines is still continued by William Richards and Co. at the sign of the spread Eagle, in Market Street, near the Courthouse in Philadelphia.—*The New-Jersey Gazette,* Vol. 11, No. 67, March 17, 1779.

PRACTITIONERS OF PHYSIC

May be supplied with the following medicines (of the first quality) by applying at the house of Jonathan Morrell, half a mile from New-Providence meeting-house; peruvian bark, rhubarb, tartar emetic, cantharides, opium, glauber salts, camphor, compound spirits of lavender, volatile aromatic, salt or worm-wood, &c.

N.B. At the same place may be had indigo by the barrel or dozen.— *The New-Jersey Journal,* Vol. 1, Numb. XXXII, Sept. 21, 1779.

To be SOLD

By THOMAS MORRELL,

At the house of the late Amos Potter, Esq; 2½ miles from New-Providence meeting-house, the following MEDICINES:

Best Peruvian quill bark, rubarb, tartar emetic, warranted genuine; glauber salts, cantharides, opium, sal absynthii, g. myrrh, Carolina pink root, quicksilver, red precip itit, compound spirit lavender, spirit volatile, camphor, Anderson's pills, &c.

At the same place may be had excellent Jamaica spirit by the barrel or gallon. November 2, 1779.—*The New-Jersey Journal*, Vol. 1, Numb. XXXVIII, October 26, 1779.

There has been at William Richard's store a quantity of common sweet oil, for some time; as the casks were not tight, he got John Crosley, cooper, of Trenton, to start said oil into right casks. There remains 90 gallons, as may be seen by the said Crosley's account of charges. The owner of said oil may have it, paying the damage it has done the store with storage and other charges.

There is to be sold at said place, a good assortment of medicine, snuff, mustard, bottle corks, &c.

Lumberton, May 2, 1780.—*The New Jersey Gazette*, Vol. III, No. 124, May 10, 1780.

TO BE SOLD

At the house of JONATHAN MORRELL, in Elizabeth Town:

WEST INDIA rum by the barrel or gallon, excellent bohea tea, coffee, chocolate, pepper, alspice, best indigo, plug tobacco, hard soap, black beads, Irish linen, with a variety of the best glazed Philadelphia earthen ware, consisting of large and small dishes, cups, mugs, bowls, &c.

At the same place may be had the following M E D I C I N E S:—Peruvian bark, rhubarb, glauber salts, tartar emetick, cantharides, opium, quicksilver, red precipitit, compound spirits lavender, spirit volatile, aromatic, &c &c.—Nails of all sizes made and sold. Emquire as above.—*The New Jersey Journal*, Vol. II., No. LXXIX., August 23, 1780.

The following short extract reveals that the bodies of executed criminals were used for dissection.

Philadelphia, November 8.

Tuesday last Peter Mennell was executed at Gloucester, pursuant to his Sentence, for the Murder of his Master's Daughter; his Body was afterwards delivered to the Surgeons to be anatomized.—*The Pennsylvania Gazette*, No. 2185, Nov. 8, 1770,

That knaves usurped the name of "doctor" even in colonial times, can be readily inferred from the following clippings relative to "Dr." Ogle and "Dr." Hunt:

SALEM, WEST NEW JERSEY, APRIL 19, 1769.

TWELVE DOLLARS REWARD

Absconded from his usual Place of Abode, on the 16th Instant, a certain Doctor THOMAS OGLE, born in Ireland, about five Feet six or seven Inches high, pitted with the Small-pox is given to Liquor, and when in Drink talks much of his Skill in Physic and Surgery, has had one of his Legs broke, and commonly wears a Handkerchief about it; had on, when he went away, a half worn Beaver Hat, Bearskin Coat, Buckskin Breeches, Worsted Stockings, and good Shoes, with Pinch back Buckles. He took with him a Silver Watch, a Silver Face, Maker's Name Wm. Clayton, London, No. 2450, rode a sorrel Horse, with a Blaze in his Face; and had a Couple of Boxes, with Medicines in them (like a Pedlar's Pack) and a Suit of Fustian, not made up. Whoever takes up the said Dr. Ogle, and secures him in any of his Majesty's Gaols, shall receive the above Reward.

THOMAS HARTLEY, DANIEL LITHGOW, PETER AMBLER.

N.B. All Watch-Makers are desired to stop the said Watch, if offered for Sale, or otherwise.—*The Pennsylvania Gazette*, No. 2105, April 27, 1769.

Philadelphia, August 21, 1779.

Whereas a certain person, who calls himself Doctor John Hunt, made his escape from me out of Brunswick gaol, in the county of Middlesex, and state of New Jersey, on account of horse-stealing, and since has been in gaol in the city of Philadelphia, there discharged from confinement by a number of villains, associates of his, on the 19th instant; any person apprehending the said HUNT, and securing him in any gaol on the continent of America and giving me information thereof, shall receive EIGHTY DOLLARS Reward, paid by JOHN VANKIRK, late Sheriff of said county and State. The above fellow goes some times by the name of *John Whitmore* and *John Campbell*.

—*The Pennsylvania Gazette*, September 1, 1779.

TRENTON, October 20.

Last Thursday evening Major Joseph Brearley, of Maidenhead, knowing that there was a band of robbers in the neighbourhood, collected a small party of men, and formed an ambuscade on a lane where they suspected they would pass; about midnight they came along, and were all seized, and are now safely lodged in gaol. The fellows taken are the noted Dr. John Hunt, whose real name is Abraham Whitmore; John Carr, a notorious horse-thief, who lately broke from Morris gaol, and Samuel Slack, who lately escaped from the gaol of Philadelphia. They were all well armed; they had stolen two horses the night they were taken, and were on their way to rob a house in the neighbourhood. They were examined before the chief-justice, and one of them made a pretty simple confession which has discovered a number of their accomplices, several of whom have since been taken with a considerable quantity of stolen goods.—*The New Jersey Gazette*, Vol. 11, No. 95, Oct. 20, 1779.

Even the colonial practitioner had his domestic difficulties:

Philadelphia, January 23, 1753.

Whereas the subscriber, wife of doctor William Leddel, of Elizabeth-Town was advertis'd last week in this paper, as having eloped from her husband's bed and board, which is known by the major part of the people in said town to be false; she hereby gives notice, that the reason of her leaving him was, that her life was in danger from the ill usage she received from him; that he kept another woman, by whom he had two children, and after having spent Four Hundred and Fifty Pounds Sterling, of her money obliged her to leave his house.

LOUISA LEIDEL.

—*The Pennsylvania Gazette*, Jan. 23, 1753. No. 1257.

The following piece, of particular interest to veterinarians, is too juicy a morsel to miss:

NOTICE TO THE PUBLICK

That Augustus Steuart, of New Jersey, has prepared a HORSE POWDER, which, for its qualities and operations exceeds any thing hitherto contrived for the benefit of that animal. In all disorders to which those creatures are liable, it gives quick relief, purifies the blood, makes the beast more than ordinary lively, brisk, and strong, and occasions him to thrive in fatness, on almost half the provisions he in common devours. It is a great preservative against disorders of all kinds, giving only one common table spoon full of it once a week. It is to be had at Mr. Michael Housworth's, next door to W. Weyman's Printer, in Broad street, New-York, at four shillings per pound. This powder is a total poison for the botts, and carries all off by evacuation.

AUGUSTUS STEUART.

—*New York Gazette or Weekly Post Boy*, August 22, 1765.

The following transcripts are of interest with reference to the military medicine of the Revolutionary War:

Philadelphia, July 16, 1776.

The good people of this city and province, and of the province of New Jersey, are earnestly desired to send all the old sheets and other old linen they can possibly spare to Dr. Shippen, jun. for the use of the Jersey Hospital. None will refuse complying with this request, when they consider that the lint and bandages made of this linen may be used in dressing and curing the wounds of their own fathers, husbands, brethren, or sons.

The good people of New Jersey are desired to send their donations to Dr. Cowel, in Elizabeth Town.—*Pennsylvania Journal and Weekly Advertiser*, July 17, 1776.

The liberal provision made by Congress in the new medical arrangement, Joined with a humane desire to prevent the repetition of the distresses which afflicted the brave American soldiers the last campaign, have drawn men of the first abilities into the field, to watch over the health and preserve the lives of the soldiers—many of them from very extensive and profitable practice; and every species of domestic happiness. Dr. William Brown of Virginia, Dr. James Craik of Maryland, and Dr. Thomas Bond, jun. of Philadelphia, are appointed Assistant Director Generals. Dr. Walter Jones of Virginia and Dr. Benjamin Rush of Philadelphia, Physician and Surgeon Generals of the Hospitals of the middle department. Under these none but gentlemen of best education, and well qualified, are employed as senior Physicians, Surgeons, &c. The Eastern and Northern departments are filled with gentlemen of the first characters in those countries; and the public may depend on it, that the greatest exertions of skill and industry shall be constantly made, and no cost spared, to make the sick and wounded soldiery comfortable and happy. As a consequence of the above liberal arrangements of the Honorable Congress, we do, with great pleasure, and equal truth, assure the public (notwithstanding the many false and wicked reports propagated by the enemies of American liberty, and only calculated to retard the recruiting service) that all the *military hospitals* of the United States are in excellent order, and that the *army* enjoy a degree of health seldom to be seen or read of. W. SHIPPEN, jun. Director General of the American Hospitals. JOHN COCHRAN, Physician and Surgeon General of the Army in the Middle Department. Head Quarters, Middle Brook, June 4, 1777. ...It is requested that the above may be published in all the newspapers on the continent.—The *Pennsylvania Evening Post*, June 5, 1777.

Colonial headline accidents requiring medical aid included traumatic injuries sustained from gun powder explosions, mine blasts, falls from and kicks of horses, falling trees, being crushed by the wheel of a grist mill, lightning flashes, falls from stage coaches, riding chairs and ladders and into wells, and the bites and scratches of wild beasts (wildcat and panther). Frostbite and illness from exposure while lost are also frequently mentioned.

Chapter Eleven

THE CAROLINAS

A GROUP OF Spaniards from Culba visited the coast of South Carolina in 1520. In 1562, Jean Ribaut and a party of French Protestants vainly tried to establish a colony near the mouth of the Broad
River.

After receiving a patent for colonization from Queen Elizabeth,
Sir Walter Raleigh, in April 1584, despatched Philip Amodas and
Arthur Barlowe to explore the area bordering on Florida. These men
returned with great praise as to the suitability of the coast of what is
now North Carolina, for colonization.

On April 9, 1585, one hundred and eight colonists led by Ralph
Lane sailed from Plymouth in seven small boats navigated by Sir
Richard Grenville. On August 17, 1585, a colony was founded on
the northern end of Roanoke Island and a short time later, Grenville
left for England for more supplies. Fierce Indians combined with
imminent starvation caused all the original colonists to return to England on June 19, 1586 with Sir Francis Drake. A few days after
their departure, Grenville returned with more colonists, fifteen of
whom remained when he weighed anchor.

Discouraged but undaunted, Raleigh sent one hundred and twenty
one colonists under John White with instructions to reestablish the
colony on the shores of Chesapeake Bay. The sailors refused to take
them farther than Roanoke Island where they arrived on July 22,
1587 to find that none of the preceding fifteen colonists had survived.
White left for supplies, not returning until 1591, at which time no
trace of his colony was found. There is evidence to support the
belief that this group of pioneers went off and intermingled with
friendly Indians.

In 1629, Sir Robert Heath received a royal grant from Charles I, of all the territory lying from ocean to ocean between the 31st and the 36th parallels but no attempts at colonization were made.

In 1663, this same parcel of land was given to the Earl of Clarendon (1609-1674), and six others by Charles II. Two years later a second charter extended the limits to 29° and 36° 30'. The proprietors were to legislate for the colony "by and with the advice, assent and approbation of the freemen" and freedom of religion was left up to the proprietors. In 1663, and 1665, concessions or immigration circulars were issued offering liberal terms to prospective colonists, but this broad policy was soon cancelled.

In 1669 the Fundamental Constitution was adopted by which John Locke and Lord Ashley (1621-1683) established a complex feudal system of government that would have been retrogressive even in Europe. Modifications in 1670, 1682 and 1698 moderated the original plan but such a system could not help but arouse great discontent among the colonists which paved the way for the War of Independence. The Fundamental Constitution directly encouraged the large plantation system and thus paved the way for the slave-holding aristocracy and the Civil War.

In April 1670, the first permanent English settlement was established at Albemarle Point, on the west bank of the Ashley River. Climatic conditions here were not advantageous so the seat of government and most of the population moved in 1680 to the neck between the Ashley and the Cooper rivers, the site of the present city of Charleston, South Carolina. The settlement gradually fanned out along the coast in both directions, but avoided delving into the interior. Three coast counties soon materialized: Berkeley, extending from the Stono River to the Sewee and including Charleston; Craven to the north of the Sewee; and Colleton to the south of the Stono. Augmenting those settlers who had come directly from England, there were many Englishmen from Barbados and French Protestants. This large Barbadian influx rendered South Carolina more closely associated with the island than with the continental colonies.

From the start, the Carolina Territory tended to divide into two distinct sections: northern and southern. The northern district, at first called Albermarle, then "that part of our province of Carolina that lies north and east of Cape Fear," finally, in about 1689, became known as North Carolina. This area was primarily settled by Pennsylvanians whose sympathies were closely allied to the continental inhabitants of the colonies.

South Carolina's story, during the colonial period, seethes first with the struggle between the people and the proprietors and later between the people and the Crown. The practical points of issue between 1670 to 1700 were the refusal of the settlers to subscribe to the Fundamental Constitution and disputes over the collection of quit-rents. Concessions were eventually effected which brought the government under more democratic control. The division of the legislature into two houses was effected in 1692, and one year later the House of Commons elected by the people obtained the right of initiating legislation.

Following the compromise, Churchmen and Dissenters went at each other's throats. A test act requiring members of the assembly to conform to the Church of England and to take the sacrament of the Eucharist according to the rites and usages of that Church (1794) was successfully defeated only via the intervention of the Whig House of Lords in England. However the act of November 30, 1706, which stood on the books until the War of Independence, made the Anglican the established religion.

A few years of peace and prosperity were culminated by another attack upon the proprietors and the revolution of 1719 which led to the downfall of proprietary rule. Chief Justice Nicholas Trott (1663-1740) foolishly convinced the proprietors to employ a reactionary policy by vetoing various popular laws. The refusal of the proprietors to amply protect the colonists from the attacks of the Indians further incensed the populace. The people rebelled, overthrew the existing government and chose their leader, James Moore (1667-1723), as governor. The Crown accepted this turn of events and South Carolina at once came under royal control.

North Carolina refrained from joining South Carolina in the revolution of 1719 and remained under proprietary rule until 1729, when an act was passed by parliament establishing an agreement with seven of the Lord Proprietors for the yielding of their claims to both provinces. Lord Carteret, however, would not sell his claim and he maintained a one-eighth individual share until 1744, at which date he surrendered his claim in return for a large strip of land in North Carolina lying between latitude 35° 34′ and the Virginia line (36° 30′).

Although South Carolina and the North Carolina were supposed to constitute a single province, the fact that the settlements were far apart made it necessary to maintain separate local governments. Until 1691 each Carolina had its own governor. From 1691 to 1712 there was usually a governor at Charleston and a deputy for the northern settlements. After 1712 separate governors were again in power. An attempt at boundary definition was made in 1732, but it was not until 1815 that mutual agreement was reached.

The constitutional development of South Carolina was little effected by the change from proprietary to crown government. The popular branch of the legislature continued to fight for the powers of the governor and council. By 1760 the members of the council were largely reduced to figureheads who rarely instituted or amended any bill and never a revenue measure. Public officials theoretically appointed by the General Assembly were in fact named by the lower house. The governor found himself progressively more entangled in the nets of the committees of the Assembly. The people of South Carolina appear to have effectively achieved considerable freedom even prior to the War of Independenc, and the demands of the crown after 1760 do not appear to have been especially unreasonable or tyrannical.

Regarding South Carolina, Thomas Lynch (c. 1720-1776), Christopher Gadsden (1724-1805), and John Rutledge (1739-1800) attended the Stamp Act Congress of 1765. In 1773 an intercolonial committee of correspondence was appointed. Delegates were sent to the Continental Congress in 1774 and 1775. In June 1775, a council of safety appointed by a Provincial Congress practically took charge of the government. On September 15, 1775, the Assembly was formally dissolved and Governor William Campbell fled from the town.

Regarding North Carolina, the vessel which carried tax stamps and stamped paper to Wilmington in 1766 was not permitted to land. The stampmaster himself was forced to swear that he would not exercise his legal functions. Governor Tryon, however, succeeded in preventing the Assembly from sending delegates to the Stamp Act Congress.

North Carolinians were further aroused by the attempt to enforce the acts of trade and navigation and by the 1764 statute passed by parliament forbidding the issue of bills of credit. The ire of the Scotch-Irish element was fanned by the 1771 enactments permitting Presbyterian ministers to perform the marriage ceremony and allowing the founding of Queen's College for Presbyterians in Mecklenburg County. The "back county" was so infuriated by burdensome fees and taxes and the violent methods of collecting them that a popular uprising, called the Regulation, finally took place in the spring of 1768. The Regulators were put down by Governor Tryon after two military expeditions and some bloodshed.

In the War of Independence, the South Carolinians proved to be seasoned fighters. There had been wars with the Spanish in 1686, 1702-04, and 1740, with the Spanish and French in 1706, with pirates in 1718, with the Yemassee Indians in 1715 and the Cherokees in 1760-61, and a slave uprising in 1739.

The Carolinas bore great wounds during the War of Independence, the numbers and influence of the Loyalists serving to embitter the conflict. In the summer of 1776, the British, under Sir Henry Clinton and Sir Peter Parker attempted to capture Charleston and summon the South Carolina Loyalists to their standard, but on June 28, 1776, the British fleet was repulsed in an assault on Fort Moultrie. In 1780, Clinton returned, surrounded the city on all sides with an overwhelming army and forced General Benjamin Lincoln and his 7000 men to surrender on May 12, 1780. The English overran all of South Carolina and until near the close of the war, a new American army, first under Horatio Gates and later under Nathanael Greene, was engaged in driving them out. The principal engagements fought within the state were Camden (Aug. 16, 1780), King's Mountain (Oct. 7, 1780), Hobkirk's Hill (April 25, 1781), and Eutaw Springs (Sept. 8, 1781).

At Brandywine and Monmouth, the citizens of North Carolina fought valiantly under Washington. They took a very active part in the Southern Campaigns of 1778-1781. North Carolina was invaded by the British in 1776 and again in 1780-81 and the Battle of Moore's Creek (February 27, 1776) and Guilford Court House (March 15, 1781) were fought on her soil.

The author is deeply indebted to the works of Dr. J. I. Waring for much of the information on South Carolina.

Some of the early writers are profuse in their praise of Carolina as a health resort, and at times, the virtues are applied so thickly that one can almost feel the hand of the proprietors between the lines.

In 1670, Stephen Bull wrote:

Wee conceive this to be as healthful A place as ever was settled wee have lost but fower p'sons since wee satt down heere. & those was sickly p'sons & in A declininge condicon of health before wee landed there is some p'sons that have had feaver and Ague butt we observe little mortality in the distemper neither is the distemper neere soe high as is usuall in other Places...May itt please yor Honor our govrnor is ill of the feavr & Ague & being aged & falen into A relapse I doe much feare his recover.

In 1682, Samuel Wilson went on record to the effect that

Such, who in this Country have seated themselves noear great marshes are subject to Agues...etc: divers Persons who went out of England Phisical and consumptive, have recovered and others, subject in England to frequent fits of Stone, have been absolutely freed from them after they have been there a short time; nor is the Gout there, yet known. The air gives a strong appetite and quick digestion; nor is it without suitable effects; men finding themselves apparently more lightsome more prone, and more able to all youthful Exercises than in England; the Women are very fruitful and the children have fresh complexions.

In 1682, another author declared:

The air of so serene and excellent a temper, that the Indian natives prolong their days to the extremity of Old Age—and where the English hitherto have found no Distemper either Epidemical or Mortal, but what have had their Rise from Excess or Origine from Intemperance. In July and August they have sometimes touches of Agues and Fevers, but not violent, of short continuance, and never Fatal. English children there born, are commonly strong and lusty, of sound constitutions and fresh ruddy complexions.

Speaking of the herbs of the colony, he mentions a

...variety of such whose Medicinal Vertues were rare and admirable. The China grows plentifully there, whose Root yields us that pleasant Drink which we know by the Name of China Ale in England: In Medicinal uses it's far more excellent... It mundifies and sweetens the Blood. It's good in Fevers, Scurvy, Gonorrhea, and Lues Venerea. They have three sorts of the Rattle-Snake Root which I have seen: the Comous, or Hairy, the Smooth, the Nodous, or Knotted Root: All of which are lactiferous or yielding a Milkie Juice. They are Sovereign against the Mortal Bite of that Snake, too frequent in the West Indies. In all pestilential Distempers as Plague, Small Pox, and Malignant Fevers it's a Nobel Specifick; when stung, they eat the Root, applying it to the venemous Wound; or they boyl the Roots in Water; which drunk fortifies and corroborates the Heart, exciting strong and generous sweats; by which endangered nature is relieved; and the Poyson carried off and Expelled." He refers to the Sea-Cow, which "...hath a stone in the Head which is a gallant Remedy against the Pains and Dolor of the Stone; so are the Bones of its Body to provoke, Urine, when pulverized and exhibited in convenient Liquors.

Notwithstanding the salubrious climate, the need for a physician was early recognized by Governor West:

Here is wanting amongst us a good Doctor, and a chest of good medicines, those few people yt have dyed amongst us, I believe most part for want of good lookeing after, & that wch is fitt for men: Wee have not (thankes be to God) had one dyed out of our ffamily since wee came ashore which I looke upon as a very great ffavour from God: Ou Servants have bene sickly as well as others but now they are indifferently healthfull, and I hope season'd to the Country... wee find that one of our Servts we brought out of England is worth 2 of ye barbadians, for they are soe much addicted to Rum, yt they will doe little but whilst the bottle is at their nose.

In 1672, the colony at Charles Town had grown to about 500 people. By 1680, as the Huguenots and Barbadians began to arrive, the population reached the twelve hundred mark, and by 1682, nearly 4000 inhabitants lived in this metropolis. The year 1684 marks the appearance of the first epidemic disease in South Carolina's colonial history —probably malaria. This epidemic was of such proportions that the proprietors were led to lament in June 1684:

We are by all people informed yt Charlestowne is no healthy situation and yt it hath no good Water in it and all people that come to the province and landing there & the most falling sick it brings a Disreputation upon the whole Country wherefore wee desire that you will cause some other place to bee Searched out upon Cooper River nere the T to build a port towne on for that River & let it be Reserved for that Use until you have informed us of it & Received our opinion thereon.

Colonists arriving from Scotland in October 1684, reported:

We found the place so extrordinerie sicklie that sickness quickly seased many of our number and took away great many of our number and discoraged others, insomuch that they deserted us when we wer to come to this place (Port Royal) and sold of their servants....We came here the beginning of November, sicklie as we wer, we must confess the countrie is verie pleasant and desirable and promiseth well enough, better by far than any other place in Carolina that we had occasione to see. We setled ourselves altogether in a verie convenient place for a toun being about twentie miles from the mouth of the river Port Royall...free of swamps and marshes, a high bloffe land excellently weell watered, of such wholesome air as many of us quickly recovered, and none have contracted sickness since we came tho many died of the sickness they contracted at Charlestoun at our first arravell.

It is related that soon afterwards, a ship from Londonderry docked at Port Royal and subsequently lost twenty-nine persons from disease contracted at this place. A few years later, a depressing account of the Carolina country stated that "Two young men have just arrived from Carolina, who give some news of the country. In the first place they say that they have never seen so miserable a country nor an air so unhealthful. They have fevers all year long from which those attacked seldom recover; that, if some escape, they become all tawny as are these two who have arrived, who are pitiable to behold. Moreover, the heat there is so intense that it is almost unbearable, and this infects the water, and in consequence, diseases are caused, there being no other drink there. They also bring tidings that, before their departure, a vessel came from London with 130 persons, including the crew, of whom 115 are dead, all from malignant fevers which spread among them."

Henry Woodward was one of the earliest physicians of Carolina. Arriving in 1666, with the expedition to Port Royal, he voluntarily remained with the Indians and established himself so firmly with the red men that he retained a great influence among them. Woodward was subsequently captured by the Spaniards and imprisoned at St. Augustine, but effected his escape when Searle assaulted this city. He later served as surgeon aboard a privateer, and eventually was shipwrecked on Nevis. He joined the first colonists as they passed through Nevis, on their trek to Carolina to colonize and settle at Charles Town. Tranquillity was never destined to persist long, for this colorful Carolina pioneer. He was accused of giving aid to the Westo Indians who were waging war against the settlers, and went to England to stand trial. A full bill of innocence was the verdict handed down. His influence with the Indians and his personal worth and ability were always put to use to the benefit of the young colony, but just how much medicine he practiced is a mooted question.

Mention is made of one Dr. Will Scrivener, deputy for Lord Berkeley, who took part in local politics and died in 1671. "Doctor Tho: Smyth," the Landgrave, is listed as an early arrival, and his will bequeathing "all my instruments that belong to Chirurgery and one half of all my medicines—alsoe my large brass mortar and pestle" to his son George Smith, is indicative of the fact that he engaged in active medical practice. The younger Smith is said to have taken a medical degree at Edinburgh in 1700 at the age of 28, to become the first permanent resident of Carolina to obtain a medical degree from a college.

Dr. William Clarke, and Dr. Peter Bodett arrived before 1678. Clarke referred to himself as "Chirurgeon" in his will, and lived in Charles Town while Bodett settled on Goose Creek. One Joseph Blake, a surgeon, active in local politics, is mentioned as is also his friend James Williams, who settled in Colleton County in about 1683. In Berkeley County, Dr. Charles Burnham, a New England Quaker, achieved prominence in politics.

The following interesting anecdote with reference to Dr. John Hardy is worthy of mention:

In the troublous administration of James Colleton, 1686-1690, Hardy became involved in disputes with the Governor, and, when the latter proclaimed martial law in 1689, the doctor decided to quit the country. According to a partisan of Colleton's, Hardy left pending a suit against the latter for 150 pounds "For Physick and as a phisitian and for some small merchandise." The Governor brought a counter suit, and, "It was proven by concuring proofs that the Gov and his lady gave him (Hardy) 10 lib in gold as a reward for his attendance as a physitian.... It ended in Hardye's being 7 pund in the Gov. Debt."

Although Colleton's tyrannical government was quickly brought to an end, Dr. Hardy does not appear to have returned to South Carolina.

The records mention one Doctor William Trevellian, who resided in the Province during the sickness of 1684. This doctor together with the two Smiths, Woodward, Clarke, Bodett, Blake, Williams, Burnham, and Hardy, comprise the ten medical men known to have been on hand during the epidemic.

Regarding medico-legal activity, there is record of an act passed in 1695 for registering births, deaths, and marriages. In 1696, the Vestry of St. Philip's Parish was authorized to raise funds for the care of the sick. In 1698, there is record of an order "yt Mr. Jonathan Amory Received Do Pay Doctr Georg ffrankline out of ye Publick Money Twenty fower Dollars in full for medicines and attendance on a Poore wounded Seaman." At the same time the said Jonathan Amory had to pay Mrs. Williams and Mr. Burroughs "the Sume of Eighteene Dollars for six-weekes Dyett and Nursing a Poore Miserable wounded man," and thirty dollars for eight weeks diet and nursing care and "for ye Burriall of a Poore wounded Seaman."

There is record of an apothecary named Franklin who arrived in South Carolina in 1686 and later returned to England with some various specimens of Carolina products which eventually were incorporated in the collection of the British Museum.

Following the epidemic of 1684, the Carolinians remained relatively free of epidemic disease until the virulent wave of yellow fever in 1699. McCrady declared that "a malignant disease, with little doubt yellow fever, was brought in from the West Indies and raged in the town. The Governor and Council signed a document written in Charles Town on January 17, 1699-1700, to the effect that

...a most infectious pestilential and mortal distemper (the same which hath always been in one or more of his Majestys American plantations for eight or nine years last part) which from Barbados or Providence was brought in among us into Charles Town about the 28th or 29th of Aug. last past, and the decay of trade and mutations of your Lordships public officers occasioned thereby. This distemper from the time of its beginning aforesaid to the first day of November killed in Charles Town at least 160 persons.... Besides those have died in Charles Town 10 or 11 have died in the country, all of which got the distemper and were infected in Charles Town went home to their families and died; and what is notable not one of their families was infected by them.

Another letter survives which declares: "150 persons had died in Charles Town in a few days;" "the survivors fled into the country," and "the town was thinned to a very few people."

New arrivals died in droves including Chief Justice Bohum, the Rev. Samuel Marshall, the Receiver General Ely, and Edward Rawlins. Old colonists also were victimized. It is said that half of the members of the Assembly died. Dr. Ramsay, in 1809, stated: "this disease was generally called the plague by the inhabitants, but that from tradition and the circumstances, particularly the contemporaneous existence of the yellow fever in Philadelphia, there is reason to believe that the malady was the yellow fever, and if so, it was the first appearance of that disorder in Charles Town and took place in the nineteenth or twentieth year after it began to be built." He considers that the subsequent epidemic of 1703, renders it still more likely that this disease was the yellow fever.

In 1696, Dr. Isaac Porcher, a Huguenot refugee, came to Carolina and lived at the Santee settlement, later on Goose Creek and Wassamassaw. Porcher became famous in the annals of South Carolina.

Mention is made of the Huguenot John (Jean) Thomas in the Journal of the Grand Council for 1692 in connection with an early autopsy in South Carolina: "Petition of John Thomas, Chyrugen, against Mr. Jonathan Amory and Mr. George Dearsley admirs of Mr. Wilson Dunston Deced for five pounds for opening the said Dunston after the disease (It was ordered that Amory and Dearsley) pay the said John Thomas fifty shillings for inspecting the said Dunston's wound after his death and alsoe for this visitt and advice in his life time." One of Dr. Thomas' patients wrote of him as "the only Pson that deserves the Name of a Phisician in this place" (Charles Town), but later the same patient, evidently disgruntled by his lack of improvement, wrote that the best of doctors in the town had "originally been no more than Barbers."

Antoine Cordes of Berkeley County, like his compatriot Isaac Porcher, was said to have studied medicine at the University of Paris. Both signed documents describing themselves as surgeons. These two, and Joseph Marboeuf de la Bruce, an apothecary, settled eventually in Craven County. Daniel Brabant was another Huguenot surgeon.

There is record of William Sallmon listed as "Doctor of Physicke" who purchased a tract from Landgrave Smith in 1684-5. Brief mention is made of one James Williams, who lived on the Wadmalaw. Nathaniel Snow, a Goose Creek Chirurgeon, witnessed a will in 1700 in which he was left "charges for burying of him, his medicines truble dyett skill and time." Dr. Atkin Williamson and Dr. Thomas Tode are mentioned in wills dated 1697. One Richard Newton, "a privateer shipp's surgeon having given parole, escaped from Charlestown but was driven back" (1692). Mention is made of Thomas Napper, Chyurgeon of Johns Island in Carolina, in the records of 1685. Dr. Jacob Burdell was instrumental in evaluating an estate. Dr. Henry Bolt appeared in a document of 1699. The will of Robert Adams, "Physition," was probated in 1697. Only the name of one Dr. William Harris survives.

In the early days of South Carolina's history, John Lining, William Bull, James Linah, Alexander Garden, Peter Dott Fayssoux, David Ramsay and David Olyphant played important roles:

John Lining (1708-1760) was born in Scotland in 1708, and travelled to America in 1730. He joined the colony at Charleston, South Carolina, and built up a fine practice. However, his interests were wider than the mere practice of medicine and he excelled as a scientist as well as a physician. He conducted pioneer experiments in electricity and Benjamin Franklin kept in touch with him. He conducted painstaking meteorological observations during 1738, 1739, 1740 and 1742, and his findings were sent to the Royal Society of London. It is said that his observations were among the first ever published in this field. To calculate the respective loss or gain in body-weight under varying thermic and meteorological conditions, Lining conducted experiments of one year's duration carefully comparing the weight of all solids and fluids ingested, with the weight of the perspiration, urine and feces. In 1747 the General Assembly appointed Lining as one of the three physicians to inspect vessels entering the port and certify as to the health of the crew. Lining's experiments were published in the transactions of the Royal Society of London. In 1751 he published an excellent history of the yellow fever.

In 1739 he married Sarah Hill, of Hillsboro, North Carolina, but no children developed from this union. He passed away on September 21, 1760.

Lining was the first American physician to describe an epidemic of yellow fever. This epidemic was the one which ravaged Charleston in 1748. Lining's article was first published in Colen Chisholm's "An Essay on the Malignant Pestilential Fever introduced into the West Indian Islands from Boullam, on the Coast of Guinea, as it appeared in 1793 and 1794." Chisholm's book was published at Philadelphia in

1799, thirty-nine years after Lining's death. Thacher mentions that Lining's account was published in November 1748, but no other record of this publication has been found.

William Bull (1710-1791) was born in South Carolina in 1710. He was the son of William Bull, lieutenant-governor of South Carolina (1738-1743). After a preliminary education in his native country, he set sail for Europe to become a pupil of Boerhaave, the famous Leyden physician. Bull was the first American to graduate from Leyden, and the first from America to complete the medical course. He served as assistant judge from 1740 to 1749, and as brigadier-general of provincial troops from 1751 to 1759. In 1751 he was also a member of the Colonial Council of South Carolina and a commissioner to treat with the Six Nations. In 1763, he was speaker of the house of representatives and from 1764 to 1780 he was lieutenant-governor of South Carolina. He was governor of South Carolina from 1760-1761, 1764-1766, 1768-1771 and 1773-1775. Although first, last and always a royalist, he was one of the most popular and capable governors that South Carolina ever had, and he remained unmolested by the revolutionary authorities. In 1782 he departed from his beloved soil for London with the British troops and he spent the rest of his life there in voluntary exile.

He was married in 1746 to Hannah Beal, but they had no children. He died in London on his country's independence day, July 4, 1791.

In 1734, he published and defended his thesis "de Colica Pictorum" at the University of Leyden. Van Swieten, his fellow student, refers to him as "the learned Dr. Bull."

James Lynah (1725-1809) was born in Dublin, Ireland, in 1725, and it was in this city that he received both his preliminary and his medical education. As a young physician, he joined the English Navy as a surgeon. When his ship was wrecked in the West Indies, he was taken to Kingston, Jamaica. From Kingston he went to Charleston, South Carolina in 1765 or 1766. He settled in the wealthy and cultured Huguenot settlement of St. Stephen's Parish and rapidly built up a lucrative practice. When the War of Independence broke forth, he without hesitation, aligned himself firmly on the side of the colonists. He served at intervals with Marion's Corps, was surgeon in Col. Joseph Maybank's cavalry regiment, and was "chief surgeon of the Regiment of Light Dragoons" of Col. Daniel Harry's cavalry. It was in this last capacity that he was present at the siege of Savannah. Count Pulaski was wounded in this battle and Dr. Lynah, with the assistance of his son and two others, carried him to safety, and extracted the bullet on the field. This bullet and a note from one of

Count Pulaski's aids-de-camp is in the possession of the Historical Society of Georgia.

When the war was terminated he removed to Charleston, South Carolina, and again resumed practice. James Lynah was one of the founders of the Medical Society of South Carolina. He died of pulmonary tuberculosis in October, 1809, and at the time of his death he was surgeon-general of the state of South Carolina. He married in Ireland, and had one son, Edward Lynah, who likewise took up medicine as a career.

Alexander Garden, (1728-1791) was born in Scotland in 1728. He studied medicine with the celebrated Dr. John Gregory in Edinburgh and at Aberdeen University (1748). In 1752, he came to South Carolina and opened his office with one Dr. Rose in Prince William Parish. Botany always intrigued him and he wasted no time in pursuing his favorite study. Poor health soon influenced him to travel northward and he was offered but declined a professorship in the New York Medical College. Instead, he returned to Charleston and started the building up of a very successful practice. At this period, he wrote the following letter to John Bartram the botanist: "Think that I am here, confined to the sandy streets of Charleston where the ox, where the ass, and where men as stupid as either fill up the vacant space, while you range the green fields of Florida." Zoology also intrigued him, especially the study of fish and reptiles, and this pastime vied with his medical practice and botanical efforts in consuming his time. He communicated with the great botanists, Linnaeus and John Ellis, the latter naming the beautiful Cape Jasmine "Gardenia" in his honor (Gardenia jasminoides).

In 1773, Alexander Garden became a fellow of the Royal Society of London and later became vice president of this scientific body.

In 1775, Garden accompanied James Glen, governor of South Carolina, when he penetrated into the Indian country and formulated a treaty with the Cherokees. It was Garden who introduced the "Spigelia marilandica" or pink-root, as a vermifuge.

Alexander Garden's only son joined Leo's Legion against the British and the elder Garden was unrelenting in his wrath toward him. His son's little daughter, named Gardenia after her grandfather's flower, was never permitted to enter his abode.

The ravages of tuberculosis began to tell on Garden's health in 1783 and he vainly hoped that "revisiting the haunts of his youth and the pleasing recollections of juvenile scenes would have salutary influence in arresting the disease." His last days were spent with his wife and two daughters in Cecil Street, off the Strand, London, striving to make permanent record of all he could of his Carolina work. He died in London on April 15, 1791.

David Ramsay (1749-1815) was born in Lancaster County, Pennsylvania on April 2, 1749. In 1765, he completed his course at the College of New Jersey (Princeton) and then engaged in the study of medicine at the medical department of the College of Philadelphia (now the University of Pennsylvania). He graduated as Bachelor of Medicine in 1772 and on May 11, 1780, he became Doctor of Medicine. Dr. Rush wrote that Ramsay was "far superior to any person we ever graduated at our college." The mandamus conferring this degree declares: ... "the Degree of Doctor of Medicine on David Ramsay, now prisoner with the enemy."

At the start of the War of Independence, David Ramsay was engaged in the practice of medicine in Charleston, South Carolina. He was appointed surgeon in the South Carolina militia and was present during the seige of Savannah. He served as a member of the State Legislature from 1776 until the end of the war. He served also in the Privy Council. During the British occupation he was sent to St. Augustine. He was elected to the Continental Congress in 1782 and three years later was elected to Congress by the Charleston district. He was president pro tem of Congress for one year during John Hancock's absence. In 1785 he published a History of the Revolution in South Carolina. In 1790 he published a History of the American Revolution. In 1801 his prolific pen turned out a Life of Washington and in 1808 his History of South Carolina went to press. He died on May 8, 1815.

Dr. Ramsay, who was imprisoned by the British with the rest of the patriots at Charleston, stated that the prisoners were packed into prison ships in such numbers that they could not lie down. Food was foul and medical attention non-existent. Of the 1900 patriots taken at Charleston and the several hundred at Camden, 800 died within thirteen months. In June 1781, when a general exchange of prisoners took place, only 740 were alive.

David Olyphant was well known in Revolutionary days as a surgeon in the hospital department of the Continental Army. He also served as a member of the Assembly of North Carolina. After peace was obtained, he served as a judge of the district court.

Dr. Olyphant, when he was Medical Director of the Southern Department, wrote as follows to General William Moultrie, who was also a prisoner:

Charleston, November 14, 1780

Dear General:—I send by the bearer the few articles you request. Enclosed is the return of our sick for last month; the mortality is great. By much the greater number of deaths happened to those patients from on board the prison ships. Within these three days there is an appearance of jail fever, from the ship "Concord". She has been a prison ship throughout the summer. No less than nine of the sick sent from that ship died in the space of 24 hours; all of them bearing the appearance of putrid, malignant fever. The unfortunate sufferers are the militiamen sent from Camden.

I have no person to look up to but you, Sir; therefore I crave and entreat your assistance.

I am,   Dr. Olyphant.

General Moultrie then wrote to Lt. Col. Balfour, who was in command:

"I must begin by calling on your humanity, and request you, for God's sake, to permit Dr. Olyphant to attend the hospital whenever he shall judge it necessary;" and more in a similar strain. Balfour made a reasonable reply, and said that he had ordered the prisoners on shore.

Peter Dott Fayssoux (1745-1795) was born in southern France in 1745. His mother came to Charleston, South Carolina, in 1746 or 1747, and the boy was raised in this city and educated under the auspices of his stepfather, James Hunter. He graduated from Edinburgh in 1774 or 1775.

He was an avid patriot and on July 13, 1778 was rewarded by being appointed first lieutenant to the South Carolina Regiment. On the fateful day of May 12, 1780, he was taken prisoner at Charleston and taken to St. Augustine, Florida for incarceration. On May 15, 1781, he was appointed chief physician and surgeon of the southern department of the army hospital service, a position he held until the close of the war.

Dr. Olyphant entrusted the care of the Continental hospital at Charleston to Fayssoux, who was a chief physician and surgeon in the Southern Department. Fayssoux wrote to Dr. Ramsay as follows:

Sir: In compliance with your request, I now send you some of the remarkable facts relative to the treatment of American prisoners, the sick in particular, received during their captivity in Charleston. The Director General (Dr. Olyphant) having been confined, the immediate charge of the American hospitals devolved on me. I can therefore answer for the truth of the account, as every circumstance was within my knowledge....

After the defeat of General Gates our sufferings commenced. The unhappy men who belonged to the militia, and were taken prisoners on Gates defeat, experienced the first effects of the cruelty of the new system. These men were confined on board of prison ships, in no means proportionate to the size of the vessels; immediately after a march of 120 miles, in the sickly season of this unhealthy climate.

The vessels were in general infected with the small-pox, very few of the prisoners had gone through that disorder. A representation was made to the British commandant, and permission was obtained for one of our surgeons to inoculate them. This was the utmost extent of humanity—the wretched objects were still confined on board of the prison ships and fed on salt provisions, without the least medical aid, or any proper kind of nourishment. The effect that naturally followed was a small pox with a fever of the putrid type; and to such as survived the small-pox, a putrid dysentery—and from these causes, the deaths of at least 150 of the unhappy victims. Such was the appearance and such the termination of the cases brought to the general hospital after the irruption of the small-pox; before on irruption, not a single individual was suffered to be brought on shore. If anything can surpass the above relatio¬ in barbarity it is the following:

The Continental troops, by the articles of Capitulation, were to be detained prisoners in some place contiguous to Charleston; the barracks were pitched on as the proper place; this was agreed to by both parties.... Confined in large numbers on board these vessels, and fed on salt provisions, they naturally generated a putrid fever from the human miasma. This soon became highly contagious. The sick brought into the general hospital from the prison ships generally died in the course of two or three days, with all the British Commissary of Prisoners and the vast increase of the number of deaths, pointed out....

In consequence of this, Mr. Fisher, our Commissary, and Mr. Fraser, who acted as British Deputy Commissary, were ordered to inspect the vessels. This report confirmed the truth of what had been advanced.... My hopes were sanguine, but they were frustrated by a person from whom I did not expect it. Dr. John McNamara Hayes, physician to the British Army, who had been taken at the capture of Burgoyne, who had received the politest treatment from the Americans when a prisoner..., was ordered to report on the state of the prisoners. To my astonishment, he replied that the ships were not crowded, perfectly wholesome and no appearance of infections or disorders amongst the prisoners!

I then determined to make one more effort.... I had two dead bodies kept in the area of the hospital, and upon Dr. Haye's daily visit, I remarked to him the appearance of the subjects, whose bodies were highly tinged with a yellowish suffusion, petechiated over the breast and trunk, with considerable ecchymoses. I inquired if it was possible to doubt the nature of the disorder, and expressed surprise at the report he had made. The words of his reply were "that the confinement of the prisoners in prison ships was the great eyesore, and there was no help for it, that it must be done." The disorder in consequence continued until the cold weather. The number of deaths, joined with the number that were compelled by the treatment to enlist with the British, removed in a great measure, the cause.

The hospital at this time was reduced to the greatest distress imaginable, the sick without clothing, covering, or any necessary, but one pound of beef and bread, very little sugar, no wine, and rarely a small allowance of rum....

It was scarcely possible for men to support such an accumulated load of misery; but when least expected a relief was administered to us. A subscription for the support of the sick was filled by people (of the city) of every denomination with amazing rapidity. Several of the ladies of Charleston, laying aside the distraction of Whig and Tory, were instrumental and assiduous in procuring and preparing every necessity of clothing and proper nourishment for our poor, worn out, and desponding soldiers....

I am sir, with esteem, yours...
Peter Fayssoux.

In 1786 he was elected to the Legislature and served also as a member of the Privy Council.

It is thought that Dr. Fayssoux was the spark plug behind the activity to organize the Medical Society of South Carolina. In December, 1789, at his residence, Dr. David Ramsay and Dr. Alexander Barron met with him to seek means of starting this society. Fayssoux was elected the first president of this infant organization. On February 2, 1795, at the age of 50, he died suddenly of a massive cerebral hemorrhage.

Let us now, for a brief interval, under the guidance of Dr. J. I. Waring, visit with the inhabitants of Charleston, S.C., during the years 1750 to 1775.

This period was a happy and progressive one in South Carolina. Pioneer days were over and both George I and George II were favorably disposed toward the colony. During the administration of Governor Glen, Charleston expanded and became prosperous. The indigo, pelts and rice of South Carolina were carried from this port primarily to England and the West Indies in over 220 sailings per annum. The population of the state at the start of this period was 64,000: 25,000 whites and 39,000 colored folk. In 1775, the whites alone numbered 65,000. Charleston alone, in 1770 had 5000 white inhabitants and 6000 negroes.

Dr. W. H. Welch declares:

There was no more cultivated and attractive group of medical men in the third quarter of the eighteenth century in America than that in Charleston, S.C.... Of these Bull was a pupil of Boerhaáve, and Chalmers, Moultrie, Lining, and Garden were trained in Edinburgh. These men were abreast of the knowledge of the day: some were naturalists as well as physicians, their names being perpetuated in those of plants, fellows of the Royal Society, and correspondents of Linnaeus, Fothergill, and other European savants.

Josiah Quincy, on a visit from Massachusetts to Charleston, speaks in superlative tones of the city.

This town makes a most beautiful appearance as you come up to it, and in many respects a magnificent one. I can only say in general that in grandeur, splendour of buildings, decorations, equipages, numbers of commerce, shipping, and indeed in almost everything it far surpasses all I ever saw or ever expected to see in America.... The number of shipping far surpasses all I have seen in Boston. I was told that there were not so many as common at this season, though about three hundred and fifty sail off the town, which struck me very greatly; and the new exchange, which fronted the place of my landing, made a very handsome appearance.

The academic facilities were good and many natives had the advantage of European educations. The theatrical world flourished. But, notwithstanding the culture of the remarkable city, life still had its moments of suspense. The hurricane and flood of 1752 wrought extensive damage including floating the Sullivant's Island pesthouse up the Cooper River, nine people drowning en route. In a few years, the Indians began to act up until Governor Lyttleton made a treaty with the Cherokees in 1759—a treaty which was not long-lived. In 1753 and 1755, a mild form of yellow fever occurred. Smallpox prevailed in 1760 and 1763.

Dr. Waring has gleaned the following information from *The South Carolina Gazette* in the files of the Charleston Library Society:

There is a very flattering obituary notice of Doctor, and Judge, Thomas Dale, a highly esteemed medical man and statesman.

An advertisement is printed of a Doctor Thomas Chalmers, who "offers a charitable cure to any poor people.... who are unable to answer a physician's charge," and gives the advice that a good method of prevention of the diseases here is to boil the drinking water with a little snake-root in it. Advertisements of importations of drugs mention many of the popular secret medicines of the day: Radcliff's elixir, Daffey's elixir, James' powders, Lockyer's pills, Speedman's pills, Pectoral Balsam, all associated with prominent practitioners of varying standing at London and elsewhere.

The South Carolina Almanack for 1759 makes mention of Dr. Tennant's (of Virginia) cure for pleurisy, Sampson's cure for rattle-snake bite and Mr. Howard's cure for yaws. Howard's cure appeared in detail in 1759, and consisted of bleeding and purging, and drinking large quantities of sarsaparilla, china root, guiac, etc. Howard personally thanked the House of Assembly for the provision made for his discovery. A week later, a notice from the Commons appeared directing that the cure be published for the benefit of the public. The virtues of the treatment did not go unchallenged, for shortly thereafter came a letter in very broken English, stating that Howard's cure was absurd, and advising that people with any sign of cancer go to the writer, one Dr. August Gottfreed Jehne, for treatment.

The printer of the *Gazette* himself sold Pierce's Styptic, and published many articles on diseases and cures. He likewise sold several editions of "Every Man His Own Doctor," a family medical book, and conveniently inserted an occasional plug for some of his pet medicines. Advertisements of Dr. Keyser's antivenereal pills with money-back guarantee appeared several times. Maredant's anti-scorbutic crops, "The most effectual Medicine that has ever yet been offered to the Public" were to be had at the printers, along with the warning that one bottle might aggravate, but that six or seven bottles would surely cure whatever ailed the purchaser.

In 1765, Andrew Judah, physician, announced his intention of practicing at the corner of King and Queen Sts., and of setting aside daily hours for the free treatment of the poor.

In 1765 a bill was defeated which would have required that persons desiring to practice Physick or Surgery must first be examined and licensed.

The following news item appeared in 1773:

Lately arrived in town, a Gentleman who, though he was not born or bred in Scotland, nor has received any University Education, proposes to lay waste the whole Materia Medica, and raise a New System upon its Ruins. There are no disorders incident to Human Nature (except the Gravel, Stone, and Dropsy) for which he had not an infallible Remedy—the Materials taken from the Neighborhood of Georgetown. No Bleeding, Blistering, Purging, or Vomiting.

This enterprising gentleman, perhaps, was the William Vernon Turner who was attacked violently in a long letter appearing later on and signed by a noncommittal "Jeremiah," who doubted vigorously Turner's claim as to association with the Hunters and others, and his intimate knowledge of the herbs of America.

An advertisement of about 1770, is to the effect that T. Lowden, late midwife and apothecary to St. Peter's Hospital, Bristol, announced his intention to practice, and likewise to establish a sort of dispensary, in that he would give free service to the poor every afternoon from 12 to 3, in Church St., opposite John Izard.

Regarding sanitation legislation, in 1750 an act for keeping the streets of Charleston clean was passed. In 1758 a letter emphasizes the need of drains and a scavanger, and attributes sickness in the town to filth and odors. The Grand Jury several times deplores the state of the streets, the feeding of cattle in the same, the lack of lamps, wells, and pumps, the increase of Dram Shops, and indicts Thomas Lamboll for keeping a stagnant pond on White Point, whence numberless insects arose.

Most interesting is Nigger Caeser's cure for poison. According to *The South Carolina Gazette* of May 9, 1750, the Assembly published "Nigger Caeser's cure for poison." The General Assembly purchased Nigger Caeser's freedom from slavery and granted him 100 pounds a year for life as the price of his formula, which consisted of roots of plantain and wild hore-hound, 3 oz., boiled together in 2 quarts of water, until the entire volume had evaporated down to 1 quart, following which the preparation was strained. Of this, one-third was to be given every morning, fasting for three consecutive mornings. The postscript is added that if in three days of such therapy no benefit results, it is a sign that the patient has either not been poisoned or has been poisoned by a substance that Caeser's antidote will not counteract.

A rumor as to an outbreak of smallpox was denied in 1754. In 1758 an announcement was made that smallpox had left the province, and had affected only Mr. deSaussure's family of twenty-four persons, all of whom had contracted the disease and recovered. In 1759, it was reported that smallpox had devastated the Catawba Indians, and destroyed half the population. It was said that the diseased Indians hurled themselves into the river as soon as they found themselves ill, in a vain attempt to check the disease. Smallpox was next prevalent among the Chickesaws, and finally four cases were quarantined on Sullivant's Island.

An epidemic early in 1760 was traced to the premature release of a patient from the pest house, but the spread was slow, and the Governor informed the Faculty of Physic that inoculation was not to be done unless the disease spread from White Point.

The *Gazette* printed severel letters on inoculation including a reprint of one by Kilpatrick, who had achieved fame as an inoculator in earlier times in Carolina and in England. In February 1760, it was noted that 2000 persons had been inoculated, and that one gentleman had upwards of 600 patients. By April six thousand had had the disease by inoculation or naturally, with a mortality of over seven hundred. The Governor nervously declared a day of fasting and prayer to check the epidemic and to revitalize the war with the Cherokees.

By December the outbreak was over, but inoculation continued to be so popular that in 1763 there appeared a letter complaining that the physicians were perpetuating the disease by their activities in that line. To this the physicians responded by an agreement to discontinue inoculation for six months, provided no one inoculated in any way. The names signed to this agreement are no doubt the list of reputable practitioners of the time: John Cleiland, Robert Wilson, William Loocock, John Swint, Wm. Pillane, John Haly, John Moultrie, Lionel Chalmers, Alexander Garden, David Olyphant, John Murray, George Milligan and Samuel Carne. In July it is noted that inoculation "is entirely dropt," and that refugees are returning to town. Just previous to this step, a crop of small hospitals for the accommodation of those desiring inoculation had sprung up. Elizabeth Giradeau, Drs. Carne and Wilson, Dr. Swint in King St., Dr. William Loocock in Broad Street opposite Union Street and others managed these hospitals, and most of them offered insurance against the dangers of inoculation.

It is likely that these institutions were reopened in 1763, when smallpox reappeared among the Negroes, and inoculation became popular once more. An exodus of about 1500 persons from the infected city left only about the same number who had not had the disease, and these were favored with a mild epidemic.

In 1771 a brig from the West Indies brought passengers with smallpox and these were promptly shut up in the pest house and infected no one. In 1772 a ship from Belfast brought smallpox, but the people on board were quarantined on Sullivant's Island and again there was no outbreak. Apparently the pest house was not a very desirable residence, for it drew some criticism from the editor, who remarked that "if the Pest House on Sullivant's Island was made tight, warm, comfortable...and if some proper Person was appointed constantly to reside on the Island...who would say, we wanted common Humanity?" Excepting a single case in 1773, smallpox disappears from the press until after the Revolution.

Two other epidemic diseases appeared in the colonial period. In 1772 measles is spoken of as "very mortal" in the town. It was thought that a child developed the disease on board a vessel bound from New

York to Charleston, but recovered completely before reaching port. The master and the mate of the vessel, answering more or less truthfully the questions asked at Fort Johnson that there had been no contagion aboard when the vessel sailed and none when she landed, managed to slip the incubating cases through the ineffectual red tape and spread the disease over the city. These men came in for much public criticism, and replied rather lamely through the press, but escaped prosecution.

In 1759, the editor of the *Gazette* referred to "that violent and present reigning Disorder, called the Whooping Cough," and a number of articles concerning its treatment were published, although no indication of the actual extent of the epidemic is given in the papers.

A lengthy abstract of Cadogan's essay on Gout appears in the *Gazette* as do several articles on child care. One of the latter cautions parents and nurses with regard to the manner of holding their infants, and describes the changes in an infant produced by improper holding.

Advertisements of and for wet nurses, both white and black, are frequent. A quotation entitled a "Receipt for Asthma" gives the following advice:

> If ven'son pasty's set before ye
> Each bite you eat memento mori,
> and:
> Be not in haste, nor think to do
> Your business with a purge or two:
> Some if they are not well at once,
> Proclaim their doctor for a dunce:
> Restless from quack to quack they range,
> When 'tis themselves they ought to change.

In the archives of the *Gazette*, Dr. John Moultrie is mentioned as president of Saint Andrew's Club, Dr. Alexander Garden as president of the St. Cecilia Society (1767), Dr. David Olyphant as vice president of the same body, Dr. Peter Fayssoux (who lived in Meeting Street, the third house below the "White Meeting") as manager of the same Society and Dr. Alexander Barron as a member of the Library Society (and later, Curator of the Charleston Museum). Dr. Robert Wilson is mentioned as dissolving partnership with Dr. Carne, and resuming medical practice on the Bay. Notice of his trip to Rhode Island is also carried. Dr. David Olyphant is referred to as a member of the Council of Safety and Dr. Loocock as a surgeon. Reference is made to Dr. George Milligan as serving in the Cherokee War and as selling drugs. Dr. Carne and Dr. John Lining are also mentioned as selling drugs.

Beginning with 1760 it was the custom for the candidate for a medical degree to go through a preliminary apprenticeship before departing for Edinburgh or elsewhere for his regular course. In 1771 a list was compiled of "natives of the Province who have been graduated and had the highest degree in Medicine conferred upon them." This list includes Peter Fayssoux, Charles Drayton, Isaac Chanler, Thomas Caw, and Tucker Harris. The last are mentioned as still being abroad. A later note adds the names of Dr. William Roberts, and Capt. Angus as graduates, and those of Mr. Robert Peronneau, Mr. Baker, and Mr. Logan as students at Edinburgh.

We find Dr. Lewis Mottet in 1762 advertising that he will prepare "Belloste's" pills for fevers if he can get a number of subscribers. He then offers for sale a "compleat and neat pharmacy" and books and instruments. In 1764 we find this versatile gentleman entering a race-horse at the New Market Course. In 1769 he unsuccessfully proposed to the Commons House of Assembly that it establish an experimental pharmacy, botanical garden, and laboratory for the analysis of vegetables, animals and minerals, and that he be made director of the same, and utilize his own apparatus, provided a loan of six thousand pounds be made to him. J. Johnson mentions Mottet on several occasions. There is one instance in which a young man sick with intermittent fever failed to carry out the prescribed treatment. Mottet proceeded to give the patient a vigorous whipping, producing a rage and a perspiration which apparently cured the patient of his fever but not of his vexation. A lawsuit ensued with Mottet protesting his innocence on the grounds that he had only applied a stimulant and a rubefacient. In his broken English, Mottet protested that he should not be charged with "sault and batter," which were for the cook and not for the physicians to use. Only one shilling damages were exacted. Mottet's jealousy of Garden was well known. When he heard about the naming of the gardenia, he sarcastically remarked that he too had discovered a very beautiful native plant, and had named it "Lucia" after his cook "Lucy."

J. Johnson presents the following account of Dr. John Haley's duel:

In 1771, on the 16th of August, an altercation arose, at the genteel house of entertainment in St. Michael's alley, between Dr. John Haley and Delancy, an elegant, accomplished royalist, of New-York, a brother of Mrs. Ralph Izard. Delancy being irritated, probably from being foiled in argument, insulted Dr. Haley, by giving him the "lie." Haley immediately challenged Delancy to fight with pistols at that house, and proposed that they should go together to an upper room, alone, and without seconds. Delancy accepted the challenge, and the proposed arrangement. He took one of the pistols offered to him by Haley; they fought across a table, fired at the same moment, and Delancy was killed.

Dr. Haley was an Irishman by birth, and an eminent practitioner of medicine in Charleston. He actively and violently opposed the royalists and became a leader in the revolutionary cause. As Delancy was held in high esteem by the royalists, they were infuriated by his death. The whigs defended Dr. Haley stoutly and concealed him until the trial. During this period of concealment, deprived of his usual occupations of mind and body, he became depressed and this depression was increased by an accidental occurrence. In passing, after dark, across the enclosure where he was secluded in the country, a clothesline caught him by the throat, and stopped his course. He considered this to be an omen of his fate. His cause, however, became symbolic of the party dispute. Thomas Heyward, the Pinckneys and the Rutledges defended him in his trial. They demonstrated that Delancy was the aggressor; that he not only accepted the challenge, but the terms also; that he took Haley's proffered pistol voluntarily; that without coercion he followed him upstairs into a private room, as had been proposed, and that he fired with intent to kill Haley with his own pistol, for the two balls with which it was loaded were taken out of the wall just back of his adversary, one on each side of where he stood. Haley was acquitted, and his acquittal was considered a great triumph by the whigs and popular party.

In 1755, a meeting of the Faculty of Physic was held at Mr. Gordon's Tavern protesting against inadequate fees and unnecessary hardships imposed by patients. This meeting accomplished little and merely acted to give rise to a series of letters and verses either supporting or condemning the medical men.

The following continental medical officers were captured at Charleston and imprisoned from May 12, 1780, to the last of 1781:

David Olyphant, Director; Peter Fayssoux, Physician and Surgeon; Thomas T. Tucker, Physician and Surgeon; James Houston, Physician and Surgeon; Henry C. Flagg, Surgeon 1st Regiment; Joseph Blythe, Surgeon N.C. Regiment; Andrew Smith, Senior Surgeon; James Lockiman, Senior Surgeon; James West, Senior Surgeon; Wm. S. Stevens, Ephraim Brevard, John E. Payos, Jr., James Hunter, Joseph Hall Ramsay, John Caine, Apothecary; Evan Lewis, Deputy Apothecary; Richard Mercer, Purveyor; Bellamy Cranford, Clerk and Dan Smith, Clerk.

The following South Carolina physicians served in a professional capacity in the Continental Army:

—— Airs (died 1777), Nathaniel Alexander, Samuel Axon, Nathan Brownson, John Carne, Patrick Carnes, Lionel Chalmers, John Clieland, John Crane, Jonathan Dayton, ——de la Horne, Benjamin Elliott, Field Farrar, Peter Fayssoux, Samuel Ferguson, Henry C. Flagg, Alex Garden, Abraham Gillett, —— Gould, —— Haig, John Haley, Oliver Hare, Tucker Harris, James Houston, William Irvine, Robert Johnson, Charles Lockman, John Lockman, James Martin, Daniel McNeil, George Milligan, Lewis Mottet, John Moultrie, William Neufville, David Olyphant, Benjamin Perry, E. S. Poinsette, John Poyas, P. S. Prealean, James Prescott, Joseph Ramsay, Jesse H. Ramsey, Isaac Rasche, William Read, William Reed, Alexander Rogers, Hugh Rose, Robert Smith, Sylvester Springer, William S. Stephens, Frederick Sunn, Benjamin Tetard, Anthony Toomer, Thomas Tucker, Andrew Turnbull, —— Vaughan, Joseph Vickers, Samuel Vickers, Samuel Vidian, John Wallace, J. Weatherspoon, Robert Wharry, Samuel Wilson and John Witherspoon.

The Hospital Department of the Southern Army always operated as a separate entity. After General Lincoln allowed his army to be shut up in Charleston and captured intact on March 9, 1780, General Gates was given the Southern command. His headquarters were located at Hillsboro, North Carolina. Cornwallis maintained about 5000 men in South Carolina. Both British and American troops were in bad physical condition, suffering primarily from dysentery and malaria; yet few died.

Dr. Jackson, surgeon's mate of the 71st British Regiment, wrote:

The position occupied by the 71st at the Cheraws, on the River Pedee, was singularly unhealthful. The disease was of a charackter similar with that which prevailed at Ebenezer—of the remitting class, but with remissions scarcely perceptible. Two thirds of the regiment were sick; and of course there were persons in all stages of the disease. The enemy advanced in force and the 71st was ordered to retire, for it was the advance of the army (American). Some part of the sick were embarked in boats, in order to be conveyed to Georgetown by water.... There were, however, about 120 who were transferred in open waggons. They were exposed to dews by night, to a scorching sun by day, and to occasional showers of rain. At the end of the third day they arrived at Lynch's Creek, about half way between the Cheraws and Camden. The Regt. was ordered to half and take a position. The sick, during the march, had little opportunity of taking medicine; yet no one had died, some had gotten entirely well; and, in the others the form had changed to distinct intermittent.

In 1780, as the summer progressed, Cornwallis gained control of the major portion of the Carolinas. However, the amount of sickness during the summer months both in 1780 and 1781 prevented large scale campaigns. At one time, Cornwallis' entire staff was sick and a short time later, he himself became so ill that he was forced to transfer his command to Lord Rawdon. Cornwallis declared:

This climate (except in Charleston) is so bad within one hundred miles of the coast, from the end of June until the middle of October, that troops could not be stationed among them (sic) during the period, without a certainty of their being rendered useless for some time, for military service; if not entirely lost.

Without warning the 71st Regiment located at the Cheraws, was violently overwhelmed by a "fever and ague" (malaria?). Within nine days, two thirds of the personnel was incapacitated and unable to engage in active duty. To avoid this dread disease, Major M. C. Arthur transferred his regiment to the east branch of Lynch's Creek (July 24). He planned to send one hundred of the sick to Georgetown in boats (via the Peedee) but as soon as he departed from Cheraw, the British militia made their royalist officers prisoners, took the boats into custody and transported the sick group to North Carolina.

Gates decided to take advantage of the events by moving southward to Charlotte. The British troops were held concentrated at Camden, where Cornwallis joined them early in August. At that time he had about 1400 regulars, out of which 800 were too sick to fight.

De Kalb's group of 1400 patriots from the Maryland and Delaware Line had reached North Carolina from Morristown, New Jersey, in May. In July they joined Caswell's Brigade at Charlotte. On July 25, Gates arrived to command all the units. Early in August he moved his army south intending to attack Cornwallis at Camden. Cornwallis, getting wind of these events, left his 800 sick soldiers at Camden and marched north with 2000 men. The two armies met thirteen miles north of Camden on August 16th. Gates' army was annihilated. General Smallwood escaped to Salisbury with some Maryland remnants and some sick and wounded. Seven hundred patriots were killed or wounded and nearly one thousand were imprisoned. Most of the latter died horribly in foul military prisons. Gates gathered the remains of his ill-omened army at Hillsboro.

On August 18th, Tarleton overtook Sumpter at Catawba Fords, killed 100 of his men, captured 300 and released 250 British prisoners.

Following these catastrophic events, the British were the undenied masters of the Carolinas. But Cornwallis' great victory at Camden was not without its detriments.

On August 23, Cornwallis wrote:

I am at present so hurried with business, with everybody belonging to me sick.... Our sickness is great and truly alarming. The officers are particularly affected; Doctor Hayes (John M. Hayes) and almost all the hospital surgeons are laid up. Every person of my family (official) and every Publick officer of the Army is now incapable of doing duty.

Six days later, he stated:

The number of prisoners was a great Inconvenience to us, here in a small village, so crowded and sickly. I was afraid that the close places in which we were obliged to confine them might produce some pestilential fever during the excessive hot Weather. I therefore sent them off as early as possible, by divisions of 150 men each.

Incidentally Marion intercepted the first division on the road to Charleston and set the prisoners free.

Dr. Hugh Williamson, chief medical officer to the North Carolina State Militia, whose biography has been described in the Pennsylvania chapter, received permission to enter the British lines at Camden and help care for the wounded. On December 1, 1780 he wrote:

Sir:
                                                          Dec. 1. 1780.
After the Battle of the 16th of August (Camden) as soon as I overtook General Caswell, he gave me a Flag to return to the Enemies' Lines for the relief of our wounded; I was also instructed to ask for a return (muster roll) of the prisoners.

This return I have made to the present Commanding Officer, but, as the Publick may be desirous of knowing the fate of their Brave Men who bled on that Memorial Day, I shall take the liberty to mention such facts as seem the most interesting. I wish I could say that our loss after the Battle, either by wounds or sickness was inconsiderable; but we labored under many difficulties. It was our misfortune that the Countenance we showed immediately after the Battle was not calculated to command the respect which is due to an army of the United States. The greatly overrated did not increase their Humanity. For eight or ten days after the Battle our people suffered under great neglect. After the Bitterest Complaints and most urgent importunity our supplies became more liberal.

Williamson wrote the following letter to Dr. John M. Hayes, Physician General and Inspector General of Hospitals of the British Army in the Carolinas:

Sir:

The articles you was so kind as to order have not been received. Our hospital patients are near 250, many of them dangerously wounded. They are lodged in six small wards, without straw or covering. Two of them have not any cloathing besides a shirt and pair of trowsers. In the six wards they have only 4 small Kettles, and no Canteen, Dish or Cup, or other Utensil. We have hardly any medicines and not an ounce of Lint, Tow, or ounce of meal to be used for Poultices. In a word nothing is left for us but the painful Circumstances of viewing wretches who must soon perish if not soon relieved.

Williamson also wrote as follows:

We were also weak in Medical Help. Our Militia Surgeons disappeared after the Battle and the Commander in Chief (Lord Cornwallis) had not yet turned his attention to the wounded Prisoners. It happened that one of the Continental Surgeons fell into the hands of the Enemy. It may be supposed that with his assistance, tho' he was indefatigable, I found it impossible to give the desired help to 240 men who Laboured under at least 700 wounds. After three weeks we were happily reinforced by Dr. Johnson (Dr. Robert Johnston) a senior surgeon of great Skill and Humanity in the Continental Service.

Included is a list of the wounded Militia, also the only return I could get of the Prisoners in general. It is not satisfactory, for the Commissary of Prisoners, one Boothe Boote, whose Character did not appear to be diversified by a single Virtue, would never do anything that would prove acceptable to us.

The number of wounded brought into Cambden from the actions of the 16th and 18th of August was 240. Of this number 162 were Continental troops, 12 were South Carolina Militia, 3 were of Virginia militia, and 63 were of the militia of this State, of whom the list is enclosed (North Carolina).

On the 7th of September, 18 of our militia having recovered from their wounds, were sent to Charles Town; 9 of the militia, having recovered, escaped at different times; 10 of them remained on the 13th of October, chiefly well. We had the misfortune to lose 5 Privates who died of their wounds; 9 by the Small Pox, 1 by a Putrid fever, and 4 by the Flux. Two officers died of their wounds and 2 by the Small Pox.

It will be observed that we paid a heavy tribute to the Small Pox. However, we have the comfort to recollect that, having formed the most alarming apprehensions from that disease, no means in our power were omitted by which we might avoid or palliate its dangerous effects. The British Camp generally contains the Seeds of Small Pox. It has been in Cambden for some time. We were not suffered even to inoculate those men who would admit of that operation with safety. Lord Cornwallis showed much displeasure at the Inoculation of an Officer who had a slight wound, and was quartered apart in a private Home. Desirous that some of our Surgeons might be permitted to inoculate the prisoners who were sent to Charles Town, I made an application to his Lordship on that Subject, and received the inclosed answer, from which nothing could be expected. Immediately after that I was called to see two of the Inhabitants of South Carolina who were sick in Prison. They had the Small Pox in a small room with 17 others, State Prisoners, who were yet to take it. I wrote Lord Cornwallis on so pursuing a Tryal of Humanity, Stated the Cases fully, and assured his Lordship that Confinement in such a Room, putrescent as the Atmosphere there was, must be followed by death, equally certain as immediate execution. The two sick men were enlarged (sic), but the others were detained; they were not inoculated; most of them died. About the 22nd of September we obtained Permission to inoculate such of our men as had hitherto escaped. At that time the State Prisoners in Jail, many of them very sick, were committed to my care. Such as were then in health, and were inoculated, suffered very little by the Small Pox. During the whole of our attendance on the wounded and Sick we had occasion to remark that most of the Prisoners were visited by the Flux, which prevailed in Cambden; we did not lose a single man by that disease, unless those who had broken thighs or Legs.

That small Boys suffered most by Flux; that the sufferings of our Men was greatly increased by the want of Sugar, Tea, Coffee, Vinegar, and such other palatable antiseptic Nourishment as is best suited to the Sick. The cry for these Articles was constant, while our supplies were so scanty as hardly to deserve the name, nor was anything of that Kind to be purchased for Money, unless in very trifling Quantities. From a transient view of our misfortunes it is clear that we should save many Lives by any kind of military Establishment which would admit of the troops being inoculated before they took the Field.

It is also clear that a moderate supply of Sugar, Rice, Tea, Coffee or such other wholesome Nourishment for the sick and invalids of our militia as would tend Greatly to reconcile them to the hardships of a Campaign & would save the lives of many. Your most obedient and very humble Servt.

Williamson.

Williamson unsuccessfully attempted to have the American prisoners inoculated. He wrote to Major England:

Cambden 30 August 1780.
I presume that Lord Cornwallis is informed that of the North Carolina Prisoners lately sent to Charles Town, who I apprehended are from 3 to

400, hardly a single man has had small Pox. There is, I presume, the utmost danger of those men taking the Disease in the Natural way, unless well inoculated. Be so kind as to inform me whether Lord Cornwallis is willing these Troops should be inoculated, and by whom he wishes it should be done. You will excuse the mention I have made of the subject, but having the chief Medical Care of the Troops of that State, I conceive it to be my duty.

Major Despond replied:

Cambden Sept. 1, 1780.

Sir

I have had Lord Cornwallis's orders to acquaint you that, with respect to the American prisoners sent to Charles Town being inoculated, his Lordship will give proper orders.

In the early days of North Carolina's history, Dr. Armand John DeRosset, Dr. John Brickell, Dr. Martin Kalberlahn, Dr. Nathaniel Alexander and Dr. Ephraim Brevard all deserve mention.

The famous DeRosset family afforded North Carolina six physicians, all of whom spent most of their lives in Wilmington and who practiced without a break, for one hundred and forty-six years. The progenitor of this family was Armand John DeRosset (1695-1760), who received an M.D. degree from the University of Basel. A Huguenot, he sojourned from Narbonne, France, to New Liverpool (now Wilmington), North Carolina. His wife and three children accompanied him on his voyage.

John Brickell (1710?-1745) was born in Ireland in 1710. It is possible that he came to North Carolina with Governor George Burrington in 1724. While in North Carolina he resided at Edenton. In 1730, he was one of the ten, who, with two Indian guides, explored the interior of the province for two months. The records show that Brickell was still at Edenton in 1731. Soon after this he went back to Ireland for good.

In Dublin, in 1737, John Brickell published his famous "The Natural History of North Carolina." This volume includes 408 pages, including various copper plates "whereon are curiously engraved several strange Beasts, Birds, Fishes, Snakes, Insects, Trees and Plants." It included considerable material from John Lawson's "History of Carolina" (1714). Brickell included considerable first hand information in his volume. Concerning the rattlesnakes, he writes: "They are a majestick sort of creature and will seldom or never bite (except they are provoked) which they cannot do until they gather themselves into a Quoit or Circle"..... "They shake and shiver with wonderful nimbleness."

In 1745, Brickell published in Dublin, a "Catalogue of American Trees and Plants which will Bear the Climate of England."

One of North Carolina's pioneer physicians was Martin Kalberlahn (?-1759). Kalberlahn was born in Drontheim, Norway, and received his preliminary education at a Lutheran school. He then apprenticed himself to an older physician, from whom he learned the medical and surgical arts. When his training was completed, he travelled about for a year, visiting leading hospitals and physicians. He paid for his travelling expenses by performing surgical procedures and practicing medicine in the cities and villages along the path of journey. While in Copenhagen, he became friendly with several Moravians who induced him to join their Church. He was accepted into the Unity of Brethren in Herrnhaag. Forsaking the good living and relatively easy life of a Copenhagen physician, Kalberlahn set out for North Carolina. En route, he visited Zeist (Holland), London and New York. Prior to departing for Wachovia, North Carolina, he spent a short time at Christian's Spring, in Pennsylvania.

These facts, as well as the following directly quoted extracts, are taken from Adelaide L. Fries' fine work entitled "The Road to Salem." In this volume, Dr. Fries has rendered a smooth and excellent translation of the manuscript containing the autobiography of Anna Catharina, one of the early leaders of the Moravian Church in America. The narrative is told in the first person by Anna Catharina:

On June 21st (1758), I left our congregation of Heidelberg, accompanied by Brother Casper Schmidt, who was on his way to Bethlehem (Pennsylvania), from his home in Manakasy, Maryland....

Perhaps I too was preoccupied and less careful than I should have been, for suddenly my horse shied and I was thrown heavily to the ground. My escort hastily dismounted and came to my assistance, but when I tried to rise I found that my right leg was badly cut and bruised, and my knee appeared to have been strained. There was a farmhouse in sight, and Brother Schmidt insisted on going there for help, but I felt ashamed of my accident and remembered my father's advice: "If you are thrown, mount again at once, never let a horse think he has the best of you," and I insisted that Brother Schmidt help me to the saddle and take me on to Bethlehem. I was probably dazed from the fall and my leg somewhat numb from the injury, or I could not have stood the pain of the next hours. As we journeyed on for more than twenty miles, our discomfort was increased by the coming of a storm with heavy rain. This convinced me of the folly of trying to reach Bethlehem, and I agreed to stop at the inn on the south side of the Lehigh. A chair was brought, and I was carried to a room and helped to bed, where I spent a night that

I will never forget. Meanwhile Brother Schmidt sent an urgent message to Bethlehem, asking that the doctor be sent as soon as possible.

Next morning the innkeeper's wife came to my room and told me that the doctor had arrived from Bethlehem, and I asked her to bring him in. Imagine my surprise when instead of Brother Otto, the Bethlehem doctor, I saw a man whom I had never met, but whom I recognized as the blond young doctor I had seen in the group about to start for Wachovia five years before. He explained that Brother Otto was away from home, and that he had been sent to attend to my injury and take me to Bethlehem in the one-horse chaise which Brother Joseph had provided.

My leg had become very painful, but even so there was a certain pleasure in the short ride, conscious as I was of that intangible something which had given my doctor such a far-reaching reputation in North Carolina. Little was said, but he did explain that he had left Bethabara after Easter, had reached Bethlehem during my absence, and expected to remain in Pennsylvania for some months before returning to Wachovia.

When we reached the Sisters House several of the Sisters received me with expressions of sympathy. To my surprise my doctor picked me up as though I were a child and carried me to the sickroom, where the Sisters put me to bed, and he did all that he could to make me more comfortable. Brother Otto was away for that length of time, and I found myself looking forward to his brief visits and to the casual conversations between the doctor and myself, and the Sisters who were nursing me.

When Brother Otto returned he took charge of my case, and as I improved slowly the days began to seem long and tiresome, and I wanted to be up and about again. Not even to myself would I admit how much I missed the visits of the younger doctor.

When I had been sitting up a little for a day or two, Sister Rosel came to see me. At once I sensed her purpose, and my heart beat faster as I wondered whose name I would hear.

"Sister Catharina, I bring you a proposal of marriage from Brother Martin Kalberlahn," she said gravely, and I stifled my emotion and asked steadily: "It has the approval of the Elders and of the Lord?" to which she answered, "Yes, certainly." At that time I had never been present when a marriage proposal was referred to the Lord through the *lot*, but we all knew that such a matter was first considered by the Elders, and if they approved, affirmative and negative *lots* were prepared and the Lord was asked to signify whether it would have His approval if they submitted the question to the Sister whose name was proposed. If the *lot* was negative the matter was dropped; if affirmative the question was taken to the Sister and she was at liberty to accept or reject, for the *lot* decision governed the action of the Elders, not of the men and women who were to wed. We believed that the approval of the Lord, given through the *lot*, guaranteed the wisdom of any move that was being discussed; so with the comforting assurance that I was following Divine leading (as well as my own inclination), I gave my answer as "Yes."

There was a short delay until I was able to walk a little, and then my wedding day arrived.

On that 29th day of July, in the year 1758, I had thought only for the solemn questions, the grave answers, the new life and responsibilities to which we were pledging ourselves.

"Dear Little One," said Martin, "I did not dream that love could come like this to a Moravian Brother, but when I saw you lying all forlorn in that inn room my whole heart went out to you, and I wanted to take you in my arms and carry you home."

"Was that why you carried me into the Sisters House?" I asked.

"Really it was," he answered with a smile, "though if the question had been raised then I would probably have explained that I hoped to make moving less painful for you than it had been when we took you out of the inn."

"The Sisters wondered," I told him rather shyly.

"And you?"

"Oh, I assured them it was just because you were such a good doctor, that it was merely professional sympathy."

"No, Dear Little One," he said, looking down at me with a smile, "I have felt professional sympathy for many persons, but this was something different."

With my face turned away and my cheeks burning I murmured: "It was new to me too," an inadequate answer, but one with which he seemed quite content.

One day I ventured the question: "Why did you come to Bethlehem?" more because I wanted to hear his answer than because I needed the information.

"Wife hunting," he replied rather grimly, as if half ashamed of the deliberate action. "I needed a wife to cook my meals, and wash my clothes, and look after my house, and leave me free to look after my patients."

"And how did you expect to find that wife?"

"I expected to say to the Elders: 'Please select a suitable wife for me,' and I expected calmly to accept whatever they offered, trusting that their judgment would be good!"

"You certainly did not expect to marry the head tailoress of the Sisters House!"

"Dear Little One, I could not have expected you, because I did not know."

And I, who had been the eldest of the family, who had been given important office before I was twenty-one, and ever since had been held responsible for the well-being of others, I thrilled each time he used his affectionate diminutive, reserved for my ears alone. To others we were a sedate married couple, quite settled and mature, but in our hearts we knew that we were young and very much in love.

The remainder of the year passed quietly at Bethlehem.

In the latter part of April, 1759, we set out for North Carolina, accompanied by the other five Brethren from Bethabara and their wives. It was not a long journey, only one month, for our wagon was drawn by six horses and we had others for riding; so we made good time.

The shoe-shop in Wachovia was near the path leading to God's Acre (cemetery), and Martin stopped there and introduced me to Brother Pfeil. "Had any more rat-hunts?" asked Martin, smiling.

Brother Pfeil's eyes twinkled, and as he took his pipe from his mouth he said, "You enjoyed the last one, didn't you?" Then turning to me he asked, "Did Brother Kalberlahn tell you about it?" I shook my head and he told me that the rats had swarmed in, no one knew from where, and had taken possession of his shoe-shop, nibbling the wax and gnawing the leather and driving him nearly distracted. "The doctor will not admit it, but I suspect he invented the idea of the rat-hunt. He certainly planned it that the men and boys were armed with stout sticks. Then as the carpenters took down the logs of the shop, and the rats ran out, everybody got after them, and had a fine time, chasing and killing them."

"The boys buried thirty of them in an unhallowed grave while the men were laying up the logs again," chuckled Martin; and Brother Pfeil said that since then there had been much less trouble, "though I suppose one never gets entirely rid of rats, even on the frontier," he said.

On July 19th, during dinner, announcement was made of the departure of Sister Rogers, after an illness of eight days. This was the beginning of a great time of sorrow for Bethabara—and for me. A strange kind of fever had broken out amongst us, and most of those living in Bethabara had it in a more or less serious form. My doctor was much worried, for the usual treatment for fever gave little relief, and it nearly broke his heart that his friends should look to him in vain.

"Oh Martin, don't worry so," I begged. "You are doing your best, and no one could do more."

"Dear Little One," he answered, "my best is not enough; they suffer and I cannot give them ease; they pass away and I can do nothing to hold them back."

"And if that be the Lord's will, Martin, can you not submit?"

"Dear Little One, you are wiser than I, come, let us pray to the Saviour for His help and comfort," but beginning with those petitions he soon was uttering such fervent appeals for help for himself in his great task, such an agonizing prayer that where he failed the Lord would aid, that I burst into tears.

"There, there, Dear Little One," and turning he took me in his arms. "Continue to stand by me and we will trust and not be afraid." And of this faith we were to have greater need than we knew, and he stood the test much better than I.

Of those who left us Sister Rogers was the first, but not the last. I helped to nurse her and she had asked me to take her baby girl. So when the end came her little Salome was placed in my care, where she remained until she was six years old and could be sent to the school for little girls in Bethlehem.

Next came Catharine Seidel, and it seemed almost impossible that, only a few short weeks before, she had traveled south with us, filled with high hopes of service in her new home. Her husband was submissive, but missed her sadly, and it was only a few days later that he returned from a visit to Bethania, oppressed by the feeling of utter weariness which we were learning to recognize as the first symptom of the disease. He did not seem very ill at first, but when hope was expressed for his recovery he shook his head, saying, "No; life was lonely without my Catharine and I asked my Lord to take me to Himself, and He has heard and answered." And so it was, and his remains were borne up the steep path to the little God's Acre on the hill.

And then my Martin! Perhaps because of his unremitting efforts for others he was seriously ill from the first. He saw what was coming and sent for Brother Jacob Lash, made his will, and advised that Brother Jacob Bonn be taken again as community doctor. Brother Bonn had served during Martin's absence, returning to Pennsylvania shortly before we came; then he had conducted Brother Spangenberg hither and so had been able to help Martin during the epidemic and could continue the work without interruption.

For me the following days were full of anguish, and yet they were precious days. His burden of responsibility lifted, Martin's every thought was for me, and he bade me think beyond the present and try to realize what heaven would mean when we were reunited there.

"Our time together has been short, Dear Little One, but it has been a happy time. Let us forget that we must separate, and think only of the eternity which lies ahead, where there shall be no more pain nor any crying, for the Lord Almighty will have wiped away all tears and will have conquered all disease and death itself."

"Oh Martin, I love you so; I cannot give you up!"

"Not even when it means that I need suffer no longer?" for his pain was intense, as it always was in the earlier stages of the fever.

"Oh my dearest, yes, if it is best for you."

"Then stay by me and hold my hand, hold it tight." And when fever mounted, when the terrible red splotches broke out on his body, when delirium came, he still felt my presence, and was quieted as I held his hand in mine, spoke gently to him, or sang some of our best loved hymns. Then he became unconscious of pain or weariness; but we were still hand in hand when the call came that took him to the eternal home where none shall ever say, "I am sick."

Others followed him up that steep hill and were laid to rest beside him, but I was stunned and rebellious and nothing seemed to matter much. Why was so beloved and able and much needed a man taken? Why must Bethabara lose pastor and doctor and so many others? Why must there be such pain and suffering in the world? Why was I brought this long distance only to be left desolate? Why could I not have stayed in the quiet Sisters House in Bethlehem? Why was I left untouched when so many others were ill? Why? Why? Why?

The aforementioned quotations from Dr. Fries' book tell more about the life and times of this pioneer North Carolina physician than any abbreviation could possibly do. The fatal epidemic may well have been typhus fever.

Dr. Fries, in a personal communication, mentions that Dr. Jacob Bonn substituted for Dr. Kalberlahn while the latter went north in 1758 and 1759. He took the position of community doctor in Bethabara after Dr. Kalberlahn's death. After a later absence he returned to Wachovia as doctor in Salem and was here during the Revolutionary War.

Nathaniel Alexander (1756-1808) was born in Mecklenburg County, North Carolina on March 5, 1756. He graduated from Princeton University in 1776, following which he studied medicine. Alexander was surgeon in the North Carolina Continental Line from 1778 until 1782. When peace was secured, he hung up his uniform and engaged in actual medical practice, first at the High Hills of the Santee, South Carolina, and then in Charlotte, North Carolina. He was elected to the North Carolina House of Commons in 1797 and to the State Senate from 1801-1802. He was elected to the United States Congress from 1805 until 1807.

Dr. Nathaniel Alexander was a staunch exponent of popular education. He served as president of the board of trustees of the University of North Carolina from 1805 to 1807. As governor, he did his utmost to demonstrate to the legislature the need for establishing a system of public education. Besides being a great statesman, Alexander found time to become a "physician of eminence in Mecklenburg."

He died at Salisbury, North Carolina on March 8, 1808.

Dr. Ephraim Brevard, after graduating from Princeton College, undertook the study of medicine. He opened his office in Charlotte, North Carolina. Brevard was instrumental in promulgating the Mecklenburg Resolution on May 20, 1775, at a public town-meeting in Charlotte. This resolution antedated the Declaration of Independence, and postulated many of its principles. During the War of Independence, Brevard served as surgeon in the Continental Army. The English took him in custody when they captured Charleston. Brevard died shortly after his release.

The following nine pre-Revolutionary laws in the Carolinas are listed by Toner:

(1) 1706: An act relating unto the office and duty of a coroner, and settling and ascertaining the fees of same.

(2) 1715: An act appointing coroners.

(3) 1721: An act for the more effectual preventing the spreading of contagious distempers.

(4) 1752: An act for the better preventing the spreading of contagious and malignant distempers in this Province.

(5) 1754: An act appropriating for a pest-house and other purposes.

(6) 1759: An act to prevent malignant and infectious distempers being spread by shipping imported distempered persons into this Province, and repealing the former acts heretofore made for that purpose.

(7) 1760: An act for preventing as much as may be the spreading of smallpox in Charleston, and the further spreading of that distemper in this Province.

(8) 1764: An act for preventing as much as may be the spreading of the smallpox.

(9) 1774: An act for reviving and amending the act of 1759; an act to oblige vessels having contagious distempers on board to perform their quarantine.

The following medical men from North Carolina served in the War of Independence:

Joseph M. Alexander, John Baker, Joseph Blyth, Hugh Boyd, Ephraim Brevard, Robert Brownfield, Thomas Bull, Thomas Burke, Tasquar Campbell, Samuel Cooley, John Davis, James Fergus, James Geekie, James Green, Isaac Guion, Robert Hall, Charles Harriss, Oliver Hart, William Hart, J. Ingram, Joseph Kennedy, William Lewis, Jonathan Loomis, David Love, William McLean, James Martin, John R. Martin, William McClure, John McElyea, William McLean, Bennett Morgan, William Parton, William Pasteur, Alex

A. Peters, William Porter, Robert Williams, Hugh Williamson and Robert Wilson.

The following newspaper extracts dating from 1773 to 1788, are of interest with reference to the practice of medicine in North Carolina.

The Cape Fear Mercury, dated December 29, 1773, contains the following:

Dr. Ward wishes to thank the public for the kind reception given to his purging cake. Ward's Anodyne Pearls 16 in a paper for only 1s and that to be returned to any buyer who shall say they have not answered the character here given.... To preclude the attempts of imposture, by any imitation, Doctor Ward will sign his name with red ink, on every paper of printed directions that will be given along with them.

The North Carolina Gazette for February 24, 1775 includes the following advertisement:

To be sold.... Stoughton's excellent London Bitters, being a grand Preventative against the Ague and Fever, and giving Strength and Digestion to the Stomach: Also some Cases of genuine Cordials.

This same paper, on February 16, 1786 advertised:

Any person that will dispose of their Front Teeth (slaves excepted) may receive Two Guineas for each, by calling on Doctor Laymeur. For further particulars enquire of the Printer.

The State Gazette of North Carolina contained the following brief item on March 2, 1788:

For sale, ... Dr. Stephany's incomparable gold tincture, also his infallible ague pills (sold by no other person in this state).

Chapter Twelve

PENNSYLVANIA

ANY EVALUATION OF Pennsylvania's colonial history must empha-
size the fact that in this largest and most successful of proprietary
provinces, Quaker tolerance and religious freedom maintained a
large measure of harmony among the heterogeneous conglomeration
of Dutch, Swedish, English, Welsh, Irish, Scotch-Irish and German
settlers representing such religious sects as Presbyterians, Catholics,
Quakers, Episcopalians, Lutherans, Moravians, Mennonites, Dunkers
and Schwenkfelders.

The earliest European settlements were trading posts, established
by the Dutch and the Swedes in the lower Delaware valley during the
period from 1623 to 1681.

As early as 1650, George Fox and other Quakers began to urge
the establishment of a colony in America as a haven for Friends who
were being persecuted under the "Clarendon Code." By 1666, William Penn added his influence to the fight.

After Penn's charters of 1680-1682 and the establishment and
growth of Pennsylvania, boundary disputes with Maryland, Virginia
and New York arose. All were settled more or less amicably.

When Penn passed away, his widow became proprietary and
named Sir William Keith as deputy. Keith practically abolished the
council but courted the favor of the assembly. Mrs. Penn discharged
him after he had an open run-in with James Logan, secretary of the
province. Keith was succeeded by Patrick Gordon and George
Thomas who served under John, Thomas and Richard Penn.

The assembly became antagonistic to George Thomas and refused
to grant him salary or supplies because of his efforts to induce the
colony to actively support the Spanish War. During the Seven Years'
War, the assembly again resisted Governor Morris' demands for financial support for military purposes.

None-the-less the assembly did assist General Braddock's expedition to organize and outfit. After Braddock's defeat, all western Pennsylvania was at the mercy of hostile Indian attacks. The proprietors then subscribed £5000 to protect the colony, following which the assembly withdrew for a short time its pressure to tax proprietary estates. In 1766 Benjamin Franklin achieved the victory of forcing the proprietors to pay a tax to the colony. By this time, the growing number of Scotch-Irish immigrants plus the fact that the proprietors had gone back to the Anglican fold, made them very unpopular.

Franklin in 1755 organized a voluntary militia which within a year began to check the Indians. However, until the suppression of Pontiac's conspiracy, frontier raids by the Indians continued.

In December 1763, six Christian Conestogas were massacred by the "Paxton boys" from Paxton (near present Harrisburg). Other Indians who had escaped and were kept in Lancaster for safety, were murdered also by this group, which marched upon Philadelphia in 1764. Quakers and Germans organized to protect Philadelphia and civil war was averted only by Franklin's intervention. The Paxton Affair demarcates the close of the period of Quaker supremacy and the start of the era of Scotch-Irish power in Pennsylvania, for the colonists were fed up with the lack of protection afforded by the Quakers.

Pennsylvania's central position made its attitude with respect to England very important. As the War of Independence approached, the British party appeared powerful because of the number of Anglican colonists and the neutrality of many Quakers, Mennonites and Dunkers. Most all colonists were satisfied with the liberality of rule in Pennsylvania, but the Whig party gathered momentum under Dickinson, Mifflin and Reed and gained ascendency in Pennsylvania. Both men and money were plentifully supplied by Pennsylvania toward the colonial cause.

The two Continental Congresses (1774 and 1775-1781) met in Philadelphia except during the British occupation. The Declaration of Independence was adopted by the second Congress, although the Pennsylvania delegation, Franklin excepted, thought this document premature at the time. However, no state supported the Declaration better than did Pennsylvania.

During the War of Independence, major engagements were fought at Brandywine, Paoli, Fort Mifflin and Germantown in 1777. Washington's army spent the winter of 1777-1778 at Valley Forge. Philadelphia was occupied by the enemy from September 26, 1777 to June 18, 1778.

In 1776, the Penns lost their governmental rights and in 1779 the

Penn territorial interests were vested in the commonwealth in return for a grant of £120,000 and the guarantee of title to private estates held in severalty.

The Federal Government was established in Philadelphia and remained there until its removal to Washington in 1800, except for a short time in 1789-1790.

The article by Francis R. Packard entitled "The Practice of Medicine in Philadelphia in the Eighteenth Century" proved most valuable in the preparation of this chapter. ·

The history of Pennsylvania in its early days seems to be quite divorced from the history of medicine. Gabriel Thomas wrote concerning Pennsylvania in 1697 as follows: "Of lawyers and doctors I shall say nothing, because the country is very peaceable and healthy."

Notwithstanding, the staff of Æsculapius did reach into Pennsylvania. When William Penn came to Philadelphia in 1682, Thomas Lloyd, Thomas Wynne (1631-1692) and Griffith Owen accompanied him. Lloyd and Wynne do not appear to have practiced medicine in the new country, Lloyd becoming Deputy Governor of the Province and Wynne Speaker of the first Provincial Assembly.

It is interesting to note that previous to 1700, all the Philadelphia physicians were natives of Wales, notwithstanding the fact that Welsh immigrants formed only a fraction of Philadelphia's population. Thomas Wynne left Deal, England, on August 30, 1682, aboard the *Welcome*. He arrived in America on October 27, 1682. Wynne brought with him the experience of thirty years active practice and was unquestionably a well trained physician. As fate would have it, smallpox broke out on the *Welcome* during transit to the New World. With only a few ship's remedies and hopelessly inadequate medical facilities to treat the one hundred passengers, Wynne served as both physician and nurse during the fifty-three day voyage and helped conquer the epidemic, although thirty died of smallpox en route.

Wynne was born in Flintshire, North Wales, in 1631, the fifth son of Sir John Wynne, of Gwydryr, and Sidney, daughter of Sir William Gerard, Chancellor of Ireland. In 1650 he went to London and entered the Royal College of Surgeons. Later he was duly licensed as a surgeon and physician. In 1656, he was married to Mary Bultall. Subsequent to his landing with Penn in Philadelphia, Wynne became a member and president of the first Provincial Assembly of Philadelphia and an eminent Friend. Penn's regard of Wynne is illustrated by the fact that present Chestnut Street, one of the major highways of the new city, was named Wynne Street.

Mention should be made of the fact that Wynne's daughter, Mary, married Edward Jones, and their daughter, Martha Wynne Jones, became the wife of John Cadwalader, the father of Thomas Cadwalader. Thus Wynne was the great-grandfather of Thomas Cadwalader. Wynne bought five thousand acres of land in Sussex County, Delaware, and lived there for a time. He, however, came back to his beloved Philadelphia, where he passed away on January 16, 1692.

Dr. Griffith Owen engaged in medical practice until he died at the age of seventy. His patients and friends dearly loved and respected him and William Penn referred to him as "tender Griffith Owen who both sees and feels." Thomas Story states that Owen performed the first amputation in Pennsylvania: In 1699 a salute was fired in William Penn's honor at Chester, and a young man present had his arm extensively traumatized. While Owen was operating, some spirits in a basin ignited and set his clothes aflame. ". . . and there being a great crowd of spectators, some of them were in the way and in danger of being scalded, as the surgeon was, upon the hands and face, but running into the street, the fire was quenched; and so quick was he, that the patient lost not very much blood, though left in that open bleeding condition."

Any listing of the physicians in early Pennsylvania would be incomplete without reference to the famous physician and conjuror, Dr. Christopher Witt (1675-1765).

Born in Wiltshire, England, in 1675, he emigrated to America at the age of twenty-nine to join the theosophical colonists on the Wissahickon in 1704.

Famous as a naturalist and skilled physician be became equally famous as a metaphysician and as an astronomer. His mystic colleagues and his patients all held him in the highest regard. Following the death of Kelphius, Dr. Witt and Daniel Geissler moved their abode to a parcel of land owned by Christian Warmer.

Dr. Witt's good botanical education came to the fore in Germantown, for there he established a large garden, probably the first botanical garden in America. This collection antedated Bartram's celebrated garden by twenty years. Dr. Witt corresponded regularly with Peter Collinson of London, whose letters mention the high esteem and regard in which Dr. Witt was held by the English naturalists. In later years there was an exchange of letters between Dr. Witt and John Bartram.

Dr. Witt was also a capable mechanic, personally constructing the first clocks made in Pennsylvania, and probably in America. He was noted as an artist and a musician. He built and played a large pipe organ.

Dr. Witt was an astrologer of note. He cast horoscopes and nativities and was respected greatly as an expert on these arts. It is likely that he was the only physician in Philadelphia's medical history who practiced urinoscopy and he constantly made his diagnosis and prescribed therapy by inspection of the urine. He accumulated a fortune which he left to some people who had been kind to him on his voyage to this country by giving him a hat to replace his own which was lost on the trip over.

At the age of eighty his eyesight failed him. Robert, a slave, carefully took care of him until his death in the latter part of January, 1765, at the age of ninety. He was buried in the Warmer burialground in Germantown. Incidentally, this location became known as Spook Hill, and tall tales were concocted which have survived to the present time, how upon the night following the burial of the old mystic, spectral flames were seen dancing around his grave.

John Bartram (1699-1777), whom we have just referred to in connection with Dr. Witt, was born on March 23, 1699 in Derby, Delaware County, Pennsylvania. Orphaned at the age of thirteen, the timely inheritance of a farm in Derby placed him in a fairly sound financial position.

Here is how John Bartram relates the events that led to his becoming America's number one botanist:

"One day I was very busy in holding my plough (for thou seest that I am but a ploughman) and being weary I ran under a tree to repose myself. I cast my eyes on a daisy; I plucked it mechanically and viewed it with more curiosity than common country farmers are wont to do and observed therein very many distinct parts, some perpendicular, some horizontal. What a shame, said my mind, that thee shouldst have employed thy mind so many years in tilling the earth and destroying so many flowers and plants without being acquainted with their structures and their uses..... I thought about it continually, at supper, in bed, and wherever I went,.... on the fourth day I hired a man to plough for me and went to Philadelphia. Though I knew not what book to call for, I ingeniously told the book-seller my errand, who provided me with such as he thought best and a Latin grammar. Next I applied to a neighboring schoolmaster who in three months taught me Latin enough to understand Linnaeus, which I purchased afterwards. Then I began to botanize all over my farm. In a little time I became acquainted with every vegetable that grew in the neighborhood.... By steady application of several years, I acquired a pretty general knowledge of every plant and tree to be found on our continent. In process of time I was applied to from the old countries whither I every year send many collections."

Haller's "Bibliotheca Anatomica" refers to Bartram as a physician and there is no question that he practiced both medicine and surgery. He arranged the notes and appendix to the American edition of Short's "Medicina Britannica," which was published by Benjamin Franklin in 1751. He purchased land three miles from Philadelphia on the Schuylkill River and erected a house on this plot by his own labor. It was here that he established his botanical garden. He spent a great amount of his time in specimen hunting and he let no obstacles deter him. He explored mountain tops and river sources at a time when travel among the Indians was most dangerous. He explored the shores of Lake Ontario in 1743 and wrote a scientific dissertation on the inhabitants, climate, soil, rivers and productiveness.

This amazing man at the advanced age of sixty-six set out from Philadelphia to explore east Florida. As botanist to the king, he had been instructed to discover the source of the St. John River. He sojourned four hundred miles making accurate observations of the river, its lakes and branches, the soil, flora, fauna and climate. In 1766 he published in London: "Description of East Florida with a Journal kept by John Bartram, Botanist to the Floridas."

Joseph Breitnall, a Philadelphia merchant, took some of Bartram's collections to Peter Collinson, the London botanist. This was the start of an intercontinental correspondence between Bartram and such botanists as Linnaeus, Sir Hans Sloane and Fothergill. Bartram was elected to the Royal Society in London and Stockholm.

John Bartram's son, William Bartram (1739-1823) settled in North Carolina and engaged in business. At the age of twenty-nine he gave up this venture and went with his father to Florida where he settled on the banks of the St. John's River and cultivated indigo. After 1771 he moved back to his father's botanical gardens and gave his attention to botany and wrote on his travels in the Carolinas, Georgia and Florida. In 1782 William Bartram was elected professor of botany at the University of Pennsylvania but declined this appointment because of poor health. William Bartram illustrated John Bartram's "Elements of Botany" and published the most complete list of American birds up to his day. William also wrote the biography of his father.

John Bartram was a great humanitarian born truly in advance of his time. He emancipated his slaves before the Revolution and they sat at the lower end of the dining-table eating his plain but plentiful foods.

He died on September 22, 1777, approaching the age of eighty. It is said that his last words were: "I want to die."

It was not long before the population and wealth of Philadelphia induced physicians to settle there. A few years before the death of "tender Griffith Owen," Dr. John Kearsley arrived from England.

John Kearsley, Sr. (1685-1772) came to Philadelphia in 1711, and built up a large and lucrative practice. Dr. Cadwalader, Dr. Shippen, Dr. Zachary, Dr. Redman, and Dr. Bard were all his apprentices. Kearsley served as a member of the Pennsylvania Assembly. He was an architect of renown and designed Christ Church in Philadelphia.

In 1750 Dr. Adam Thomson published an article "On the Preparation of the Body for the Small-pox." Dr. Kearsley attacked Dr. Thomson's conclusion in a publication entitled "Remarks on a Discourse on Preparing for the Small-pox" (1751). Dr. Alexander Hamilton, of Annapolis, Maryland, replied in "A Defense of Dr. Thomson's Discourse," and wrote "The Case of Mr. Thomson."

Kearsley died in January, 1772, aged eighty-seven, leaving a large part of his property to found Christ Church Hospital, a still flourishing institution for the support of poor widows who are members of the Episcopal Church.

Bard left this picture of his experiences: At the age of 14 or 15 years he was, "according to the custom of the day, bound apprentice to Mr. Kearsly (sic), an English surgeon of good talents, but of so unhappy a temper, that his presence banished cheerfulness from his family. He treated his pupils with rigor and submitted them to the most menial employments." Bard says that life would have been impossible were it not for the kindness of Mrs. Kearsley, a friend of his mother's. The apprentice's duties were manifold. As there were no apothecary shops in the Colonies at that time, the apprentices had to prepare their master's prescriptions personally.

Lloyd Zachary and John Redman chose the long, expensive and dangerous voyage abroad to enhance their medical education.

Lloyd Zachary (1701-1756) was born in Boston, Massachusetts, on November 15, 1701. His medical knowledge was obtained with Dr. Kearsley, Sr., in Philadelphia. In 1723 he travelled abroad to supplement his medical studies and in 1726 he opened his office in Philadelphia. He was one of the founders of the College of Philadelphia and of the Pennsylvania Hospital. He was one of the members of the latter institution's first medical staff. At his death he left 350 pounds and a number of books to the Pennsylvania Hospital. He was at one time health officer of the Port of Philadelphia. He died on September 26, 1756, while attending a patient.

His pupil, Dr. John Jones referred to him as "A person whose whole life had been one continued scene of benevolence and humanity."

John Redman (1722-1808) was born in Philadelphia on February 27, 1722. He attended Rev. William Tennent's school and later studied medicine under Dr. John Kearsley. His medical apprenticeship completed, he went to Bermuda to start his practice. He soon went to Edinburgh and later to Paris to study new methods. He obtained an M.D. from Leyden in 1748. He then went to England and spent some time at Guy's Hospital, following which he returned to Philadelphia and built up a fine practice.

Redman is described as "somewhat below the middle stature, his complexion was dark, his eyes black and uncommonly animated; and his gesture and speech such as indicated a mind always busy and teeming with new and original conceptions of humane and divine things."

In 1751 he was elected a member of City Council. In 1762 he was appointed trustee of the College of Philadelphia until it joined the University of the State of Pennsylvania and became the University of Pennsylvania (1791), when he resigned. He was a member of the American Philosophical Society from 1768.

In 1748 he published an article "De Abortu." In 1751 he was elected a consulting physician to the Pennsylvania Hospital which position he maintained for twenty-nine years. From 1787 to 1805 he served as president of the College of Physicians, being the first president of that body. In 1759 he published "A Defence of Inoculation." An article on the "Yellow Fever in Philadelphia in 1762," was read before the College of Physicians in 1793, when a worse epidemic was raging. His therapy was based on purgation "with Glauber's salts sustaining the patient with cordials or wine, with an antiemetic of tartar vitriolat gr. x and a half or whole drop of ol. cinnamon in a spoonful of simple mint and two spoonfuls of decoction of snakeroot every two hours." To diminish the danger of contagion, he kept a bowl of vinegar in the room with a hot iron occasionally plunged into it. He always kept tobacco in his mouth to prevent the swallowing of saliva, the only precaution used, as he found the use of many preservatives to effect his mind "with such fears as I thought were likely to render me more susceptible of infection than the omission of them."

Redman survived two attacks of fever. In 1762 he developed a liver ailment which necessitated him limiting his practice until his retirement in 1784. Rush and Shippen remained for all times his loyal students.

Other Philadelphians also left their beloved shores to become polished physicians. Thomas Cadwalader (1708-1779) received a course of instruction under Cheselden, the leading surgeon of his day in London. Cheselden's cataract extractions and lithotomies were known the world over. He was known to remove a stone in the bladder by the lateral operation in fifty-four seconds. When Cadwalader came back to Philadelphia he gave demonstrations to his professional colleagues. He presented anatomical lectures as early as 1730. He wrote an "Essay on the West India Dry Gripes; with the Method of Preventing and Curing that Cruel Distemper" (Trenton 1745). This disease was very prevalent in Philadelphia because of the citizens' affection for Jamaica rum which was distilled in leaden pipes and produced lead poisoning. Dr. Cadwalader's kindness and courteous manners were part and parcel of his character. The story is told that one Lieutenant Brulman of the British Army was seized with a homicidal mania and decided to shoot the first man he might meet. Dr. Cadwalader was the first whom he saw but the greeting he received from him was so generous that the lieutenant did not have the heart to kill him. Shortly thereafter, the lieutenant met one Robert Scull and promptly murdered him, for which crime he was executed.

Thomas Bond (1712-1784) must forever be remembered in American medical history because of the part he played in establishing the first major hospital and the first medical school in colonial America: the Pennsylvania Hospital and the medical department of the University of Pennsylvania.

Born in Calvert County, Maryland, in 1712, he studied medicine under Dr. Alexander Hamilton, following which he sojourned and studied at the Hotel Dieu, Paris. He started practice in Philadelphia in 1734. Two of his sons, Thomas and Robert also became physicians. His younger brother, Phineas arrived in Philadelphia from Maryland in 1738 and the two practiced together and demonstrated great interest in matters of municipal health in the infant City of Brotherly Love.

It is said that Dr. Bond customarily visited his patients in a two-wheel sulky drawn by a black horse. Such a mode of transportation was permitted only to aged and infirm physicians and it is likely that Dr. Bond's health was poor. Thacher says of Bond: "Dr. Bond was of a delicate constitution and disposed to pulmonary consumption for which he went on a voyage when a young man to the Island of Barbadoes. By unremitted care to his health, the strictest attention to diet, and to guard against the changes of temperature and also by frequently losing blood when he found his lungs affected, he lived to an age which the greater part of mankind never reach."

Bond, in his early practice had considerable experience with diseases common to immigrants and he maintained friendly relations with two physicians of the port of Philadelphia: Dr. Thomas Greene and Dr. Lloyd Zacharay. He probably saw considerable yellow fever and he refers to five epidemics of typhus in the introduction to his clinical lectures. From 1740 to 1754, Dr. Bond frequently visited suspected vessels, isolated suspicious cases and fumigated infected houses or ships. He reduced dislocations, splinted fractures, incised breasts, lanced "impostumes" (abscesses) of livers, scarified "mortifying" feet, amputated legs, tapped legs, chests and abdomens, attended difficult confinements, and treated a considerable number of cases of measles, smallpox, and other infectious diseases. Benjamin Rush states that Bond introduced mercury in medical practice in Philadelphia. He employed it therapeutically in all cases which resisted the regular methods of treatment. Bond was an ardent physiotherapist. He employed external heat, external cold, vapor, warm air and baths in the treatment of disease. He insisted that baths be introduced into the Pennsylvania Hospital. He discovered the Bond splint, still employed in fracture of the lower end of the radius. The records of the Pennsylvania Hospital demonstrate that Dr. Thomas Bond performed a successful lithotomy at the Pennsylvania Hospital on October 29, 1756. A letter written in 1772 by one who saw Bond operate declares:

I had the curiosity last week to be present at the hospital, at Dr. Bond's cutting for stone, and was agreeably disappointed, for instead of seeing an operation, said to be perplexed with difficulty and uncertainty, it was performed with such ease, regularity, and success that it scarcely gave a shock to the most sympathizing bystander, the whole being completed, and a stone of two inches in length, and one in diameter, extracted in less than two minutes.

Dr. Bond early saw the need for adequate hospital facilities and he frequently discussed this need with his friends and patients. When Bond approached Benjamin Franklin with his idea, things began to click.

Benjamin Franklin's Autobiography disclaims all personal credit of having been the founder of the Pennsylvania Hospital, and generously passes it on to Dr. Bond. Thomas Bond, his brother Phineas and Lloyd Zachary, formed the first medical staff of the Pennsylvania Hospital. Thomas Bond was one of the founders and the first vice-president of the American Philosophical Society.

Bond instituted the first systematic courses of clinical or bedside lectures in America in 1766, one year after the Medical Department of the University of Pennsylvania, the first medical school in this country, was founded by Drs. John Morgan and William Shippen, Jr. As a trustee of the College of Philadelphia (University of Pennsylvania), Bond greatly aided in the establishment of the medical department. Dr. Bond received permission from the Board of Managers of the Pennsylvania Hospital to utilize its facilities for clinical lectures. Bond lectured regularly at the Hospital until his death. We have Dr. Osler's word, in his Occasional Notes on American Medical Classics, that the first lecture to be given in a hospital in America was given by Dr. Bond in the Pennsylvania Hospital on Dec. 3, 1766.

Bond made several communications to the Philosophical Society and frequently read letters from physicians both in England and in some of the English colonies. In 1779 he presented a paper before the Society on the "Means of Pursuing Health and the Means of Preventing Diseases." "Medical Observations and Inquiries," contains a clinical article by Bond, amusingly named: "A Worm and a Horrid One found in the Liver." This presents the symptoms of a patient in his practice who allegedly was afflicted with a liver worm. There is a description of the autopsy and an engraving of the postmortem findings. Another article in the same work by Bond was on the "Use of Peruvian Bark in Scrofulous Cases." His "Introductory Clinical Lectures," are his greatest medical literary achievement.

He died on Friday, March 26, 1784, at the age of seventy-two, after a short illness.

Phineas Bond (1717-1775) studied medicine in Leyden, Edinburgh, Paris and London. He not only was on the staff of the Pennsylvania Hospital, but as trustee of the College of Philadelphia (University of Pennsylvania), he exerted great pressure in 1765 to establish the proposed medical school. He was one of the group who organized the American Philosophical Society.

Cadwalader Evans (1716-1773) studied medicine in England. He joined the staff of the Pennsylvania Hospital in 1759 after practicing for several years in Jamaica. Prior to the opening of the Pennsylvania Hospital in 1751, the colonies maintained numerous almshouses, some of which in later years became hospitals. The great Philadelphia General Hospital is a definite development of the almshouse established in Philadelphia in 1731. However, the first instance of the appointment of any physician to attend the sick in this institution goes back to 1769, when Thomas Bond and Cadwalader Evans were "re-elected" physicians to the Almshouse. It is not known how long they had held their positions prior to this date. Bond and Evans each received a salary of £50 a year with the stipulation that they had to provide the necessary medicines. Prior to 1788, "there is no evidence that the medicines requisite for the sick were prepared in the house, or that persons instructed in medicine resided in the institution." In 1788, an apothecary shop was established within the hospital with a pharmacist in charge.

The first building occupied by the Pennsylvania Hospital was a house rented on High Street, near Seventh. In 1755 the Hospital moved into the buildings at Eighth and Pine Streets which location it still occupies. The cornerstone was laid on May 18, 1755, and contains the following inscription written by Benjamin Franklin:

IN THE YEAR OF CHRIST
MDCCLV
GEORGE THE SECOND HAPPILY REIGNING
(FOR HE SOUGHT THE HAPPINESS OF HIS
PEOPLE)
PHILADELPHIA FLOURISHING
(FOR ITS INHABITANTS WERE PUBLICK
SPIRITED)
THIS BUILDING
BY THE BOUNTY OF THE GOVERNMENT
AND OF MANY PRIVATE PERSONS,
WAS PIOUSLY FOUNDED
FOR THE RELIEF OF THE SICK AND
MISERABLE;
MAY THE GOD OF MERCIES
BLESS THE UNDERTAKING.

Franklin tells in his Autobiography how he successfully obtained a grant of money for the Hospital from the Legislature. The country members objected to such a grant because they said such an institution would only benefit the city population. They also were of the opinion that there was little desire for a hospital among the populace. Franklin pushed through a bill granting the Hospital 2,000 pounds, provided that a like sum be raised by voluntary subscriptions. Of course the country members felt that he could never raise such a huge sum and that they could safely assume credit for being philanthropists by voting for the bill, without it costing them a penny. They did not reckon with the man Franklin, however, to whom nothing was impossible. He cleverly used their consent as a lever to influence people to give money enough to raise the necessary amount. Franklin writes: "I do not remember any of my political maneuvers, the success of which at the time gave me more pleasure; or wherein, after thinking of it, I more easily excused myself of having made some use of cunning."

The first minutes of the Board of Managers are in Benjamin Franklin's own handwriting. Remaining in the background, Franklin had Joshua Crosby, an influential merchant, elected first president and when Crosby died in 1756, Franklin was elected president of the Board.

Benjamin Franklin (1706-1790) was born on January 17, 1706, the youngest of seventeen children of Josiah Franklin of Boston, Massachusetts.

Benjamin Franklin made his living as a printer and a publisher. His manifold talents as a statesman, diplomat, pioneer investigator in electronics, inventor, engineer, scientific agriculturalist, oceanographer, author, philosopher, meteorologist, botanist and physicist are common knowledge. Yet, Benjamin Franklin was also a keen and observant medical scientist.

Although not a graduate of any medical school, Franklin was elected a member of several medical societies and there is an old engraving by P. Maren which has under the bust the inscription, "A. Benjamin Franklin, Docteur en Medicine."

Franklin wrote an article, "Diet and its Effect on Health and Disease," in which he insisted that "in general, mankind, since the improvement of cooking, eat about twice as much as nature requires." He observed that bathing could quench thirst and stop diarrhea, and that in the case of fevers, bathing or sponging with water or spirits would reduce the temperature by evaporation. He wrote on the heat of the blood and the cause thereof. He expounded on the motion of the blood and kept in his library a glass machine demonstrating this motion through arteries, veins and capillaries. He discussed learnedly the absorbent vessels and sweat glands of the skin and engaged in experimentation to prove his theories. Night blindness, sleep and deafness, all occupied his mind.

Every presbyopic person is directly indebted to Benjamin Franklin for he was the inventor of bifocal lenses.

In 1784, at the age of seventy eight, Franklin served as ambassador to France, and had great difficulty without glasses to "distinguish a letter even of large print." Franklin states:

Before that year I had used two pair of spectacles which I shifted occasionally, as in travelling I sometimes read and often wanted to regard the scenery. Finding this change troublesome and not always sufficiently ready, I had the glasses cut and half of each kind (of lens) associated in the same circle.

It was thus that the first pair of glasses was devised to provide for both near and distant vision.

John Pringle, president of the Royal Society of Medicine, asked Franklin to discuss the beneficial effects of electricity on paralytic cases. Franklin sagaciously replied:

I never knew any advantage from electricity in palsies that was permanent..... And how far the apparent temporary advantage might arise from the exercise in the patient's journey and coming daily to my house, or from the spirits given by the hope of success, enabling them to exert more strength in moving their limbs, I will not pretend to say.

Franklin was greatly concerned with the scientific study of vital statistics and the mortality of different diseases. The high mortality rate of foundlings and babies not nursed by their own mothers worried him greatly. He was apprehensive of the growing habit among the French mothers to neglect this duty. He wrote concerning the possibility of infection remaining for periods in dead bodies after burial.

Franklin was even a comparative anatomist as is evidenced by a description he wrote of some fossil elephant teeth. His pamphlet entitled a "Dialogue between Franklin and the Gout," dealt with the hygiene and treatment of Gout and was written during one of his visits to Passy. His statements concerning gout were personal observations and accurate in detail.

Franklin was principal founder and president of the Pennsylvania Hospital and he wrote "Some Account of the Pennsylvania Hospital from its First Beginning to the Fifth Month, called May, 1754." Fifteen hundred copies were printed on his own press.

Franklin's was a vehement voice in the fight against smallpox. Franklin lent his weight to the side of those advocating inoculation after losing a son from this dread disease in the days that he was against this practice. Franklin influenced William Heberden, distinguished London doctor, to write a pamphlet entitled "Some Account of the Success of Inoculation for the Small Pox in England and America, Together with Plain Instructions by Which any Person May be Enabled to Perform the Operation and Conduct the Patient through the Distemper (1759)."

Heberden printed this brochure at his own expense and, to its eight pages, Franklin added a four page preface in which he declared there was no longer any doubt as to the value of inoculation. Franklin wanted the benefits of medical science to reach the masses, so to train poor parents to inoculate their own children, he distributed 1,500 copies of this pamphlet gratis in Philadelphia.

Dr. Jan Ingenhousz, the court physician to Maria Theresa and Joseph II, consulted Franklin before inoculating the young princes of the imperial family.

Always concerned with advancing medical education, he helped many young medical students in their desire to study abroad, including Rush, Morgan, Shippen and Kuhn.

Franklin maintained a modern attitude toward that widespread disease, the common cold, which still defies adequate therapy. Ignorant of bacteria and virus, he more-the-less deduced that colds are contagious in character and conveyed by "particular effluvia in the air."

He asserted that colds are disseminated by crowds gathered in unventilated quarters where foul and stagnant air is inspired. This concept led to his theories on air conditioning.

To prevent colds, Franklin advised frequent bathing (in an era when baths were regarded as unwholesome), routine physical exercise, sound diet and fresh air.

Franklin's keen observation and judgment did not let him be taken in by Mesmerism or other spectacular "cures." According to this great American, "Quacks are the greatest liars in the world—except their patients."

Early in 1784 Mesmerism was riding a tidal wave of popularity in Paris. Even Lafayette was an ardent believer in Mesmer's cult. As Franklin was a member of the Royal Medical Society of Paris, he was appointed by King Louis XVI to serve on a commission examining Mesmer's doctrines and experiments. Franklin's report led to the debunking of Mesmer's claims.

When Samuel Johnson was ailing with "fever and ague", Franklin in a letter dated September 13, 1750, advocated that he not "omit the use of bark too soon"....."Remember to take preventing doses faithfully.....If you take the powder mixed quick in a tea cup of milk, 'tis not disagreeable, but looks and even tastes like chocolate. 'Tis an old saying: That an ounce of prevention is worth a pound of cure,—and certainly a true one, with regard to the bark."

In 1745 Franklin sent a letter to Cadwallader Colden expounding on the dilatation of the ventricles of the heart and the cure of the yaws. An undated article entitled "A Conjecture as to the Cause of the Heat of the Blood in Health and of the Cold and Hot Fits of Some Fevers" was found in Franklin's handwriting among the papers of Mr. Colden.

Benjamin Franklin's brother, John, asked him to devise a flexible catheter, for use in catheterization of bladders, and in December, 1752, Franklin constructed the first flexible catheter known in American medical history. Franklin states: "I went immediately to the silversmith's and gave directions for making one (sitting by till it was finished that it might be ready for this post)." In 1768, Franklin wrote to Cadwalader Evans that he had long believed lead poisoning to be due "to a metallic cause only; observing that it affects, among tradesmen, those that use lead, however different their trades: as glaziers, letter founders, plumbers, potters, white-lead makers and painters."

Franklin avowed from his personal experience as a printer that lead poisoning among typesetters was directly produced by particles of metal swallowed with their food by careless workers who ate their meals without washing their hands.

Franklin received the Copley Medal from the Royal Society in recognition of his discoveries in electricity and held the LL. D. from St. Andrews and the Yale and the Harvard A.M. for the same reason.

He died in Philadelphia on April 17, 1790, at the grand old age of eighty-four. He did not live to fulfill the obscurity his early modesty had predicted when he wrote the following epitaph for himself:

THE BODY

OF

BENJAMIN FRANKLIN

LIKE THE COVER OF AN OLD BOOK

ITS CONTENTS TORN OUT

AND STRIPPED OF ITS LETTERING AND GILDING

LIES HERE, FOOD FOR THE WORMS.

BUT THE WORK SHALL NOT BE LOST,

FOR IT WILL, AS HE BELIEVES, APPEAR ONCE MORE

IN A NEW AND MORE ELEGANT EDITION

REVISED AND CORRECTED

BY

THE AUTHOR.

There are a number of interesting features in the history of the Pennsylvania Hospital. A precedent was established in the institution that doctors render their services gratis. Drs. Thomas and Phineas Bond and Lloyd Zachary comprised the regular staff and Drs. Graeme, Cadwalader, Moore and Redman were to be called in as consultants in difficult cases.

Occupational therapy in the form of large and small spinning-wheels, two pairs of cards, and some wool and flax, "to employ such patients as may be capable of using the same" was provided for at this institution. A place for the insane to exercise was provided. As the hospital at first was surrounded by an open lot not walled off, the curious began to gather about the Hospital to stare at and tease the insane. A fence was constructed but to no avail. On May 10, 1762, the Managers stated:

"The great crowds that invade the Hospital give trouble and create so much disturbance, that Samuel Rhoades and Jacob Levis are directed to employ a workman to make a suitable hatch door and get an inscription thereon notifying that such persons who come out of curiousity to visit the house should pay a sum of money, a Groat, at least, for admittance." This abominable practice was not discontinued until 1791.

In the other Colonies some of the best medical men were Tories. In Philadelphia, however, all were patriots except John Kearsley, Jr., and Abraham Chovet. As the managers of the Pennsylvania Hospital were mostly Quakers, and pacifists, four were exiled to Staunton, Va., by order of the Council of Safety.

The first public medical library in the Colonies was founded at the Hospital in 1763. In 1762 John Fothergill presented a book "An Experimental History of the Materia Medica" by William Lewis, F.R.S., to the Hospital. In May, 1763, the staff of the Hospital addressed the following proposal to the Managers:

"As the Custom of most of the Hospitals in Great Britain has given such gratuities from those students who attend the Wards of the Hospital to the Physicians and Surgeons attending them, we think it properly belongs to us to appropriate the Money arriving from thence. And we propose to apply it to the founding of a Medical Library in the Hospital which we judge will tend greatly to the Advantage of the Pupils and the honor of the Institution."

The Managers accepted this proposal and the Library grew quickly. By 1884, it contained 14,500 bound volumes.

The Pennsylvania Hospital instituted the practice of giving ward instruction to students. A certificate to students was granted after completion of their studies. In 1773 a policy of taking apprentices into the Hospital was adopted. The term of indenture was five years, after which a suitably inscribed certificate and a suit of "cloathes" were awarded. This system was given up in 1824 when the system of taking only graduate physicians as resident medical officers was instituted. This was the beginning of the present system of internship.

The lives of Hugh Mercer and Henry Stoy are of importance to this period:

Huge Mercer (1725-1777) was born in Aberdeen, Scotland, in 1725. After completing his preliminary studies at the University of Aberdeen, he attended the Medical School of Marshall College, graduating from this institution in 1744. An open exponent of Prince Charles Edward the Pretender and a member of his army at Culloden, he succeeded in effecting his escape and sailed from Leith for Philadelphia in Autumn 1746. After reaching his destination he made his way to the western part of Pennsylvania and settled near Green-castle (now Mercersburg). We have it on the authority of Toner that Hugh Mercer actually is the founder of Mercersburg.

Until the French and Indian War, he practiced in this wild and poorly populated area. When this war broke out, he joined Brad-dock's army as captain of a company and was present with the ill-fated expedition against Fort DuQuesne. In this campaign he was wounded and left behind, but he cleverly made the dangerous trip through the wilderness and rejoined his comrades.

In 1756 he was appointed captain of one of the companies raised to protect the residents against the Indians and their French allies. His company was stationed at McDowell's Fort (now Bridgeport). In this location he also engaged in medical practice both in caring for his men and the civilian population. In a battle with the Indians he was again wounded and again abandoned, but this man of indomitable courage undertook a journey through over one hundred miles of forest to again join his comrades at Fort Cumberland. During this back-breaking trek, he subsisted on roots and herbs, and rattlesnake meat, and so closely did the enemy keep after him that on one occa-sion he had to hide in the hollow trunk of a tree, around which the Indians squatted. Mercer was wounded a third time while command-ing one of the companies which captured an Indian settlement at Kittanning in 1756.

The Corporation of Philadelphia awarded Mercer a note of thanks and a memorial medal for the part he played during these perilous times. In the summer of 1757, he was placed in command of the garrison at Shippenburg and in December of the same year he was promoted to the rank of major and placed in command of the forces of the province of Pennsylvania west of the Susquehanna. In 1758, he commanded part of the forces under Gen. Forbes in the expedition sent against Fort DuQuesne, and it was during this campaign that Mercer met Washington and became a life-long friend of his. It was Mercer who advised Washington to make Virginia his residence.

The French and Indian War over, Mercer moved to Virginia and settled in Fredericksburg where he dwelt and practiced until the start of the War of Independence. An English traveller who visited Fredericksburg during this War published the following statement in 1784: "In Fredericksburg I called upon a worthy and intimate friend, Dr. Hugh Mercer, a physician of great eminence and merit, and a man possessed of almost every virtue and accomplishment."

Mercer's consultation room and apothecary's shop were still stand-ing in 1908 situated on a corner of Princess Ann and Amelia Streets. The start of the War saw Mercer abandoning his large practice so that he could raise and drill troops more efficiently. He entered the army of the new country as colonel of the third Virginia continentals. He was promoted to the rank of brigadier-general on June 5, 1776.

Mercer energetically devoted all of his talents to the campaigns of Washington. On one occasion, refusing to surrender against hopeless odds, he was clubbed and bayonetted, and left for dead at Princeton. The seven bayonet wounds of the body and the numerous bludgeon wounds did not immediately finish this man of iron. He was removed to a farmhouse, where he was cared for by Mrs. Clark and her daughter, the wife and child of the owner of the house, and by Major Lewis, whom George Washington dispatched to the scene. Benjamin Rush and Archibald Alexander attended him with the best that medical science had to offer, but he died on January 12, 1777, and was buried in Christ Church yard, Philadelphia.

Years later his body was exhumed and transferred to Laurel Hill Cemetery and a monument erected to his memory by the St. Andrew's Society, of which organization he had been a member. This monument, dedicated on November 26, 1840, is inscribed as follows: "Gen. Mercer, a physician of Fredericksburg, in Virginia, was distinguished for his skill and learning, his gentleness and decision, his refinement and humanity, his elevated honor and his devotion to the cause of civil and religious liberty." A resolution was passed in 1777 to erect a monument to his memory at Fredericksburg, but it was not until June 28,1902 that by act of Congress, this was carried out.

Henry William Stoy (1726-1801) was born in Herborn, Germany, on March 14, 1726. His studies prepared him for the priesthood and he was ordained in America in 1752.

He first settled in Lebanon County, Pennsylvania, but in 1756 he moved to Philadelphia and married Maria Elizabeth Maus. His congregation did not like his marriage and he resigned under pressure and moved to Lancaster in October, 1758. In 1763 he returned to Europe and went to the city of his birth, Herborn, and studied medicine under John Adam Hoffman, professor of the university until 1773.

In 1767 he returned to America and accepted a pulpit at Tulpehocken, the present Host Church in Berks County. However, the church authorities in Pennsylvania again refused to receive him as a member of the Coetus, or Synod, not because they accused him of sin, but because of his disputes with the ministry and the fact that he was looked upon as a "stirrer up of strife."

He resigned from the Host Church in 1772 or 1773 and went to

Lebanon where he engaged in medical practice. He found time to preach at several rural congregations during this period. He was very active in politics and in 1779 wrote a letter to Joseph Reed, president of the Supreme Executive Council of Pennsylvania, on "The Present Mode of Taxation," in which he energetically advocated a single tax on land. He thus was the first single tax advocate to be recorded in America.

In 1784, he was elected to the Pennsylvania Legislature.

His remedy for hydrophobia and his hysteric drops, or "mutter tropfen," made his fame penetrate wide areas. General Washington's account book, contains the following: "Oct. 18, 1797. Gave my servant, Christopher, to bear the expenses to a person at Lebanon in Pennsylvania celebrated for curing persons bit by wild animals, $25.00."

The hydrophobia preparation consisted of one ounce of the herb, red chickweed, four ounces of theriac and one quart of beer, all well digested, the dose being a wineglassful. The hysteria cure consisted of opium, castor, saffron and maple seed, of each one dram, and Lisbon wine four ounces. Stoy avidly recommended inoculation for smallpox at a time when there was much prejudice against this practice. He passed away in Lebanon, on September 14, 1801, at the age of seventy-five, and was buried at the Host Church, in Berks County.

One of the first Edinburgh-trained native Americans to employ his medical education for the advance of his native country was William Shippen, Jr., but first a word about his father, William Shippen, Sr.

William Shippen, Sr. (1712-1801) was born in Philadelphia on October 1, 1712. His grandfather, Edward Shippen, had served as mayor of Philadelphia after he had come to the New World from Cheshire, England, in 1668. William Shippen, Sr., early undertook the study of medicine and soon developed a large practice. He was elected to the Continental Congress in 1778 and returned to this body in 1779. He enjoyed membership in Benjamin Franklin's "Junto." He served as president of the American Philosophical Society. From 1753 to 1778 he served as physician to the Pennsylvania Hospital. His name is included in the list of founders of the University of Pennsylvania and he served as trustee to this institution from 1749 to 1779. He was a founder of the College of New Jersey (later Princeton) and trustee of this college from 1756 to 1796.

It is said that his charity to the poor not only included free professional services but also large sums of money. Always a robust out-door man, it is said that shortly before his death he took a six mile hike. He died at the grand old age of eighty-nine, on November 4, 1801.

William Shippen, Jr., (1736-1808) was born in Philadelphia, on October 21,1736. He attended the famous academy supervised by the Reverend Samuel Finley at Nottingham, in which John Morgan and Benjamin Rush were also pupils. In 1754 the College of New Jersey (Princeton) awarded him an A.B. At his graduation exercises, he was valedictorian. Whitefield, the famous colonial preacher, who witnessed his speech stated that it was an excellent oration. Young Shippen then undertook the study of medicine with his father, Dr. William Shippen. In 1758 he went to England to enhance his medical knowledge. The elder Shippen wrote as follows: "My son has had his education in the best college in this part of the country, and has been studying physic with me, besides which he has had the opportunity of seeing the practice of every gentleman of note in our city. But for want of that variety of operations and those frequent dissections which are common in older countries, I must send him to Europe. His scheme is to gain all the knowledge he can in anatomy, physic, and surgery."

Young Shippen made good on his father's hopes. He studied anatomy with John Hunter and obstetrics with William Hunter and Dr. McKenzie. He personally observed the work of Sir. John Pringle and Dr. William Hewson. It will be recalled that Hewson is the one whose studies on blood coagulation and the lymphatic system have given him a rightful niche among the medical great, even though he died when he was only thirty-five years old. Dr. John Fothergill, the famous Quaker physician, personally befriended Shippen. This attachment later was instrumental in influencing Fothergill to aid the Pennsylvania Hospital, and the medical department of the College of Philadelphia. The hospital benefited by his gift of crayon illustrations and casts of the anatomy of the human body, which had been executed by Van Rymsdyck, the best anatomical artist of his day. The Pennsylvania Hospital still has these pictures.

Shippen received his M.D. from Edinburgh University, and his doctoral thesis was named "*De Placentæ cum Utero Nexu.*" In Edinburgh he remained close to Monro "primus" and Cullen. He then managed to get to France, in spite of the fact that England and France were at war, through the influence of Sir John Pringle, the great military surgeon.

Shippen returned to Philadelphia in 1762, with the Fothergill pictures.

Fothergill wrote as follows, to the managers of the Pennsylvania Hospital:

I need not tell thee that the Knowledge of Anatomy is of exceeding great use to Practitioners in Physic and Surgery and that the means of procuring subjects with you are not easy, some pretty accurate anatomical Drawings about half as big as the Life have fallen into my hands and which I propose to send to your Hospital to be under the care of the Physicians and to be by some of them explained to the Students or Pupils who attend the Hospital. In the want of real Subjects these will have their Use and I have recommended it to Dr. Shippen to give a Course of Anatomical Lectures to such as may attend, he is very well qualified for the subject and will soon be followed by an able Assistant Dr. Morgan both of whom I apprehend will not only be useful to the Province in their Employments but if suitably countenanced by the Legislature will be able to erect a school for Physic amongst you that may draw many students from various parts of America and the West Indies and at least furnish them with a better Idea of the Rudiments of their Profession than they have at present the Means of acquiring on your Side of the Water.

Shippen's first series of lectures attended by ten pupils was announced in a newspaper letter dated November 11, 1762:

.... a course of anatomical lectures will be opened with winter in Philadelphia for the advantage of the young gentlemen now engaged in the study of physic in this and the neighboring provinces, whose circumstances and connections will not permit of their going abroad for improvement to the anatomical schools in Europe; and also for the entertainment of any gentlemen who may have the curiosity to understand the anatomy of the human frame. In these lectures the situation, figure, and structure of all the parts of the human body will be demonstrated, their respective uses explained, and as far as a course of anatomy will permit, their diseases, with the indications and methods of cure, briefly treated of. All the necessary operations in surgery will be performed, a course of bandages exhibited, and the whole concluded with the explanation of some of the curious phenomena that arise from an examination of the gravid uterus, and a few plain general directions in the study and practice of midwifery. The necessity and public utility of such a course in this growing country, and the method to be pursued therein, will be more particularly explained in the introductory lecture, to be delivered on the sixteenth instant, at six o'clock in the evening, at the State House, by William Shippen, Jr., M.D. The lectures will be given at his father's house in Fourth Street. Tickets for the course to be had, of the doctor at five pistoles each; and any gentleman who may incline to see the subject prepared for the lectures and learn the art of dissecting, injecting, etc., is to pay five pistoles more.

His first lecture was presented in the State House on November 16, 1762. The following ones were given in his father's house on Fourth Street. Some years later he built an anatomical theater for himself. Shippen's anatomical lectures became progressively more popular and for one course it is said that he had two hundred and fifty students in attendance.

Strong opposition and mob violence attended those who dared "violate" the human body with dissection. Shippen was stoned on several occasions and the windows of his anatomical laboratory broken by frenzied citizens. Shippen would not be cowed, but to moderate public opinion, he announced in letters to the newspapers that the bodies he used were those of persons who had committed suicide or been legally executed, except "now and then one from the Potter's field."

Dr. Shippen started the first lectures on obstetrics to be given in America in 1765. Although midwifery was largely in the hands of female attendants, Shippen, by giving this branch much time, did much to place it in competent medical hands. Shippen illustrated his lectures with "anatomical plates and casts of the gravid uterus at the hospital." Shippen established the first lying-in hospital in America, "under the care of a sober, honest matron, well acquainted with lying-in women."

Women were permitted to attend his obstetrical lectures, for he strove most of all to elevate the standards of obstetrics. The an-announcement of the course states:

"In order to make the course more perfect, a convenient lodging is provided for the accommodation of a few poor women, who otherwise might suffer for want of the common necessaries on these occasions, to be under the care of a sober, honest matron, well acquainted with lying-in women, employed by the Doctor for that purpose. Each pupil to attend two courses at least, for which he is to pay five guineas.

The female pupils to be taught privately, and assisted at any of their private labors when necessary."

Dr. Shippen was appointed professor of anatomy and surgery at the medical department of the College of Philadelphia. In 1791, when the College of Philadelphia and the University of Pennsylvania formally united, Shippen received the post of professor of anatomy, surgery, and midwifery. Dr. Caspar Wistar was appointed adjunct professor in the same branches.

Wistar described Shippen thusly: "His person was graceful, his manners polished, his conversation various, and the tones of his voice singularly sweet and conciliatory. In his intercourse with society he was gay without levity, and dignified without haughtiness or austerity. He belonged to a family which was proverbial for good temper. His father, whom he strongly resembled in this respect, during the long life of ninety years had scarcely ever been seen out of humor. He was also particularly agreeable to young people. Known as he was to almost every citizen of Philadelphia, it is probable that there was no one who did not wish him well."

Shippen served on the staff of the Pennsylvania Hospital in 1778 and 1779, resigning because of his military activities. In 1791 he was again elected to the staff and served until 1802, when he again resigned. Shippen was an active member of the American Philosophical Society and a founder of the College of Physicians of Philadelphia. He was president of the College from 1805 to 1808.

Shippen's first military appointment was as medical director of the Flying Camp in the Jerseys. In this position he was subordinate to Dr. John Morgan. Morgan's eventual dismissal from the position of director-general of the military hospitals and physician-in-chief of the American Army and Shippen's subsequent appointment by order of Congress on October 9, 1776 to the directorship of the hospitals on the west side of the Hudson River, thus placing him on an equal footing with Morgan, led to Morgan's open accusation that Shippen had insidiously bored from within and effected his overthrow. On April 11, 1777, Shippen was appointed to succeed Morgan as director-general of the military hospitals and physician-in-chief of the American Army, an appointment he held until his resignation in January, 1781. In August, 1780, he was courtmartialed and declared innocent of charges that he had improperly handled funds and supplies. The available evidence, however, tends to throw doubt on his innocence.

In 1798 Shippen was shocked by the loss of his son, and Caspar Wistar, in his Eulogy of Shippen delivered before the College of Physicians shortly after his death, says that this loss cut him to the quick and deadened his interest in all things. He gave up most of his lectures and let his practice to go pot. He died in Germantown on July 11, 1808.

Shippen's courses in anatomy and obstetrics had been going on for several years when John Morgan returned to Philadelphia in the spring of 1765.

John Morgan (1735-1789) for all times must be remembered as the guiding genius behind the first medical school in America. One of that remarkable group of Philadelphia physicians of Welsh ancestry, John Morgan temporarily left his native city to attend the Academy at Nottingham, Maryland, which was run by the Reverend Samuel

Dr. John Cochran (1730-1807)

Dr. John Cochran helped found the New Jersey Medical Society and served as president of this organization in 1769. In 1781, he became Director General of the Hospitals of the United States.

Upper left, DR. DAVID OLYPHANT was well known in Revolutionary days as a surgeon in the hospital department of the Continental Army. (*Courtesy of Mr. Murray Olyphant and Frick Art Reference Library.*) *Upper right*, DR. ALEXANDER BARRON met with Dr. Peter Dott Fayssoux and Dr. David Ramsay in December 1789, to seek means of starting the Medical Society of South Carolina. (*Courtesy of St. Andrew's Society and Frick Art Reference Library.*) *Lower left*, DR. JAMES LYNAH (1725-1809) was one of the founders of the Medical Society of South Carolina. (*Courtesy of Frick Art Reference Library.*) *Lower right*, DAVID RAMSAY, M.D. (1749-1815), who was imprisoned by the British with the rest of the patriots at Charleston, declared that the prisoners were packed into prison ships in such numbers that they could not lie down. (*Courtesy of Carolina Art Association and Frick Art Reference Library.*)

Beginning of Memoir of Dr. Martin Kalberlahn (?-1759). Photostat supplied through the courtesy of Dr. Adelaide L. Fries who furnishes the following literal translation:

4

Memoir of our dear Brother Hans Martin Kalberlahn. He was born in Drontheim, in Norway, on the 30th of March, 1722. In the Lutheran fashion he was sent to school regularly, and in his fifteenth year he was admitted to the Communion. Then he became a student and learned surgery. In the year (17)43 he went on his travels, and came by way of Bergen, Hamburg, and Lubeck, to Travemunde, and of this he wrote: Here for the first time I experienced the forgiveness of sins. The next year he came to Copenhagen, and from there went to Slagelsee, with the purpose, as he wrote, that he there would lead a godly life, as he . . . .

Upper left, WILLIAM BARTRAM (1739-1823). Poor health prevented William Bartram from accepting the professorship of botany at the University of Pennsylvania. (*Courtesy of the Philadelphia College of Physicians.*) *Upper right*, DR. LLOYD ZACHARY (1701-1756) was one of the founders of the College of Philadelphia and of the Pennsylvania Hospital. (*Courtesy of the Philadelphia College of Physicians.*) *Lower left*, THOMAS CADWALADER, M.D. (1708-1779) presented anatomical lectures as early as 1730. (*Courtesy of the Philadelphia College of Physicians.*) *Lower right*, JOHN REDMAN, M.D. (1722-1808) was elected first president of the College of Physicians of Philadelphia. (*Courtesy of the Philadelphia College of Physicians.*)

Upper left, DR. PHINEAS BOND (1717-1775) wielded great influence in establishing the University of Pennsylvania Medical School. (*Courtesy of the Philadelphia College of Physicians.*) *Upper right,* DR. HUGH MERCER (1725-1777). Seven bayonet and numerous bludgeon wounds did not immediately finish this man of iron. (*Courtesy of Mercersburg Academy.*) *Lower left,* WILLIAM SHIPPEN, JR., M.D. (1736-1808). In 1765, Dr. William Shippen, Jr. presented the first lectures on obstetrics to be given in America. (*U. S. Army Medical Museum. Neg. No. 44948.*) *Lower right,* DR. BENJAMIN CHURCH, the first medical director of the Continental Army, was convicted of treason and dishonorably discharged. (*U. S. Army Medical Museum. Neg. No. 42549.*)

JOHN MORGAN, M.D. (1735-1789)

Dr. John Morgan for all times must be remembered as the guiding genius behind the first medical school in America. (*U. S. Army Medical Museum. Neg. No. 42773.*)

Left, Dr. James Hutchinson (1752-1793). It is said that with six assistants, Dr. James Hutchinson inoculated 3,496 men at Valley Forge for smallpox. (*Courtesy of the Philadelphia College of Physicians.*) *Right*, Edward Hand, M.D. (1744-1802). In 1777, Dr. Edward Hand was promoted to the rank of brigadier-general, and he took an active part in the battle of Trenton. (*Courtesy of the Philadelphia College of Physicians.*)

Surgeon's Field Case—Revolutionary War (*U. S. Army Medical Museum. Neg. No. 47274.*)

BENJAMIN RUSH, M.D. (1745-1813)

Dr. Benjamin Rush is considered by many as the greatest colonial physician. (*Reproduced from Army Medical Bulletin #25.*)

Finley. In 1757 Morgan attained the degree of A.B. from the College of Philadelphia, graduating with the first class to complete the course of this infant institution. He then apprenticed himself to Dr. John Redman, spending thirteen months as resident apothecary to the Pennsylvania Hospital. He writes, "I had an opportunity of being acquainted with the practice of other eminent physicians in this place; particularly of all the physicians of the hospital, whose prescriptions I put up there above the space of one year." Following his apprenticeship he served for four years as surgeon to the Pennsylvania troops in the French and Indian War. The quality of his performance at this task is attested to by Rush as follows: "I well remember to have heard it said that if it were possible for any man to merit heaven by his good works, Dr. Morgan would deserve it, for his faithful attendance upon his patients."

The year 1760 saw him in London, with the Hunters, and later in Edinburgh. Benjamin Franklin, then living in London, felt that Morgan "will one day make a good figure in the profession, and be of some credit to the school he studies in, if great industry and application, joined with natural genius and sagacity, afford any foundation for the presage." In 1763 he received his M.D. at Edinburgh, his thesis being entitled "De Pyopoiesis." In this monograph he presented the view that pus is a secretion formed by the blood-vessels in conditions of inflammation. He then sojourned to Paris, where he further engaged in anatomical investigations, and read a paper on "Suppuration" before the Royal Academy of Surgery in Paris. He also presented a demonstration of the methods employed by the Hunters in injecting and preserving anatomical specimens. "On the Art of Making Anatomical Preparations by Corrosion," was presented to the Academy a short time later and he was elected a member of this body.

Morgan then went to Italy and met the great Morgagni. Rush states that Morgagni "was so pleased with the doctor that he claimed kindred with him," from the resemblance of their names, and on the blank leaf of a copy of his works, which he presented to him, he inscribed with his own hand, the following words: "affini suo, medico praeclarissimo. Johanni Morgan, donat Auctor." The veracity of this anecdote is open to serious question.

Morgan was elected a member of the Belles Lettres Society of Rome. He also was elected to the Royal Society of London and was made a licentiate of the Royal College of Physicians.

When Morgan returned to his native Philadelphia in 1765, he brought a letter from the proprietary, Thomas Penn, to the Board of Trustees of the College of Philadelphia, endorsing his plan to establish a medical school associated with the college. On May 3, 1765, he was elected professor of the theory and practice of medicine in the college, this marking the advent of the first medical school in the colonies—an institution which still continues as the department of medicine of the University of Pennsylvania.

On May 30, 1765, Morgan presented "A Discourse upon the Institution of Medical Schools in America," which had been written by him in Paris with the approval of Fothergill, William Hunter and Dr. Watson, of London. He advocated a very comprehensive preliminary education preparatory to the study of medicine. Morgan continued his professorship until his death and was succeeded by Dr. Benjamin Rush.

Morgan also was one of the founders and active members of the American Philosophical Society. Morgan founded a Medical Society in 1765, the "Philadelphia Medical Society," which later became the American Philosophical Society, after an independent existence for three years. Upon settling in Philadelphia to practice he resolved that he would neither compound his remedies nor do any surgical work and he tried to introduce the English custom of presenting the physician with his fee at the time of each visit.

Dr. Benjamin Church, the first medical director of the Continental Army, was convicted of treason and dishonorably discharged, and Congress, in October, 1775, appointed Morgan to the post. With all of his energy and ability he set to work to organize the army Medical Department on a sound basis. He instituted rigid examination of those desiring to enter the medical service, and personally supervised the work of the entire department. The meager finances of the Continental Army during Dr. Morgan's career as chief of the medical department fell to a pitiful level. Necessary hospital supplies could not be obtained and jealous regimental surgeons fought diligently to have Morgan relieved of his post of director-general. On July 17, 1776, Congress passed a law promulgated by Dr. Morgan which standardized military discipline, salaries for physicians and medical regulations.

Dr. Samuel Stringer, in charge of army medicine in northern New York State, let medical practice under his area of jurisdiction fall into a sad state of disrepair. Morgan assailed Stringer's alleged misconduct in Congress, which settled the argument by firing both Stringer and Morgan. Morgan vehemently objected to this miscarriage of justice in the famous pamphlet "A Vindication of His Public Career in the Station of Director-General of the Military Hospitals and Physician-in-chief to the American Army," Anno 1776, by John Morgan, M.D., F.R.S., Boston, 1777.

Morgan was greatly aroused by the appointment, on October 9, 1776, of Dr. William Shippen, Jr., as director of the hospitals on the west side of the Hudson River, for Shippen had previously been in charge of the hospital of the Flying Camp in the Jerseys, and subject to the authority of Dr. Morgan. Under this new appointment, Shippen reported directly to Congress over the head of Morgan. On April 11, 1777, Shippen was appointed to succeed Morgan in the post of director-general and physician-in-chief of the army. Morgan promptly withdrew from public affairs.

Morgan served the Pennsylvania Hospital from 1773 until 1783, when he resigned under somewhat peculiar circumstances, notwithstanding the fact that the minutes of the hospital declare his action was "to the grief of the patients, and much against the will of the managers, who all bore testimony to his abilities, and great usefulness to the institution."

Morgan's fine art collection and library were destroyed by the British at Bordentown, New Jersey, and Danbury, Connecticut, where they were stored to escape the ravages of war. Such were the vicissitudes of Morgan's fate. He died on October 15, 1789, and is buried in St. Peter's churchyard, Philadelphia.

Edward Hand and James Hutchinson were two important Revolutionary medical figures:

Edward Hand (1744-1802) was born in Clyduff, Kings County, Ireland, on December 31, 1744. In 1774 he emigrated to America as surgeon's mate with the Eighteenth Royal Irish Regiment. He promptly gave up his appointment and settled down to practice medicine in Pennsylvania. When the War of Independence broke out, he was appointed lieutenant-colonel in the Pennsylvania Line. He was quickly promoted to the rank of colonel and was present during the retreat of the American Army from Long Island. During the engagement he served as commander of the First Regiment of the Pennsylvania Line. He left an account of the part he played in this retreat. In 1777, he was promoted to brigadier-general, and took an active part in the battle of Trenton. In 1778 he led a group of troops at Albany and later he joined General Sullivan in his drive against the Six Indian Nations. In 1780 he was appointed major-general and in 1781 he was made adjutant-general. During 1784-85, he was elected to Congress from Pennsylvania. He died from cholera at Rockford, near Lancaster, Pennsylvania on September 3, 1802, at the age of fifty-eight.

James Hutchinson (1752-1793) was born in Wakefield, Pennsylvania on January 29, 1752. Paul Preston afforded him his preliminary education and then he attended an academy in Virginia. When his father, a Quaker farmer, passed away, he moved in with an uncle, Israel Pemberton, who lived in Philadelphia. He attended the College of Philadelphia and was first in his class when graduation took place. He apprenticed himself to Dr. Cadwalader Evans of Philadelphia, and later attended the Philadelphia Medical College. In 1774 he was awarded a gold medal to commemorate his perfection in chemistry.

Dr. Hutchinson's patriot sympathies led his uncle to send him to London, patently to study under Dr. Fothergill, but actually to get him away from the brewing conflict. His uncle's ulterior motive was destined to failure for he returned home via France in 1777 with important dispatches from Benjamin Franklin to his Government. Undaunted when his ship was attacked by a British man-of-war off the American coast, this man of destiny left the ship in an open boat, and landed with his valuable documents under British fire. The vessel which he had left was captured by the English and the medical library which he had painstakingly collected in England and France went to the bottom of the sea.

Setting foot on American soil, Hutchinson quickly joined the army as surgeon and later became surgeon-general of Pennsylvania, a position he maintained until peace was won. The Friends and his uncle felt violated by Hutchinson's breach of their sacred doctrine of non-resistance, but a letter from Dr. Fothergill, of London, advising him to pursue the course he did, inhibited them from casting him out of the Society.

This avid patriot served from the end of 1778 to February, 1781. While Senior Surgeon to the Flying Hospital in the Middle Department, it is said that with six assistants, he inoculated 3496 men at Valley Forge. When the battle of Monmouth was over, he joined the regiment sent out against Rhode Island, commanded by General Sullivan.

After the British were driven out from Philadelphia, Hutchinson was appointed one of the famous Committee of Safety, and exercised his functions intelligently and with great integrity. The Legislature selected him to be a trustee of the University of Pennsylvania at the age of twenty-seven, and he continued in this capacity for ten years. The chair of professor of materia medica was given to him and after 1791 he was also appointed to the professorship of chemistry. He was a member of the Philosophical Society and served on the medical staff of the Pennsylvania Hospital. Hutchinson was first secretary of the College of Physicians. During the 1793 yellow fever epidemic, he worked feverishly day and night without thought of his own health. He contracted the dread disease and died on September 5, 1793.

Benjamin Rush (1745-1813), considered by many the greatest colonial physician, was born in Byberry Township, Philadelphia County, on December 24, 1745 of Quaker stock. In his youth he attended Reverend Samuel Finley's academy at Nottingham. In 1760 he was awarded a B.A. by Princeton, following which he apprenticed himself to Dr. John Redman. During this period he translated the "Aphorisms of Hippocrates" into English. He at all times maintained a thorough medical notebook and it was from this that the only eye-witness account of the yellow fever epidemic of 1762 in Philadelphia was obtained. Rush attended the first course of lectures on anatomy given by Dr. William Shippen, Jr.

He received his M.D. from Edinburgh in 1768. Concerning his graduation monograph, *De Coctione Ciborum in Ventriculo,* Thacher states that it was written in classic Latin "without the help of a grinder of theses." While Rush was at Edinburgh, his erstwhile preceptor at the academy, Samuel Finley, then president of Princeton College, died, and the famous Dr. Witherspoon, of Paisley in Scotland was appointed as successor. It was only by the forceful efforts of Rush that Witherspoon was influenced to accept the office. After leaving Edinburgh, Rush went to London and then to France to study, returning to Philadelphia in 1769, to be elected professor of chemistry in the College of Philadelphia, to augment the professorships of John Morgan, William Shippen, Jr., and Adam Kuhn. As previously intimated, clinical lectures correlated with their teaching were also given at the Pennsylvania Hospital by Dr. Thomas Bond.

When John Morgan died in 1789, Rush succeeded him to the professorship of the theory and practice of medicine. In 1791, the merger of the College of Philadelphia, with the University of the State of Pennsylvania, led to the appointment of Rush as professor of medicine and clinical medicine in the new institution.

It is said that during the forty-four years in which Rush was actively engaged in teaching he instructed 2,250 pupils. His lectures became famous as models of clarity and thoroughness and his pupils could not help but become affected by the contagiousness of his enthusiasm and lust for medical knowledge.

Let us for a moment consider Cullen's method of disease classification and therapy. According to this method so popular in Rush's day, every ailment had to fit into the classification and receive a specific treatment. Basic principles of physiology, pathology and pharmacology were unnecessary to this artificial classification of diseases and their treatment. Rush vehemently and effectively attacked such an unscientific system of medical practice. A physician of the "old school" thus complimented Rush's method:

In his public instructions, the name of the Disease is comparatively nothing, but its nature everything. His system rejects the nosological arrangement of diseases. . . . . It rejects, likewise, all prescriptions for the names of diseases, and by directing their application wholly to the forming and fluctuating state of diseases, and of the system, derives from a few active medicines all the advantages which have been in vain expected from the numerous articles which compose European treatises upon the materia medica. This simple arrangement was further simplified by considering every morbid state of the system to be of such as neither required repletion or stimulation.

The broadness of Rush as a man and scientist was his greatest attribute. Always ready to admit any error, he steadfastly, without swaying to the right or left, strove to learn the truth about medicine.

Phlebotomy and calomel formed the basis of his therapeutic armamentarium. During the yellow fever epidemic of 1793, Rush and other physicians of Philadelphia were frantically seeking a form of treatment to favorably control the course of this dread plague. Rush chanced to find among some papers in his library a manuscript which had been presented to him by Benjamin Franklin some years previously containing an account of the yellow fever of 1741 in the Province of Virginia, written by a Dr. Mitchell. In this document the author presented the strongest claims of the value of free purgation in the treatment of yellow fever, even in those cases in which an extreme degree of debility and a very feeble pulse had developed. Rush felt that the feeble pulse seen in so many cases was directly caused by "an oppressed state of the system." Grabbing at this straw, he at once proceeded to administer large doses of calomel and jalap to all his yellow fever patients. He also employed bleeding, low caloric diet, high fluid intake and local applications of cold water. He advised that the temperature of the sickroom be kept low.

His method appears to have been attended with great success for his notebook for September 10 declares: "Thank God! out of one hundred patients whom I have visited or prescribed for this day, I have lost none." Rush freely disseminated his method to his colleagues. Patients flocked to him. He himself became afflicted and responded well to his own therapy. He then went back to his patients and worked unceasingly until the epidemic subsided.

Like all great men of undeviating policy, Rush gathered many enemies along the road. When he vehemently declared that yellow fever was directly caused by the filthy condition of the city streets, many Philadelphians openly assailed him. William Cobbett, in *Peter Porcupine's Gazette*, vilified his name unmercifully and Rush successfully sued him for defamation of character. He presented the $5,000 which the court awarded him to charity.

During the yellow fever epidemic if 1797, Rush firmly adhered to his doctrine of bleeding and purgation and again avowed that the disease originated from the filthy condition of certain parts of the city. Dr. Ross in the *United States Gazette* publicly denounced Rush, and Rush's son, John, dispatched a vitriolic reply to Dr. Ross, and later, when words failed, actually caned him. Dr. Ross then challenged Dr. Benjamin Rush to a duel but Rush declined the challenge and published the whole correspondence in the newspapers. The controversy over the yellow fever epidemic of 1797 led to the resignation of Rush from the College of Physicians and the founding of the "Academy of Medicine of Philadelphia" by the adherents of Dr. Rush. Dr. Physick served as the first president of the Academy.

Rush was elected physician to the staff of the Pennsylvania Hospital in 1783 and served in this capacity until his death. It is said that he never missed a daily visit to the institution and was never more than ten minutes late. Numerous reforms and advanced methods were instituted by Dr. Rush in the treatment of the insane.

Rush served as a member of the Provincial Congress of 1776, and as such, signed the Declaration of Independence. On April 11, 1777, Congress appointed him surgeon-general of the medical department of the Continental Army. He became embroiled in the Conway Cabal. Since he openly supported Gates and Samuel Adams in their criticism of what they termed the Fabian policy of Washington, with the collapse of the famous Conway Cabal, Rush realized that his military career was shattered. He therefore resigned and went back to private practice. Rush, of course, was never a conspirator—only a reformer. Washington realized this and later became his personal friend. His military experience led to his writing the "Directions for Preserving the Health of Soldiers," data which was published by order of the Board of War. This is a capable production on military hygiene and camp sanitation. Rush refused all compensation for military services. In 1799 he was appointed Treasurer of the United States Mint, and served in this capacity until his death.

He was an active member of the American Philosophical Society. He was the guiding influence in the founding of the Philadelphia Dispensary in 1786. He assisted in founding the institution now known as Franklin and Marshall College, at Lancaster, Pennsylvania, and also Dickinson College, at Carlisle, Pennsylvania.

He earnestly fought for the freeing of the Negroes, the abolition of the death penalty, and the restriction of the immoderate use of alcohol and tobacco.

Rush's premature philosophy: "Medicine is my wife; science is my mistress; books are my companions; my study is my grave; there I lie buried, the world forgetting, by the world forgot" in later years, after he married and had thirteen children, gave way to "Celibacy is a pleasant breakfast, a tolerable dinner, but a very bad supper. The supper is not only bad, but, eaten alone, no wonder it sometimes becomes a predisposing cause to madness."

A collection of Rush's works was published in seven volumes. He edited various English works including Sydenham. He wrote scientifically on thermic fever, in "An Account of the Disease occasioned by Drinking Cold Water in Warm Weather." His monographs on climatic disease are excellent. His "Medical Inquiries and Observations, on the Diseases of the Mind," found an international market.

Mrs. Rush wrote to Dr. Mease soon after his death, thus describing his last hours:

At nine o'clock in the evening of Wednesday, the fourteenth of April, 1813, Dr. Rush, after having been as well as usual through the day, complained of chilliness and general indisposition, and said he would go to bed. While his room was prepared and a fire making, he became so cold that he called for some brandy and drank it; he then went to his room, bathed his feet in warm water, got into a warm bed, and took some hot drink; a fever soon came on, attended with great pain in his limbs and in his sides; he passed a restless night, but after daylight a perspiration came on, and all the pains were relieved except that in his side, which became more acute. He sent for a bleeder, and had ten ounces of blood taken from his arm, with evident relief. At ten o'clock Dr. Dorsey called and saw him, heard what had been done, and approved of the treatment; observed that his pulse was calm, but rather weak, and advised him to drink plentifully of wine whey, which was immediately given to him. He remained the rest of the day and on Friday with but little apparent disease, though never quite free from fever, and always complaining when he tried to take a long breath. On the morning of Saturday he awoke with an acute pain in his side, and desired that the bleeder might be sent for; to this I objected on account of the weak state of his pulse. I proposed sending for Dr. Dorsey, but Dr. Rush would not consent to his being disturbed; he reminded me of his having had a cough all the winter, and said "this disease is taking hold of my lungs, and I shall go off in a consumption." At eight o'clock Dr. Dorsey saw him, and, upon feeling his pulse, objected to his losing any more blood, and called in Dr. Physick, who agreed in the opinion that bleeding was improper. The pain in his side, however, continuing, and his breathing becoming more difficult, Dr. Physick consented to his losing three ounces of blood from his side by cupping; this operation relieved him so that he fell into a refreshing sleep, and towards the evening of Saturday his fever went off and he passed a comfortable night, and on Sunday morning seemed free from disease. When Dr. Physick saw him, he told me that Dr. Rush was doing well, that nothing now appeared necessary but to give him as much nourishment as he could take; he drank porter and water and conversed with strength and sprightliness, believing that he was getting well, until about four o'clock in the afternoon when his fever returned, but in a moderate degree. At five o'clock Dr. Physick and Dr. Dorsey visited him, and found him not so well as in the morning, but did not appear to apprehend what so soon followed, for at that time nothing was ordered different from the morning. At nine o'clock they again visited him, when they found him so low as to apprehend a fatal termination of his disease. Stimulants of the strongest kind were then administered; you, my friend, know with how little effect!

Benjamin Rush's scientific spirit and open-mindedness become apparent upon reading the preface to the second volume of his "Medical Inquiries and Observations":

The candid reception of a small volume of Inquiries and Observations, published in the year 1788, has encouraged me to offer a second to the public, with the same title. Three of the inquiries were published several years ago; two of them in pamphlets, and the third in the second volume of the American Philosophical Transactions. They are now republished, in their present form, at the request of several of my friends, with the addition, chiefly, of a few notes.

I am aware of the fate of every attempt to introduce new opinions into medicine. My apology for this attempt in some of the following essays is, that I believe the want of success in the treatment of those diseases which are thought to be incurable, is occasioned, in most cases, by an attachment to such theories as are imperfect or erroneous. I do not say, by a want of theory altogether, for it is impossible for a physician to prescribe, without a theory of some kind. I believe further, after all that has been said against theory, and in favour of simple observation in medicine, that uniform and complete success can never be obtained, but by combining with observation a perfect knowledge of all the causes of diseases. Perhaps it would be equally just to assert, that observation will always be extensive, accurate, and useful, in proportion as it is directed by principles in medicine.

I have one more excuse to offer for my temerity in proposing the new opinions which are contained in the following inquiries, and that is, they were not fought for, but obtruded upon me, and that too in spite of a conviction of the certain loss of reputation which follows a change of opinion upon any subject; for I well knew the world was not disposed to admit as a justification of this change, that it is always the necessary effect of the discovery or adoption of new truths; and that stability in principles and practice, in an imperfect science, is, for the most part, the effect of a timid or slothful perseverance in ignorance or error.

In departing in some things from the system of Dr. Cullen, in which I was educated, I do not relinquish the whole of his principles, much less do I reject indiscriminately the systems of authors, whether ancient or modern, of less reputation. Truth in medicine, as far as it has been discovered, like truth in religion, appears to exist in greater or less proportions in different systems; but the fabric which shall include a knowledge of the causes and cure of every disease, remains yet to be completed, by an application to its unfinished parts, of the successive labours of Physicians in generations, or perhaps ages, yet to come.

Had I yielded to personal considerations, I should have kept these papers a few years longer from the public eye, in order that they might have become more correct from the influence which time alone exerts upon all literary performances; but I have preferred at every hazard, sending them thus early into the world, from a desire that my opinions and practice may be corrected, or supported, by the auxiliary observations and reasonings of my medical brethren; and that several formidable diseases may thereby be opposed, not by an individual only, but by the confederated exertions of men of different talents, and situations, in every part of the republic of medicine.

I had another reason for committing these Essays to the press, in their present immature state, and that was, I have observed freedom in thinking, to be necessarily connected with freedom in communicating the result of inquiries after truth. I consider this volume therefore, with all its imperfections, as a pledge of equal boldness, and I hope, of more success, in all future investigations.

PHILADELPHIA,
    4th July, 1793.

In any history of the early days of medicine in Pennsylvania, the names of Samuel Griffitts, William Currie, Hugh Williamson, Adam Kuhn, Abraham Chovet and John Kearsley, Jr., must not be forgotten.

Samuel Powel Griffitts (1759-1826), famous as the founder of the Philadelphia Dispensary, was born in Philadelphia on July 21, 1759. His father passed away while he was still in his infancy and his mother raised him in such a religious atmosphere that his entire life became imbued with religion. Each morning he read from the New Testament in Greek or Latin. Later he became a Friend, and rose high in the estimation of the Society. He attended the College of Philadelphia, received a fine classical education, and learned to speak Latin and French fluently. College completed, he studied medicine under Dr. Adam Kuhn, then professor to a class of materia medica and botany in Philadelphia. He worked with Kuhn until he received his M.D. from the University of Pennsylvania in 1781. Then he furthered his medical education abroad. He studied at Montpellier, travelled through Southern France, studied for several months in London and tarried for a time in Edinburgh, where he studied with Cullen. He returned to Philadelphia in 1784 and practiced medicine there for the rest of his life.

Dr. Griffitts showed his intense zeal for furthering the public health by being the first person to establish a dispensary. The Philadelphia Dispensary was founded in 1786. As manager and attending physician, he served this institution daily. Griffitts was a member of the Pennsylvania Abolition Society, the Society for Alleviating the Miseries of Public Prisons, the Humane Society, and the American Philosophical Society. In 1787 he became one of the original members of the College of Physicians, serving this body as vice president in 1817. He helped organize a pharmacopoeia for the College and in 1795 issued a revised edition of "Buchan's Domestic Medicine."

In 1792 the University of Pennsylvania appointed him professor of materia medica. He helped compile the United States Pharmacopoeia and he read a paper concerning it on June 1, 1820, before the Pharmacopoeial Convention. He died of pneumonia after a short illness on May 12, 1826.

William Currie (1754-1828) was born in Chester County, Pennsylvania, in 1754. His father, a Scotch emigrant and Episcopal minister educated him for the clergy and young Currie received a thorough education in Latin and Greek, and some knowledge of Hebrew. Always intellectually honest, even when young, he sincerely objected to some of the opinions promulgated in the Thirty-nine Articles, and therefore he refused to make his profession the ministry. Instead, he apprenticed himself to Dr. Kearsley and then attended the medical lectures at the College of Philadelphia. However, he never received a diploma.

Soon after the War of Independence commenced, he entered the American Army as a surgeon and in 1776 was assigned to the military hospital on Long Island, and later transferred to Amboy. After the War he entered upon the practice of medicine in Chester. In 1792, he was elected to the American Philosophical Society. He wrote for volume four of the Transactions of this society an article "On the Insalubrity of Flat and Marshy Situations; and Directions for Preventing or Correcting the Effects thereof." On December 6, 1820, he authored a report to the joint committee of the City Councils relative to the yellow fever epidemic of 1820 published in the "Report of the Malignant or Pestilential Disease of the Summer and Autumn of 1820, in the City of Philadelphia," 1821. He served on the Board of Health and was senior physician of the Magdalen Asylum.

It is said that Dr. Currie treated the poor unstintingly and without charge, and even gave money to the most needy, that his knowledge of medical literature was unsurpassed and that his practice was large and lucrative. He was unpretentious in dress and manner. Occasionally he satirically would give vent to his distaste for some of the foibles of his medical opponents, but he never let malice enter the issue. He unhesitatingly gave credit to his enemies when he deemed that such was due.

His health permanently failed in 1816, after his wife most unfortunately died, and he became senile. He died on June 12, 1828, at the age of seventy-four.

Hugh Williamson (1735-1819) was born in West Nottingham, Chester County, Pennsylvania, on December 5, 1735. He received a good preliminary education, and then enrolled in the College of Philadelphia. He received an A.B. from this institution in 1757. The University of Pennsylvania awarded him an A.M. in 1760 and an LL.D. in 1787. At first his inclinations led him toward the clergy and he even became a licentiate. Religious friction and a respiratory ailment, however, combined in directing his attention toward medicine. He pursued his medical studies at Edinburgh and in London and then received his M.D. at Utrecht in 1772.

All sciences intrigued this amazing man. In 1769, he wrote with others on the transit of Venus. He formulated theories concerning the comet of 1769. He wrote an article on the "Variation of Climate in North America." This scientific monograph brought him honorary memberships from Holland and an honorary LL.D. He then interested himself in collecting funds from the West Indies and England for the Academy of Newark, Delaware. The King of England thought enough of Williamson personally to give a donation in spite of the fact that he was on the outs with his American subjects.

Williamson was first to bring tidings of the Boston Tea Party and he advised the Privy Council to employ conciliatory measures. After the War of Independence began, Williamson, always wide awake, learned of the secret correspondence to crush young America which was transpiring between Hutchinson and the British Cabinet officers.

He cleverly made off with these letters and sent them to Franklin. Naturally, he departed from London the next day.

In the midst of these adventures that rocked the foundation of nations, Williamson found time to engage in scientific experiments with John Hunter and Franklin. He presented a paper before the Royal Society in London entitled: "On the Gymnotus Electricus or Electric Eel." After the signing of the Declaration of Independence, Williamson hastened back to Philadelphia to search for a post as army surgeon. Finding no suitable opening available, this versatile man bought a sloop and engaged in mercantile voyaging to the West Indies with his brother from South Carolina.

While in South Carolina he took time off to travel to Newbern and inoculate for smallpox. The year 1779 saw the metamorphosis of the merchant back to the doctor again. He was appointed surgeon to the North Carolina Militia and served capably in treating his own troops and prisoners. When the war ended, he was elected for three years to the House of Commons of North Carolina. In 1787 he was sent to Philadelphia as delegate to the United States Constitutional Convention.

He wrote a monumental work entitled "Climate from a Medical Point of View" and another on "The Fevers of North Carolina."

In 1805 he published his "Report as Commissioner to Inquire into the Origin of the New York Yellow Fever Epidemic in 1805." In 1812 his two-volume History of North Carolina appeared. The death of his elder son in 1811 deeply affected him but drove him even more zealously to engage in constructive enterprise for country and state. It is said that he arrived to the first month of his eighty-fifth year, with "the punctuality and ability he had brought to his never decreasing duties being a continual source of surprise to his juniors."

On May 22, 1819, a very hot day, while taking his customary ride, he suddenly dropped dead.

Adam Kuhn (1741-1817) was born at Germantown near Philadelphia on November 17, 1741. Dr. Adam Simon Kuhn, his father, emigrated from Hellbronn and reached Philadelphia in September, 1733. The younger Kuhn completed his preliminary medical studies under the tutelage of his father. He then left for Europe in 1761 and travelled to London and then to Upsala.

The elder Kuhn must have indeed been a proud father when he received the following letter from Linnaeus himself dated February 24, 1763, written in classical Latin: "He is unwearied in his studies and daily and faithfully studies materia medica with me. He has learnt the symptomatic history of diseases in an accurate and solid manner.

In natural history and botany he made remarkable progress. He has studied anatomy and physiology with other professors."

Kuhnia eupatoriodes (Linnaeus) named by the old master for his American disciple commemorates their friendship as do numerous personal and friendly letters. One declares: "I pray and entreat thee send some seeds and plants among which I ardently desire the seeds of the 'Kuhnia,' which perished in our garden."

In 1764, Kuhn went to London to continue his studies. In 1767 Edinburgh awarded him an M.D. degree. His doctoral dissertation, dedicated to Linnaeus, was named "De Lavatione Frigida." Kuhn also sojourned for a brief time in France, Holland and Germany. Then he came back to Philadelphia and in 1768 was appointed professor of materia medica and botany at the University of Pennsylvania. In 1774 it is reported that he was busy immunizing the population against smallpox during the great epidemic. Kuhn's signature as professor of materia medica and botany in the College and Academy of Philadelphia is imprinted upon the diploma of John Archer, dated 1768. The College of Physicians and Surgeons, Baltimore, prides itself on this possession.

Dr. Charles Caldwell is responsible for this more or less unfriendly picture of him:

He was by far the most highly and minutely furnished specimen of old-school medical production I have ever beheld. He wore a fashionable curled and powdered wig, his breeches were black, a long skirted buff or white waistcoat, his coat snuff colored. He carried a gold headed cane and a gold snuffbox; his knee and shoe buckles of the same metal. His footsteps were sternly and stubbornly regular; he entered the sick-room at a given minute and stayed a given time and never suffered deviation from his directions. "Doctor, if the patient should desire toast, water or lemonade he may have it?" asked the nurse sometimes. He would turn and reply with oracular solemnity, "I have directed weak sage tea. Good morning, madam."

Kuhn served as physician to the Pennsylvania Hospital and consulting physician to the Philadelphia Dispensary. He was one of the founders of the College of Physicians of Philadelphia, and in 1808 was elected president of this august body. He was professor of the theory and practice of medicine at the University of Pennsylvania in 1789, and when the two medical schools merged, he was appointed professor of the practice of physic (1792-1797). He either did not produce much medical research or his writings have been lost down through the years. A short letter addressed to Dr. Lettsom has survived concerning "Diseases Succeeding Transplantation of Teeth."

He denounced Rush's regime in yellow fever when he published his own in *The General Advertiser* (September 11, 1793).

He did not marry until he was thirty-nine after which he had two sons, by his wife Elizabeth, daughter of Isaac Tartman of St. Croix.

Adam Kuhn died on July 5, 1817, after a short illness.

The progress of anatomy in the new world was further assisted when Abraham Chovet arrived in Philadelphia in 1774.

Abraham Chovet (1704-1790) was born in England on May 25, 1704. It is recorded that he joined the Company of Barber-Surgeons in London on February 5, 1734 and that on August 15, 1734 he was appointed demonstrator of anatomy to this guild. As early as 1732, Chovet published "A Syllabus or Index of all the Parts that enter the Composition of the Human Body" in London. This work describes wax models which he had constructed that covered the whole field of anatomy. He also explained the method of making corrosion specimens including facsimiles of the arteries made by injecting actual blood vessels with colored wax and then destroying the tissues by means of caustic alkalis or acids. Chovet made his residence in Leicester Square, London, later the abode of John Hunter, and successfully practiced surgery. It should be stated that prior to William Hunter and his insistance on actual dissection in the teaching of anatomy (London, 1746), this science was studied with the aid of wax models. It was under Chovet that the old fashioned pre-Hunterian methods reached their peak of perfection. The following advertisement appeared in December, 1733:

"To be seen this day and for the future, price 5s. at Mr. Lamark's, Surgeon, in Orange Street, Leicester Fields, Mr. Chovet, the surgeon's New Figure of Anatomy, which represents a woman chained down upon a table, suppos'd opened alive; wherein the circulation of the blood is made visible through glass veins and arteries; the circulation is also seen from the mother to the child, and from the child to the mother, with the Sistolick and Diastolick motion of the heart and the action of the lungs. All which particulars, with several others will be shown and clearly explained by Mr. Chovet himself. Note, a Gentlewoman qualified will attend the ladies."

Dr. Physick, of Philadelphia, explained why Chovet left England by giving credence to the story that Chover had performed a tracheotomy on a criminal prior to hanging with the result that he carried on an excellent conversation after the hangman was through with him. The authorities of law and order, of course, did not appreciate such a demonstration of surgical skill and Chovet found it best to seek a healthier climate.

More authentic records show that in 1754 a prize ship arrived in the Barbados with a quantity of wax and that Chovet, then residing at this port, employed some of this wax to make some anatomical models. The year 1759 found him in Kingston, Jamaica, accompanied by his wife and widowed daughter. He set sail for Philadelphia to avoid a slave insurrection.

The *Pennsylvania Journal and Weekly Advertiser* and *The Pennsylvania Gazette* for October and November, 1774, carried advertisements listing the time and place in Philadelphia of lectures on anatomy and physiology by Abraham Chovet. Accounts of his first lecture which was attended by "his Honour the Governor, the Trustees and Faculty of the College, the Clergy, the Doctors of Physic, the Students of Medicine, and a considerable number of the most respectable inhabitants of the City" were also included.

The following announcement is also of interest:

AT THE ANATOMICAL MUSEUM

in Videl's Alley; Second Street, on Wednesday, the Seventh of December (1774-5) at six in the evening

Dr. Chovet

will begin his course of Anatomical and Physiological Lectures, in which the several parts of the human body will be demonstrated, with their mechanism and actions, together with the doctrines of life, health and the several effects resulting from the actions of the parts; on his curious collection of Anatomical wax-works, and other natural preparations; to be continued the whole winter until the course is completed. As this course cannot be attended with the disagreeable sight or smell of recent disease, or putrid carcases, which often disgust even the students in Physick, as well as the curious, otherwise inclined to this useful and sublime part of natural philosophy, it is hoped this undertaking will meet with suitable encouragement.

Thus, Chovet capitalized on the cleanliness of his exhibit in comparison with the foul stench present at the exhibits of his competitors such as Shippen who used actual cadavers.

In his house on Water Street, Chovet accumulated an anatomical museum. In 1777 he built an amphitheater in which he gave his lectures in 1778. We have it on the personal observation of John Adams, who examined the specimens in 1774, that they were finer than those used by Dr. Shippen in the University of Pennsylvania. The eminent Frenchman, Marquis de Chastellux, visited Chovet in 1780 and declared that his models were of a higher quality than those used at Bologna. Thomas G. Morton describes Chovet's collection as "A very remarkable collection of anatomical preparations including dried, injected and painted specimens, together with a series of beautiful wax models."

Chovet was a small man with a great sense of humor always on the look-out for a chance to perpetrate a practical joke. He was one of the group that organized the College of Physicians of Philadelphia in 1787. Chovet remained a vehement Royalist during the War of Independence, but he was so well liked that no one persecuted him for his outspoken convictions. He passed away on March 24, 1790. Chovet's anatomical collections were eventually bought up by the Managers of the Pennsylvania Hospital to join the Fothergill group in the hospital museum. Unfortunately, while exhibited at the University of Pennsylvania, the collection was destroyed by fire (1888). The Pennsylvania Hospital owns a wax medallion of Dr. Chovet, inscribed "Abraham Chovet, born May 25, 1704, drawn May 25, 1784, by his servant Dr. Eckhout."

The following description is of Dr. Chovet in his last years:

This aged physician was almost daily to be seen pushing his way in spite of his feebleness, in a kind of hasty walk, or rather shuffle, his head and straight white hair bound and hanging forward beyond the cape of his black old-fashioned coat, mounted by a small cocked hat, closely trimmed upward upon the crown behind, but projectingly and out of all proportion cocked before, and seemingly the impelling cause of his anxious forward movements, his lips, closely compressed (sans teeth) together, were in constant motion, as though he were munching something all the time; his golden-headed Indian cane, not used for his support, but dangling by a black silken string from his wrist; the ferule of his cane and the heels of his capacious shoes, well lined in winter time with thick woolen cloth, might be heard jingling and shaking the pavement at every step; he seemed on the street always as one hastening as fast as aged limbs would permit him to some patient dangerously ill, without looking at any one passing him to the right or left.

Chovet died "of an acute disease" on March 24, 1790, at the age of eighty-six, and was buried in Christ Church Cemetery, Philadelphia.

The only other prominent Tory physician in Philadelphia was John Kearsley, Jr., nephew of the architect of Christ Church, who emigrated from London to practice with his uncle in Philadelphia. Unquestionably a talented physician, he wrote on the "Angina Maligna" or "Putrid Sore Throat." He was instrumental in establishing the Philadelphia Medical Society in 1766.

On August 6, 1775, Isaac Hunt, a Tory lawyer was forced by a frenzied mob to parade about the streets and express publicly the error of his opinions.

Hunt was taken to the corner in front of Dr. Kearsley's house for another recital. Kearsley, in a rage threw open his window, pulled out a revolver and fired twice upon the crowd. The mob thereupon rushed into his house, overpowered him, disarmed him, and forced him, although wounded in the hand, to go to the Coffee House. No terrors or ignominy could get the doctor to publicly proclaim the error of his ways. The crowd, with drum beating, then paraded him through the streets, eventually taking him back to his house. The Associators, who guarded him, did not permit tarring and feathering, but after they had gone, his house was ravaged by the angry patriots.

In October, 1775, Kearsley was arrested for treasonable correspondence with the British, which crime included the sending of a map and military information to the enemy. At first he was sent to Lancaster. The Council of Safety at Philadelphia learned that he was seeking his release after he had "insinuated himself in the good Graces of a number of your Inhabitants and that they have applied for his enlargement, in order to attend them as a physician." He then was sent to Carlisle, where he appears to have lost his mind completely. He died in November, 1777.

The College of Philadelphia was originally located in a building on Fourth Street which had been built by voluntary contributions to make room for the crowds that came to hear the preaching of the Reverend George Whitefield in 1741. Medical lectures were also given in this building. Dr. Shippen, however, gave his courses in anatomy and midwifery in rooms in the rear of his father's house, at Fourth Street above Market.

The idea to establish the College of Physicians of Philadelphia goes back to 1767 when John Morgan proposed such an organization to Thomas Penn. In 1783, Samuel Powel Griffitts stated that the concept of a College of Physicians had occurred to him several times previously. It was not until September, 1786, that the College was actually partially organized and the first election of officers took place in October, 1786. The first meeting of the full organization took place on January 2, 1787. The officers of the College during this meeting were John Redman, president, John Jones, vice president, Gerardus Clarkson, treasurer, James Hutchinson, secretary, William Shippen, Jr., John Morgan and Benjamin Rush, censors, and Adam Kuhn.

The constitution of the College of Physicians was duly signed by the aforementioned officers and by Samuel Duffield, Thomas Parke, George Glentworth, Abraham Chovet, Andrew Ross, William W. Smith, James Hall, William Clarkson, William Currie, Benjamin Say, Samuel Powel Griffitts, Benjamin Duffield, John Morris, John Carson, John Foulke and Robert Harris. The constitution was published in the *Pennsylvania Packet and Daily Advertiser* on February 1, 1787.

The constitution declares the purposes of the College to be

.... to advance the Science of Medicine, and thereby to lessen Human Misery, by investigating the diseases and remedies which are peculiar to our Country, by observing the effects of different seasons, climates, and situations upon the Human body, by recording the changes that are produced in diseases by the progress of Agriculture, Arts, Population, and Manners, by searching for Medicines in our Woods, Waters, and the bowels of the Earth, by enlarging our avenues to knowledge from the discoveries and publications of foreign Countries; by appointing stated times for Literary intercourse and communications, and by cultivating order and uniformity in the practice of Physick.

On March 26, 1789, "An Act for the Incorporation of the College of Physicians" was passed and this enactment served as the charter for the infant organization.

The first home of the College of Physicians between the years 1787 and 1791 was the old college of the University of Pennsylvania.

Chapter Thirteen

GEORGIA

GEORGIA, THE LAST English colony to be founded on American soil, was named after King George II of England. James Edward Oglethorpe, the spark plug behind the establishment of the colony, unquestionably sought to protect South Carolina from the French in Louisiana and the Spanish in Florida as well as to provide a haven for the persecuted Protestant groups and various worthy indigent classes in Europe.

In 1732, a charter and 10,000 pounds were granted by the crown and parliament for this new colonial enterprise. Oglethorpe personally directed the establishment of the first settlement at Savannah in 1733. The original groups of colonists consisted of Piedmontese, German Lutherans (Salzburgers), Moravians, Scottish Highlanders, Swiss, English and Portuguese Jews. However, extensive colonization did not begin until 1752, when large numbers began arriving from the Carolinas and Virginia.

The "Trustees for establishing the colony of Georgia in America" suggested the cultivation of wine grapes, silk, hemp and medicinal herbs in the new colony for the purpose of making England independent of foreign trade for these products. They insisted that the settlers raise mulberry trees (silkworm culture), and forbade the sale of rum, which was a major commercial staple. They did not permit negro slavery. But the economy of the colony proved to be unsuccessful and unremunerative. The industries did not flourish and, as labor was short, restricted importation of slaves was begun in 1749. The prohibition on the sale of rum was relaxed at about the same time. The year 1753 saw the original charter expire and Georgia became a royal province.

Under direct British rule, Georgia rapidly became a land of prosperity. It is an unquestioned fact that the people of Georgia joined the War of Independence out of sympathy with the other colonies and not out of personal animosity toward the mother country. Revolutionary doctrines flourished, particularly in St. John's Parish, which was colonized primarily by New Englanders from Dorchester, Massachusetts. The Loyalist section of the Georgia population was so powerful that only five of the twelve parishes bothered electing representatives to the First Provincial Congress and the Georgia delegates to the Continental Congress did not feel justified in claiming any seats. However, one half year later, all the parishes elected representatives to another Provincial Congress, which met on July 4, 1775. The royal government then rapidly lost all power and colonial administration was taken over by a council of safety.

In certain respects, the War of Independence inflicted deeper wounds in Georgia than elsewhere, for the Revolutionary and Loyalist parties were about numerically equal. Savannah was conquered by the English in 1778 and the occupation of this heart of Georgia was continued until 1782. In 1779, Augusta and Sunbury were captured. After 1780, the Revolutionary forces gradually gained the upper hand.

In the formation of the United States government, Georgia's policy was one of maintaining a powerful central government. On January 2, 1788, Georgia was the fourth state to ratify the Federal Constitution and one of the three states to do so unanimously. However, a series of conflicts between the Georgia state government and the Federal government led to a decline in nationalistic sentiment and an increase in the influence of those who fought for states rights.

The excellent articles of Dr. J. Calvin Weaver and Dr. Joseph Krafka, Jr. provide the basis for this chapter.

The medical history of Georgia begins back in England when one Mr. Cox, surgeon, at a meeting of the Trustees of the Colony of Georgia in November 1732, at Palace Court, London, proffered his medical services gratis to the emigrants for one year with the stipulation that a house be built for him and that his land be cared for by the other colonists. At this meeting a resolution was passed to secure a set of instruments and a chest of medicine for the good surgeon. However, the latter stipulation was later rescinded.

There is no proof that Mr. Cox ever came to Georgia. Certainly no headstone in Savannah bears his name. However, there is record that in July 1733, Garden 52E was allotted to Frances, relict of Dr. Wm. Cox.

The minutes of the meetings of the trustees show that various medicinal products were dispatched to Georgia by friends of the settlers. These include two barrels and three bottles containing twenty-three deer skin's weight of "Bears Oyl" and packages of sassafras, sumac, sea rod, snake root, rattle-snake root, China root and contrayerva.

On November 17, 1732, Oglethorpe and his party set sail for Georgia. About one hundred and thirty passengers from about thirty-five families were on board. The vessel reached the coast of Charleston on January 13, 1733, and was dispatched to Beaufort, while Oglethorpe investigated to find a suitable location for the colony.

It took a month to locate a suitable site and receive permission from the old Indian Chief, Tomochichi, to use the area. The settlers then made their home near Yamacraw Bluff, the location of a trading post, and habitat of a tribe of Yamacraw Indians ruled by the aforementioned chief. Tomochichi remained on friendly terms with the colonists all the days of his life.

On February 13, 1733, the colony left Beaufort and arrived in Savannah. Four stately pines were grouped on the bluff and these supplied shade for the four tents that were pitched for the colonists. The settlers were soon greeted by the local Indians:

In front advanced, with antic dancings, the 'medicine man,' bearing in each hand a spreaded fan of white feathers, fastened to a rod hung from top to bottom with little bells; marching behind this jingling symbol of peace and friendship, came the king and queen, followed by about twenty others, making the air ring with their uncouth shouts. Approaching Oglethorpe, who walked out a few steps from his tent to meet them, the 'medicine man' came forward with his fans, declaiming the while the deeds of their ancestors, and stroked him on every side with the emblem of amity.

The first trained physician known positively to have landed on Georgia's shore was Noble Jones. Shortly after his arrival he wrote to the Trustees about the location of Savannah, as follows:

Our people are all in perfect health. I chose the situation for the town upon high ground, forty feet perpendicular above high water mark; the soil dry and sandy; the water of the river fresh and springs coming out of the hill. I pitched upon this place not only for the pleasantness of the situation, but because, from the above mentioned, and other signs, I thought it healthy.

It is said that General Oglethorpe himself was possessed of considerable information concerning the medical art and it is a fact that his friend, Colonel Noble Jones, had received an M.D. degree. Jones originated from Lambeth County, Surrey, England, and appears to have been adept in the art of politics as well as medicine. He served as member of the King's Council, as assistant to Patrick Graham, President of the Colony, as Treasurer of the Province and as Military Commander. Jones became the first judge of the General Court under Gov. Reynolds, some twenty years after his arrival.

The "Early Epitaphs in Georgia" contains the following epitaph of the elder Jones:

DR. NOBLE JONES

Noble Jones, Esquire, of Wormsloe, Senior Judge of the General Court and acting Chief Justice of the Province of Georgia. For twenty-one years member and sometimes President of his Majesty's Council, Colonel of the First Georgia Regiment, died Nov. 2, 1775, aged seventy-three.

Dr. Hans Sloane, famous Court Physician, personally supported a botanist in New Spain, so that valuable medicinal herbs might be sent to the new colony of Georgia. The Apothecary Company was desirous of raising ipecac, tolu, Jesuit's bark, and contrayerva in Georgia. This company fought energetically to crack the Spanish monopoly on cochineal. It should be recalled that the cochineal industry involved a highly remunerative trade. Eight hundred thousand pounds of dried scale reached Europe in 1734, valued at 15,500,690 francs. The Spanish monopoly in Mexico was maintained by inflicting the death penalty on anyone attempting to break it. It is related that Thiery de Menonville succeeded in surreptitiously obtaining a stock of the insects in violation of this decree. He succeeded in transplanting them but the revolution at Port au Prince in one fell swoop destroyed his collection.

Dr. Sloane appointed one Dr. William Houstoun to the highly important post of Botanist to the Trustees, but he died six months later. Then Dr. Sloane selected Robert Millar to replace him. Millar was a member of the Royal Society.

It is said that Dr. Sloane was the first British physician to be made a baronet and that he personally supervised the inoculation of Princesses Amelia and Caroline in 1722 and Prince William in 1724. Sloane was a charter member of the Royal Society and eventually became its president. As editor of the 4th edition of the *London Pharmacopeia*, he included in this monumental work numerous American drugs including ipecac, stramonium and seneca.

The famous Rev. Dr. Stephen Hales, also took a keen interest in the founding of Georgia. It was Hales who devised a method of direct blood pressure recording. He inserted a glass cannula into the carotid artery of a horse. Trustee of the new colony, he solicited financial aid for the colonists from the congregations of England. Hales concerned himself greatly with the converting of the Indians. He collected the following for the infant Colony: 200 Primers, 200 Horn Books, and 500 *Friendly Admonitions to Drinkers of Brandy*. When Lord Egmont was away, Dr. Hales frequently presided at the meetings of the Board of Trustees.

Notwithstanding the eminence of Sloane and Hales, we find the medical chests of one of the vessels sailing to Georgia containing one thousand of Dr. Ward's pills. Ward and his remedies became famous in the annals of quackery.

Robert Millar's importations into Georgia consisted, among other things, of one tub of white mulberry plants, two papers of Egyptian kali or potash seed, one box of tellicherry bark, one paper of cotton seed, one tub of Burgundy vines, two gallons of lucerne seed, one olive tree, over fifty caper plants, and one tub of madder root. In a letter from Kingston he declared that he would try to get jalap, sarsaparilla, contrayerva and cochineal. In another letter, he writes that the Spanish have forbidden him to search Florida for medicinal herbs. After colliding with a bulkhead of official opposition he appealed to the Duke of Richmond to obtain a license for him from the Court of Spain. In 1737, the Duke of Richmond obtained this license signed by the Count de Montijo and addressed to Lord Don Joseph Vizarron, Bishop and Vice Governor of Mexico.

Millar departed from Jamaica on the South Sea Company ship, the *St. Thomas*. He sojourned to Porto Bello and then to Panama in his quest for Jesuit's bark and Balsam of Peru. His quest was not very successful for only a few seeds are listed among the contents of his shipment to his brother in Chelsea.

Carrying his valuable epistle to the governor, Millar sailed to Cartagena on the *Don Carlos*. He at once departed for Mompon to look for ipecacuanha and gum capaiva. He sailed on the *Charming Jolly* to Campeche to obtain contrayerva transplants, and shipped to Vera Cruz to obtain the much desired lac cochineal. In this case, however, he was forcibly kept on board ship by order of the governor. His protests to Don Manuel Lopes Pintado, Admiral of Florida, were in vain and he was returned to Havana on a man of war. The captain had Millar transferred to an English ship just prior to their reaching the Spanish port.

Millar states remorsefully in a letter that "there is no getting the jesuit's bark." He suggested the culture of indigo, as a substitute.

Millar's health was finally affected by his lengthy peregrinations. He stated that he was a victim of the "severest sickness,—except for the long dismal touch last in London." Changes of climate did not help ameliorate his recurrent bouts of fever. Relapse after relapse would follow any apparent partial recovery. Millar's quest ended when war with Spain was declared in 1740, and there were no further large scale efforts to introduce foreign plants into Georgia.

The illnesses suffered by the early colonists are worthy of some discussion. Thomas Stephens died of cancer of the foot. Lord Egmont ailed from the gout. Col. Harvey, governor of North Carolina, died of a stroke and Captain Lacy, founder of Augusta, died of drink. "Fevers" and "bloody flux" were widely disseminated.

The trip to Georgia was certainly not conducive to good health. All meats carried on board were pickled. John Brownfield mentions that when a barrel of beef on board ship was opened, the meat, which had been pickled in August, was definitely unfit for human consumption. The opened barrel was then generously donated to the channel pilot and five other barrels of similar antiquity were sent back to London to be sold in the public market.

The lengthy delays while the ships lay wind bound in the Channel harbors were conducive to considerable imbibing of spirits. The aforementioned Brownfield insisted upon the poor white servants attending to their personal hygiene, and he deported two women for drunkenness. A surgeon's servant was returned because of an itch. When the vessel upon which Brownfield made the journey eventually put into Charleston harbor, the captain ordered fresh water aboard in order that the servants might wash their dirty linen. This water was obtained at a price of one pound sterling. Captain Shubrick reported an outbreak of ship's fever among his passengers while his vessel lay wind bound in West Cow Road.

The mortality produced by such unhygienic conditions naturally was often high. On one voyage, out of 172 who started the trip, 40 died in transit.

Epidemical malignant fever (considered by some authorities as yellow fever) struck Savannah in 1742. William Stephens refers to this ailment as a contagion that seizes people in the head, causing it to swell. He states that some drop dead from this disease. The Georgia climate was more moderate than in Spain and the drinking water of Savannah was of good quality. "Rum Fever" developed in Charleston, but not in Savannah. John Wesley personally vouched for the fact that one could sleep without harm from rain or dew. A high mortality of the newborn was recorded.

Mention is made of a few local popular methods of therapy. Daffy's Elixir and "capillaire" are referred to. It should be recalled that Bousquet's Capillaire, made in London, is referred to in the *Autobiography of Benjamin Franklin.* Reference is made to the fact that "Miss Becky was bled four ounzes and died." Laporte gave the Trustees a bottle of Salistrum seed, "a cure for the flux."

President Stephens' journal makes mention of a visit to Ebenezer to inspect the saw-mill. While in this city he noted a Moravian servant "with a full-blown crop of smallpox" and yet working without difficulty.

Colonial Georgia had its unethical and base physicians as well as its medical heroes. Dr. Patrick Tailfer (Taillfor) (Tailfeur), an apothecary surgeon, arrived in the colony in its first days. His patron was Dr. Robert Houston of Glasgow, who paid his "consideration moneys." By 1739, Tailfer gave up farming to engage in the rum trade. Many of the citizens of Savannah managed to get in his debt. As leader of the "Scot's faction," he was anxious to legalize both rum and slaves. Nightly orgies were held at Jenkins' Tavern. Vile and underhand letters were sent to General Oglethorpe. Anonymous rabble-rousing proclamations were posted in the public square. Minor enmities between officials were fanned into hot fires. Tailfer succeeding in keeping Causton and Thomas Jones in a constant belligerent state and turned young Stephens against his father. Horse-racing and betting poured huge sums into his pockets. He sought vast profits as leader of the negro slave trade.

Tailfer's star flew high but not for long. In 1739 the Spanish attacked Amelia and he appointed himself Captain of a "company of Juntillo" to defend Savannah. He quickly showed his true character, however, by turning over his business enterprises to Duchee, the potter, and fleeing for his personal safety to Charleston. In 1741, while in Charleston, he published a denunciation of Oglethorpe.

Leaving this medical reprobate, let us probe into the life of Doctor Patrick Graham. Graham served as both surgeon and apothecary for the Trustees and helped make his living by farming. He accumulated 50 pounds from the sale of mulberry seedlings collected at Purrysburg at the rate of a penny a plant. Graham presented a bill for physic administered at Savannah from Nov. 30, 1737, to Oct. 4, 1739. This bill, among other things, was for medical service rendered to soldiers sick at Savannah while on their way to Frederica, during the war with Spain. In March, 1740, Graham married the widow of Captain Cuthbert, allegedly to complete her cure.

He became the third president of the colony in the interim between the withdrawal of Oglethorpe and the appointment of royal governors. The first appointee was Reynolds and Graham acted as his chief adviser in his capacity as head of the King's Council, in 1754. When Graham died in 1755, the Council granted his widow an additional tract of land even though he had already built up a good estate.

Some of the less conspicuous or less known physicians were Dr. Christian Thylo (Thilo), surgeon to the Salzburgers, who was the only physician in the northern part of the province in 1742, and Henry Garret, "chymist." One Dr. Precott, whose abode fronted on the Ogeechee River, received a land grant. Dr. Perkins lived on Cathead Creek, near William MacIntosh's place on the Sapello.

The story of Dr. Samuel Nunez Ribiero must be mentioned in any history of medicine in colonial Georgia. White received the information in the following account from M. M. Noah, Esq.:

Dr. Samuel Nunez of Lisbon was one of the foremost practitioners in that city at a time when the Jews were already being persecuted under the Inquisition. Colleagues, begrudging the good man his well earned success, denounced him to the tribunal of the Inquisition and he and his family were arrested and thrown into the dungeons as heretics.

This was one of the many sad epochs in Jewish history. Jews who could not openly seek their Lord according to their faith, customarily got together secretly in each other's homes and read Hebrew prayer-books pulled out of secret compartments in the seats of the chairs. Spies of the Inquisition readily ascertained that many Jewish families spent their Sabbath in concealed Jewish prayer, even though they outwardly accepted the State religion and attended mass. Promptly the Hebrew prayer-books were confiscated and their owners taken into custody.

Dr. Nunez, a man of fine personality and proven medical skill, became physician to the Grand Inquisitor himself. The Grand Inquisitor did his best to ameliorate the sufferings of the doctor's family. None-the-less, his kinswoman, Abby de Lyon, who passed away in Savannah, carried to her grave the impression left by ropes on her wrists when put to the question.

Lisbon soon missed the medical services of Dr. Nunez and the ecclesiastical council, spurred by the Grand Inquisitor, freed him and his family. Two officials of the Inquisition were appointed to live with his family to prevent another relapse into Judaism.

Dr. Nunez's fine estate on the banks of the Tagus was often visited by the nobility. One summer's day, as was customary, a dinner party was held at the mansion. This was not unusual but what was out of the ordinary was the fact that the captain of an English brigantine anchored in the river attended the affair. As the rest of the guests enjoyed themselves on the lawn, the captain, innocently enough, invited the Nunez family and, of course, the spies of the Inquisition, to board his vessel and partake of a repast. While all were below in the cabin, the anchor was pulled in, the sails unfurled, and the ship soon left the Tagus and was out at sea. The entire group was conveyed to England without mishap. Of course, this entire desperate adventure had been arranged between Nunez and the captain and the latter received one thousand moidores in gold for his services. Dr. Nunez had converted as much of his wealth as he could into gold which was distributed among the gentlemen of the family and carried in hidden compartments in their leather belts. The ladies had secreted their jewels on their persons. Needless to say, Nunez's estate, mansion, furniture, servants and equipage, were all subsequently seized by the Inquisition and confiscated to the State.

It happened that at the time Dr. Nunez and his family reached London, the settlement of Georgia was the subject of much favorable speculation. The entire group promptly joined the party of Oglethorpe which was embarking to the new colony. It is said that not a single one of these people who were to become founders of Georgia could speak the English language.

Zipra Nunez married Rabbi David Machado, minister of the Hebrew congregation of New York. Major Noah remembered that his great-great-grandmother, Zipra Nunez, was a very practical personage, who lived until nearly ninety years of age. Zipra in her prime was said to have been both beautiful and accomplished. She is said to have spoken several languages fluently. Whenever the clock struck, it was her habit to repeat a silent prayer referring to her imprisonment during the Inquisition.

All members of the Nunez family adhered rigidly to their religion. Two of her brothers, who came aboard the same vessel from London, lie buried in the Jewish cemetery in Chatham Square, New York. Many of the descendants of the Nunez family living in Savannah, Charleston, Philadelphia and New York, still adhere to the Hebrew faith.

It is recorded that on July 11, 1733, Dr. Nunez and his mother, Mrs. Nunez, Daniel, Moses and Sipia Nunez, and Shem Noah, their servant, arrived with a party of about forty Jews. The Trustees vehemently objected to granting land to the Jews in Georgia, and informed Oglethorpe accordingly. Oglethorpe, none-the-less, submitted a eulogy of Dr. Nunez's medical services rendered to the settlers (1734). The Trustees eventually directed Oglethorpe to reimburse this fine physician for his services. Dr. Nunez, besides treating the colonists, also maintained a pharmacy—probably the first in Georgia.

Dr. Nunez, in spite of the great good he had wrought, soon realized that he was not welcome in the new colony. "Israelite that he was, a gentleman of education, a humane and skillful physician, when notified that the benevolent effort to improve the condition of the settlers of Georgia did not extend to Jews and Roman Catholics, removed at once, in 1740, with his family, to a more generous community. He made his home in Charleston, in the colony of South Carolina. Not many years later, the grand spirit of freedom that pervaded the land led to the declaration that our government was not a respector of religious creeds, and that Jew and Gentile should find equal protection under its liberal institution." Dr. Nunez was lost to Georgia, and Georgia's loss was South Carolina's gain.

The following poem illustrative of South Carolina's tolerance was addressed to the editor of the *Georgia Gazette* on April 14, 1774:

> The generous, open, scientific mind
>   Its true benevolence extends,
> The wise respect alike all human kind
>   Stern foes to vice, to virtue steady friends,
> Truly to grace the Carolinian name,
>   Let naught like envy influence your views,
> Urbanity in every act proclaim
>   Whether to Indians, Georgians or to Jews.

That Dr. Nunez passed on before 1800 is indicated by the fact that Mrs. Zipporah Jacobs, "daughter of the late Dr. Nunez" is recorded as having died in Philadelphia on November 19, 1800 at the age of eighty-six.

Another Jewish colonist, Abraham de Lyon, by name, deserves mention as the vigneron of the colony, and the introducer of valuable foreign plants and drugs into the colony. He strove in every way to improve Georgia's horticulture.

East of Savannah, a ten-acre tract was set aside as a Public Botanical Garden and this was probably supervised by de Lyon. This garden was situated partially on a hill with part of it touching the Savannah River. It contained numerous trees, including bay, oak, orange, mulberry, sassafras, evergreen, pellitory, hickory, American ash and the laurel-tulip and a collection of West Indian plants sent over by Dr. Houston from the Spanish West Indies.

On March 12, 1734, seventy eight Salzburgers including forty families, sailed in the harbor at Savannah, the great voyage marking the culmination of the events that transpired since their exile from Bavaria. The earlier colonists extended to them a raucous and heartfelt welcome.

Mr. Balzius' Journal under the date, March, 1734, reads as follows:

"At the place of our landing almost all of the inhabitants of Sa-vannah were gathered together. They fired off some cannon and cried 'Huzza.' A good dinner was prepared for us. We, the Com-missary and Doctor Twiffler, our physician, were lodged at the house of the Rev. Mr. Quincy, the English missionary."

The Salzburgers were desirous of settling inland in a hilly terrain with abundant spring of water, for they wanted their new country to be as similar as possible to their native haunts. A party including Dr. Twiffler, their physician, Gen. Oglethorpe and some Indians, com-posing the Corps of Observation, set out to find such an area. Thirty miles inland on the banks of a crystal clear river, they found such a place. Dr. Twiffler helped select this territory where pure water was abundant and where good drainage prevailed, Oglethorpe marked out a town site which he called Ebenezer ("Stone of Help"). Later this ground was in St. Matthew's Parish and still later in Effingham County.

In February, 1735, a party of Moravians departed from London aboard *The Two Brothers* and landed in Savannah on April 8, 1735, after nine and a half weeks on shipboard.

On the long voyage to Georgia, it was found expedient to select one Moravian as nurse for the passengers. On one occasion at least, he was incapacitated by sea sickness. The records show that quite a few of the Moravians became dangerously ill on the journey. Four of the Swiss immigrants passed away and were buried at sea. Two Moravians were selected as nurses for the Swiss patients. It is recorded that their faithful attention to the sick coupled with the medicine provided by the Trustees made the ailing fairly comfortable en route.

One week after their arrival, "Either from the noon day heat, or other conditions to which they were not acclimated, Gotthard De-muth and George Haberland became seriously ill, causing Spang-enberg, their leader, much anxiety, for he did not feel at liberty to send for a physician, as they could not afford to pay for medicine, so resort was had to bleeding—then an approved practice—and to such remedies as remained from their voyage. One of their number was fortunate enough to shoot a grouse, which gave them some much needed palatable meat and broth. Perhaps the most serious case was Gottfried Habernicht's, who suffered for several days with fever resulting from a cut on his leg. Finally oak leaves were heated and bound about his limb which induced free perspiration and quickly relieved him so that he was able to return to work."

The "First Company" to be dispatched to the colony included

ten Moravians. Each individual of the group was not only a "good and true son of God, but a skillful workman as well." The Trustees selected the place for them to locate near Fort Argle on the north side of the Ogeechee River. However, various factors prevented them from occupying this location and when the "Second Company" disembarked early in the following year, the original group was still in Savannah proper.

According to the records, the first Moravian to die in Georgia was a mason named Riedel. Several months after his arrival in Georgia, he was overtaken by a severe fever, but he recovered from this. Three days after the boat left Savannah with the group to survey Zinzendorf's Tract, Riedel took sick. Upon his return, he was bed-ridden and developed delirium. His brother Moravians attended him assiduously and prayed for him earnestly, but their efforts were to no avail. Although the delirium subsided, he none-the-less passed away on September 30, 1735.

As Riedel was being dressed for burial, one John Regnier came to the door and offered to make some pewter spoons. Regnier, a native of Switzerland and the son of a physician, after his father passed away, had embarked for Pennsylvania intending to engage in the practice of medicine. He had the misfortune, however, while en route, to have all his belongings, funds and books stolen. He was thus forced to sell his services for seven years as a redemptioner. However, his health failed after five years of the period of servitude, and his master threw him out. The Moravians received John Regnier with open arms and he soon became a fundamental part of their community. He mended clothing and shoes efficiently and showed great ability in nursing the sick.

When a man from a neighboring village begged for help in controlling hemorrhage from a severed blood vessel, Regnier answered the call and efficiently effected a complete cure in two weeks.

When a destitute Scotchman with extensive dropsy was found in a wretched plight on the floor of his hovel, the Moravians magnanimously took him in and nursed him until he died.

Most of the Moravians had their share of sickness. The medicine brought from Europe was eventually exhausted and the cost of the medicine available in Savannah was prohibitive. Besides the Moravians were unfamiliar with their use. They therefore sought simple remedies and depended on good nursing care. They employed readily available turpentine. Spangenberg secured an herb which he thought was camomile and used this therapeutically. The records show that with the advent of cooler weather most of the party recovered their health.

Roscher was thought to be ill with consumption when he reached Savannah. Regnier did not agree with this diagnosis and when Roscher died he obtained permission to perform an autopsy. John Wesley assisted in this postmortem examination. This appears to have been the first autopsy performed in Georgia.

John Wesley's great interest in medicine led to the publication a few years later of his "Primitive Physic," or an "Easy and Natural Method for Curing Most Diseases" (1747).

It is related that George Haberland died on September 30, 1741, from "flux."

It is related that many colonists were afflicted with nausea and swollen feet, and that the drinking water was held responsible for this syndrome. A sassafras beer was concocted, therefore, which was imbibed until the people became acclimated and were able to tolerate the local water.

Like Dr. Nunez, the Moravians left Georgia when the Trustees passed enactments against them.

During the winter of 1739-40, John Regnier became infuriated by some remarks of Schulius and left the colony for Europe. Later, he sailed to Pennsylvania and joined the colony of Moravians there. Some of this group had come from Georgia.

On August 10, 1739, John Michael Schober, the ninth Moravian to be buried beside the Savannah River, passed away of a malignant fever and delirium.

In February, 1740, George Whitefield returned to Savannah on his second voyage and brought furniture for the Moravians. Their town house was subsequently rented to Whitefield's followers to be used as a hospital.

After arriving in Georgia, Whitefield organized an orphanage containing nearly 70 inmates. The hospital, originally started in the town house of the Moravians, was turned over to the management of one Dr. Joseph Hunter, from Bristol, England. Hunter was a surgeon and an apothecary, who had accompanied Whitefield from England out of devotion to this man of God.

Whitefield's own "Account of the Orphanage in Georgia," relates how the first hospital and the first free clinic were established in Georgia:

I chose to take over only a Surgeon and a few more of both sexes, that I thought would be useful in carrying on my Design. These cheerfully embarked with me, desiring nothing for their Pains but Food and Raiment. I likewise erected an Infirmary, in which sick people were cured and taken care of gratis. I have now by me a List of upwards of a hundred

Upper left, SAMUEL POWEL GRIFFITTS, M.D. (1759-1826) was the founder of the
Philadelphia Dispensary. (*Courtesy of the Philadelphia College of Physicians.*) *Upper
right*, ADAM KUHN, M.D. (1741-1817) was appointed professor of materia medica and
botany at the University of Pennsylvania in 1768. (*Courtesy of the Philadelphia
College of Physicians.*) *Lower left*, DR. ABRAHAM CHOVET (1704-1790). Although a
vehement Royalist, Dr. Abraham Chovet was so well liked that no one persecuted
him for his outspoken convictions. (*Courtesy of the Philadelphia College of Physicians.*) *Lower right*, DR. JOHN KEARSLEY, JR. was instrumental in establishing the
Philadelphia Medical Society in 1766. (*Courtesy of the Philadelphia College of
Physicians.*)

Upper left, DR. BENJAMIN SAY, *upper right,* DR. GEORGE GLENTWORTH, *lower left,* DR. JOHN FOULKE, *lower right,* DR. THOMAS PARKE. These physicians signed the constitution of the College of Physicians of Philadelphia. (*Courtesy of the Philadelphia College of Physicians.*)

JOHN WESLEY

John Wesley's great interest in medicine led to the publication of his
"Primitive Physic," or an "Easy and Natural Method for Curing Most
Diseases," in 1747. (*Courtesy of the Georgia Historical Society and the
Savannah Public Library.*)

and thirty Patients, which were under the Surgeon's Hands, exclusive of my own private family. This Surgeon I furnished with all proper Drugs and Utensils, which put me to no small expense.

The Salzburgers at Ebenezer already were running a small orphanage when Whitefield established Bethesda. Construction on the first hospital in Georgia was started on May 25, 1740. Drugs were also compounded in this institution for to the rear of the main house was the infirmary and a still house for the apothecary.

Dr. Hunter lived in the original orphanage, until he was appointed universal apothecary at Savannah. Then he moved to that city and became famous.

It is related that Hunter adopted fourteen year old William Wiley from Bethesda. In 1743 young William was accidentally shot while hunting. Dr. Hunter, who feared a bad prognosis, nevertheless attended the lad until he recovered.

In August 1742, Jonathan Barber, the chaplain, and Dr. Hunter, the house surgeon, were arrested at Savannah and imprisoned for a week on the charge that they had insulted two clergymen in private conversation.

In 1747 Wesley published his "Primitive Physic" which Dr. George Dock has termed "a strange combination of good sense and superstition."

Prior to the publication of his famous work, Wesley, together with an apothecary and a surgeon, opened a dispensary in Bristol. This project was so successful that he organized others in New Castle and London. Wesley early foresaw the need of treating the indigent sick in their homes in conjunction with clinic operations—a proposition which is widely neglected today.

"Primitive Physic" was published in twenty three editions during Wesley's lifetime, and nine others after his death. Thus, thirty-two editions in all rolled off the presses—a great tribute to the esteem in which his home compendium of medical practice was held. His preface places the blame for illness on sin and divine retribution: "As man knew no sin, so he knew no pain, no sickness, weakness or bodily disorders." Later, however, he declares: "The seed of wickedness and pain, of sickness and death, are lodged in our inmost substance; whence a thousand disorders continually spring even without the aid of external violence."

Wesley's objections to polypharmacy are far in advance of his time: "Experience shows that one thing will cure most diseases, at least as well as twenty put together. Then why add the other nineteen?" Wesley believed in the efficacy of Indian remedies, and acquired considerable medical knowledge from the Indians while he served as a missionary in Georgia.

Wesley felt that electricity "comes the nearest an universal medicine of any yet known in the world." He denounced the substitution evil in the preparation of prescriptions. Wesley advocated keeping away from the face of the sick if one is desirous to avoid catching infectious fevers. He was of the opinion that all insane people are cowards. However, he stated that they should be bound only—never beaten. Thus he anticipated Dr. Pinel's reform by fifty years. "Cleanliness is next to Godliness," was his dictum. He thus followed the biblical dictum of the Hebrews.

Wesley's diary, small and duodecimo in size, leather-bound and 168 pages long, contains a mine of information. From its contents it is apparent that the author had suffered from numerous sicknesses. He frequently refers to seizures of "cholick." He became afflicted with "St. Anthony's Fire," which disease "smarted much." Shocking headaches, intermittent fever, violent and protracted nausea, dysentery and boils were also his lot.

Soon after his arrival in Georgia, Wesley heard the following story of the first suicide in the new colony:

Charles and John Wesley had left Skidaway to have communion. About ten families were present in addition to the garrison at the fort. After riding on horseback to the home of Mr. DeLacy, this gentleman told them the following story:

Captain Wright brought a man to me and I bought him, paying as much as his passage was worth. The next day this man, named David Jones, told me his history.

He was a saddler by trade, and meeting the Captain at Bristol the latter proposed that he go with him to Georgia, that the business of saddler flourished there, and he would furnish him with tools and a shop, for which he could repay him at his own convenience.

On reaching Savannah, instead of the shop and tools, he was told that as the ship would return to England in a few days, he must have his passage money at once. As he was unable to pay this he was sold. I, of course, knew nothing of the circumstances, as I bought just as the others do and the law seems to allow.

He was a delicate looking man, but there was no work except to go into the forest with the servants.

He had an intellectual face, and when resting from his work would sit under the oaks near the river bank and apparently watch the water.

One day I sent him to my large plantation some four miles from here, but he did not return Saturday night with the other servants, sending word that he would go hunting. When they returned to their work Monday morning they found him on the shore with part of his head blown off, his gun at his side. In his pocket was a small paper book containing some poetry. Here it is, and you may keep it.

Mr. Wesley took the little worn book and read:

"Death could not a more sad retinue find—
Sickness and death before, and darkness all behind."

It is said that at the age of eighty-five, Wesley delivered eighty sermons in eight weeks. Wesley unquestionably was the outstanding physician-minister of early Georgia.

Frederica was universally hailed as the healthiest settlement in infant Georgia. Lieutenant Dunbar testified that, despite exposures, "the men are kept so healthy that often no man in the camp ailed in the least and none died except one man who came sick on board and never worked at all."

Dr. Thomas Hawkins, surgeon of the regiment raised to defend Georgia against the Spanish, saw considerable service during the siege of the Spaniards in Florida. The troops were in bad condition mainly because of malaria, putrid drinking water and the intense and humid heat. It was customary for fifty or so soldiers to seek attention from Hawkins each day. As the siege progressed, about fifty English soldiers were killed and about fifty wounded.

Oglethorpe himself was overcome by a fever, probably malaria, and returned to Frederica, his home. He remained under Dr. Hawkins' care for several weeks.

The white man's best friend among the Georgia Indians, Tomochichi, passed away on October 5, 1739 at the ripe old age of ninety-seven, after a lingering illness. Later the same month, the difficulties between England and Spain developed into an out and out declaration of war. Until Oglethorpe departed from Georgia for the last time on July 23, 1743, he was continously engaged in warfare with the Spaniards.

The Colonial Records show that Oglethorpe commissioned one Capt. Will Thompson to deliver drugs and medicines to Thos. Hawkins to the value of £29, 9s and 6d.

During the Battle of Bloody Marsh, which took place near Dr. Hawkins' home, some five hundred Spaniards were wounded, killed or taken prisoner. The regimental surgeons, doctors Hawkins and Bowler, did yoeman service in treating the wounded. Dr. Hawkins' bill for one shilling to be paid Richard Hughes for sharpening surgical saws, is an index of the quantity of surgery performed. Moses

Lidesmos received fifteen shillings for cleaning and grinding surgical instruments.

The energetic Dr. Hawkins, used boat as well as horseback to reach his patients. However, a bill of £5 for services of his boat and two servants was not accepted by the Trustees.

Hawkins also engaged in considerable obstetrics. In 1740, 55 babies were born in Frederica alone.

Dr. Hawkins wrote the following letter to the Trustees on May 23, 1736:

Frederica, the 23 of May, 1736.

To the Hon. the Trustees for the Establishment of the Colony of Georgia at their Office in Old Palace Yard, Westmester, Hon. Gentlemen:

I have by this Opertunity remitted my Accounts of the two last months, which I have the Satisfaction of Doing without the loss of any, but one Infant and Mrs. Humble (a Woman aged upwards of 60 who died of old Age rather than illness).

The Chief illness that happ'd was a Cows During Our Passage. There most Complaint of Coughs and Colds occasioned by the Change of weather and Living, dureing our Stay together with want of Exercise. At our passing the Tropic we had but few Complaints either of Headache or over Costiveness, at our Arrival here Some few had Pains in their limbs and Rhumatic Disorders, Inflammation of their feet, and Leggs, most of which Cured by Strong Purgatives; and as Occasion required, Fomentations of the Discuttient Kind; as Yet Fluxes have not prov'd So Obstinate as we could reasonably expect, the following was my General Method of treating them; they Vomited with the Ipecacuanha in the Evening, the next morning if necessary I gave them a purge, and in the Evening a Small Draught of Burnt Rice Liquor, or the white Drink of Burnt Hartshorn with 20 drops of Laudanum; with which only several have recovered, their Drink was chiefly of the same liquor.—and The following Electuary has proved very Serviceable, viz., Concerve of Roses and Luceallhus Balsam of each an Ounce Bole and Sperma Ceeti of each 2 drams made into an Electuary with a Sufficient quantity of Diacodium, of which the Patient took a Small Quantity 5 times a day, in a Draught of his Rice or Hartshorn drink; In Cases of any Continuance a Little Burnt Clarret Releevd them when weak and Languid. Feevers have Yielded to Bleeding, and the uses of the Lapis Contreyarva, drinking either Barley Liquor, or an Emulsion of Indian Corn; and few have as yet required Blistering, wounds of all kinds are very Difficult to Cure, our Blood Abbounding with Scorbutic Salts. I attribute my Success on the Above account owing in a great Measure to Your Honors Prudent Prohibition of Rum and Spirituous Liquors, which if had not ben we might have ben half lost, I thought it my duty to acquaint you with my Proceedings here, in which I have the Satisfaction not to diminish a Person of the Number entrusted to my Care, Assuring you Hon Gen that my utmost Eendeavrs Shall be allways ready for the Interest of the Colony and the Health of the Inhabitants I am,

Yr very Humble
and Obedient Servant,
THOS. HAWKINS.

Hawkins' patients, not unlike their modern counterparts, often found fault with his treatments. Some declared that Claret and Florence wines were "stypticks" and not good for the flux, as used by the good doctor. President William Stephens himself failed to heed his counsel when he was bitten by an insect. Dr. Hawkins applied "maugre," which made the sore as big as a man's hand. Stephens effected a cure by employing "cooling and innocent things."

No lawyer being present in Georgia, Dr. Hawkins was appointed one of the bailiffs of Frederica. According to Stevens, "The bailiffs of Savannah and Frederica, like those of Scotland..... were magistrates of burghs. They exercised more civil and judicial jurisdiction than an English bailiff, the chief magistrate of some particular town. It was giving large powers to men with humble titles; and though it is the power, and not the title, which confers greatness, yet the majesty of law, and the dignity of the colony, demanded that its executive officers should bear a name more linked with the nobler offices of state and the higher tribunals of justice, than with a sheriff's court or a baronial steward."

It is said that Hawkins was the only bailiff in Frederica who could read and write.

It appears that William Bowler came to Georgia in May, 1738. He cared for the medical needs of two companies of General Oglethorpe's troops, stationed at St. Andrews on Cumberland Island.

He not only treated the Highlander soldiers at this location, but took care of their eighty wives and children. He also rendered medical services to the Highlanders and people associated with the scout-boat at Amelia Station. There is an order signed by Oglethorpe that Bowler be paid £45 for 18 months of medical services.

Because of the poor workability of the system of town courts, the Trustees, in April 1741, redivided the colony into two counties: Savannah County which included all the territory north of Darien, and Frederica County which included St. Simons and the Altamaha settlements. Each county had a president and four assistants.

William Stephens was selected as President of Savannah County, and when the governments of the two counties were incorporated, he became President of both. Prior to his appointment as president, while serving as secretary, he reported to the Trustees in Stephen's Journal. This diary included several anecdotes of interest:

Thursday, Dec. 1, 1737.—Walked out to see my people, how they were getting along with their work; where only four were employed, three of them being ill at home; and ever since my arrival some or other of them were ailing every day, which required a Doctor's continual attendance and like to prove very chargeable.

Friday, Dec. 2, 1737.—Another servant taken ill at his work this morning and came home.

Saturday, Dec. 17.—One of my servants came home at noon wounded by stroke of axe in leg, and in the evening another of them was taken ill. The Doctor that dressed the first and bleeded the other, gave me hopes that they would be well again in a few days. But how certain soever that might prove, it was very sure his Bill increased apace.

Jan. 5, 1738.—Mr. Brown of Highgate, in a drunken fit, with little or no Provocation, had taken his Gun loaded with drop Shot and a Ball and shot his Servant through the Thigh; and the surgeon who dressed it said the man was in a dangerous Condition.

Jan. 12, 1738.—Called on Mr. Bradley. Found him in bed complaining of his Want of Health; which he attributed to his living so much on salt Provisions, having no money to get fresh provisions. (By Saturday Mr. Bradley was able to bring list of Horses and cattle wanted Tuesday before.)

Jan. 16, 1738.—Sickness which has never yet wholly ceased among my Servants continued to pull them down; and no less than four were under the Doctor's care, one of whom we scarcely hoped would live, till this Day he began to recover.

Feb. 15, 1738.—Mr. Brown's Servant at Highgate being likely to die, as the Surgeon declared who attended him, a warrant was ordered to take Brown into Custody. (dide Jan. 5).

Feb. 17, 1738.—Mr. Bradley drew Bills on Mr. Causton for "two Doctors for attending his family and servants in their sickness." Refused.

In the early years of Georgia the Trustees did not fail to make some provision for medical care of the destitute and down trodden. One hundred pounds was appropriated for the care of sick widows and orphans in the northern part of the Province, and fifty pounds to the same group in the southern district. In 1739, five pounds was allotted a public midwife at Frederica for attending the poor and trust servants. This midwife had to answer all calls for help. In the same year, one hundred and fifty pounds was voted for care of the poor at Savannah, for medicines, drugs, nurses, and burial expenses.

It is the irony of fate that Oglethorpe himself sustained the first severe head injury in Georgia. As he was sailing, one of his cannon exploded and a piece of sail-yard struck his head and so traumatized him that blood poured out of his ears and nose.

In the spring the Georgia planters moved to the highlands. They considered April 1st, as the deadline for moving. Few dared spend a night on a rice field from this date until frost, for it was believed that the miasma arising from the rice fields at night was the etiological agent of malaria. Unquestionably the early Georgia planters recognized the mosquito as a pest, if not as a harbinger of pestilence. The sand fly was also a great nuisance. Charles Wesley declared in his diary: "At one this morning the sand flies forced me to rise and smoke them out of the hut. The whole town was employed in the same manner."

The fluxes and malignant fevers that seemed to be so associated with the summer heat often acted to destroy initiative. Many colonists became loafers and many took to drink.

Another colonial physician of Georgia was Dr. John Miliken. According to the records, on January 4, 1748, 500 acres of land were presented to him by the Court of President and Assistants in Georgia. Although little is known of him, this indicates that he had resided in the colony for at least three years, prior to the award.

Oglethorpe early appreciated the need of extending the limits of colonization toward the north. Heeding his advice, the Trustees marked out a town on the right bank of the Savannah River. Here is the earliest record of the town:

Seven miles above New Windsor, on the Georgia side, lies the town of Augusta, just below the Falls: This was laid out by the Trustees' Orders, in the year 1735, which has thriven prodigiously; there are several Warehouses thoroughly well furnished with Goods for the Indian Trade. Hither all the English Traders, with their servants, resort in the Spring; and 'tis computed above two thousand Horses come hither at that Season.

Above the town to the North West and on the Georgia side of the River, the Cherokees lived in the Valley of the Appalachian Mountains; they were about five thousand warriors; but last year it is computed they lost a thousand, partly by Small Pox, and partly (as they themselves say) by too much Rum brought from Carolina.

The Creek Indians live to the Westward of the town.

At a moderate estimate six hundred White men live by their trade in this vicinity.

Oglethorpe visited Augusta only once, in September, 1739, on his way back to Savannah after his dangerous mission to Coweta

Town, where he met in convention seven thousand Indian braves. Ailing with "a burning fever," he tarried for a few days at Augusta.

Chiefs of the Chickasaws and Cherokees visited Oglethorpe during his brief stay in Augusta, complaining that they had been poisoned by rum sold to them by the traders. It appears that certain unlicensed traders had conveyed smallpox to the Indians. The red men blamed poisoned rum for this disease.

Samuel Brown, an active trader with the Indians, became ill himself and reported "many as extremely sick thereabouts; that a great many were down in fevers, and that Lieut. Kent was so ill that it was feared he could not live."

That ".....in the autumn this malarial region, badly drained, the atmosphere impregnated with noxious exhalations from a soil recently denuded of forest trees and subjected by the plow to the direct rays of a semi-tropical sun, should have been visited by fevers of a severe type, excites no wonder."

In May, 1751, a message dispatched by the previously mentioned Dr. Patrick Graham of Augusta, reached Savannah containing the information that James Maxwell and a number of Indian traders had just fled the area occupied by the Cherokees to save their lives after two traders had been killed.

Cavalry units sought the enemy near Augusta without success, but, none-the-less, the entire country was put in a state of alert. Troops and horses were raised, and Noble Jones, M.D., was appointed Colonel, and his son, Noble Wymberly Jones, who had previously served in Oglethorpe's regiment, and who later became a prominent physician, was selected to command the dragoons. Either the alarm was premature or the Indians feared the white man's armed might, for no conflict developed from this delicate situation.

The first record of a physician in Augusta refers to Thomas Ford, who in 1759, was paid the sum of £20, s. 10 for attending the Cherokee Indians. Jones states that Dr. William Day practiced in Augusta in 1760. The first autopsy in Augusta was performed by Dr. Andrew Johnston who was paid 10 pounds for examining the body of William Miller, who was shot ten miles above Augusta in 1766.

The doctor in colonial Georgia had much to contend with. The population was widely disseminated and the doctor found it difficult to cover his territory. A medical call could turn into a full day's journey. Various physicians maintained row boats for creek and river navigation and at times had servants to do the rowing. Dr. Hawkins, for example, maintained such facilities.

The early Georgia records mention such diseases as colds, fevers, dropsy, debilitated states of the system, bloody flux, swollen feet and nausea, scurvy, tuberculosis, measles, gunshot wounds, fever and ague and smallpox.

Inoculation for smallpox was early practiced in Georgia. The *Gentlemen's Magazine* for March, 1751, suggests the following technique:

Draw a piece of thread through a ripe pustule so as that some part of the thread may be moistened with the matter. This, when dry'd by holding it a few minutes in the air, may be put into a clean box and kept for use. When the operation is to be performed, first make a slight scratch or superficial incision, either in the leg or arm as near that part of either where issues are commonly made; cut off a small piece of the thread charged with variolous matter, one-eighth of an inch, or even less, lay it upon the incision, cover with a bit of sticking plaster and the operation is performed.

In the period leading up to the war of Independence, Dr. Noble Wymberley Jones and Dr. John Houstoun, played significant roles. However, neither got to be in that immortal group who signed the Declaration of Independence. Another Georgia physician, Dr. Lyman Hall, a native of Wallingford, Connecticut, who had migrated to Georgia with the group of Puritans that had settled at Medway, was to have this honor.

Dr. Noble Wymberley Jones was born in England in 1723 or 1724. It will be recalled that his father had come with General Oglethorpe to Georgia when the colony was founded. It is believed that the younger Jones received his medical education primarily from his father. From the beginning, he took an avid interest in the events that preceded the War of Independence. Known for his oratorical ability, he was elected Speaker of the Georgia Legislature. When Charleston was captured by the British, the younger Jones was held prisoner for some months. In July 1780, he was released and sojourned to Philadelphia, where he engaged in medical practice until 1782. He served as representative from Georgia in Congress from 1780 to 1782. In the latter year he returned to Georgia, was elected to the State Assembly and thereafter became the Speaker of this body. Later Jones went to Charleston, South Carolina, where he practiced medicine until 1788, at which date he returned to his beloved Savannah, where he practiced extensively until his death on January 1, 1805.

Dr. John Houstoun, the son of Sir Patrick Houstoun, was born near Waynesboro in 1744. He as well as Dr. Noble Wymberley Jones, came to the political fore during the Provincial Assembly under Governor Wright and both men remained a harmonious

team in the Lower House for a number of years. They were instrumental in re-appointing Benjamin Franklin as Georgia Agent in
London. They both asked for clemency in the case of Joe Prine,
convicted and condemned to hang for horse-stealing on the basis of
the fact that there had been a change in the law between 1772 and
1773, the period between the date of the crime and the date set for
execution of sentence. Houstoun and Jones did not always agree,
however. Houstoun voted to congratulate Governor James Wright
on his safe return to Georgia as a baronet, but Jones who had been
treated harshly by Wright, joined LeConte in voting against the
motion. As a rule, however, they saw eye to eye. Both were included
among the four signers of a statement published in the *Georgia
Gazette*, requesting that all liberty-loving Georgians meet in front
of Tondee's Tavern in 1774. Houstoun and Jones were very active
in the organization of the Sons of Liberty.

Houstoun was elected to the Provincial Congress. He served on
the first Council of Safety and acted as a delegate to the first Continental Congress held at Philadelphia in September, 1775. He was
re-elected to the congress in 1776. Houstoun violently offset the
influence of Rev. Joachin Zubly, who had suddenly and vociferously
turned Tory and referred to a republic as "a government of the
devil." As the second "rebel governor", Houstoun led an unsuccessful
attempt to capture St. Augustine. He served as Surgeon General
of the army for a time and asked Council for the use of the church
in Augusta as a hospital. He served on the committee of 1783 that
set the northern boundary of the State. During his administration
as governor, 40,000 acres of land was granted for a state college.
He was governor again in 1784 and was later appointed Justice of
Georgia. He passed away in 1797.

Dr. Noble Wymberley Jones' son, Dr. George Jones, was taken
prisoner early in the Revolutionary War and was confined on the
prison ship in the harbor at Savannah.

Dr. Nathaniel Brownson, of Georgia, served as a member of the
Continental Congress in 1776, and as a surgeon in the Continental
Army. He became deputy Purveyor to the Southern Army on
March 27, 1781. Soon after this he was elected to the gubernatorial
chair of Georgia and was forced to give up this army post.

The Colonial Records mention James Houstoun, patriot surgeon,
David Bradie (Brydie), surgeon and captain of the eighth company
of militia, and Dr. James Habersham, third son of the famous loyalist,
and a member of the Committee of Safety in charge of slaves.

The Revolutionary Records mention one Dr. Traill of St. Phillips
Parish, who refused to sign the Articles of Association drafted by

the Provincial Assembly. Traill was given eight days to leave the colony. With the return of the royal governor and the reorganization of the King's Council in 1780, the names of Dr. Irvine and the Rev. Joachin Zubly both appear as tories.

The Provincial Congress commanded one Dr. Charles Younge to stay away from Rosedew Plantation except in his capacity as family physician. Paying no heed to this directive, he was ordered to be taken into custody. The Confiscation Act led to the taking of 150 acres from Dr. John Young.

Mention is also made of Dr. Andrew Johnston who refused to subscribe to the loyalty "test," notwithstanding the fact that he had been appointed to a captaincy in the Queensborough militia at the beginning of the war. The citizens of Augusta asked the Council to refrain from applying the test to Johnston so that he could take care of them professionally. When peace prevailed, the Banishment Act was revoked in his favor. However, he was not permitted to hold public office for fourteen years.

Dr. Frances Folliott, who was commissioned a third lieutenant in Johnston's company, was asked to vacate the "glebe" house in Augusta. Dr. Thomas Taylor was declared to be "an enemy of the state" by Dr. Humphrey Wells. Wells later served as a member of the Governor's Council under Wereat.

The Revolutionary Records mention Dr. Donald McLeod, who was accused of poisoning prisoners in the service of Great Britain. The properties of Dr. Peter Walsh (Welch) on the Great Kioka, and Dr. Lewis Johnston, at Sunbury, were also confiscated.

The Revolutionary Records state that Dr. Edward Cartledge was "allowed 2 rations" as doctor of militia. When Dr. Brownfield, surgeon at the hospital near the Great Swamp, petitioned for supplies, he was granted a cask of wine and eight bushels of salt. One Dr. Frederick Rehm is listed as Magistrate on the Little Ogeechee. A Dr. Dunwiddie is mentioned as being commissioned to collect all unidentified cattle for the state.

Here is the first quarantine ordinance to be promulgated in Georgia:

As other Provinces have greatly suffered by permitting ships with Negroes to send them on shore when ill of contagious Distempers (as particularly South Carolina has often by the Yellow Fever) proper places must be appointed for such ships as bring negroes to Georgia, to cast anchor at, in order to their being visited, and to perform such Quarantin as shall be order'd by the President and Assistants, and no Ships must be suffer'd to come nearer than those places before they are visited by proper Officers and a Certificate of Health is obtained.

And in case of any contagious Distempers on board, proper places must be appointed at a distance from the Towns for Lazarettos, where the whole Crew of the Ship and the Negroes may be lodg'd and supplied with Refreshments and assisted towards their Recovery.

You must acquaint the Trustees by the first Opportunity with the Names and Description of the proper Places for the ships to stop at, and likewise where to perform a Quarantin if there are contagious Distempers on board, and these Places may be specified in the Act.

The nearness of the slave trade, even in the earlier days when slavery was forbidden, provided a constant potential menace to health. A vessel arrived in Charleston from Angola in 1736 after having lost 250 slaves en route. In 1749, after slavery was legalized, the following regulations were enforced: No slave-carrying vessel could come nearer than Cockspur. A lazaretto was built at Tybee to shelter all slaves. Medicines were required to be provided by the ship's captain. Full quarantine was enforced under penalty of forfeiture of 500 pounds, if contagious diseases were on board.

June, 1758, saw the eruption of a virulent smallpox epidemic in Augusta. The Governor issued a proclamation on quarantine, and Rangers were stationed at Ebenezer to stop all persons coming either by water or land from infected parts of the province who could not provide a bill of good health. No leather or other pelfry, brought from infected parts of the province, was permitted to be landed. After the epidemic subsided in October, 1758, the guard was removed.

In 1759, the Governor re-issued the proclamation and a ten-day full quarantine was placed on all vessels without a bill of health. Even papers could not be removed from the ships unless they were held by a long stick dipped in vinegar and afterwards smoked.

In 1772, the Assemblymen reported a boat with smallpox on board, in from Philadelphia, and the governor was asked to issue a quarantine. Governor Habersham reported that she was too far off to spread contagion, and refused the request.

There is little question that the success of the War of Independence was greatly aided by the fact that New England was the scene of considerable oppression by the mother country. The New Englanders, in their dispersion, even reached as far as Georgia. The citizens of St. John's Parish in Georgia, for the most part hailed from New England and were keenly sympathetic with their confreres back north. Midway Settlement, a section of St. John's Parish, has been called the Southern Cradle of Liberty. It was here in about 1756 that Dr. Lyman Hall of Connecticut settled.

Lyman Hall (1731-1790) was born in Connecticut, in 1731. With Oliver Wolcott, he received an A.B. from Yale in 1747. Soon after his graduation he accepted a pastorate in Stratfield Parish, Fairfield, Connecticut. He soon got into trouble with the church fathers and resigned his pulpit. He then apprenticed himself to a local physician and it is said that he practiced for a brief interval in Wallingford. In 1752, he moved to South Carolina. With several families that had migrated with him, he engaged in an agricultural experiment with uncertain results. Then the group migrated with him to Sunbury, a small village to the south of Savannah and near the coast of Georgia. Hall became a successful country practitioner and as the War of Independence approached, he became a banner bearer of the patriot cause. His oratory was heard far and wide and when it came time to elect a delegate to the Continental Congress in 1775, Lyman Hall was the man chosen. A later act of the legislature joined St. John's, St. Andrew's and St. James' Parishes into "Liberty County." Until Georgia was fully represented in the Congress, Dr. Hall abstained from voting upon questions that came before the Congress, but he engaged in the debates and went on record with his opinions. With regard to the Declaration of Independence, Dr. Hall presented his credentials on May 30, 1776, and early in June signed for the State of Georgia, with two others. Hall served as member of Congress for three successive terms, following which he refused another nomination. On June 18, 1776, Dr. Hall was added to the medical committee of the Continental Congress, to which all contemplated medical legislature was referred. Until its discontinuance on March 28, 1781, the committee was primarily responsible for the army medical department.

When the English took the forts in Savannah, the property of Hall was naturally confiscated and the good doctor sojourned for a year with his relatives in Connecticut. After his return he settled in Burke County, Georgia, and practiced there until he was elected Governor in 1783. In 1790, he bought a beautiful plantation in Burke County intending to spend his last days there, but a few months after this he died at the age of sixty-seven, on October 19, 1790. At the site of Lyman Hall's birthplace in Wallingford, Connecticut, a memorial boulder reveals these significant words: "This rock from Connecticut soil marks the beginning of the life of one of the living stones which coming from this town, formed the foundation of our Republic." Hall County in Georgia was later named after him.

John Brickell, (1749-1809) possibly a descendant of the John

Brickell mentioned in "The Carolinas" chapter, was born in about the year 1749, in County Louth, Ireland. He emigrated to America in about 1770, and it is probable that he was the John Brickell who entered King's College (now Columbia University), New York, in 1774. He had not finished his course when the College suspended its curriculum in 1776. During the Revolution, Brickell moved to Georgia, and practiced medicine for many years at Savannah. He became renowned as a physician, scholar and patriot. His main hobby was the science of botany. He was a regular correspondent of Muhlenberg. He contributed five papers to the earlier volumes (1798-1809) of the "Medical Repository." Of these, two described plants found by him near Savannah. "Brickellia," a genus of Compositae, was dedicated to his memory by Stephen Elliott in 1823. He died in Savannah, Georgia, on December 22, 1809. Dr. Brickell's only surviving relative appears to have been his brother James, to whom he left all of his property.

Nathaniel Brownson, Lyman Hall, John Houstoun, James Sharp and John White were the principal medical men from Georgia to serve in the patriot army.

Following the Revolution, settlers from the Carolinas, Virginia and other states came in large numbers to Georgia in search of free land. The population increased by leaps and bounds, and a new group of physicians came on the scene. Cornelius Dysart probably migrated from North Carolina. At any rate, the records there mention one Doctor Dysart who bought drugs from the patriot, Dr. Brevard, of Charlotte. Dysart purchased 1,350 acres of land in Georgia which had been confiscated under the Banishment Act from William Manson in 1783. Dysart in 1784 married Elizabeth Chandler, widow of a local wealthy planter. Dysart settled in Bedford Village (now known as Lakemont) on the Washington Road, three miles from Augusta. In 1789, the records show he purchased a lot on Broad Street for $4,000. He built up extensive real estate holdings in nearby areas. In 1789, Doctor Dennis Smelt, who had studied in England, became his partner.

J. V. T. Gardner's account book, dated 1790, contains a bill for professional services rendered by the firm of Dysart and Smelt and countersigned by William Cocke. This account helps elucidate the type of current medical practice. Medical procedures such as drawing a tooth, reducing a fracture of the jaw and administering clysters are listed. Charges for lead-water, lavender, anodyne boluses, camphor, blisters and red-bark are itemized. The second entry refers to inoculation for the smallpox. No mention is made of bleeding. Smelt published an article against bleeding in 1806.

The name of William Cocke, appearing on the receipted bill, probably refers to the fact that he was apprenticed to the firm. He graduated from the University of Pennsylvania in 1798 and settled in Savannah in about 1800. He became one of the first health officers of the State.

Gardner's account book presents a complete inventory of stock carried by a general merchant. Peppermint, bergamot, musk of roses, capillaire, mosquito gauze, temple spectacles, court plaster and cat-gut are all listed.

Dr. John Murray, Dr. George Graves and Dr. Burke also carried accounts with Gardner and conducted successful practices, as is evidenced by their tax returns. The drug stock of Murray and Tindale in 1792 was registered on the tax digest as amounting to $1,500. Murray owned 1,850 acres of land. Graves owned a house in Augusta and 800 acres in Columbia County. Burke, who may have practiced as far as Edgefield, S. C., married the widow of Col. Benjamin Fishburn, of Revolutionary fame. The year 1809 saw these three men paying a professional tax of $4.00 per year to the State.

Dysart, Smelt, Graves, Murray, John H. Montgomery and William Brazier, in association, signed and published the first fee bill of Georgia in 1797. The fees for fifty-one procedures were listed. Lithotomy was done for $50. Trepannation cost $40. A delivery cost $30. The aforementioned association antedates the Georgia Medical Society of Savannah by seven years. Dysart and Montgomery, the leaders of the movement, died soon thereafter and the interest of the other men waned soon after their deaths. Doctor Hull purchased the shop of Dysart in 1798 and started to practice. Smelt died in about 1828. The firm of Montgomery and Bird, which advertised for an unlimited quantity of pink root in 1792, soon passed out of the existence.

Dr. George Sibbald, who left a memorial in a paper published on the health and climate of the pinelands, and Dr. Hugh Nesbit, also practiced in Augusta in 1800.

Chapter Fourteen

MAJOR SOURCES
AND
ACKNOWLEDGMENTS

N O ATTEMPT is made in this acknowledgment to catalogue the
literally hundreds of works that have been investigated in the
preparation of this book. There are a certain few volumes that have
been so frequently employed that they require special mention at
this time. Foremost among these are the biographical works of
Howard A. Kelly and Walter L. Burrage. These include: Howard A.
Kelly: A Cyclopedia of American Medical Biography from 1610 to
1910, W. B. Saunders Co., Philadelphia and London, 1912; Howard
A. Kelly and Walter L. Burrage: American Medical Biographies,
The Norman, Remington Co., Baltimore, 1920; and Howard A.
Kelly and Walter L. Burrage: Dictionary of American Medical Biog-
raphy, D. Appleton and Co., New York and London, 1928.

Authors of articles in these works which are quoted in the pres-
ent work include: John H. Burnhart, Alan N. Blodgett, Walter L.
Burrage, George F. Butler, Donald A. Campbell, Eugene F. Cordell,
Douglas F. Duval, Elsworth Eliot, John W. Harshberger, Howard
A. Kelly, Robert M. Lewis, John U. Lloyd, Francis R. Packard,
James E. Pilcher, Lewis S. Pilcher, Ira Joslin Prouty, Albert Robin,
Robert M. Slaughter, H. Lee Smith, James A. Spalding, Walter R.
Steiner, Arthur K. Stone, Hannah M. Thompson, J. Collins Warren,
Davina Waterson, William H. Welch, Robert Wilson, Jr., and
Lemuel F. Woodward.

Francis R. Packard's excellent work, History of Medicine in the
United States, Paul B. Hoeber, New York, 1931, has been referred to
and quoted many times and is heartily recommended to the reader.
The value of Dr. Packard's personal contributions to the history of

medicine in general and to the history of American medicine in particular cannot be overemphasized. The eleventh edition of the Encyclopædia Britannica has been a constant source of information and has been extensively employed in the preparation of the general historical summaries which precede the medical historical data in the various chapters. Malcolm S. Beinfield's fine article, The Early New England Doctor: An Adaptation to a Provincial Environment, *The Yale Journal of Biology and Medicine*, Vol. 15, No. 1, October 1942, pp. 99-132 has been employed for the region implied in the title. Louis C. Duncan's Medical Men in the American Revolution, 1775-1783, published as Army Medical Bulletin, Number 25, at the Medical Field Service School, Carlisle Barracks, Pa., is a mine of information concerning this important historical period.

Other general sources include: James Thacher: American Medical Biography, Boston, 1828; Joseph M. Toner: Medical Men of the Revolution, 1876; John A. Farmer: Genealogical Registry of the First Settlers in New England, 1861; Stephen West Williams: American Medical Biography, 1845; William B. Atkinson: Physicians and Surgeons of the United States, 1878; Samuel D. Gross: Lives of Eminent American Physicians and Surgeons (1861); and John Elliot: A Biographical Dictionary of the First Settlers in New England, 1809.

The section on the medical practices of the Amerinds (Chapter 1) is based on: Eric Stone: Medicine Among the American Indians; Paul B. Hoeber, N. Y., 1932.

In the chapter on Virginia (2), most of the material on George Percy, John Smith and Lord Delaware is taken from the following excellent and authoritative work: Narratives of Early Virginia 1606-1625, edited by Lyon G. Tyler, Charles Scribner's Sons, New York, 1907. The following other works have been referred to: Page: The Old Dominion, Charles Scribner's Sons, 1908; and Edward Ingle: Regulating Physicians in Colonial Virginia, *Annals of Medical History*, new series, Vol. IV, 1922, pp. 248-250. For a thorough coverage of Virginia's early medical history, the reader is referred to: Wyndham B. Blanton: Medicine in Virginia in the Seventeenth Century (1930) and Medicine in Virginia in the Eighteenth Century.

The History of Medicine in Massachusetts by Samuel Abbott Green (1881) is referred to in the chapter on Massachusetts (3). Dr. Stafford's "Receipts to Cure Various Disorders" is quoted from Edward Kremers' Documents Pertaining to the Medicinal Supplies Within The N. A. Colonies From 1643 to 1780; Amer. Inst. Hist. of Pharmacy; Madison, Wisconsin, 1944. This chapter also incorporates material from the following works: Henry Viets: A Brief History of Medicine in Massachusetts, Houghton Mifflin, Boston and N. Y.,

1930. Reginald Fitz: The Massachusetts Medical Society, From Cow-Path to State Road (The Annual Discourse delivered at the annual meeting of the Massachusetts Medical Society, Springfield, June 10, 1936), *New England Journal of Medicine*, Vol. 214, No. 24, June 11, 1936, p. 1181; The General Court Records of Massachusetts; The Massachusetts Historical Society Publications; William Bradford: History of the Plimoth Plantation, Commonwealth Edition, Boston, 1898; C. F. Adams: Three Episodes in Massachusetts History; E. Winslow: Good News from New England; John Ward Dean: Brief Memoir of Giles Firmin, Boston, 1806; H. U. Williams: The Epidemic of the Indians of New England 1616-1620, *Johns Hopkins Hospital Bulletin*, 20, 1909; John Brown: The Pilgrim Fathers of New England and Their Puritan Successors; Abbott Green: Centennial Address on the History of Medicine in Massachusetts; Oliver Wendell Holmes: Medical Essays IX; W. R. Steiner: Some Early Autopsies in the United States, *Johns Hopkins Hospital Bulletin*, August 1903; John Josselyn: An Account of Two Voyages to New England, London, 1674 (reprinted in Massachusetts Historical Society Collections, Series 3, Vol. 3); J. B. Felt: Annals of Salem; A Brief Rule to Guide the Common-People of New-England How to Order Themselves and Theirs in the Small Pocks, or Measels, 167$\frac{7}{8}$; Facsimile Reproductions of the Three Known Editions with an Introductory Note by Henry R. Viets, M.D., Johns Hopkins Press, Baltimore, 1937; and John Winthrop: The History of New England, Boston, 1825.

The New Hampshire chapter (4) is based primarily on The Story of the New Hampshire Medical Society, told to 1854 by Lyman Bartlett How at the Centennial of the Society in 1891, and revised and continued by Henry O. Smith; printed for the 150th anniversary of the New Hampshire Medical Society in 1941; Phaneuf Press, Nashua, N. H. and A. B. Crosby: A Contribution to the Medical History of New Hampshire; read before the New Hampshire Medical Society, Concord, June, 1870, and republished from their transactions; Nashua, 1870. Herbert Thoms: The Signing Doctors, *The American Journal of Surgery*, New Series, Vol. XXX, November 1935, No. 2, pp. 390-396, and E. L. Page: Josiah Bartlett and the Federation, *Historical New Hampshire*, Oct. 1947, pp. 1-6, have also been employed.

A considerable portion of the chapter on New York (5) is taken from Claude E. Heaton: Medicine in New York During the English Colonial Period, *Bulletin of the History of Medicine*, Vol. XVII, No. 1, January, 1945, pp. 9-37. James J. Walsh's History of Medicine in N. Y. (1900); The New York Historical Society Collections; The

Colonial Laws of New York, Albany, 1894; Documents Relative to the Colonial History of the State of New York, Albany, 1856-61; Minutes of the Common Council of the City of New York, 1675-1776; and The New York Colonial Documents, have been referred to.

The chapter on Connecticut (6) follows in part the outline laid down by Dr. George O. Summer in his address on the *Early Physicians in Connecticut* presented before the Connecticut Medical Society at its meeting in Hartford on May 14, 1851. A reprint of this dissertation is available in *The Connecticut State Medical Journal*, Vol. VI, June 1942, No. 6, pp. 459-475. Gordon W. Russell: An Account of Early Medical Men in Connecticut, *Proceedings of the Connecticut State Medical Society*, 1892 is also referred to.

Some of the material in the chapter on Maryland (7) is taken from an address entitled "Early Medicine in Maryland" presented by Dr. Thomas S. Cullen to the Medical and Chirurgical Faculty of Maryland on April 26, 1927. Dr. John R. Quinan is author of "The Medical Annals of Baltimore from 1608 to 1880," which was published in 1884. The Medical Annals of Maryland by Dr. Eugene F. Cordell was published in 1903.

The chapter on Rhode Island (8) is based on: William S. Sherman: Some Notes on Early Medicine and Surgery in Newport County, the Cradle of American Medicine (delivered before the joint meeting of the staff of the Naval Hospital and Newport County Medical Society), *The Rhode Island Medical Journal*, Vol. XIV, No. 5, May 1931, pp. 76-82; Walter L. Munro: Early Medical History in Rhode Island and the Rhode Island Medical Society (read before the Friday Night Medical Club, May 17th, 1935, and condensed to make the Annual Address before the Rhode Island Medical Society, June 6, 1935), *The Rhode Island Medical Journal*, Vol. XVIII, No. 7, July 1935, pp. 93-110; E. B. Krumbhaar: Doctor William Hunter of Newport, *Annals of Surgery*, Vol. 101, No. 1, January 1935, pp. 506-528; Records of the Colony of Rhode Island and Providence Plantations in New England, edited by J. R. Bartlett, Providence, 1856-1865; and James H. Eldredge: History of Medicine in Kent County, Rhode Island, *The Rhode Island Medical Journal*, Vol. XXIII, August 1940, pp. 135-139.

Some of the information in the chapter on Delaware (9) is obtained from an address on Delaware Doctors presented by Dr. Thomas C. Stellwagon before the Historical Society of Delaware in February 1896. This address was published by the Historical Society of Delaware as paper XIX, in 1897. The section on Matthew Wilson's Therapeutic Alphabet has been obtained from Laryngology and Otology in Colonial Times by Dr. Stanton A. Friedberg, published in *The Annals of Medical History*, (old series) Vol. I, No. 1, Spring 1917, pp. 86-101.

The chapter on New Jersey (10) is based on Stephen Wickes': History of Medicine in New Jersey, and of its Medical Men, From the Settlement of the Province to A.D. 1800, Newark, N. J., Morton R. Dennis & Co., 1879. Many of the documents employed in this chapter are taken from this work. The numerous newspaper accounts are taken from Maurice B. Gordon: Medicine in Colonial New Jersey and Adjacent Areas, *Bulletin of the History of Medicine*, Vol. XVII, No. 1, January 1945. Reference has also been made to The Transactions of the New Jersey Medical Society, The New Jersey Archives and George H. Lathrope: Dissertation on the State of Physick in the Colony of New Jersey. Being Some Account of the Foundation of the Medical Society of New Jersey, *Journal of the Medical Society of New Jersey*, Vol. XXVII, No. 1, pp. 2-10.

Much of the material in the chapter on the Carolinas (11) is taken from J. I. Waring: A Sketch of Medicine in South Carolina 1670-1700; *Journal of the South Carolina Medical Association*, Vol. XXXVII, No. 12, December 1941, and J. I. Waring: Medicine in Charlestown 1750-1775; *Annals of Medical History;* New Series, Vol. XII, No. 1, January 1935, pp. 19-26. The section on Dr. Kalberlahn is quoted from A. L. Fries: The Road to Salem, Chapel Hill, The University of North Carolina Press, 1944. The South Carolina Historical Society Collections and The Public Records of South Carolina have been referred to. J. Johnson: Traditions and Reminiscences of the American Revolution, Charleston, Walker and Jones, 1851, has also been referred to. Contemporary newspaper accounts in the *South Carolina Gazette*, the *North Carolina Gazette* and the *Cape Fear Mercury* have been valuable sources of information.

A considerable portion of the chapter on Pennsylvania (12) follows the outline delineated by Francis R. Packard: The Practice of Medicine in Philadelphia in the Eighteenth Century (The William Potter Memorial Lecture of the Jefferson Medical College, February 4, 1932); *Annals of Medical History*, New Series, Vol. V, No. 2, March 1933, pp. 135-150. A brochure entitled Benjamin Franklin's Contributions to Medical Science prepared and distributed by The National Franklin Committee (organized by The Franklin Institute) is the source of considerable information about Benjamin Franklin. Benjamin Rush's Medical Inquiries and Observations, Vol. II (1797) has been referred to. An Account of the College of Physicians of Philadelphia by G. E. de Schweinitz and W. B. McDaniel 2d (second edition) published in the *Transactions of the College of Physicians,*

Fourth Series, Vol. II, supplement No. 1, December, 1934, has been employed to obtain information about that institution.

The chapter on Georgia (13) is based primarily on J. Calvin Weaver, M.D.: Early Medical History of Georgia; *Journal of the Medical Association of Georgia*, Vol. XXIX, No. 3, March 1940, pp. 89-112; Joseph Krafka, Jr.: Medicine in Colonial Georgia; *Georgia Historical Quarterly*, Vol. XX, 1936, pp. 326-344; and Joseph Krafka, Jr.: Augusta, From Trading Post to Medical Center, *Journal of the Medical Association of Georgia*, Vol. 29, April 1940, pp. 232-236. Recourse has also been had to the histories of Georgia by C. C. Jones, Stevens and McCall. The Colonial Records of Georgia (Atlanta 1904-1916) and The Revolutionary Records of Georgia (Atlanta 1908), both ably edited by A. D. Candler, contain valuable source material. For some of the material on Lyman Hall, the article by Herbert Thoms: The Signing Doctors, *American Journal of Surgery*, New Series, Vol. XXX, No. 2, November 1935, pp. 390-396, has been referred to. Other data have been obtained from L. L. Knight: Georgia Landmarks, Memorials and Legends (Atlanta 1914).

Extensive bibliographies, to which the reader is referred for further study, are contained in most of the aforementioned works.

INDEX